CW00959754

Spiritual Bioenergetics of Homoeopathic Materia Medica

VOLUME II: ARTBOOK

Dr. Yubraj Sharma

Published by Academy of Light Ltd.

The author can be contacted through the publisher.

First published in the UK in 2006 by Academy of Light Ltd.

ISBN 1-904472-02-8

British Library Cataloguing-in-Publication Data.
A catalogue record of this book is available from the British Library.

Design: Bumblebee Design, 5 Nelson Road, Greenwich, London SE10 9JB

Printed in the United Kingdom by Goodman Baylis Ltd.

Published by Academy of Light Ltd
Unit 1c Delta Centre, Mount Pleasant, Wembley,
Middlesex HA0 1UX, UK
Tel: 0044 (0)20 8795 2695 Fax 0044 (0)20 8903 3748
Email: yubraj@academyoflight.co.uk
www.academyoflight.co.uk

This book is lovingly dedicated
to Myriam Shivadikar

and

Mita Shah, Krishna Devi, Krishan Sharma

When you meant healing crisis for my asthma, did you mean hayfever, diarrhoea, night sweats, warts, headaches and nausea all at once!
Doctor of Homeopathy

CONTENTS

CONTENTS

INTRODUCTION AND HOW TO USE THIS BOOK

Volume 2 is the illustrative companion to Spiritual Bioenergetics of Homoeopathic Materia Medica volume 1. The contents of this book closely follow the order within that publication. There is a deliberately wide range of artistic styles and sources. This includes artists of different age groups and techniques, for example, from watercolour, pastel, oils or digital art. Presented at the beginning of many remedy sections is art reproduced with permission from various museums or collections, under a heading of 'Museum art'. In many cases a seemingly novel connection is described between the artist's work and the material medica. I hope an appreciation of the spiritual, cultural and historical background to the paintings enriches our appreciation of the remedy. Some readers may note that much of this section stems from western art sources, including a large proportion of Christian art. This is in part due to the ease of researching and obtaining from such sources. No particular religious faith is promoted; instead the highest possible spiritual overtones are sought. The copyright holder is listed with each museum piece of art, but a complete index of copyrights and permissions is also listed at the end of the book with the index of artists and museums – Academy of Light not being the copyright holder of the museum images, and unable to therefore provide any permissions for re-use of certain sections of the book.

The next section, titled 'Original Art' contains artwork completed by the publisher's own team of commissioned artists. In some cases copyright also continues to reside with the artist, therefore permission to re-use may require such third party consent (contact the publisher for further details). Some of the artwork may appear quite basic or childish, as commissions were also given to children and some performed by the author himself, without formal art training. The design is based on an imaginative draft sent to the artist by the author, found on visualisation within the 'inner landscape' of his mind. Some design elements may be recognisable, as sources of inspiration have included the work of Gustave Dorè and William Blake, for example. The remedy is usually depicted in its original mineral, plant or animal form, but with symbolic representation of salient themes further described within volume 1. The description therefore provided in volume 2 is kept short to avoid repetition of material from volume 1.

The next three sections of images were all produced by the author. The Astrology section portrays a stylised orbit around the central Earth point of the planets/bodies described in volume 1. These are also colour coded as shown in the charts. I have also amended any misinterpretations that appeared in the first print of volume 1 (as found in Baryta carb, Berlin wall, Colocynthis and Gelsemium).

The Oriental section contains a Buddha-like seated figure in meditative pose showing the key internal organs pertaining to the remedy. These match the text of volume 1 and are colour-coded as shown on the next page (and reproduced for convenience at the end of this book). The organ diagnosis is not intended to be inclusive of all Oriental medical aspects of the remedy's action, but as a pointer to its essential nature from this diagnostic standpoint. Single organ pathologies do not necessarily live in isolation, for example, kidney yin deficiency tends to eventually involve liver yin and blood deficiency as well over time. Some also depict a yin-yang chi diagram to illustrate the relative balance of chi. For example, where deficiency of chi occurs this could pertain largely to the yin chi or to the yang, in which case a different pattern of symptoms arises.

The Pathology section contains line diagrams of key diseases causing the symptoms of the particulars within the remedy. It is beyond the scope of this book to provide a proper account of the anatomy and physiology underlying each pathology, but it is hoped that most students and practitioners will be able to utilise these images to visualise and understand the disease processes more effectively. The pathological parts have also been colour-coded as shown in the charts.

To avoid repetition of pathology images where they cross-over with other remedies, a related pathology images section has been listed for each remedy. This is not necessarily fully exhaustive, the reader may also therefore wish to refer to the index of pathology images on p.782 for further exploration.

Astrology	Chinese	Pathology
Sun	Wind	Normal tissue
Moon	Cold	Blood vessels/blood
Mercury	Wind-cold	Absent blood flow
Venus	Heat	Fluid lighter than csf
Mars	Fire	Nerve tissue
Jupiter	Mucus-damp	Mucus
Saturn	Yin/blood deficiency	Inflammation/allergy
Uranus	Yang deficiency	Microbes
Neptune	Chi deficiency and defence chi def	Cysts/stones
Pluto	Essence deficiency	Stones
Asteroids	Chi constraint/ stagnation	Gangrene/necrosis
Transuranian	Blood stasis/ congealed	Ectopic/misplaced tissues
Centaur	Yang collapse	Medical instruments/ devices
Miscellaneous	Yin collapse	Moles
Earth	Rebellious chi	Light rays

ACONITUM NAPELLUS

Original

'Aconite and spiritual forces of transformation', by Caroline Hamilton. Moments of crisis and catharsis are depicted by lightning bolts, streaming down from the spiritual realm above the plant. Hordes of angels are shown soaring above, ready to stabilise and support the soul undergoing intense change on Earth. Note the helmet shaped blue flowers facing forwards. The leaves are crowfoot-like, typical of the Ranunculaceae family, and the roots thick and tuber-like with the prior season's root still attached to the currently active root.

Astrology

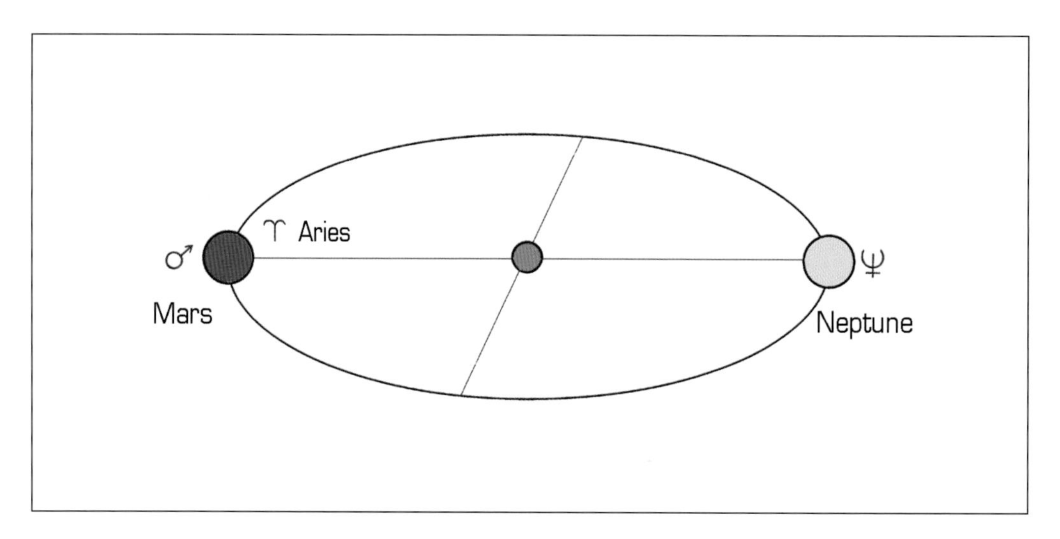

Mars in Aries opposed by Neptune.

Oriental

Heart and kidney chi collapse (yang collapse especially depicted here by the colour scheme).

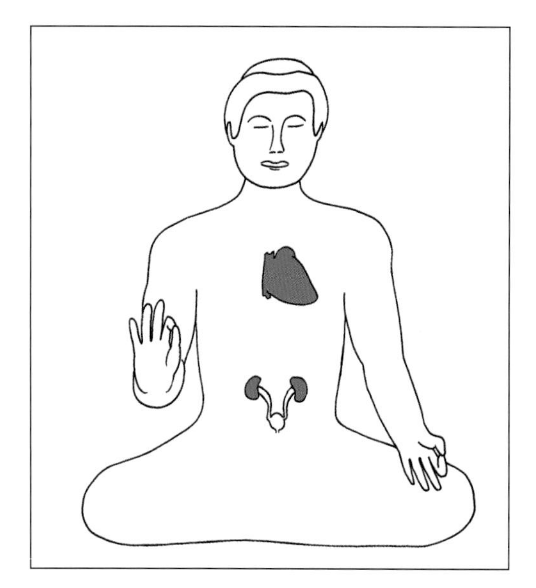

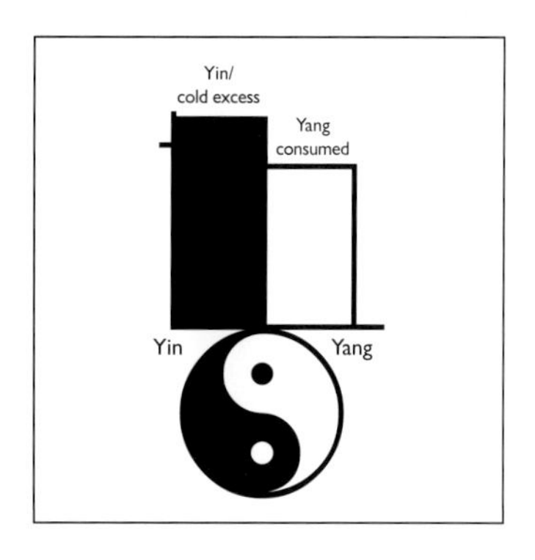

Exterior wind-cold invasion (lung invasion in this case).

Particulars

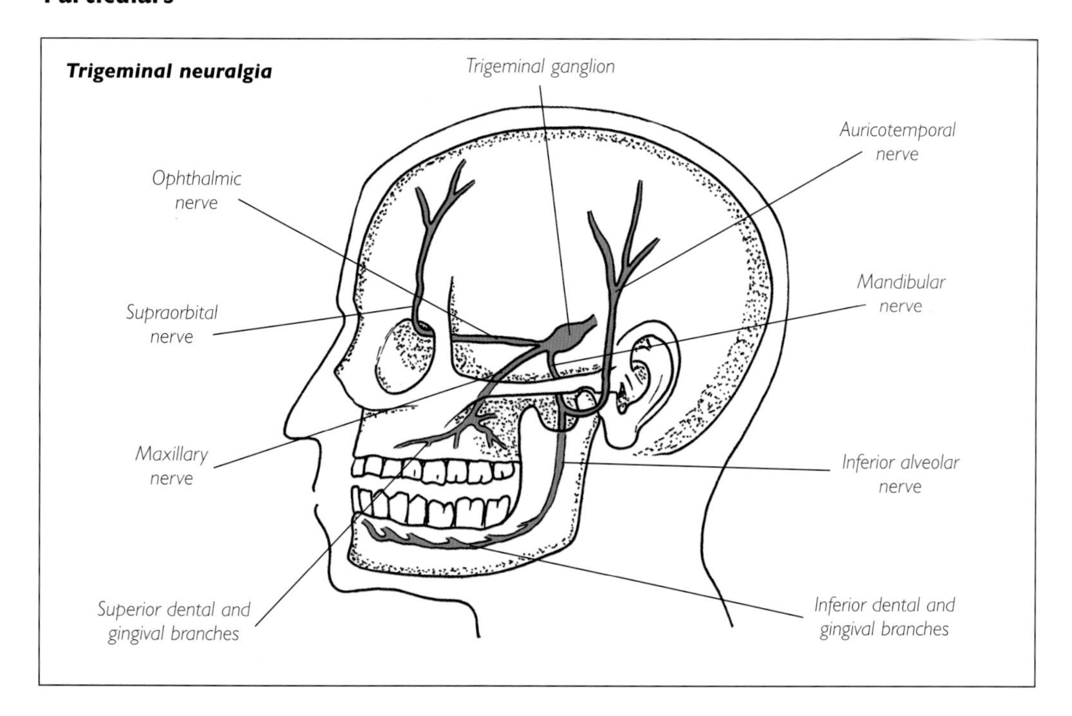

Trigeminal neuralgia (also known as tic douloureux) is a cause of headache, with sharp jolting or jabbing pain in the affected branch regions of the nerve. Pain is most common in the maxillary branch (pain at nose, cheek, upper lips, palate and teeth) and the mandibular branch (lower teeth, gums, lips and jaw pain). Pain may be triggered by touch, eating, talking, shaving or cold exposure.

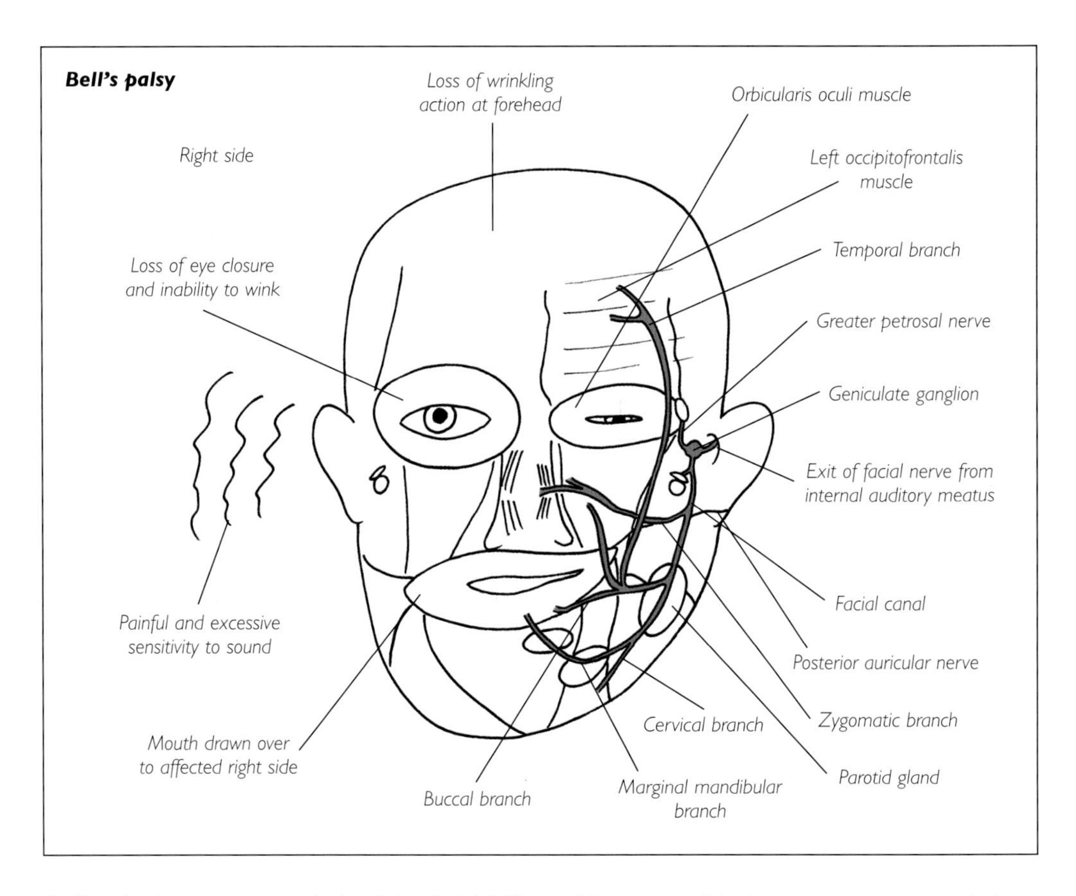

Bell's palsy is an acute paralysis of the facial (VII) cranial nerve and is the most common pathology amongst the cranial nerves. It is a mixed motor and sensory nerve, with motor supply to the facial muscles, lacrimal (watering function to eyes) and salivary glands; and sensory supply for taste (to the anterior two-thirds of the tongue) and part of the ear canal and stapedius muscle of the middle ear. The symptoms affect the same side of the face as that of the nerve affected, with inability to fully close the eye, an asymmetrical smile, pain or difficulty in hearing with an unpleasant sensitivity to sound. The cause is usually unknown, or it can occur as part of a viral or post-viral inflammation, from trauma or from a local tumour pressure. In most patients of no known cause it resolves by itself.

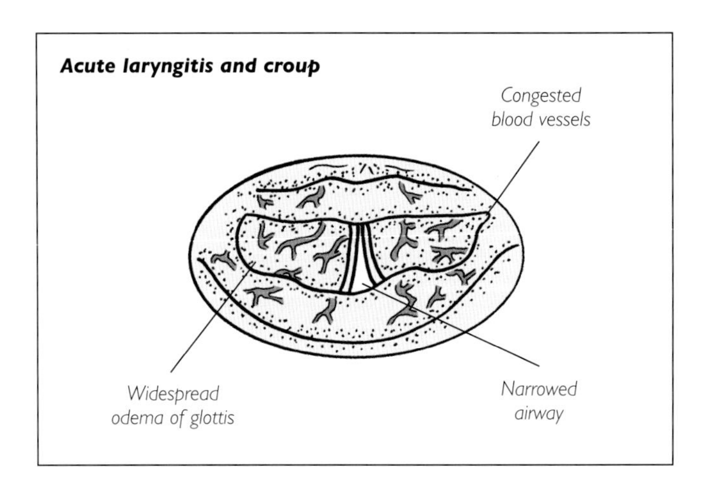

Acute laryngitis is often due to parainfluenza virus infection. There is odema, congestion and pain of the whole glottis and vocal cord region. In severe cases it can cause airway obstruction. A similar but severe swelling can also be a part of an anaphylactic or allergic reaction. The inflammation also tends to affect the pharynx above and trachea below the larynx, as in childhood croup. There is sore throat, breathlessness and fever.

Umbilical cord round neck during childbirth

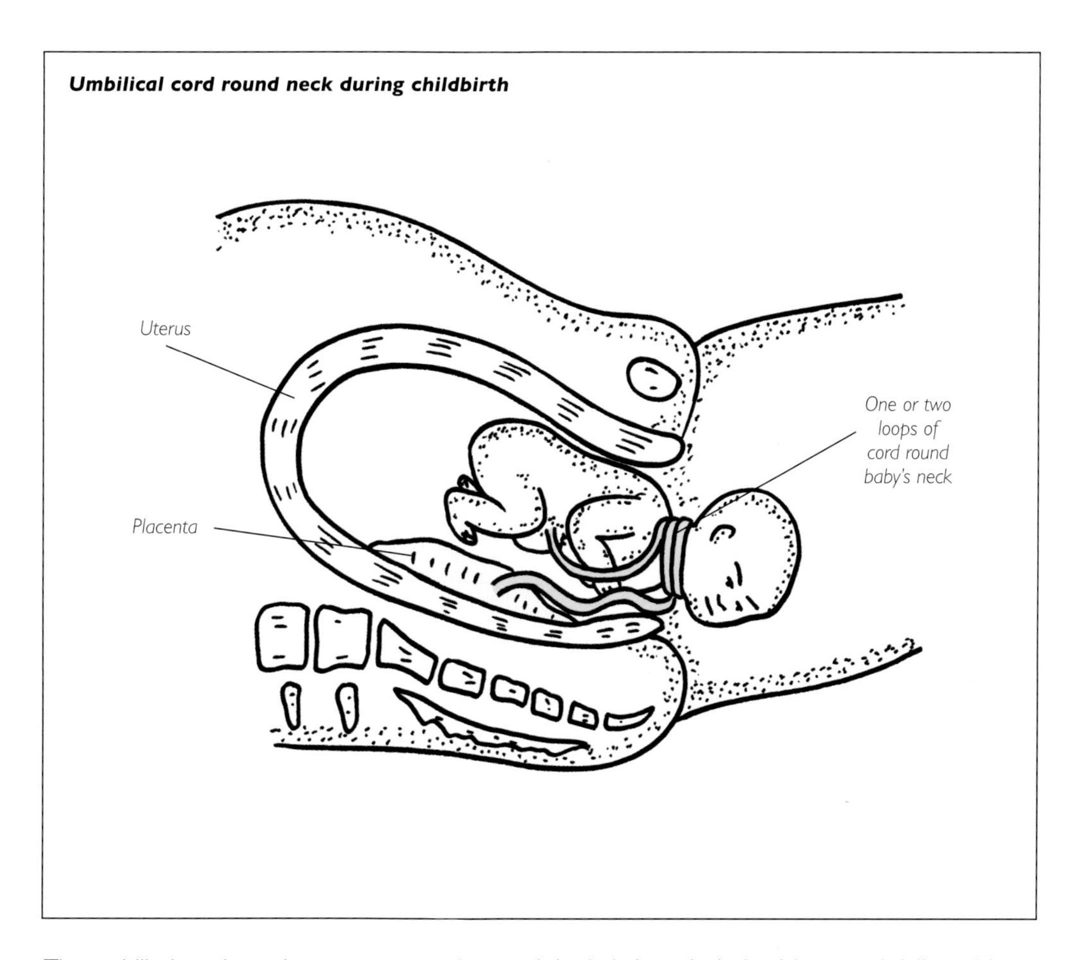

The umbilical cord may become wrapped around the baby's neck during labour and delivery. Up to 2 loops of cord round the neck are quite common and usually do little or no harm; the loops are usually clamped and cut upon exit of the neck and before delivery of the shoulders and trunk. Less commonly there are six or more loops drawn tightly round the neck, with interruption of the placental blood supply, causing foetal distress and the risk of death. Such looping is more likely with overly long cords (over 50cm in length).

Obstetric forceps

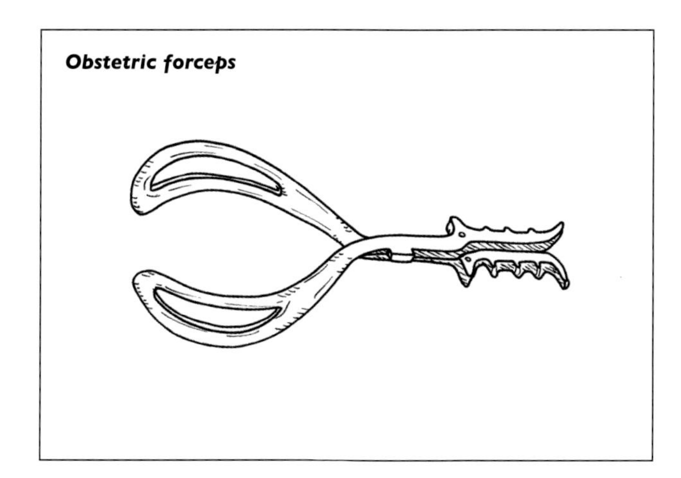

There are many different types of forceps, e.g. Wrigley's forceps is designed for a low forceps procedure when the head is on the perineum. Anderson's (Simpson's) forceps (as shown here) is suitable for a mid-forceps delivery and is longer and heavier than Wrigley's. Kielland's forceps can be used when the foetal head is even higher or above the pelvic brim, or when rotation of the head is also needed.

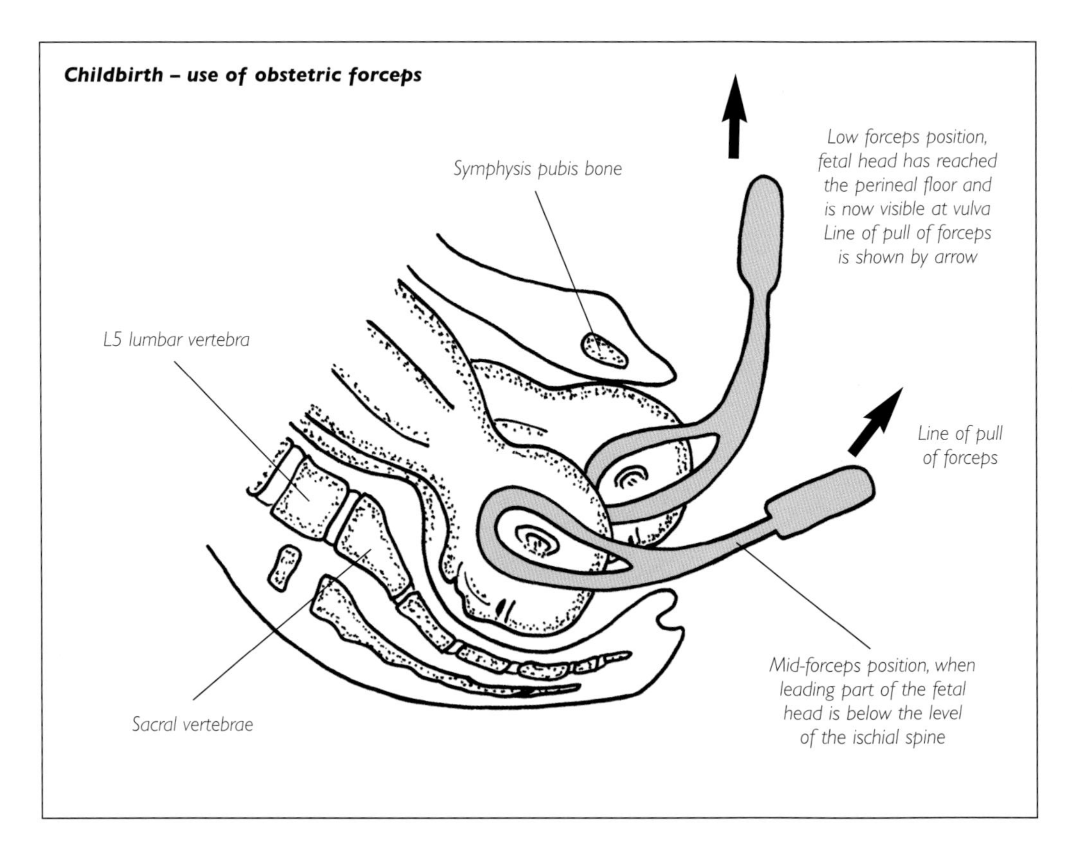

Forceps delivery is common in obstetric practice. It is indicated when there is delay in the second stage of labour (from full dilatation of cervix onward), e.g. due to poor uterine contractions or abnormal foetal head rotation. It is also used when the foetus is under distress, during maternal distress (e.g. exhaustion). To use the forceps the cervix must be fully dilated and the baby presenting its head vertex, face or its after-coming head after a breech birth. Also the head must be at least engaged within the pelvic brim. A high forceps delivery method is when the head is not engaged, and has in many centres been abandoned in favour of caesarean section. Two kinds of forceps pull are shown here, at mid and low levels of head engagement in relation to the birth canal. The procedure invariably requires local anaesthesia, and sometimes an episiotomy as well. The complications of a forceps delivery are cervical and vaginal wall tears, injury to the foetal head (e.g. bruising, facial nerve damage, depression fracture of the skull).

Related Particulars

p.144 Normal coronary angiogram
p.144 Coronary artery disease, angiography
p.103 Temperature measurement, fever
p.388 Nerve injury
p.265 Toothache, teeth innervation
p.10 Torticollis
p.10 Sciatica
p.619 Herpes zoster, shingles

AGARICUS MUSCARIA

Original

'Agaricus and the fairy/elf realms', by Antonia Chetwynd. Two examples of fly-agaric mushroom are shown, one for day, the other for night-time. Fairies encircle overhead, as well as a friendly dragon. The significance of the moon is depicted with the nearby crescent moon. At the base of the mushroom are gnomes and elves. The etheric realm of the planet is populated by nature spirits, of which the elemental beings are particularly significant. Of these, gnomes represent the forces of the earth element (undines pertain to the water element, sylphs to the air element and salamanders to fire).

Astrology

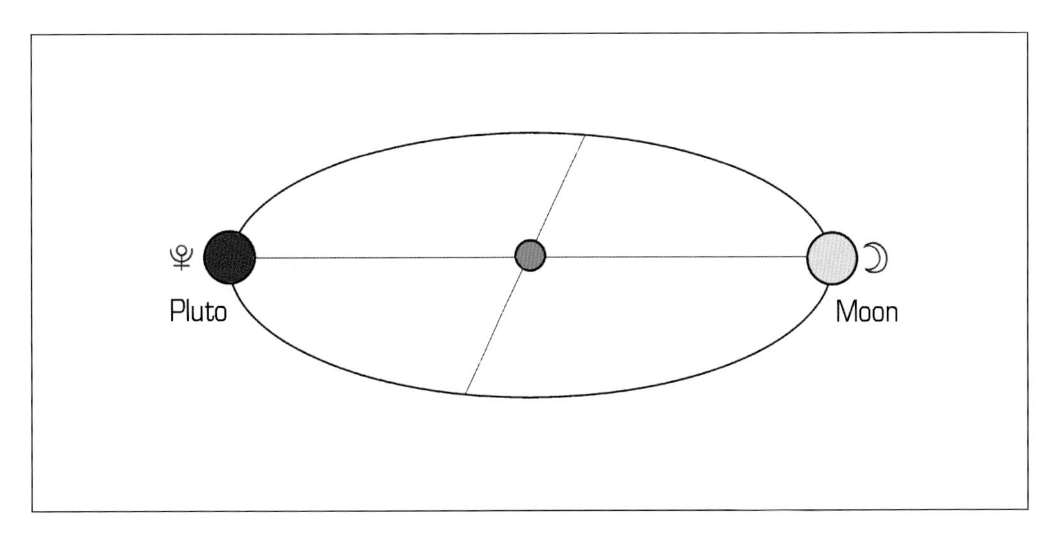

Pluto opposed by the Moon.

Oriental

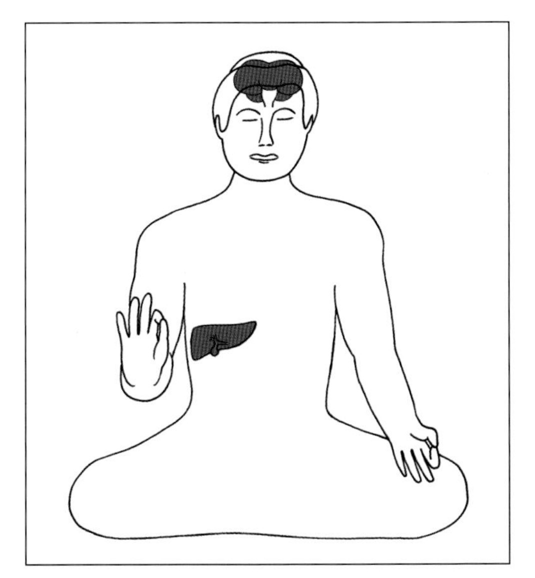

Hyperexcitation of the Hun soul, shown as entity-based and stagnant energy lodged within the liver and brain.

Particulars

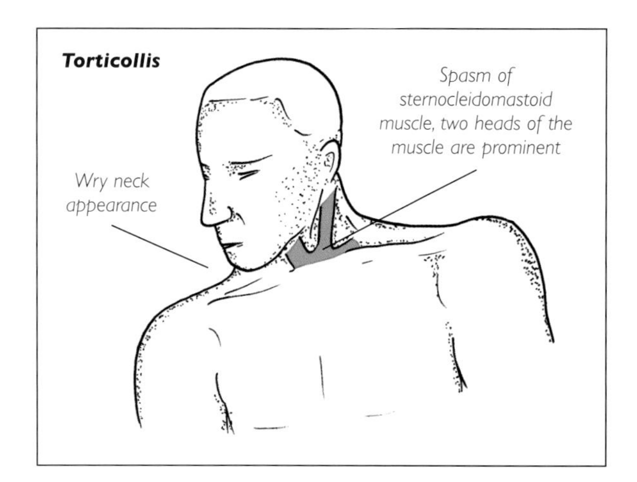

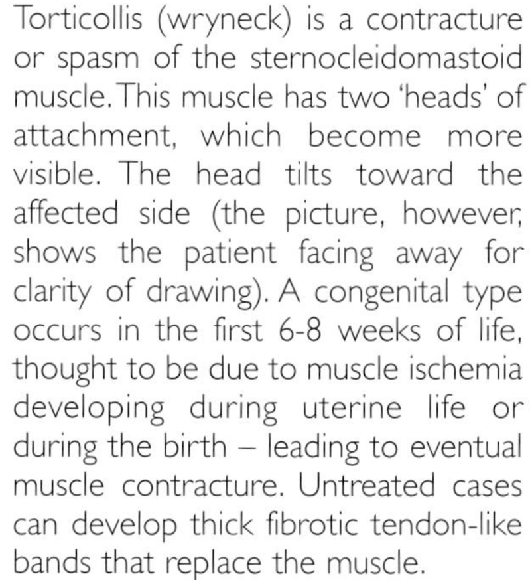
Torticollis (wryneck) is a contracture or spasm of the sternocleidomastoid muscle. This muscle has two 'heads' of attachment, which become more visible. The head tilts toward the affected side (the picture, however, shows the patient facing away for clarity of drawing). A congenital type occurs in the first 6-8 weeks of life, thought to be due to muscle ischemia developing during uterine life or during the birth – leading to eventual muscle contracture. Untreated cases can develop thick fibrotic tendon-like bands that replace the muscle.

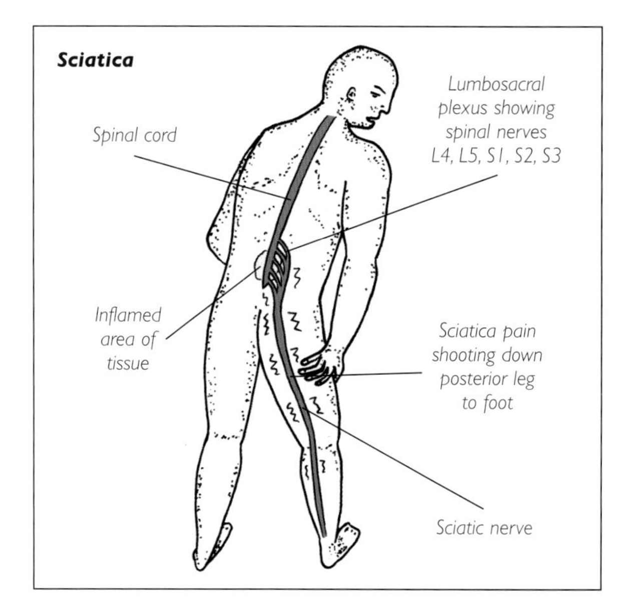

The plexus of nerve roots leaving the spinal cord may become damaged at various sites. The sciatic nerve is supplied by the nerve roots of L4, L5, S1, S2 and S3 within the spinal cord. The L5 and S1 roots are commonly compressed by prolapse of the L4-5 and L5-S1 intervertebral discs (especially where the prolapse pushes disc material laterally). There is low back pain and pain radiating down the buttock and posterior leg. Other causes of sciatic nerve injury include growth and invasion of a local tumour, or a haematoma (haemorrhage).

Related Particulars

p.18 Parkinson's disease
p.586 Muscle wasting
p.417 Myasthenia gravis
p.234 Epilepsy
p.233 Normal EEG
p.737 Fever chart, tubercular type
p.3 Trigeminal neuralgia
p.619 Herpes zoster, shingles
p.207 Cancer growth and detection

ALLIUM CEPA

Original

'Allium cepa with the liquid nature of the drop', by Loolie Habgood.The onion and its plant family are characterised by the spherical form of the fluid drop, hence the shape of the bulb. During Old Moon, when the planet was still predominantly watery, the atmosphere was misty, like a thick soup of the fluid and air elements intertwined.This family had thus not descended properly into the earthy mineral realm, retaining the soft watery nature of Old Moon, as shown by the bulb being suspended above the surface. The bulb is actually part of the stem; the root itself is represented by the thin tendrils at its base.

Astrology

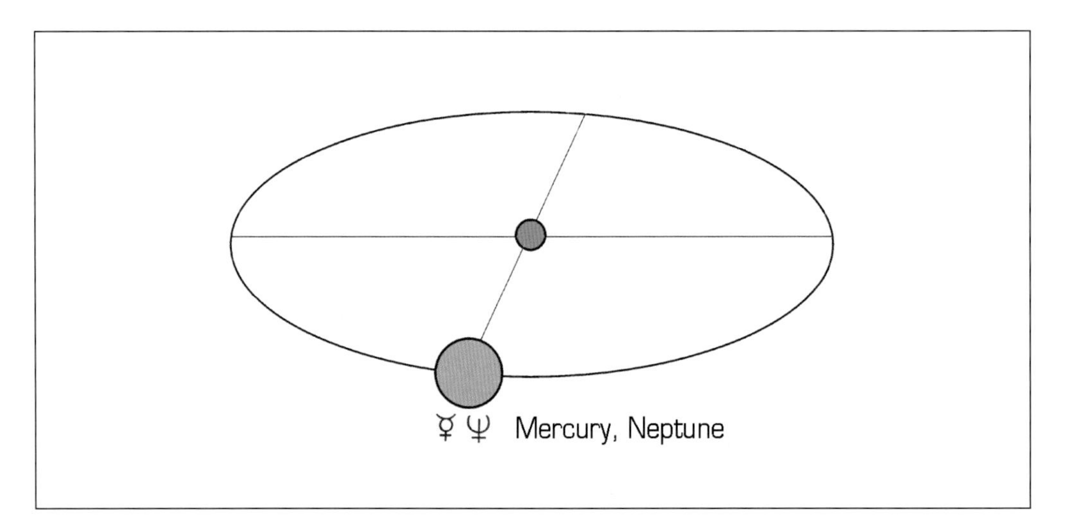

Mercury conjunct with Neptune.

Oriental

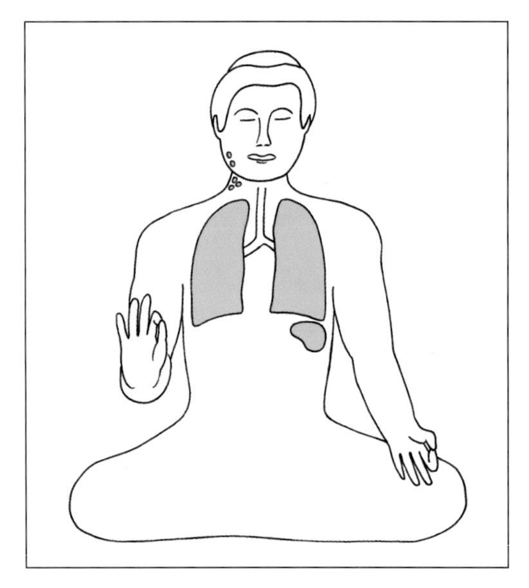

Exterior wind-cold invasion to lungs and spleen yang deficiency.

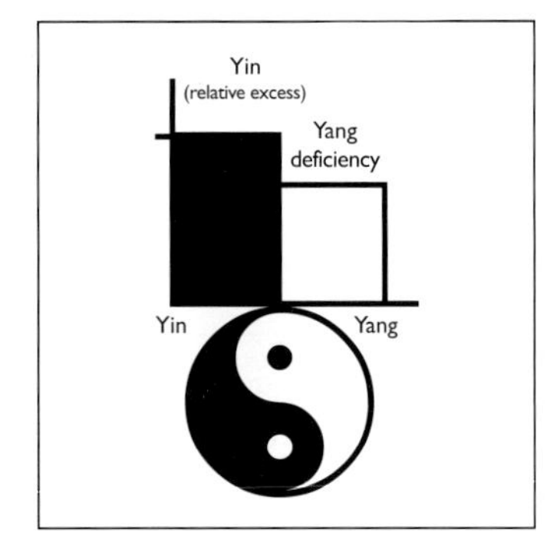

Particulars

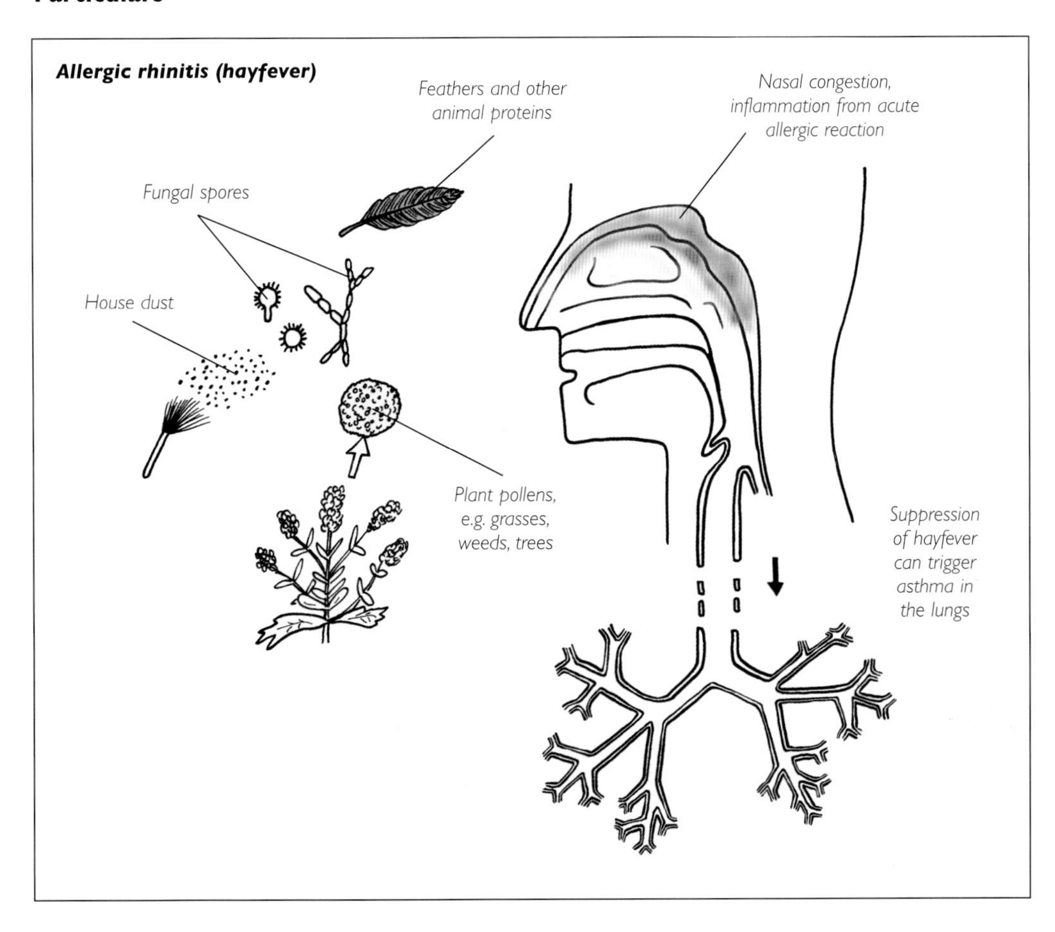

Allergic rhinitis is an allergic type of inflammation, with immediate hypersensitivity to various triggers. Symptoms are sneezing, itching and watery discharge. There is odema of nasal mucosa with infiltration of eosinophils and plasma white cells, and enlargement of mucous glands.

Related Particulars

p.408 Sinusitis and nasal polyps
p.527 Cluster headache
p.56 Conjunctivitis

ALUMINA

Museum

Dali, Salvador (1904-1989), 'The Persistence of Memory (Persistence de la memoire)', 1931. New York, Museum of Modern Art (MoMA) © 2005, Digital image, The Museum of Modern Art, New York/Scala, Florence. Oil on canvas, 9" x 13" (24.1 x 33 cm). Given anonymously. 162.1934. Dali explored the state of paranoid-criticality in many of these works from around 1930, with themes of chronic hallucination, megalomania and/or persecution complex. Here, the scene is a sparse landscape (based on the area near Port Lligat), with an amorphous object, appearing organic and strangely partly human. On the left-hand platform sits an olive tree stump with a deformed clock draped upon it. Dali himself does not provide the reasons for the associations of these objects. Nonetheless, the state of lingering memory features in states of senile dementia.

NEXT PAGE. 'Alumina and cosmic activity within the nervous system', by Crispin Chetwynd. The cerebral brain and spinal cord is depicted suspended within starry space. The spinal nerves are shown radiating from the spinal cord, with some ganglionic junction cells also attached. Thoughts are essentially mental projections from the soul-spirit self, streaming down from the spiritual realm to be received by the physical nervous system. In alumina this cosmic connection is lost, and thoughts then become regurgitated and recycled old thoughts, the end-stage of this can lead to dementia.

Original

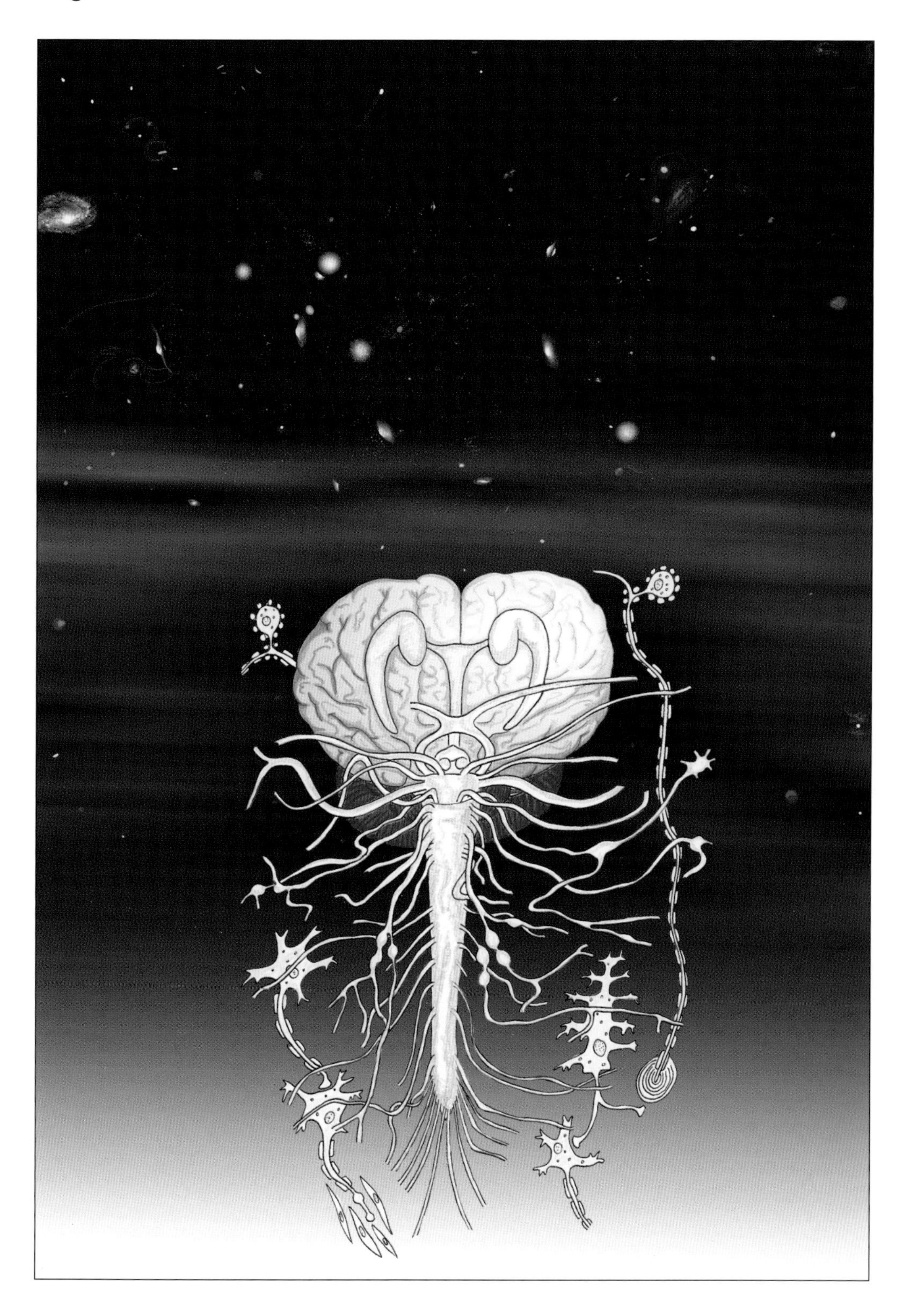

Astrology

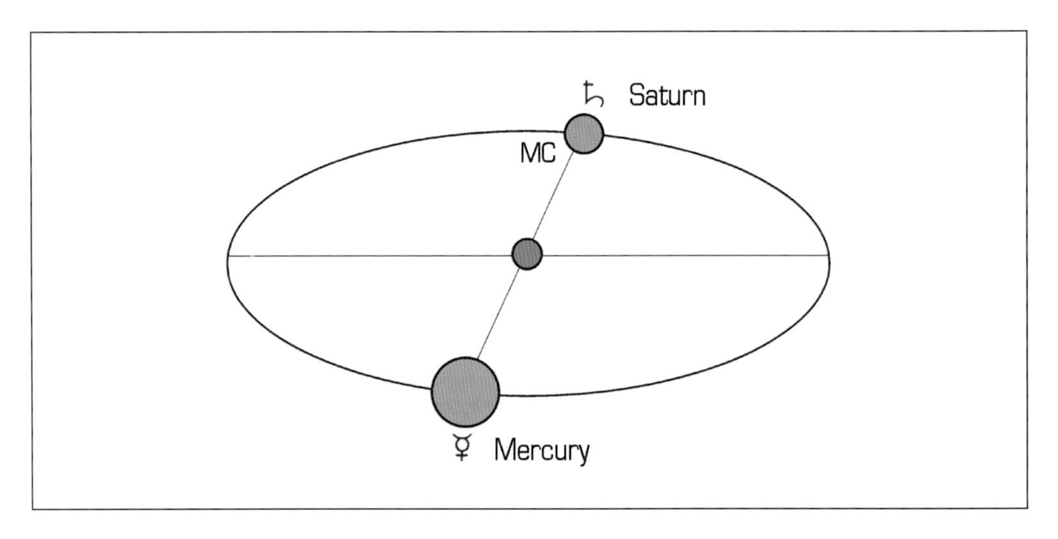

Mercury opposed by Saturn at the Midheaven.

Oriental

Kidney and brain essence deficiency.

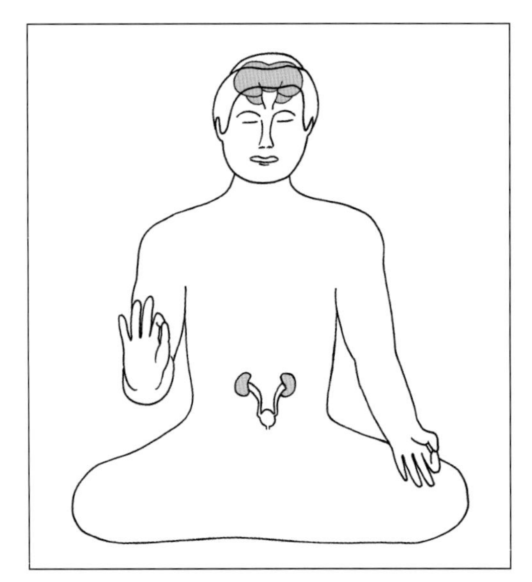

Particulars

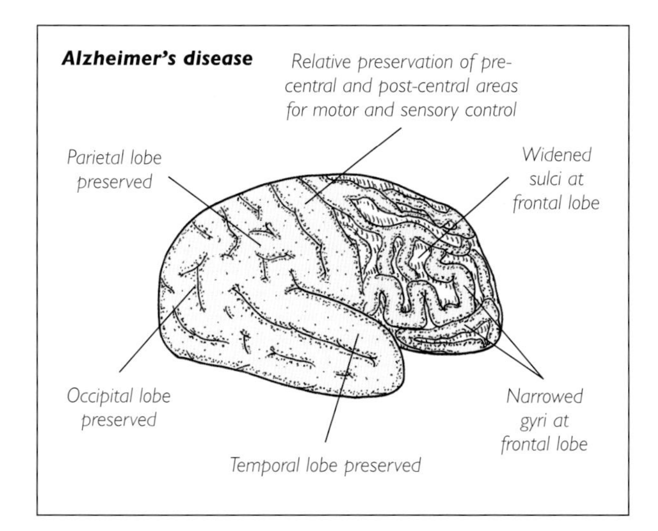

Alzheimer's disease is a type of senile dementia where certain brain regions become severely atrophied. It makes up 60% of cases of elderly dementia. The brain regions affected are typically frontal, superior parietal and inferior temporal gyri. In this example only the frontal lobe region has been shown atrophied for clarity. There is evidence of metabolic and chemical toxicity in the brain, with neurofibrillary tangles or deposits within the nerve cells and amyloid deposits at the meninges and blood vessel walls. There is global impairment of intellect, memory and personality.

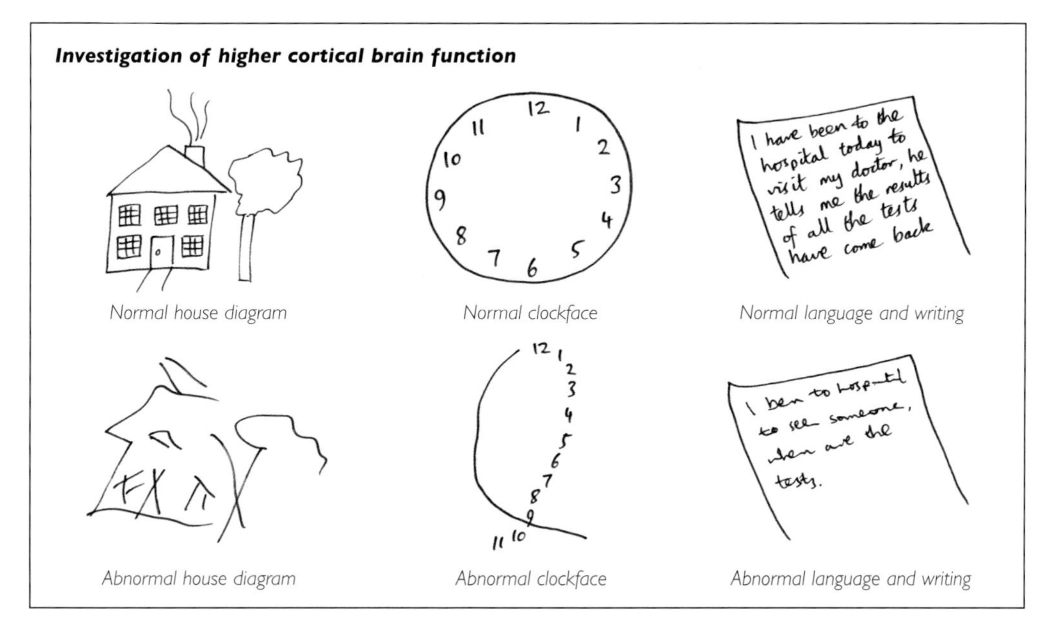

Normal house diagram / Normal clockface / Normal language and writing

Abnormal house diagram / Abnormal clockface / Abnormal language and writing

Most of the brain sustains complex intellectual and cognitive (awareness and appreciation skills) activity. There are various tests for this higher cortical functioning, much of which involves asking questions to qualitatively test the patient's ability to understand, remember, provide meaningful answers and so on. However, many quantitative tests are also available. Language functions can be tested by asking the patient to write a paragraph, e.g. providing their reason for attendance at the clinic. Abnormalities in spelling, grammar, use of words and organisation of sentences suggests damage to the area known as the parasylvian region – at the dominant cerebral hemisphere (usually on the left side of the brain). Asking the patient to draw a house and/or a clockface are good tests for organisation, line angulation and recognition of symmetry in patterns. If abnormal then a disorder of visual-spatial orientation includes damage in the right cerebral hemisphere, especially at the parietal lobe area. Other tests for higher function include questions to test the patient's memory of recent or distant events.

Parkinson's disease, pose

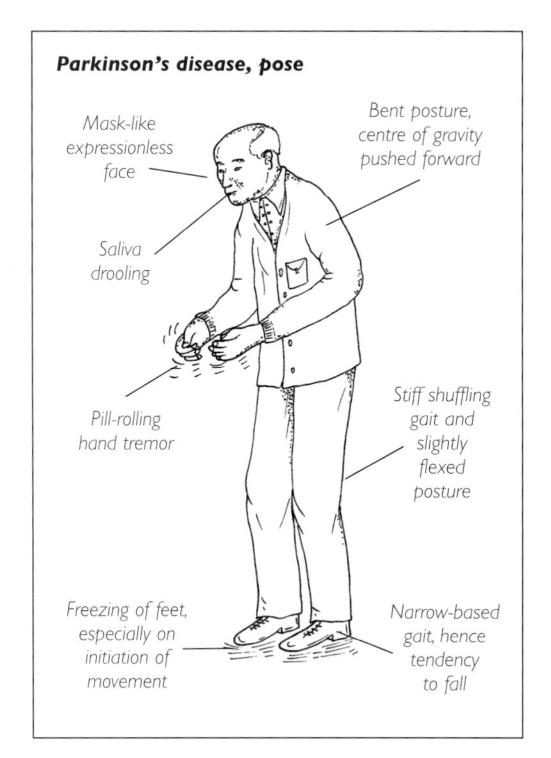

Parkinson's disease, lead-pipe rigidity

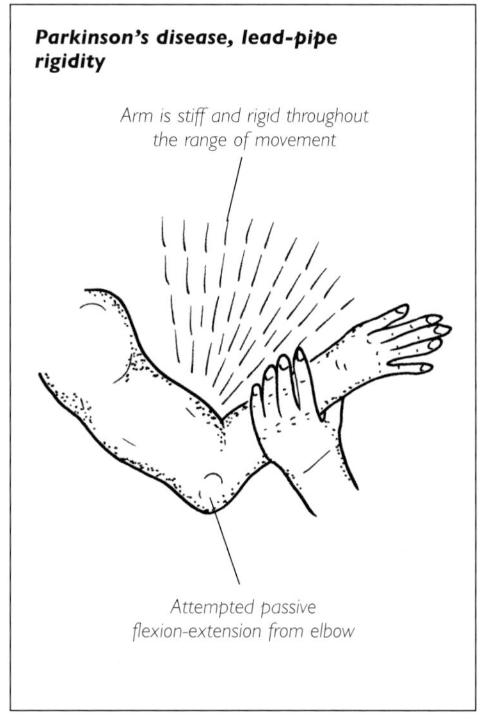

Parkinson's disease, hand tremor

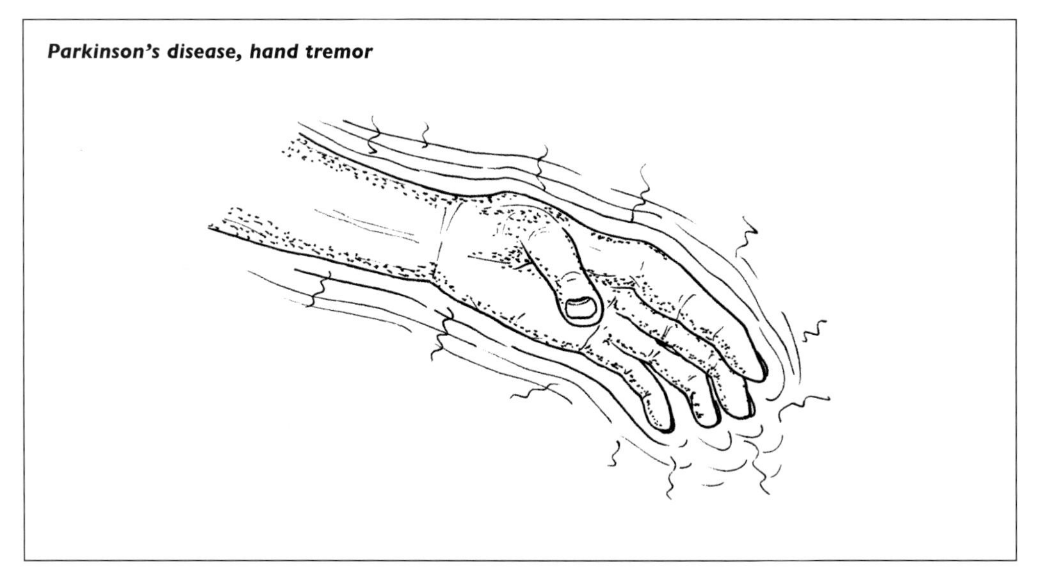

Parkinson's disease is the most common of a range of akinetic-rigid movement disorders. There is a combination of symptoms – tremor, rigidity and akinesia. The limbs feel stiff and ache, fine movements are awkward. The rigidity is throughout the whole range of movement (lead-pipe in nature). There is akinesia (absence of movement) or bradykinesia (slowness of movement). It is especially difficult to start or change movement. Writing becomes small and spidery. The tremor is a characteristic 4-7 Hz tremor at rest, aggravated by emotional stress and with pill-rolling movement between the thumb and index fingers. The stoop is forward, with a shuffling gait and poor arm swinging, lack of facial expressions and impaired balance (hence a tendency to fall).

Severe constipation with faecal impaction

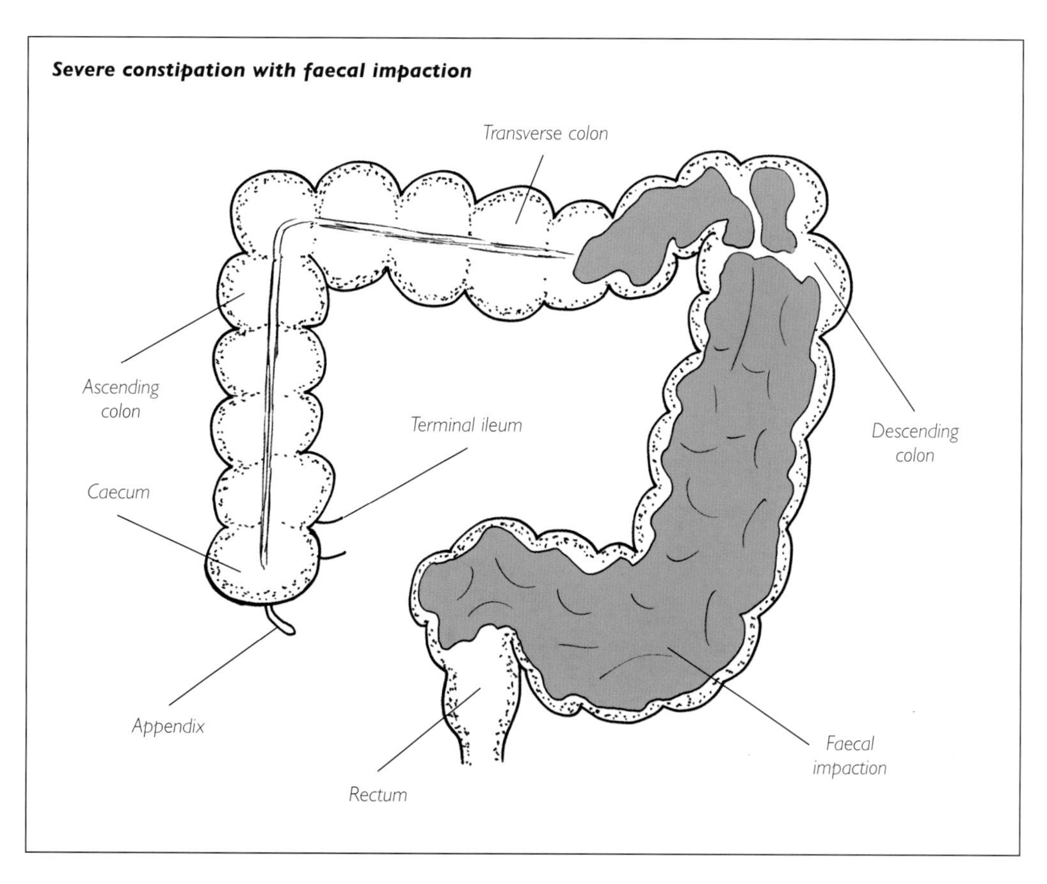

Severe constipation is common in the frail or elderly, during dehydration, on a poor diet low in fibre and during immobility. The faeces may become dry and impacted. Overflow diarrhoea can occur as liquid bowel contents are forced around the impacted faeces along the inner wall of the colon.

Related Particulars

p.574 Peripheral neuropathy
p.214 Neurogenic bladder – flaccid
p.159 Post-burn contracture
p.258 Labyrinthitis
p.260 Meniere's disease
p.158 Meconium ileus
p.71 Eczema with lichenification

AMBRA GRISEA

Museum

'Ocean Thunder', © Jeff Bedrick, artist. Although not a sperm whale, this image illustrates the power of the whale. A gray whale is breaching the ocean surface with great force. A bolt of lightning and the electric nature of the splashing water convey a sense of the astral forces at play. Esoterically, electricity is the material condensation of astral energy; popular phrases such as 'an emotional charged situation', or 'an electric atmosphere of emotion' hint at this connection.

PRECEDING PAGE. 'A sperm whale attacks a giant squid,' by A Twidle. © Wellcome Library, London. The Sperm Whale differs from some whales in having teeth, but as these are within the lower jaw only, it is unable to use them for mastication (although useful for catching and cutting food). The squid is one of the most important items of its food. Marks evidencing such titanic battles are often found in whales caught by the fishery industry.

Original

1. Killer whale
2. Wing
3. Baby condor
4. Bird
5. Animal
6. Spiral
7. Lizard
8. Tree
9. Hands
10. Spiral
11. Spider
12. Flower
13. Dog
14. Astronaut
15. Triangle
16. Whale
17. Trapezoids
18. Star
19. Pelican
20. Bird
21. Trapezoid
22. Hummingbird
23. Trapezoid
24. Monkey

(Llama not shown)

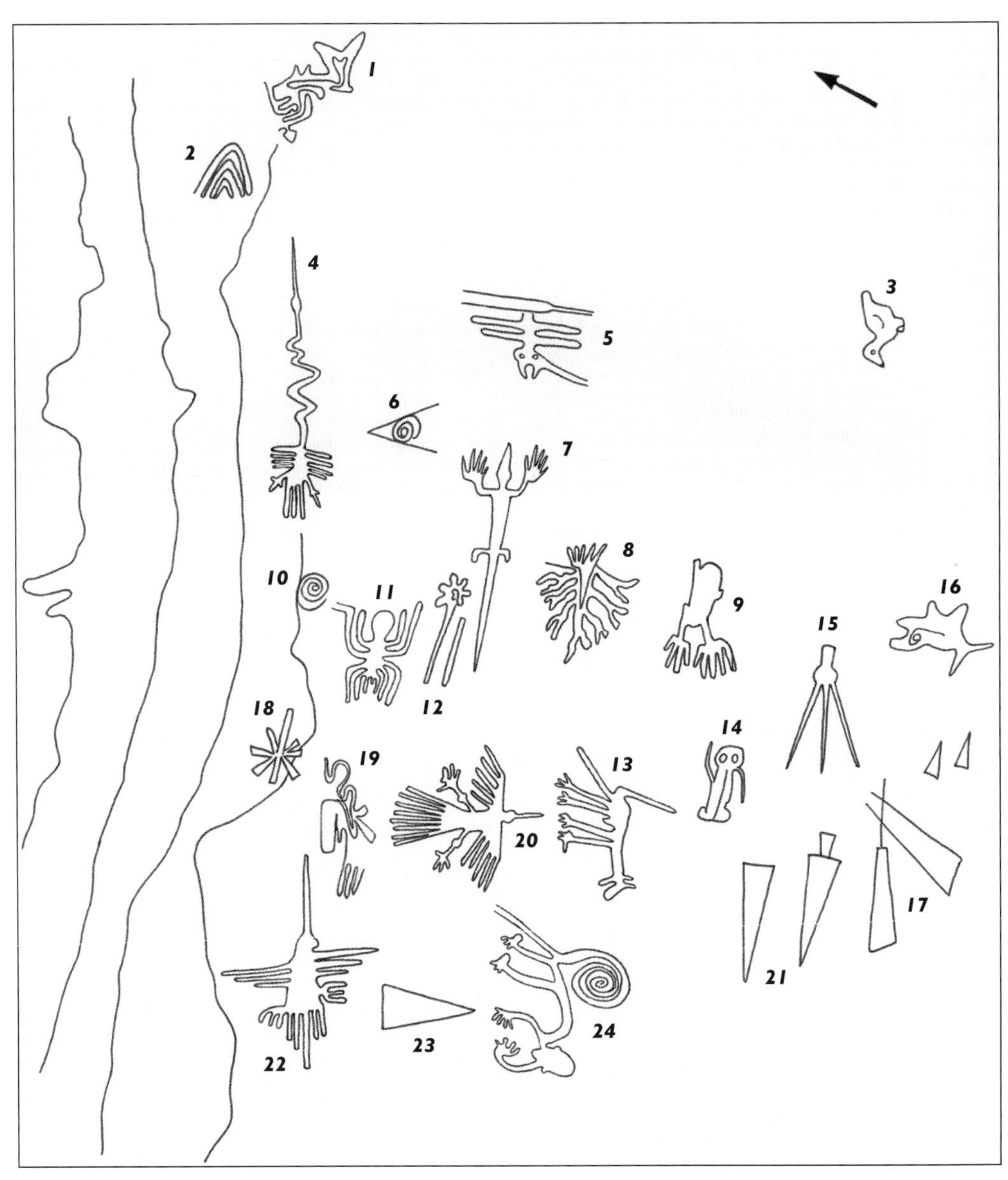

LEFT. Nasca lines, aerial photograph of the whale geoglyph.

PRECEDING PAGE. Nasca lines aerial illustrative images. The Nasca (Nazca) lines are a mystery. They are large geoglyphs within the Pampa 400km square desolate region of Peru, 400 km south of Lima. They were first noticed from commercial airflights above the Peruvian desert in the 1920's. The Pampas comprises sandy desert and slopes of the Andes. The land is unique for its ability to preserve the markings. There is extreme dryness (only 20 minutes rainfall over the year) and flat stony ground which reduces ground wind activity. Thus there is absence of climatic erosion and negligible sand or dust settlement. The surface pebbles and stones contain ferrous oxide, which form a dark patina colouration. Underneath this is lighter gypsum based subsoil. The removal of this surface gravel allows the lighter underneath to remain exposed. There are various types of designs, those of creatures and those forming geometric lines. The patterns are only properly realised from the air, e.g. at 1000 feet altitude. Of the lines which are many kilometres long there are criss-cross patterns radiating throughout the pampas. These also show angles, triangles, spirals, rectangles, wavy lines, concentric circles and so on. Man-made objects such as yarns, looms and ornamental clasps are also depicted, with well-defined entrances that could function as paths and entrances into the pattern. Many lines are, however, random and without a pattern, scattered throughout the plain, crossing and intersecting with each other. Some of the creatures are of an unknown nature. An example of this is the strange alien or astronaut being, with a rounded helmet-like head. The most famous Nasca researcher was Maria Reiche, the German mathematician and archaeologist, who believed them to be an astronomical map of constellations and zodiac, and to mark important points of the astronomical calendar (she deceased in 1998 and was buried in that valley). She purports the lines to have been constructed between 300 B.C. and 800 A.D. There have been numerous theories as to their formation and function. Those who believe the ancient Nascan people built them point to the remains of this civilisation found with the Nasca patterns on their pottery, suggesting they either knew the designs or had aerial access to the images. A portion of the lines have been found to point to the positions of the Sun, Moon and various stars 2000 years ago. The directions of the equinox and solstice points are suggested by such lines. However, computer modelling found that only 20% of the lines are configured for this purpose – which has caused some archaeologists to discount the astronomical map and calendar function as mere chance. Other theories include manufacture by extraterrestrial visitors, and later by the Nascan humans as part of a cult religion to these 'gods'. Some believe them to be a code based on the ancient system of Gematria; a type of earth geomancy. There is considered to be a global coordinate system whereby the Nasca lines, alongside other world sites (including megaliths such as Stonehenge), are integrated with the Giza pyramids in Egypt. Gematria was used to compose a system of numbers by many ancient peoples including the Persians, Babylonians, Egyptians and Greeks. It includes mathematical constants such as 'pi', and formulated the 360 degree circle, the base 10-numbering system, 12-inch foot and so on. Another theory is that the lines form the plan of a gigantic cathedral with sacred geometry. The patterns and creatures may also suggest universal archetypes, such as the flower of life, spirals of consciousness and so on. There are also many ideas of their function based on cultural and religious practices of the ancient Nascans. There are aspects of truth and overlap between these and many of the other theories. A hand-drawn map of the major discrete patterns is shown here. The key for the images is shown.

'Sperm whales swimming through outer space', by Catherine Eastman. The whales are shown carrying whole worlds and populations within their [etheric] structure. The history of a planet and the evolution of its populations are thereby held within the memory of a whale, which forms a life-support system on a collective level.

Astrology

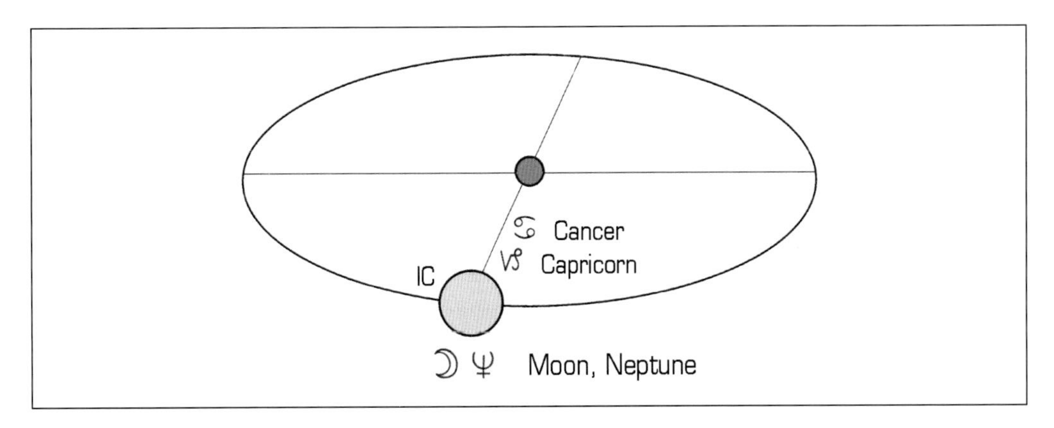

Moon conjunct with Neptune at the IC, within Cancer or Capricorn

Oriental

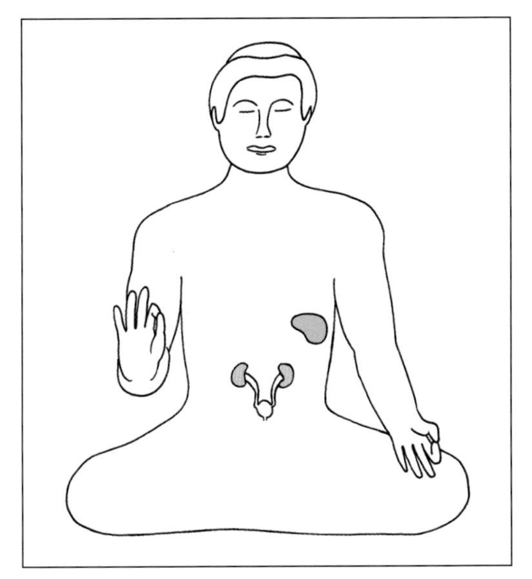

Kidney essence and yang deficiency and spleen yang deficiency.

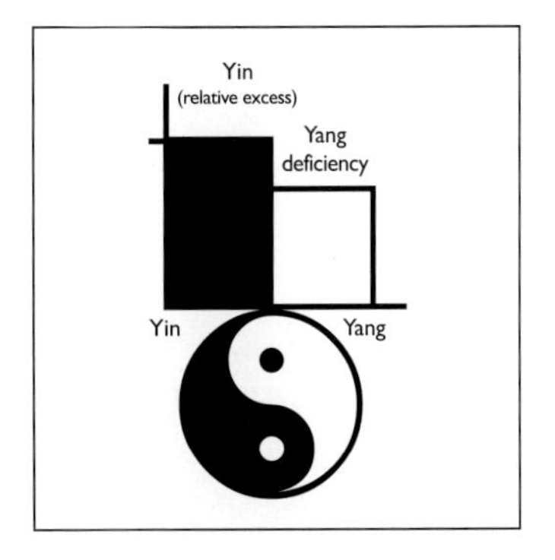

Related Particulars

p.417 Myasthenia gravis
p.232 & p.343 Multiple sclerosis
p.72 Asthma
p.264 Multifocal extrasystoles/ectopic beats

AMMONIUM CARBONICUM

Original

'Amon-Ra, the Egyptian primeval god', by Tessa Gaynn. Amon-Ra is shown standing upon a primordial fiery Earth world, with his ram-headed form reaching gigantically above the stratosphere. The air is composed of ammonia fumes and other gases, which would be noxious for present-day humans.

Astrology

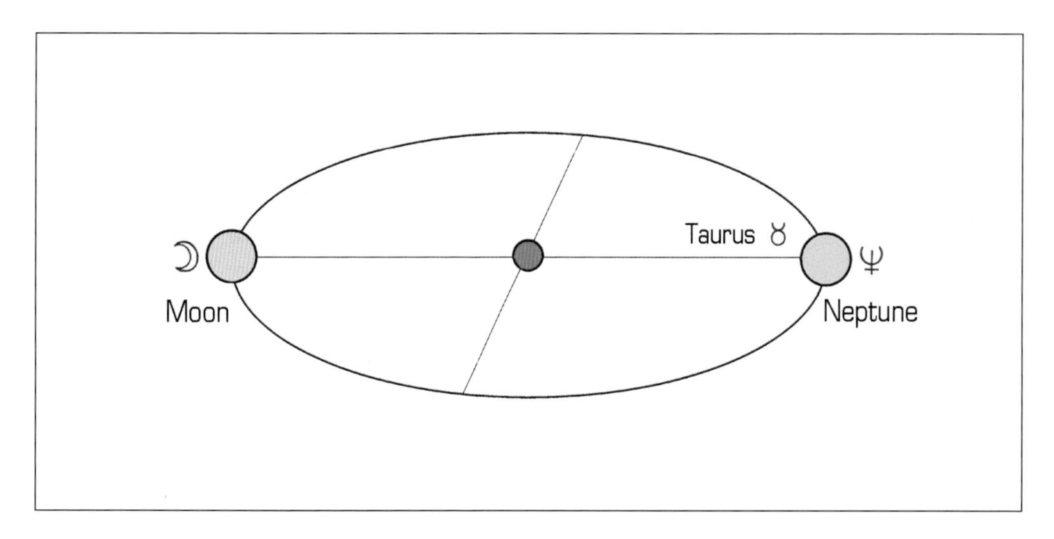

Moon opposed by Neptune within Taurus.

Oriental

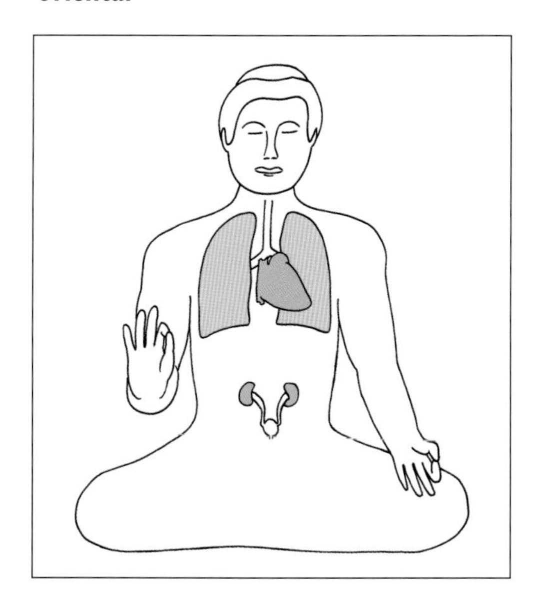

Phlegm-fluids obstructing the lungs, with heart and kidney yang deficiency.

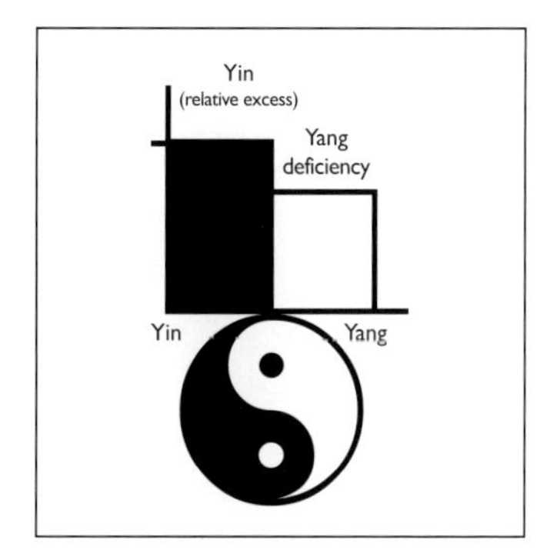

Particulars

Ammonia toxicity of lungs

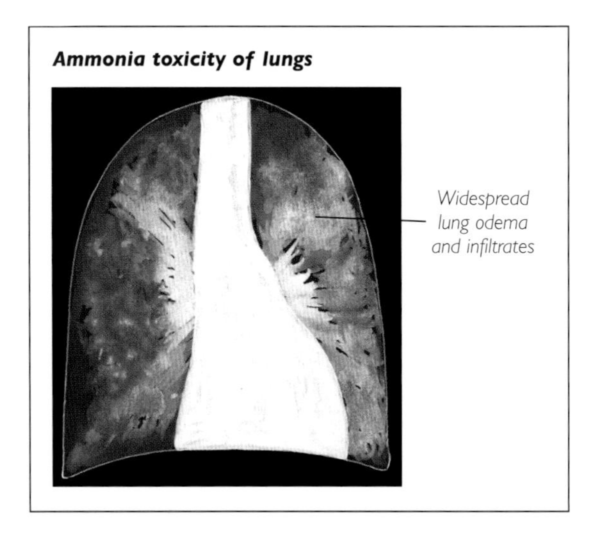

Supplementary oxygen therapy

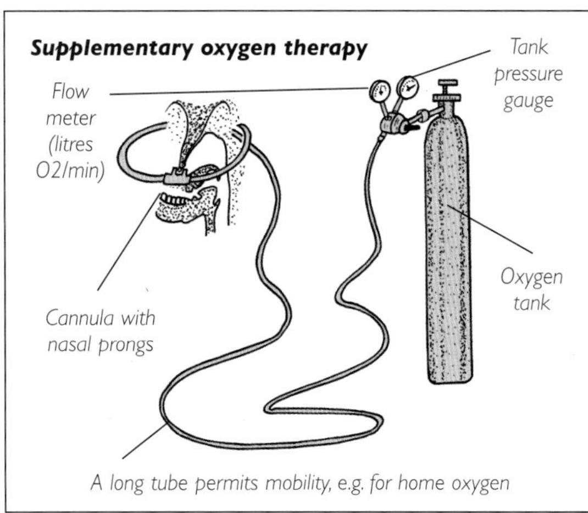

A long tube permits mobility, e.g. for home oxygen

Acute toxic damage to the lungs by ammonia fumes causes a chest x-ray appearance similar to pulmonary odema, within hours of the exposure. There is widespread alveolar and connective tissue odema and damage. If recovery is not complete then a follow-up chest x-ray (e.g. months later) can show diffuse changes of fibrosis, scarring and dilated airways compatible with emphysema.

Oxygen therapy may be required in the short-term in patients with, for example, stable chronic obstructive pulmonary disease (COPD) during high altitude, exercise or sleep. Continuous oxygen therapy (for 15-24 hours each day) is more difficult, and may be needed in, e.g. in managing patients with severe congestive heart failure, pulmonary fibrosis or unstable COPD. The oxygen is provided at low concentrations via a nasal cannula or Venturi mask (e.g. 24-28% of oxygen by concentration). It enables better oxygenation of haemoglobin, improves lung haemodynamics and exercise tolerance, also reducing hospitalisation rates. Compressed gas cylinders and liquid oxygen are typically used for home therapy. Portable systems are also available.

Related Particulars

p.13 Allergic rhinitis, hayfever
p.408 Sinusitis, nasal polyps
p.4 Acute laryngitis and croup
p.144 Normal coronary angiogram
p.144 Coronary artery disease, angiography
p.451 Myocardial infarction
p.451 Post-myocardial infarction, healed infarct
p.81 Post-myocardial infarction, ventricular aneurysm and thrombus
p.300 Pulmonary odema
p.504 Chronic bronchitis
p.198 Emphysema
p.202 Glasgow coma scale

ANACARDIUM ORIENTALE

Museum

'Buddhist Heaven and Hell', on Khoi paper, manuscript from 1860. © Wellcome Library, London. Top left shows a thorn tree for the punishment of adultery. Top right shows ghouls in hell with Phra Malai above them. Bottom right shows a poor woodcutter picking lotus flowers from a pond and on the bottom left he is presenting them to Phra Malai. The Buddhist philosophy can be summarised as: 'The wise man makes his own heaven while the foolish man creates his own hell here and hereafter.' The concept of heaven and hell is very different from that of other religions. Neither realm is eternal; a soul does not reside permanently in either. Entry into either state is self-actuated and not based on external judgement. Thus hell is a temporary place, a person caught in hell can work themselves upward and out by meritorious action; there is no need to suffer indefinitely. There are no actual real or fixed abodes to either realm, but are created as temporary states from the human mind. The last thoughts held before death are especially relevant as to where the soul is taken. The fires of this human realm and world are considered hotter than the fires of any hellish other-world. According to Buddha there are 11 kinds of physical pain and mental anguish: decay, death, lust, hatred, illusion sickness, lamentation, pain (physical and mental), grief and melancholy. Thus, hell is a condition in this world where a person is living predominantly in one or more of these states. Heaven is a condition where the soul resides in pleasure, happiness, joy, charity etc. In the human realm both pleasure and pain must be experienced, so people are in a mixture of heaven and hell. Eventually the individual must choose to step off the wheel of rebirth and follow the path to enlightenment, in which case the alternate realities of heaven and hell collapse.

Duccio Di Buoninsegna (1255-1319), 'The Temptation of Christ on the Mountain', painted between 1308-1311, tempera on panel. Copyright ©: The Frick Collection, New York. This is one of a series of panels illustrating the life of Christ painted for the Maesta, a large altarpiece for the Siena Cathedral – which was greatly influential at the time. The temptation of Christ takes place after His baptism by John in the Jordan, whence God's voice from heaven had declared: "This is my beloved Son, in whom I am well pleased". After this, from the Gospel (Matthew 4:8-11): 'Then Jesus was led into the desert by the Spirit to be tempted by the devil. After fasting forty days and forty nights, He was hungry. The tempter came and said to Him, "If you are the Son of God, command that these stones become loaves of bread." But He answered and said, "It is written, 'Not by bread alone does man live, but by every word that comes from the mouth of God.'" Then the devil took Him into the holy city, and set Him on the pinnacle of the temple. The devil said to Him, "If thou be the Son of God, throw yourself down. For it is written, 'He will give His angels charge over you; and upon their hands they will bear you up, lest you cut your foot against a stone'." Jesus said to him, "It is written further, 'You shall not tempt the Lord your God.'" Again the devil took Him to a very high mountain, and showed Him all the kingdoms of the world and the glory of them. And he said to Him, "All these things I give you, if you will fall down and worship me." Then Jesus said to him, "Begone Satan! For it is written, 'The Lord your God shall worship and Him alone shall you serve'." Then the devil left Him. And behold, angels came and ministered to Him.' Christ is depicted majestically towering over and rejecting the devil. The angels stand behind Him. By emphasising the mountain, Duccio reinforces the sense of Christ rising above the powers of darkness. The 'kingdoms of the world' are depicted as the castles of medieval Italy (especially the festive colours and crowded hill-sites of Sienna) idealising worldly glory. It should be realised that Christ could not actually be tempted, for he has no fallen human nature, no sinful urges in His body, mind or soul. The story is thus depicting that Christ is revealing the temptations within the world and the human race, and casting out the devil from the sphere of human nature. His initial baptism and blessing from God signifies his inauguration into Christed ministerial service. His fasting signifies He has disconnected Himself temporarily from spiritual sustenance, and entered into the hunger of the human soul. He seeks to reverse the sin from the Fall of humanity, when refusing to himself fall downwards. Furthermore He casts the devil from the glamour of the world. Satan expresses his doubt that Jesus is the Christ, by his use of the word 'if' in his question "If thou be the Son of God..." It is noteworthy that the devil also quotes from the Scriptures, as a means of convincing Jesus to follow him. Note, how in Anacardium a similar self-doubting state is portrayed. It symbolises the falsehood that humanity constantly faces by misinterpretation and distortion of sacred writings. Christ indicates a true interpretation of the teachings in the dialogue.

Luca Signorelli (1441-1523), 'Dannati all'Inferno'. Orvieto Cathedral, Italy. © 2000, Photo Scala, Florence. The artist was considered one of the greatest painters of his period. The fall of the rebel angels is a powerful theme of the Counter-Reformation with which the Christian church could present a propaganda against all forms of heresy. There is portrayed the triumph of light over the rebellious forces of darkness. The heavenly hosts with knight-like angels are contrasted with the brimstone of the damned below. These angels, the force of Michael being amongst them, would be involved in weighing the souls. Demons are depicted entangled and with bat-like wings. The impression is that the nude humans falling from heaven could be transforming into devils. Indeed, according to the 'Secret Book' of the Cathars and the Inquisition records, Satan was considered to be the eldest son of the God of Light and had once held a high position in his Father's realm. He fell due to his rebelliousness and jealousy of his Father, and persuaded a large group of angels to join him in his rebellion. When they fell, these angels became either demons or human souls, in accordance with their degree of rebelliousness and sinfulness. The Cathars had a dualistic based philosophy in keeping with an earlier philosophy known as Manichaeism, where the earthly sphere was considered to be the realm of the devil. With the human figures on the ground in dramatic poses the subject is also mixed with that of the Last Judgement and the Antichrist.

Original

'Anacardium orientale and the duality of thoughts within the brain', by Tessa Gaynn. The tree is shown centrally, with seeds, leaves and flowering twigs on either side. From the tree rises a brain in anterior-posterior profile, with an expanded view of cerebrospinal fluid ventricles drawn from this. The central smaller bluish chamber is the third ventricle, with the lateral CSF ventricles on each side. A demon, representing negative thinking, stands on the left hand lateral ventricle. It faces a winged angel, representing positive thoughts, on the right hand lateral ventricle.

'Anacardium orientale and transformation of the soul', by Joanna Campion. The central figure is being cleaved into two separating aspects or entities. The lower one, a tortured aspect screams in pain as it falls into greater shadow and separation. The upper aspect of the soul rises as a winged and serene angelic form.

Astrology

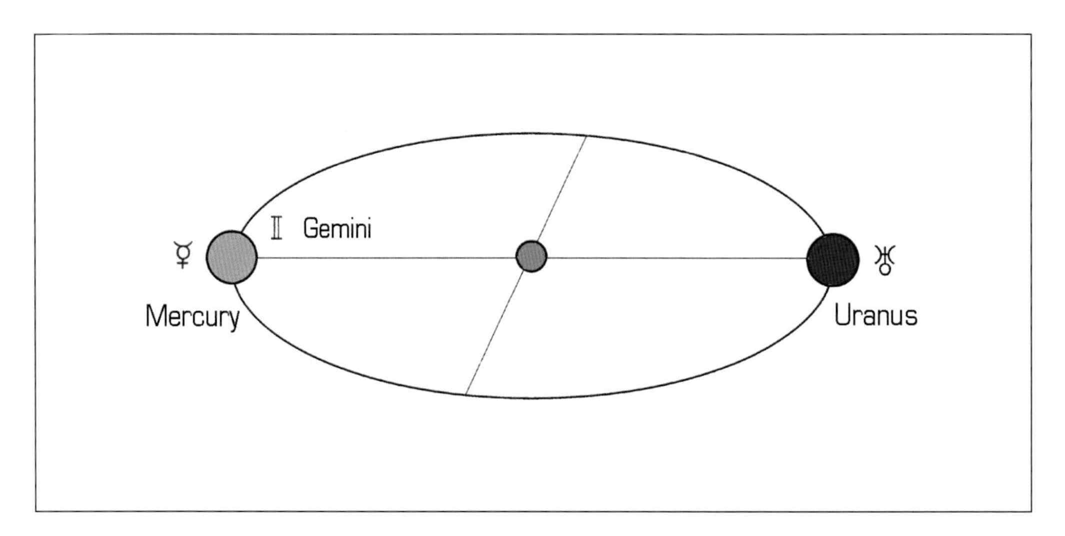

Mercury within Gemini opposed by Uranus.

Oriental

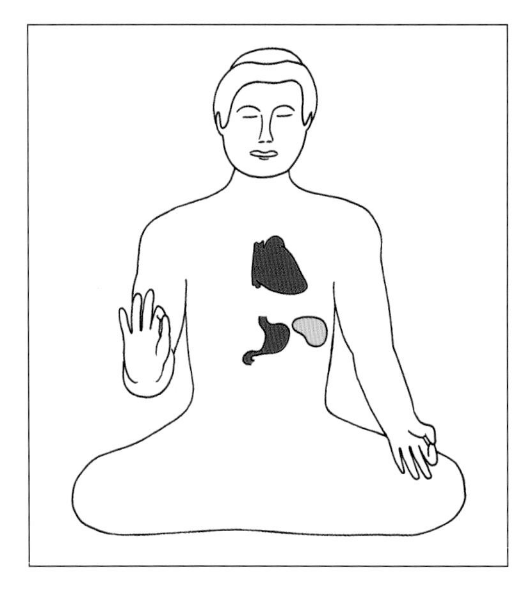

Blood stasis/congealed within heart and stomach, spleen damp congestion.

Particulars

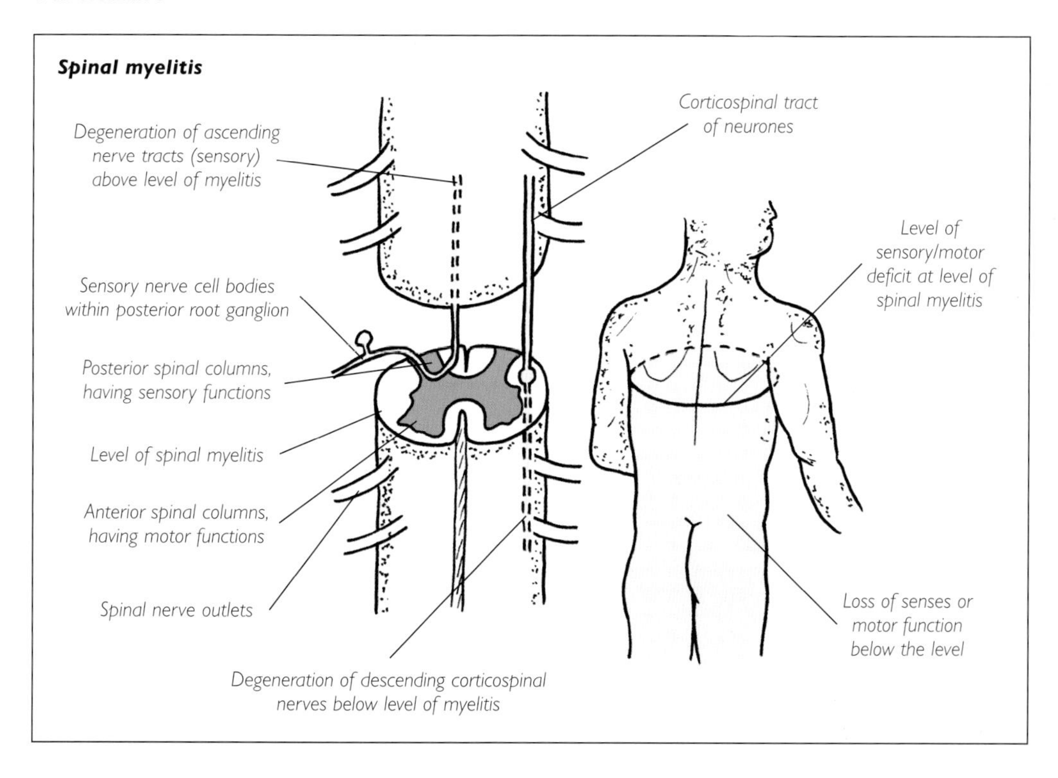

Common causes of an acute spinal cord syndrome include transverse myelitis (e.g. viral inflammation at that level), arterial infarction, or compression by a tumour. There can be a generalised disruption of both anterior and posterior grey matter (which consist of the nerve cell bodies) within the spinal columns, as well as the white matter (which consist of the nerve axonal tracts). This causes a body level, below which is a mixed sensory and motor loss. There is degeneration of many of the nerve fibres ascending and descending from that level.

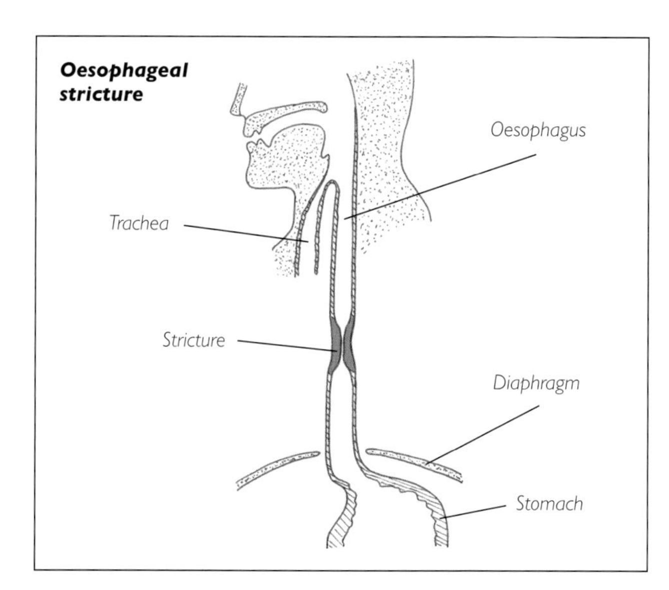

Narrowing or stricture of the oesophagus can be caused by chronic inflammation or oesophagitis (e.g. by chemical injury, reflux of stomach acid or drug-related side-effects), by a local tumour, by radiotherapy or by various nerve-muscle disorders (e.g. achalasia). Symptoms are predominantly dysphagia and difficulty swallowing. These will be progressive and deteriorating in persistent causes such as a cancer growth.

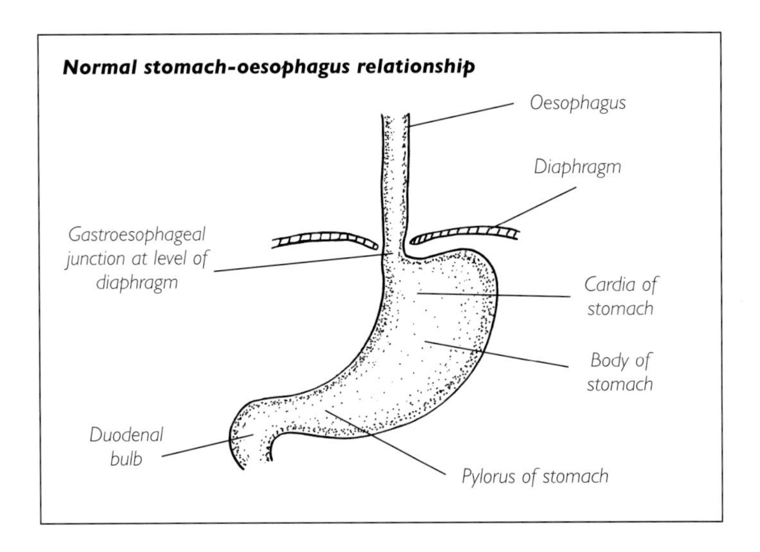

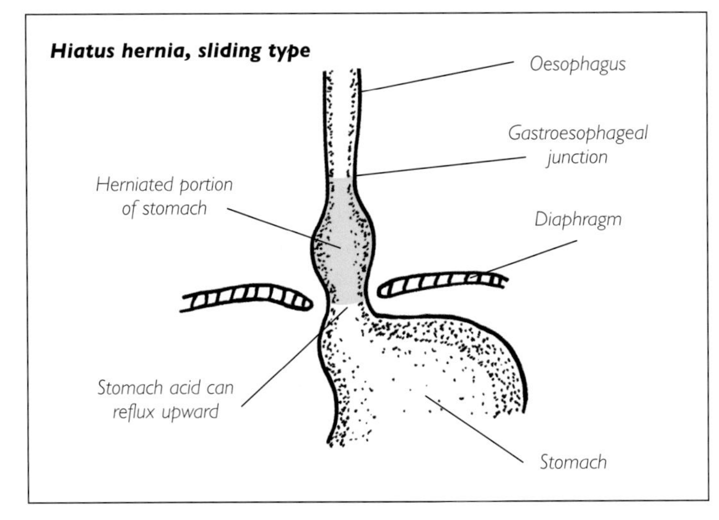

A hiatus hernia is characterised by part of the stomach herniating into the thorax. A sliding type of hernia is where the uppermost part of the stomach slides upwards to lie inside the thorax. Reflux of acid is typical with this type, causing heartburn and reflux oesophagitis.

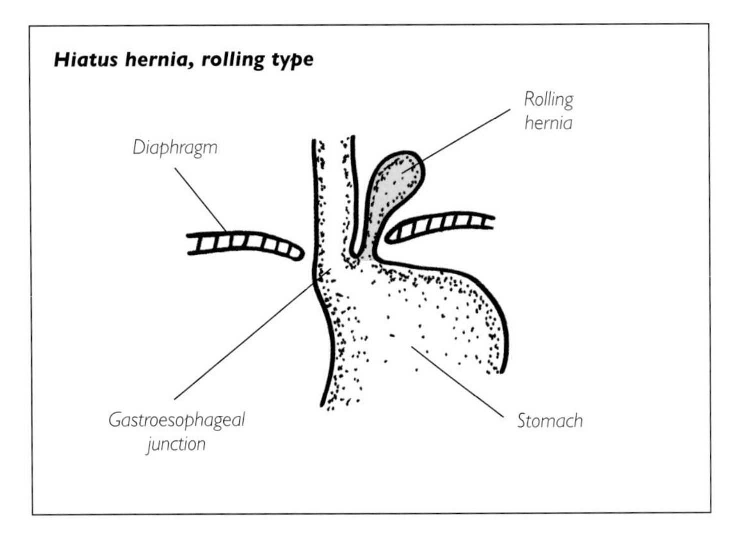

A rolling type of hiatus hernia is where a loop of stomach rolls through the diaphragm to lie alongside the gastro-oesophageal junction. There is usually no or little acid reflux in this type.

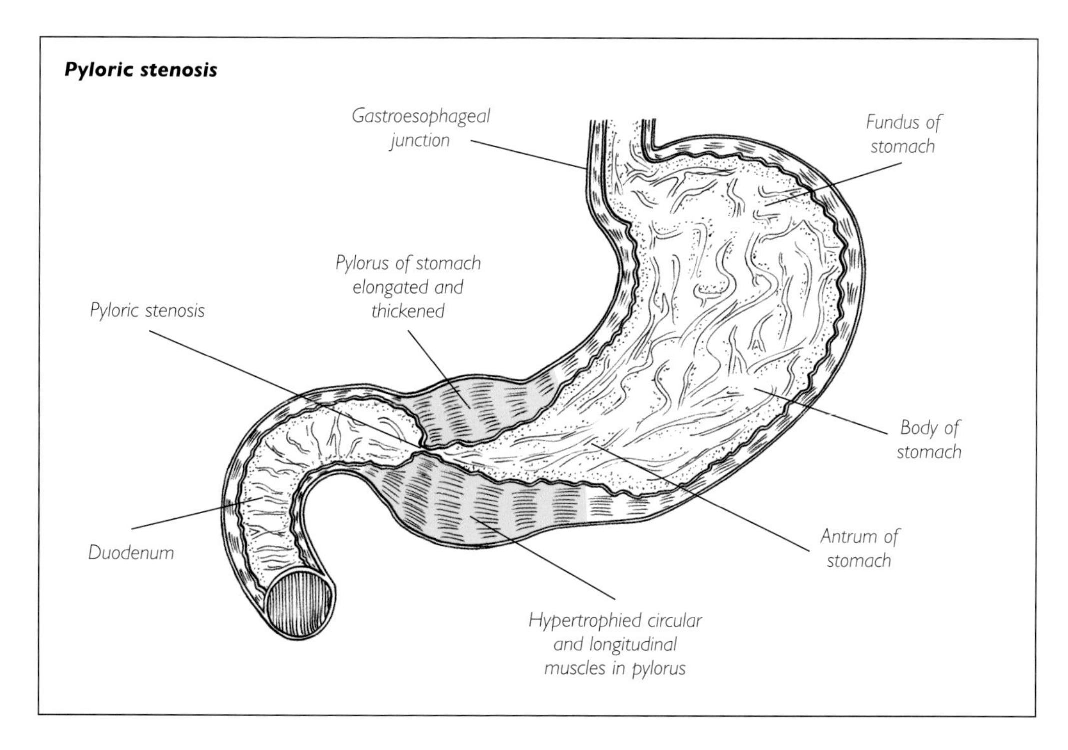

Gastric outflow obstruction may occur upon an active ulcer with surrounding odema, after healing of a stomach ulcer with scarring, or from external compression (such as from a pancreatic cancer). The type of pyloric stenosis shown here is a genetic disorder with hypertrophy of the muscle layers of the stomach pylorus. The main symptom is vomiting, projectile and huge in volume, containing the food ingested since the last vomiting phase. Fluid, electrolyte and nutritional disturbances can develop. It presents soon after birth, the baby vomiting the milk feed in such a forceful manner.

Related Particulars

p.444 Oesophageal cancer, barium swallow imaging
p.574 Peripheral neuropathy
p.277 Spinal cord infarction
p.278 Spinal cord compression, traumatic fracture
p.278 Cancer (metastatic) within vertebral body with spinal cord compression

ANHALONIUM LEWINII

Original

'Anhalonium with psychedelic landscape', by Crispin Chetwynd. The peyote plant is shown in the foreground, amidst a desolate desert landscape, with an eruption of white flowers. A vivid background of sacred geometries, patterns and dimensional portals through time and space are shown. Extraterrestrials in the foreground add to the other-worldly effect.

Astrology

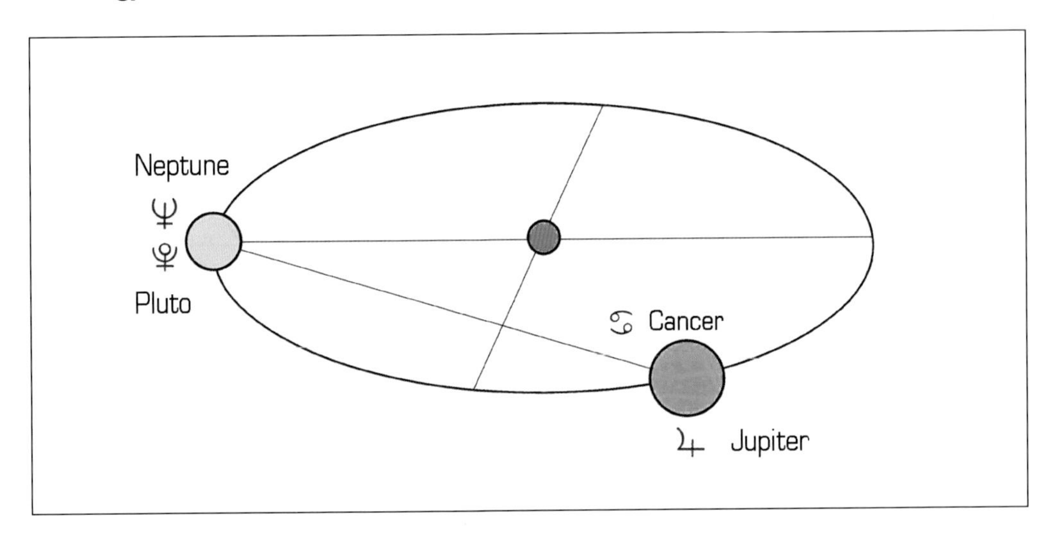

Neptune conjunct with Pluto, and trine to Jupiter within Cancer.

Oriental

Heart yang deficiency.

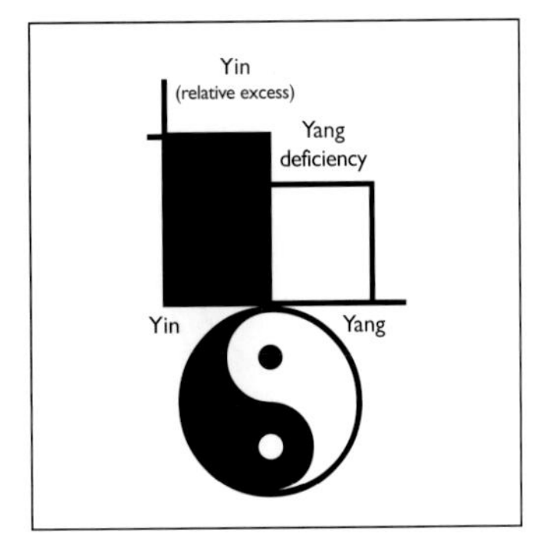

Particulars

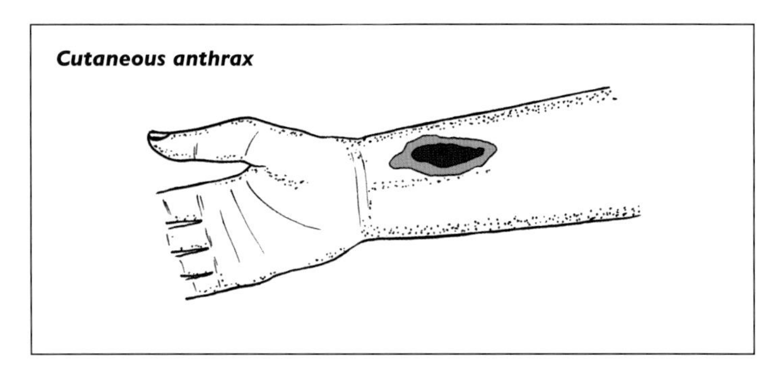

Cutaneous anthrax infection typically leads to a small erythematous (red) maculopapular eruption which is relatively painless. This then develops a vesicle or small blister, which ulcerates and forms a central black eschar.

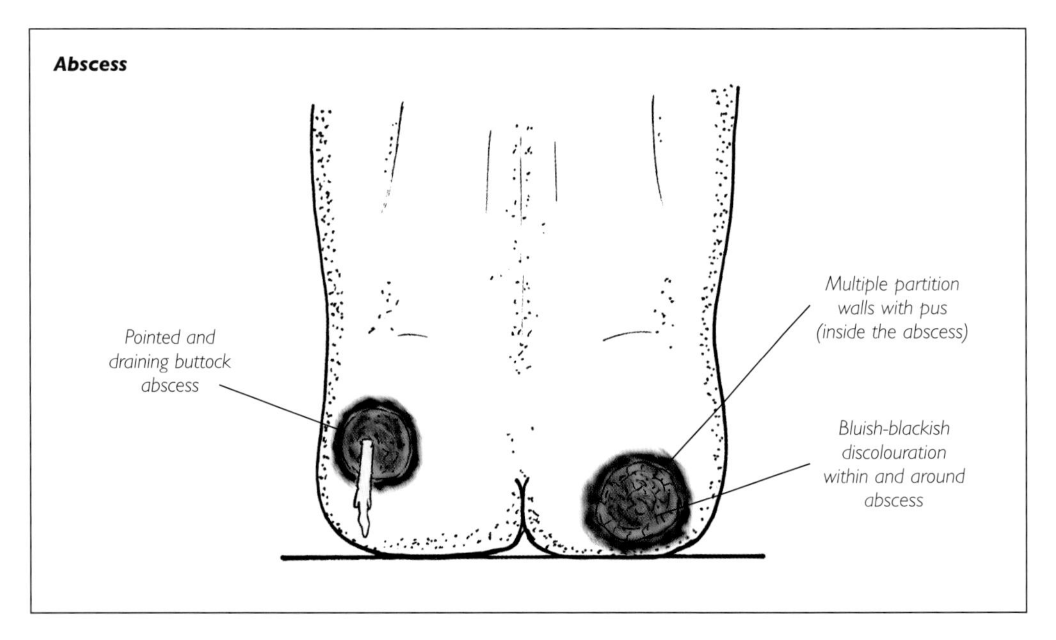

See explanation of abscess in p.368. A dusky bluish or blackish discolouration is typical in an anthrax abscess.

Related Particulars

p.300 Pulmonary odema, x-ray
p.704 Syphilitic chancre female genitalia
p.704 Syphilitic chancre male genitalia
p.71 Eczema with lichenification
p.239 Incomplete miscarriage
p.240 Missed abortion
p.642 Placenta abruption

ANTIMONIUM CRUDUM

Museum

Jan Steen (1626-1679), 'The Lovesick Girl'. Munich, Alte Pinakothek © 1990, Photo Scala, Florence. One of Steen's most favourite subjects was the visit of a doctor to a bourgeois home, and usually full of secrets, assumptions, misunderstandings and indiscretions. Above the bed is a painting of lovers, and a statue of Amor sits on the draughtscreen of the door. The maid stands next to the suitor at the door. The doctor is depicted as a quack, he is diagnosing the existence of a pregnancy through reading the smoke rising from the basin of coals in the foreground. He is taking the patient's pulse, whilst in her other hand the note has the following written words: "Daar baat gen/medesyn/want het is/minepeyn" ("No medicine can cure the pain of love").

Original

'Antimonium crudum and subconscious memories', by Selina Swayne. On and above the earth surface are shown the souls in various stages of activity and incarnation. This conscious realm is under the influence of the Sun. Below the ground, however, are caverns storing the subconscious experiences and buried memories of the soul, particularly within the chests and urns. Numerous eyes are glaring out of the shadows, suggestive of entities and ghosts. This realm is under the influence of the Moon.

Astrology

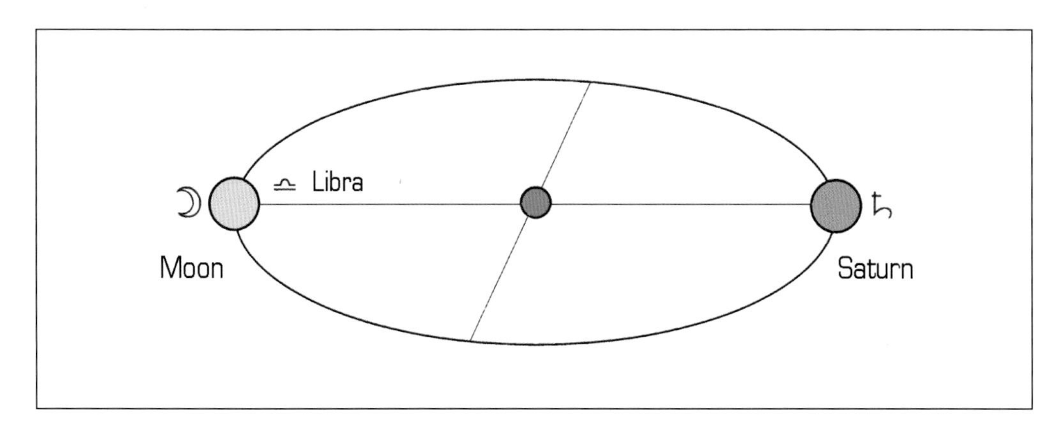

Moon within Libra opposed by Saturn.

Oriental

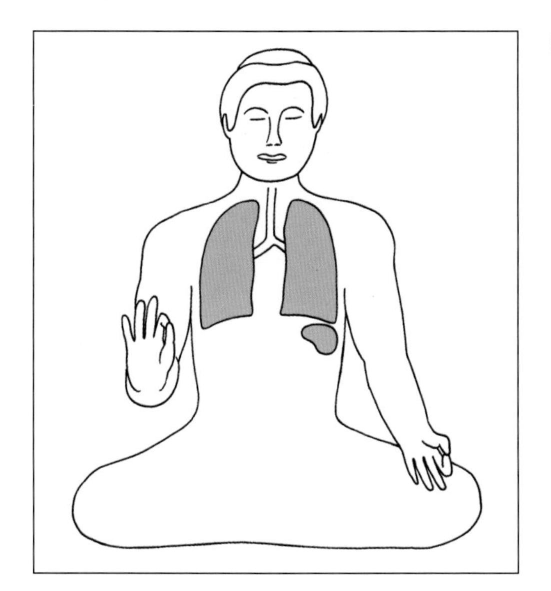

Spleen and lung chi deficiency.

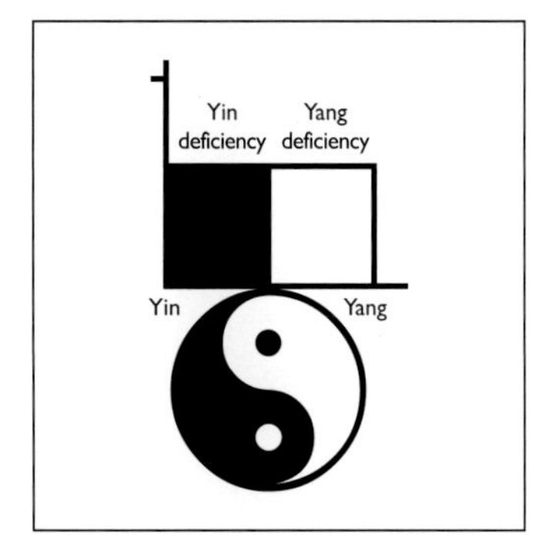

Related Particulars

p.527-528 Headaches
p.720 Condylomata
p.159 Impetigo
p.408 Sinusitis and nasal polyps

ANTIMONIUM TARTARICUM

Original

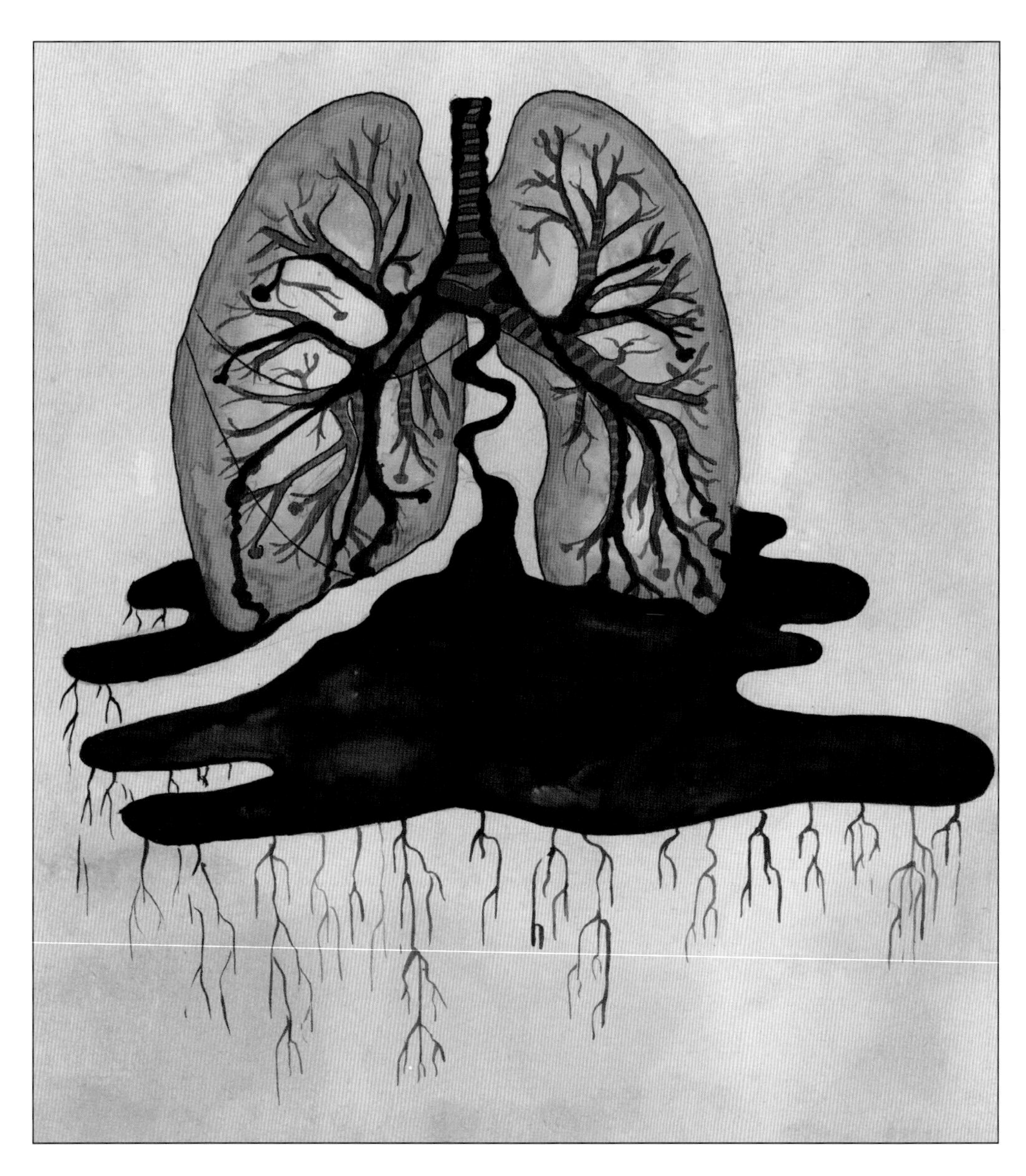

'Antimonium tartaricum and lung toxicity', by Nadine Kardesler. The trachea, bronchial tree and lungs are shown. Black dense toxicity is shown stuck within the airways and lung tissue, seeping downwards like a pool of dark mucus. As well as being physical debris, this deposition could also be stuck grief and sadness lodged within the lungs. The blackness thereby symbolises the heaviness of the mood and the tendril-like roots descending from the mucus pool bind the soul to the heavy earth.

Astrology

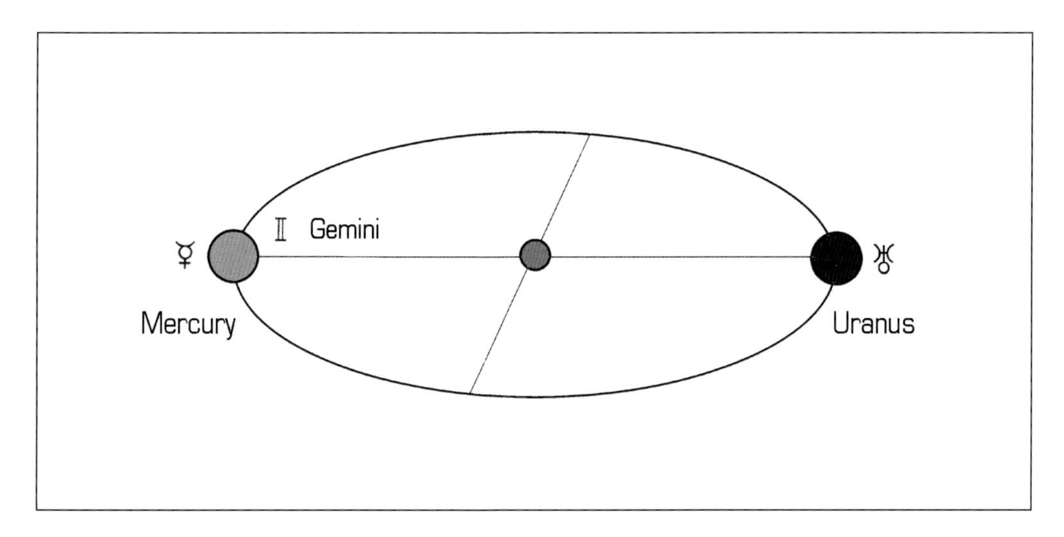

Mercury within Gemini opposed by Uranus.

Oriental

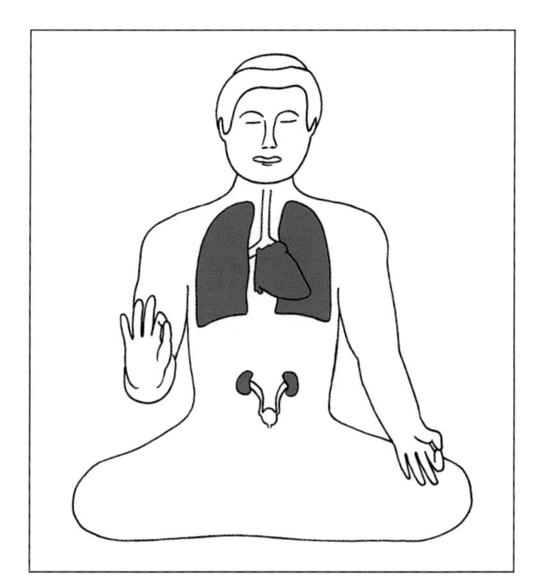

Yang collapse of heart, lungs, kidneys.

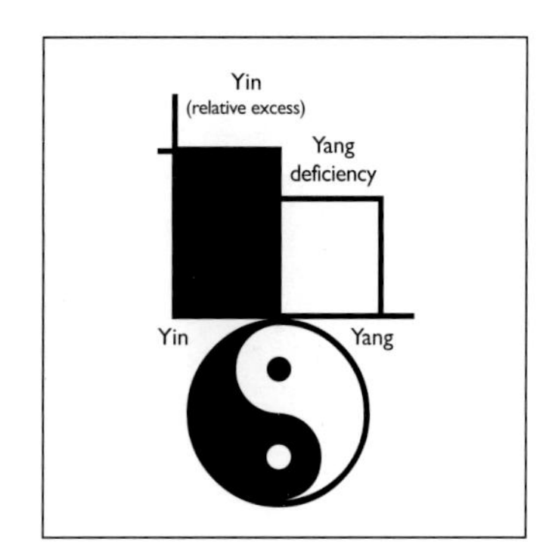

Particulars

Sleep apnoea, neural control of respiration

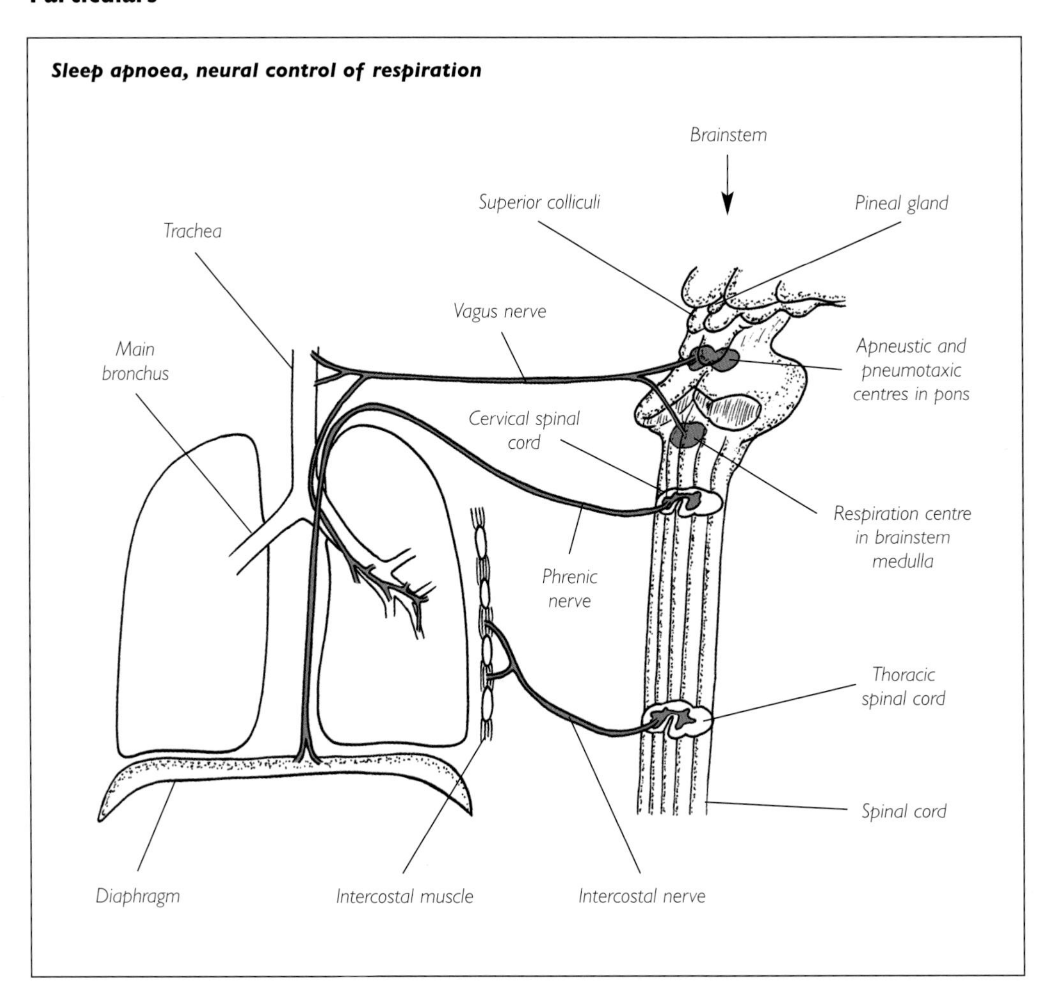

There are chemical and neural factors in the control of respiration. Breathing involves the cyclic contraction and relaxation of respiratory muscles – the nerve control centres reside mostly in the pons and medulla brainstem. There are three groups of respiratory muscles – the diaphragm, intercostals and abdominal. There are also descending nerve pathways from the motor cerebral cortex (along the corticospinal tract) which further supply the intercostal muscles of the rib cage through the spinal cord. The nerve control centres are sensitive to changes in arterial blood gases (oxygen and carbon dioxide) and pH (acidity levels). The vagus nerve exits from the brainstem control centres to supply the larynx, trachea and bronchi. The phrenic nerve exits from the cervical spinal cord to supply the diaphragm. Sleep apnoea is often taken to be obstructive in cause, due to encroachment or partial obstruction of the pharynx airway (e.g. by obesity, enlarged tonsils) or after drugs that depress the respiratory control drive (e.g. alcohol, opiate analgesics, sedatives). The opening muscles of the upper airway (at the pharynx, throat and palate) become hypotonic during sleep. The partial narrowing of the airway causes snoring, and then absent breathing (apnoea). Patients partially awake many times during the night, with a struggle to breathe (but usually do not consciously realise these episodes), leading to daytime sleepiness and fatigue. Any other factors that damage the respiratory control centres can precipitate or aggravate sleep apnoea, such as after diphtheria, tetanus and pertussis vaccination, or after complications of encephalopathy. Cot death in newborn babies is also related to weakness at these nerve control centres.

Investigation of obstructive sleep apnea

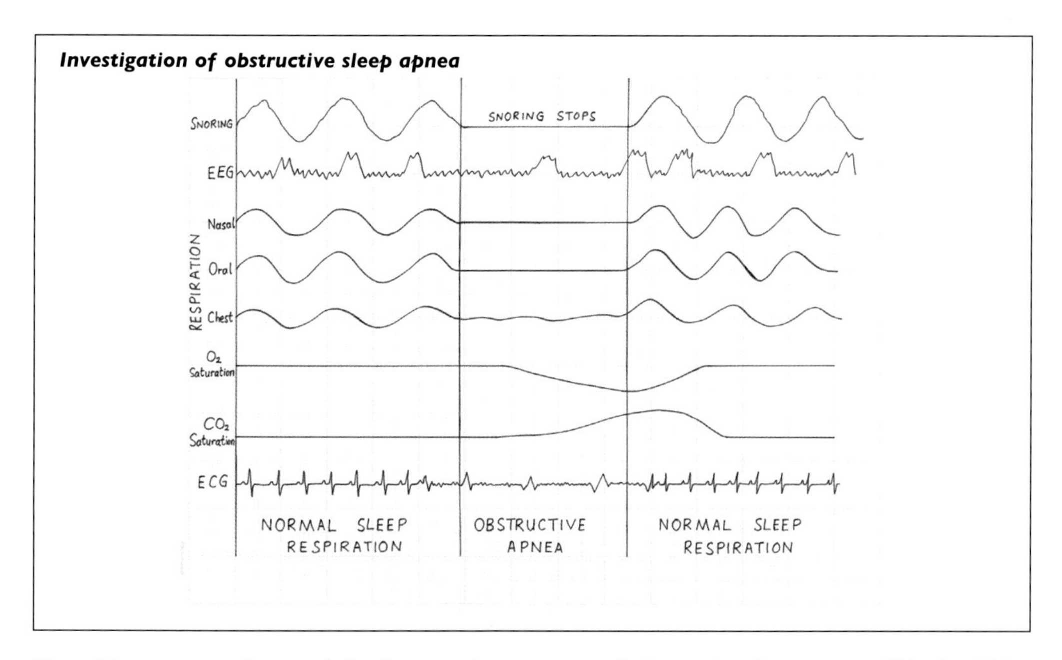

Sleep laboratory studies can help diagnose the presence of obstructive sleep apnoea. This should be suspected if there is excessive daytime sleepiness. Despite the sleep being transiently disrupted hundreds of times each night, the patient will usually claim to have sound and uninterrupted sleep. During the sleep apnoea there is disruption of the respiratory control. This can be central nervous system disruption (e.g. weakness of the brainstem centres) or peripheral (e.g. partial obstruction of the upper airways by obesity). During the sleep apnoea the respiratory rate temporarily ceases and the blood oxygen saturation falls from the impaired inhalation. The heart often enters an abnormal rhythm (e.g. bradycardia or slow heart rate in this example). Blood carbon dioxide levels rise due to loss of effective exhalation. Snoring is a typical symptom of obstructive sleep apnoea, being an attempt to keep the airway open. The brain electroencephalogram (EEG) can show brief moments of arousal or partial wakefulness, as shown by the higher amplitude wave at the end of the apnoea in this illustration. The consequences of sleep apnoea can include hypertension (of both lung and systemic circulations), chronic heart arrhythmias and late onset chronic lung disease (such as late-onset asthma).

Related Particulars

p.300 Pulmonary odema
p.300 Heart failure, right-sided
p.198 Emphysema
p.504 Chronic bronchitis
p.28 Supplementary oxygen therapy
p.95 Cystic fibrosis
p.241 Uterine contractures at labour
p.243 Partograms during labour
p.5 Umbilical cord round neck during childbirth
p.443 Neonatal apnoea
p.203 Resuscitation with face mask and bag
p.202 Glasgow coma scale

APIS MELLIFERA

Original

'Apis bee and the forces of the Sun', by Caroline Hamilton. Bees live in accordance with the laws of light and our Sun. They help regulate the warmth organism of the soul. Several bees are shown flying towards the flowers in the foreground, ready to collect the nectar and pollen within the reproductive regions. They are streaming from the Sun, within which is a hexagonal shaped honeycomb representing the solar codes of collective and personal soul destiny. The bees carry these 6-sided geometries towards the plants. The Sun contains portals for the reception of cosmic codes, which stream into it as double helical DNA-like projections. The heat and light of the Sun is therefore not created within itself. Rather, the Sun acts as a suction device for radiating cosmic heat and light.

Astrology

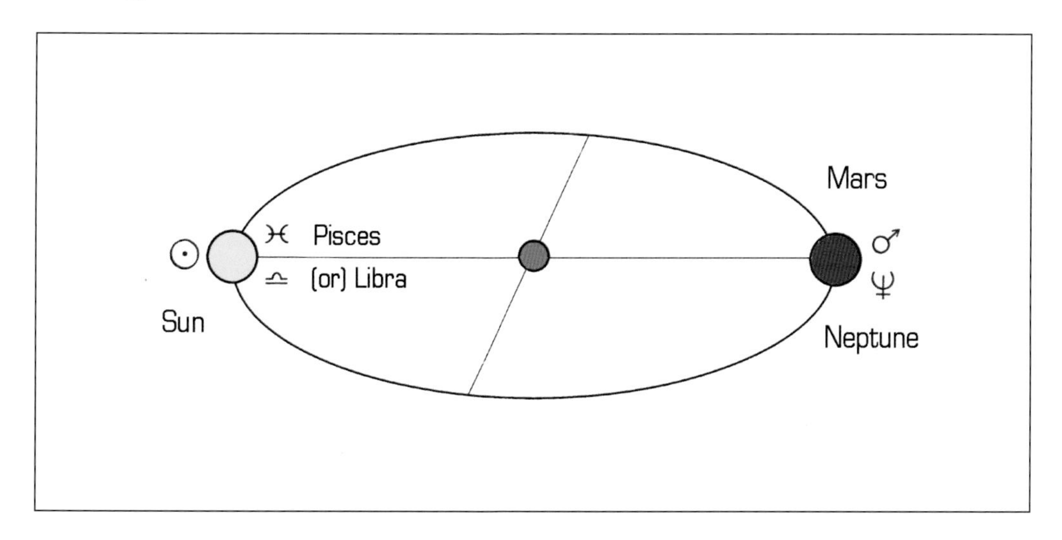

Sun (within Pisces or Libra) opposed by Mars conjunct Neptune.

Oriental

Kidney yin deficiency with heart fire.

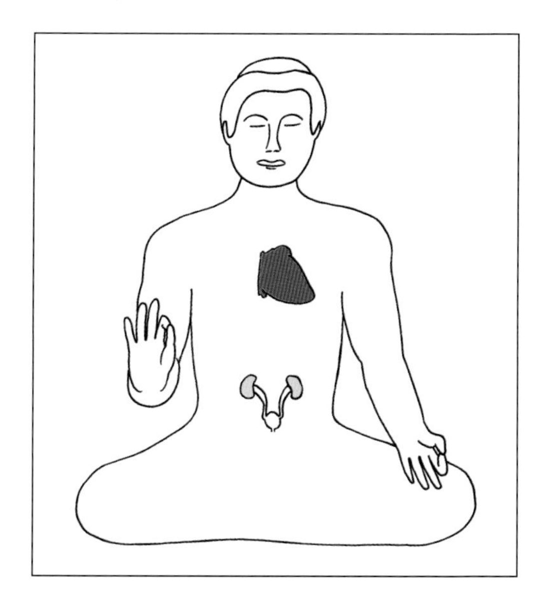

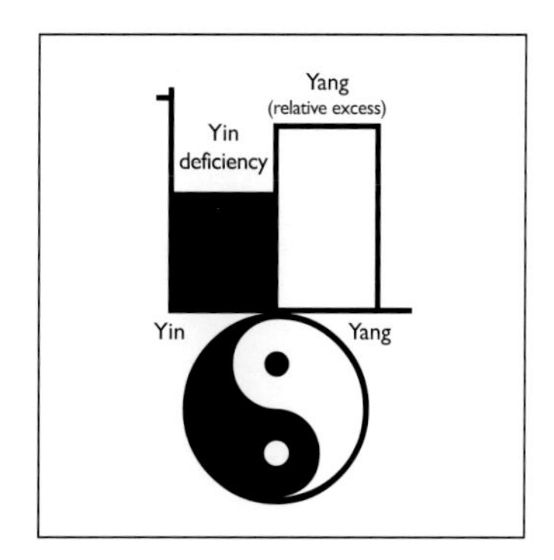

Particulars

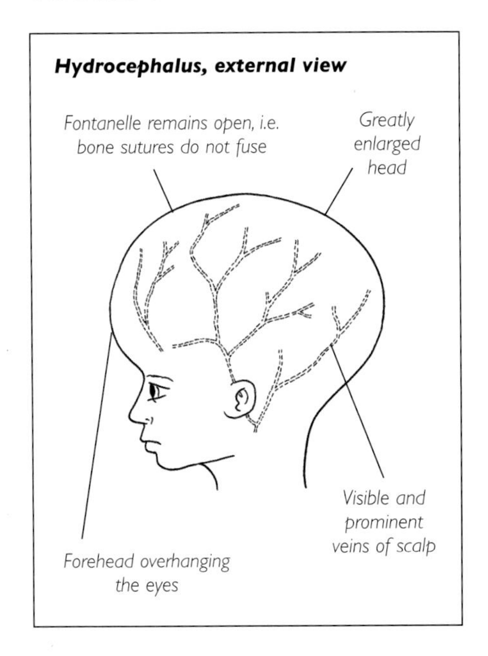

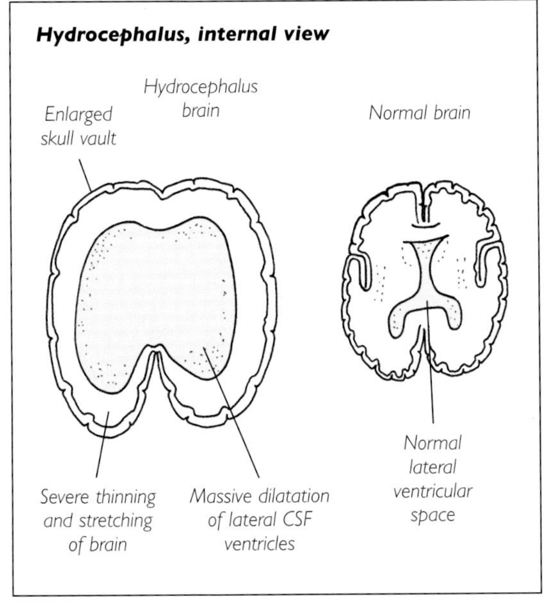

Hydrocephalus is characterised by increased volume of cerebrospinal fluid (CSF) and dilated ventricles. There is usually also an increase in intracranial pressure. The causes could be from an overproduction of CSF, obstruction to the flow of CSF or rarely from defective re-absorption of CSF. Diseases that lead to hydrocephalus include congenital abnormalities (such as congenital stenosis of the CSF aqueducts) or acquired (e.g. from an obstructing cerebral tumour). In the young child the skull is soft and pliable, and so expands to accommodate the enlarging brain, as shown here. If a CSF shunt is surgically inserted in time then this enlargement is prevented. In the older child and the adult, the skull is unable to expand like this, so instead the brain becomes compressed within the skull vault from the increased ventricular CSF pressure.

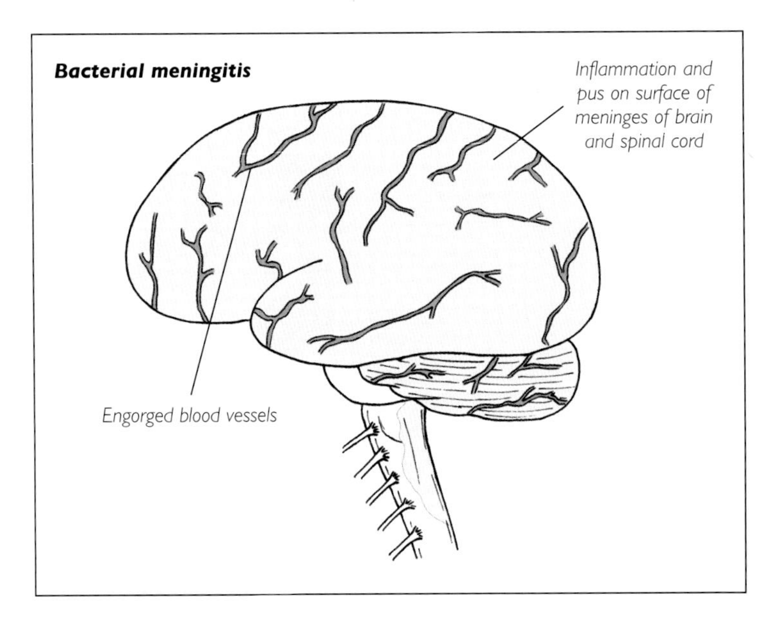

Meningitis is infection of the meningeal linings and subarachnoid space surrounding the brain and spinal cord. This is usually triggered from spread of bacteria from an infective focus elsewhere in the body via the bloodstream, e.g. middle ear infection or pneumonia. Symptoms are an acute headache, fever, vomiting, stiff neck and sometimes confusion.

Giovanni Battista Ferrari, 'Selene, Greek goddess of the Moon', book illustration, 1646, published by J. Janson, Amsterdam. © Wellcome Library, London. The Moon goddess Selene is in her flying chariot drawn by two white horses. Her brother, Helius, the god of the Sun rides beside her, the two thus depicting the passage of time. The Moon governs the past (including past incarnations) and the realm of the subconscious. The Sun governs the future (including destiny) and the superconscious. Since both the Sun and Moon affect the temperature and condition of the air, pestilent diseases and death was attributed to their interaction. Balance between the two thereby imparts health. In this context, the Moon also relates to the functioning of the lower half of the body, the Sun to the upper half.

Original

'Argentum nitricum and lunar forces', by Esther Lane. The influence of the Moon is shown, veiled by a foggy atmosphere with only a few clear areas of starlight, representing the veiling of consciousness by past-life karma. Silvery moonbeams radiate into a lake, within which are submerged soul fragments trapped within these past lives. The potential of the remedy is to bring such experiences to consciousness for a resolution.

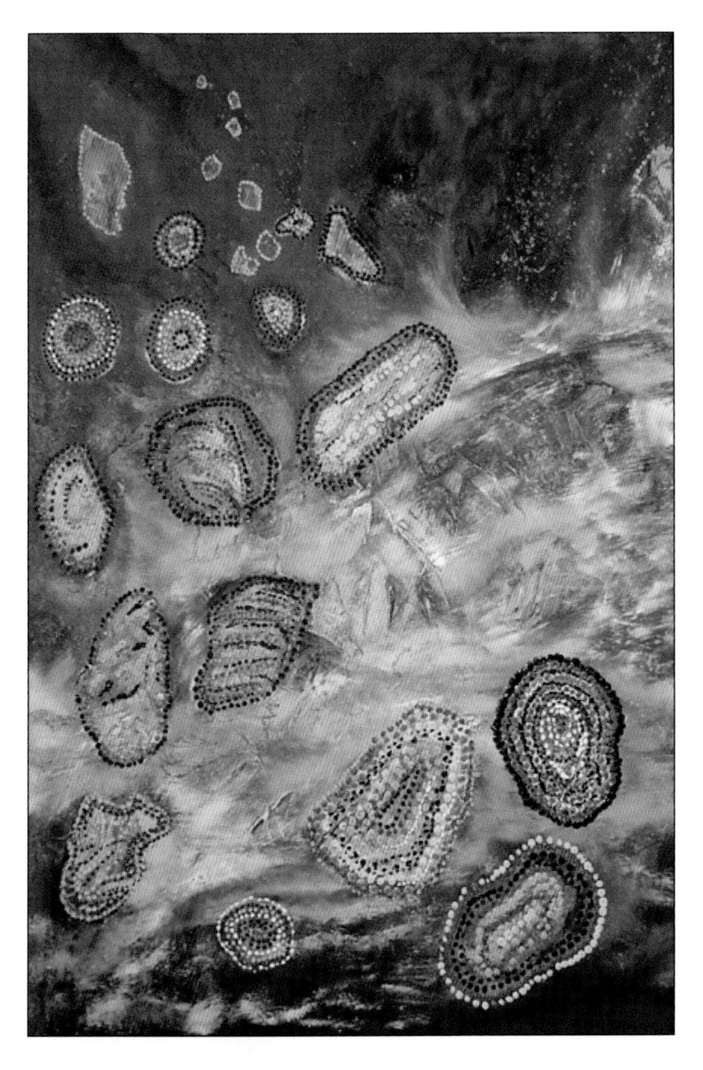

'Down under is in my mind', © Mentes Korucan (2004). This painting was discovered at an art gallery by the author during a trip to Cyprus. The Cypriot artist had travelled and lived in Australia, which had provided the inspiration for much of his exhibition work. A poem he wrote to complement the work: "AUSTRALIA. What a big continent, country… It won't live before my eyes. It's a big love and longing left in me. Years won't let me forget the memory. The nature decorated with greens and blues. The people are black and white. I travelled but couldn't finish. The aboriginal land left its memory in my mind…"

The picture has significant themes depicting the Old Moon state, in keeping with the Argentum remedy picture. During this ancient period of earth history, the world was not yet solidified. The densest level of matter was the gel state, a suspension of solid in liquid. Old Moon was also the proper beginnings of chemical reactions within a liquid phase, and the ether was influenced by colour and sound tones. Beings would have appeared to suspend themselves within a milky soup composing the half-liquid, half-airy atmosphere. These creatures were largely head focused, the body below the neck as yet having limited development. This state is largely that of the human embryo during early gestation, only portrayed at a world and collective humanity level. Even the poem is reflective of the silver state, the artist having entered a mood of nostalgia and resurgence of some ancient memory.

'Frozen Dawn' © Ruth Carthew. The painting is a Cornish landscape, in the background is a disused tin mine, in the foreground are some megalith stones of the Hurler's circles. On the right is the stone formation known as Arthur's seat. The eerie scene is, however, evocative of a lunar landscape.

BELOW. 'Argentum and the weight of lunar memory', by Tasvi Shah. This is an illustration adapted from plate 8 of the 1st chapter of William Blake's prophetic work 'Jerusalem: The Emanation of The Great Albion'. It took Blake 16 years to complete in 1820. Its poetic dream-narrative is a masterpiece in illuminated print, with 100 hundred plates. It does not follow a logical chronological sequence. Blake describes an England, known as Albion, infected with a soul disease. Her rivers are filled with blood from war with Napoleonic France. Religion is used by the monarchy and church to control the masses, greed tainting the message of Christ. Albion must become reunited with Jerusalem for humanity to become redeemed. The illustration shows a daughter of Albion pulling a Moon. It is suggestive of the weight of the subconscious realm, which heavies the soul. Such unresolved incomplete energy within the past timeline may exist at a personal, ancestral, generational, human race collective or world level of memory. Advanced souls can perceive the more worldly and collective memories, thereby transforming and releasing such experiences on behalf of the rest of the race.

Astrology

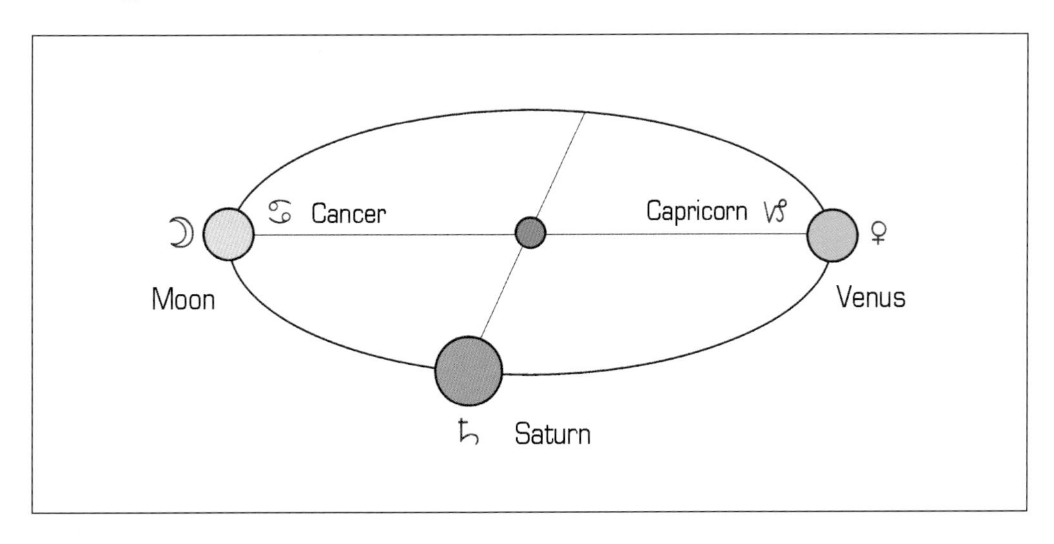

Moon within cancer, opposed by Venus within Capricorn, both squared by Saturn.

Oriental

Liver and kidney yin deficiency, with uterus blood deficiency.

Particulars

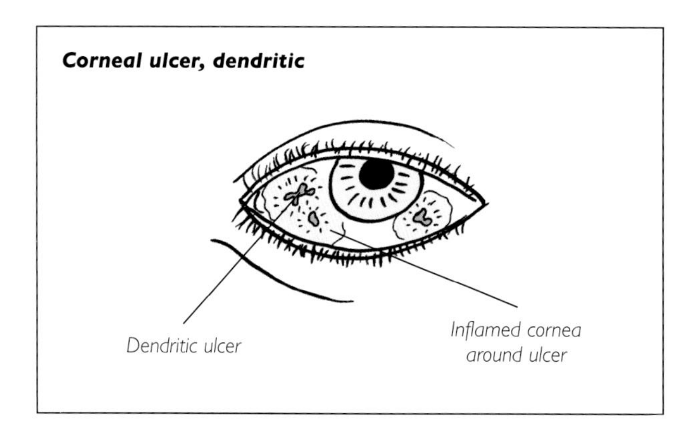

Dendritic ulceration of the cornea can occur in herpes simplex viral infection. There is a painful red inflamed eye with intense watering and photophobia (painful on light). The cornea develops small vesicles which break down to leave raw ulcerated areas, typically of an irregular branching pattern. Other types of corneal ulceration can occur in various autoimmune diseases, e.g. rheumatoid arthritis, and after trauma.

Related Particulars

p.17 Investigation of higher cortical functions, e.g. for dementia
p.17 Alzheimer's disease
p.56 Conjunctivitis
p.103 Tonsillitis
p.4 Croup
p.343 & p.232 Multiple sclerosis
p.443 Arteriosclerosis
p.233-234 Absence seizure
p.532 Skull fracture head injury
p.388 Nerve degeneration atrophy, injury

Original

'Diurnal rhythm of the astral body', by Esther Lane. The left-hand image reveals the flow of the astral body at sleep-time out of the physical-etheric body, towards the dream reality within the astral plane. The right-hand image shows the return of the astral body upon waking. The left-hand image can also be representative of excarnation (exit of the soul with its astral body at death), and the right image of incarnation (entry of the soul with its astral body at birth). The portal into and out of the astral plane (also known as the 4th dimension) is shown with a starry realm beyond. Indeed, the astral body is also known as the sidereal or star-body, an allusion to its journey into the planets and stars whilst away from the physical body. The winged astral body is portrayed with various sacred geometries. Dreams can therefore often feature flying experiences and a sense of such shapes. Fragments of mineral arsenic are depicted lying next to upper parts of the physical body to guide the astral body in and out. The astral especially connects to the heart, lungs and kidneys, and a spiral vortex is shown to indicate this flow. Disorders of the astral body can include lost or missing astral parts trapped within the astral plane after the morning incarnation. This could arise, for example, after psychotropic drugs, shock or a constitutionally weak physical-etheric body (often featuring the psoric miasm) causing loss of integration between the astral and physical. Another problem is where the astral body is unable to effectively leave the physical-etheric during the nightly excarnation, causing the classic midnight aggravation, restlessness, heating of the head (from jammed astrality at this region) and insomnia. This is similar to the situation when a soul is unable to leave at the point of physical death, e.g. when a patient's life is artificially prolonged with drugs and intensive care. This principle was of use for the ancient procedure of Egyptian mummification, where arsenic could preserve soul forces within the remnant physical body.

Astrology

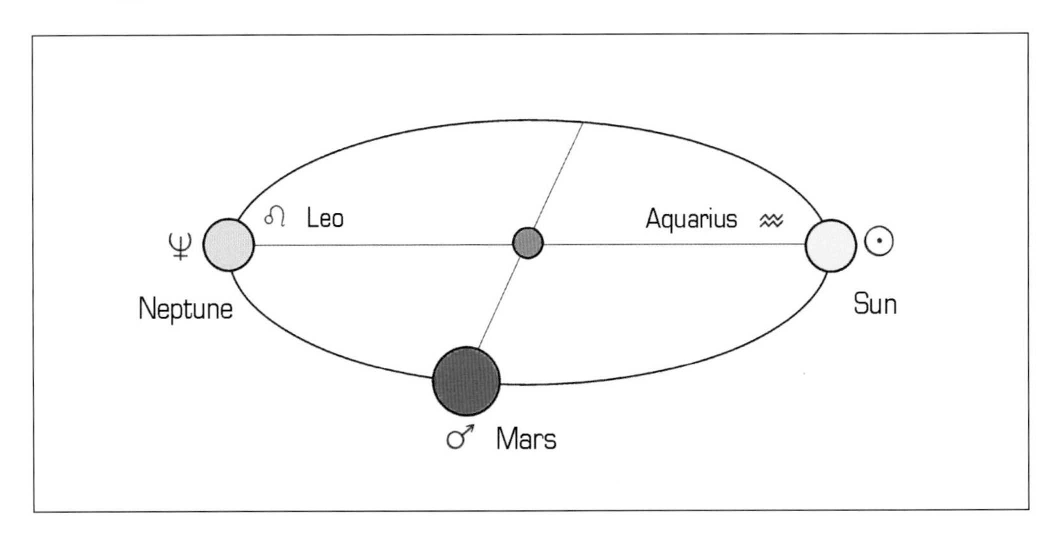

Neptune within Leo, opposed by Sun within Aquarius, both squared by Mars.

Oriental

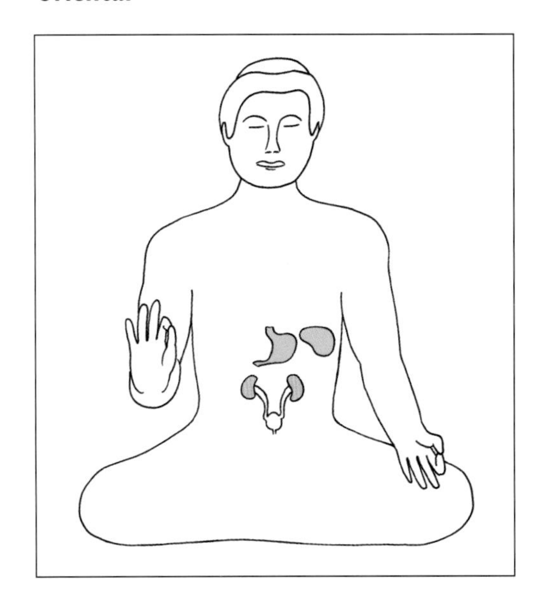

Kidney essence deficiency, with stomach and spleen yang deficiency (although yang deficiency is portrayed in the chi diagram below, significant essence deficiency also involves reduced yin).

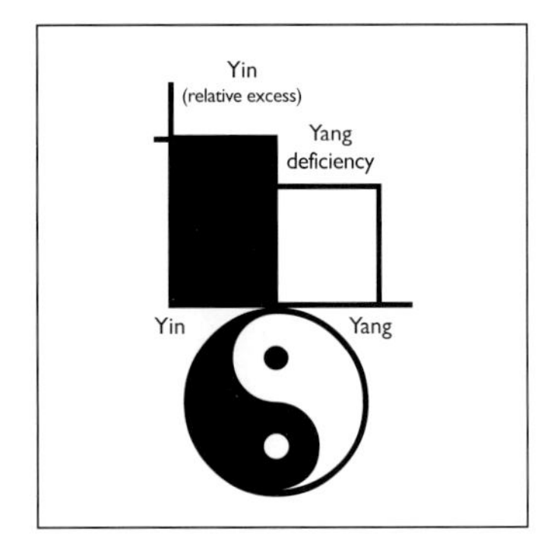

Particulars

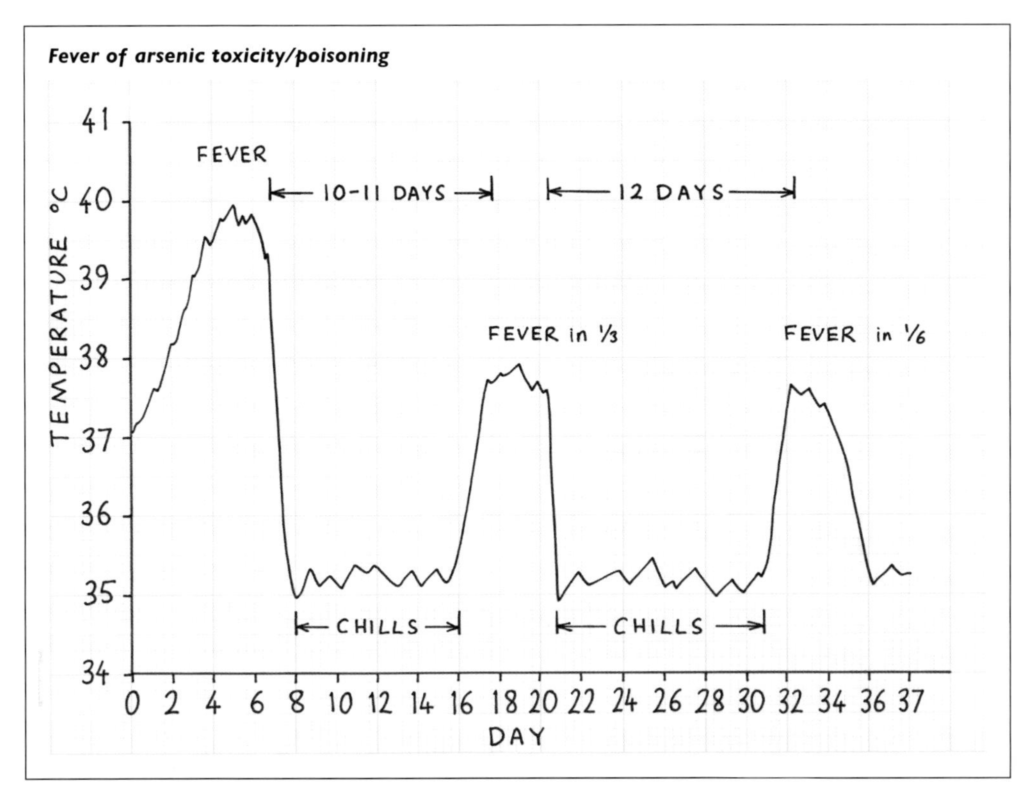

A typical fever chart induced after acute arsenic poisoning is shown. The body temperatures rise to a high fever (40°C) over the first week, lasts about 2 days and then suddenly drops to a chilly phase lasting about 10-11 days. Another fever episode occurs in one-third of victims, again lasting for about 2 days before falling again to a similar chilly phase. In one-sixth of victims another fever episode occurs after this.

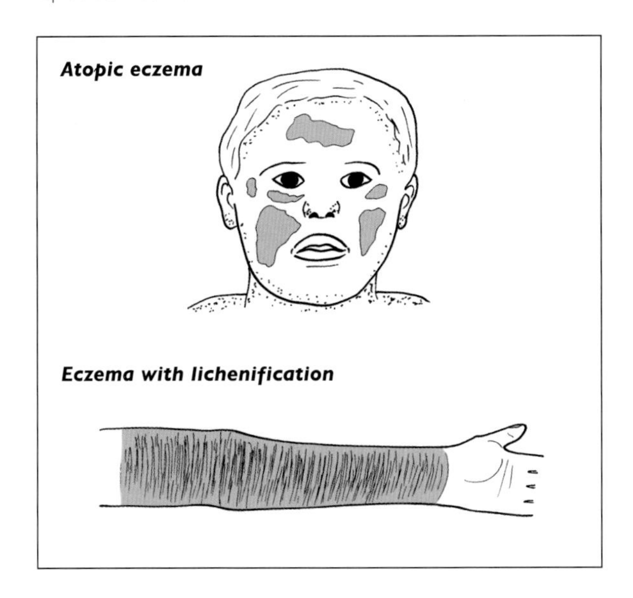

Facial eczema is shown in this infant. There is hypersensitivity/allergy to foreign proteins, often developing from 3 months after birth. Itchy red papules appear on the cheeks, or dry chapped red areas, hypopigmented skin areas and skin weeping. Another common area of involvement is at the elbow and knee flexures, wrists and ankles.

Chronic eczema with constant rubbing and scratching can lead to areas of thickened skin with markings. This is especially seen at the flexures of the arms and legs.

Bronchi – normal and asthmatic

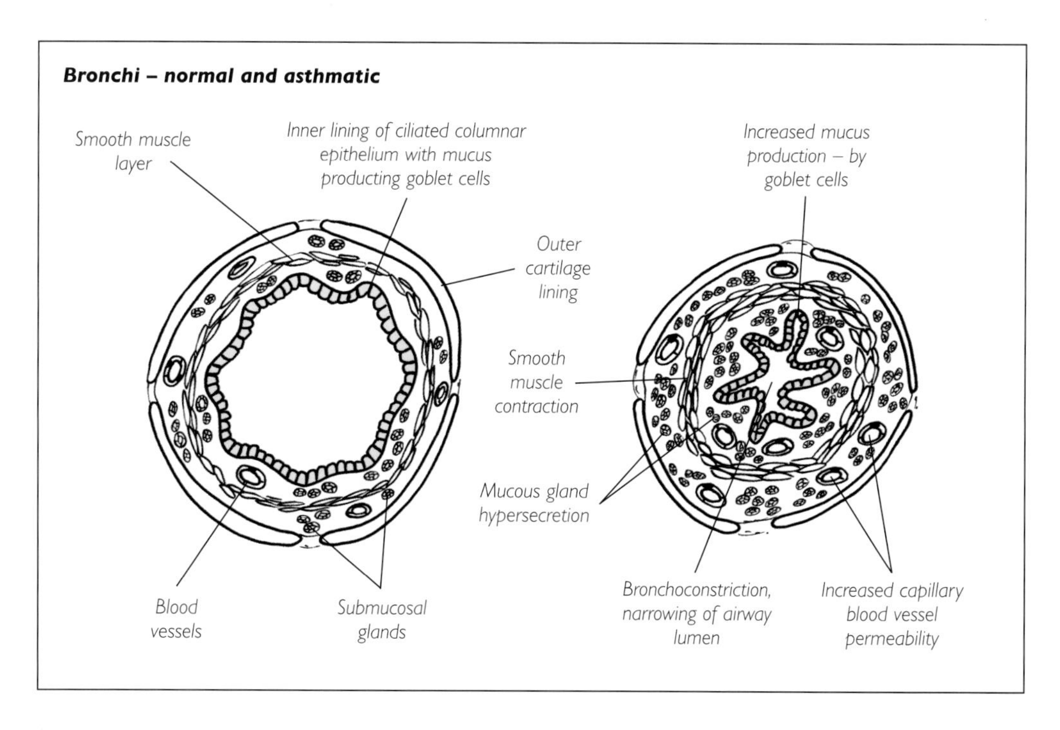

In asthma there is hypersensitivity of the airways, an aggravation of the normal defence response. There is inflammation with release of inflammatory mediators (e.g. histamine, prostaglandins), smooth muscle contraction and mucous gland hypersecretion. Constriction of the airways leads to wheezing and breathlessness.

Related Particulars

p.202 Normal bone marrow
p.376 Bone marrow suppression
p.208 Leukaemic bone marrow
p.177 Pressure skin sores
p.541 Peptic ulcer
p.36 Hiatus hernia
p.582 Infectious gastroenteritis
p.180 Gastrointestinal bleeding
p.494 Crohn's disease
p.721 Lichen planus
p.208 Malignant melanoma
p.640 Peripheral vascular disease

ARSENICUM IODATUM

Original

'Fiery throat chakra and the astral body', by Esther Lane. The astral body is shown hovering above the physical-etheric body, in a state of re-entry (e.g. during incarnation or during waking after sleep). However, the throat chakra and thyroid gland is congested with heat; which is radiating from the front and rear aspects of the chakra. The astral body is similarly fiery. A portal to and from the astral plane is shown above. This state is frequently found whenever the astral body finds it difficult to incarnate, for example, due to vaccination damage, throat chakra communication blocks or suppression of creativity.

Astrology

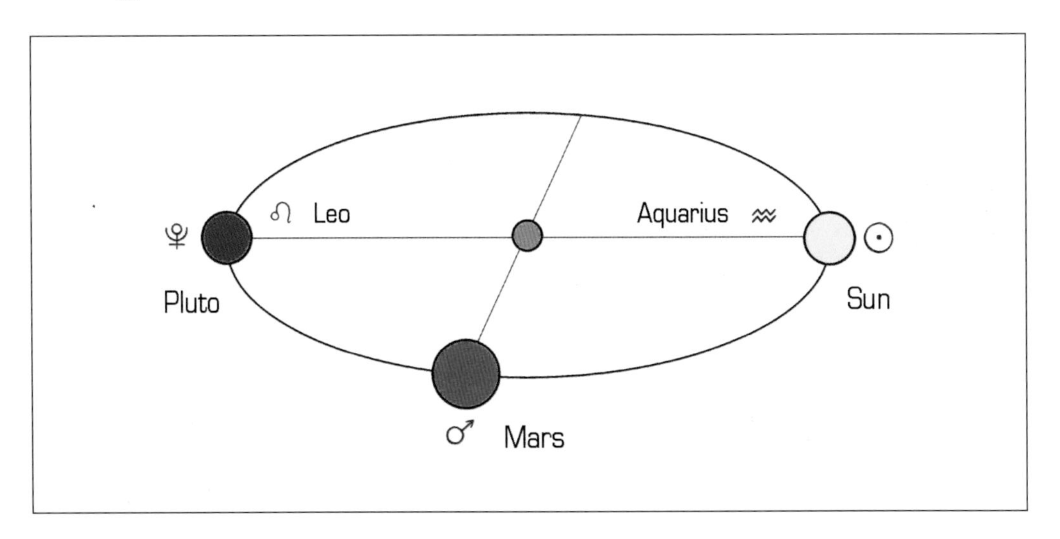

Pluto within Leo, opposed by Sun within Aquarius, both squared by Mars.

Oriental

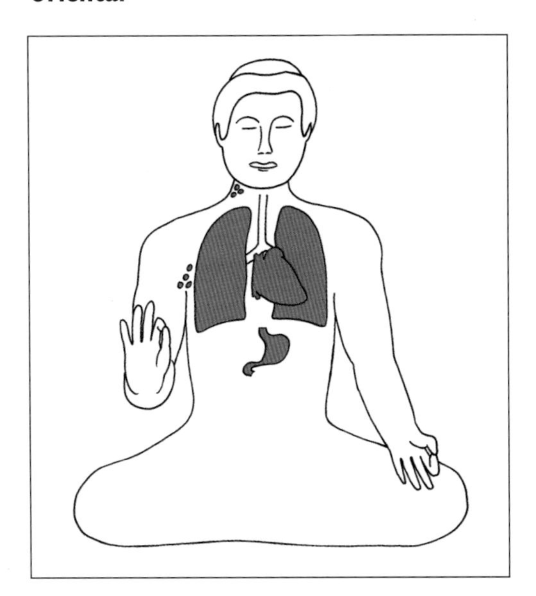

Wind-heat invasion of heart, lungs, lymph nodes and stomach.

Particulars

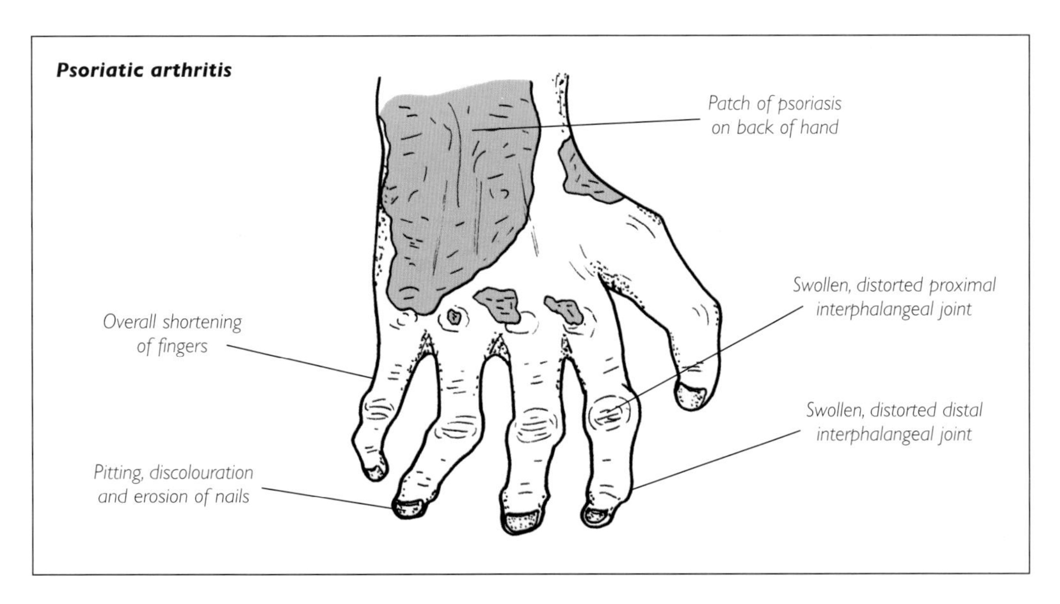

About 10% of patients with psoriasis also have associated arthritis. This particularly affects the finger joints, i.e. the proximal and distal interphalangeal joints. There are destructive and mutilating changes of the bone next to the inflamed joints which causes shortening and angulation of the fingers. The finger bones can even telescope with each other.

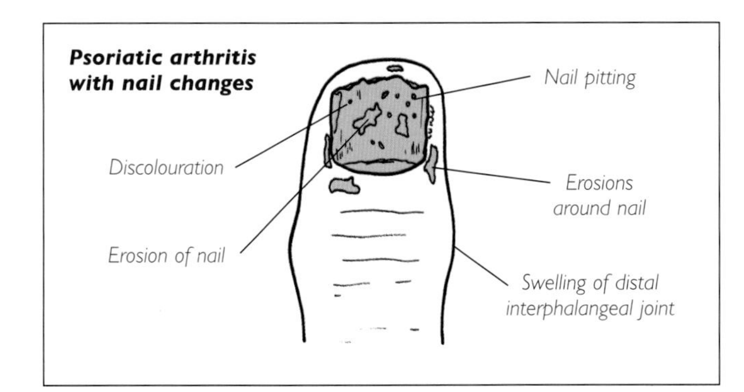

About 10% of patients with psoriasis develop inflammation of the joints, usually of the distal joints of fingers and toes. In the long term there is mutilating destruction of these joints (even to cause telescoping of bones into each other through complete loss of joint between them). Nail changes also occur with pitting, erosions and discoloration.

Related Particulars

p.732 Graves disease exophthalmos
p.729-731 Hyperfunctioning thyroid nodule
p.737 Tubercular type fever
p.737-741 Tuberculosis, primary
p.738 Tuberculosis stages of pathology
p.13 Allergic rhinitis

AURUM METALLICUM

Museum

PRECEDING PAGE. Pompeo Batoni (1708-1787), 'Sacred Heart'. Rome, Church of the Gesu' © 1990 Photo Scala, Florence. The Sacred Heart of Christ provoked some of the most intense religious debates during the period of Enlightenment, and was primarily an 18th century phenomenon deriving from a local cult in southern France. It spread across the world, to trigger an understanding of the divine nature of the human heart at all levels – from the religious to anatomical/physiological. Much Christian reform probably sparked from this impulse. The church of the Society of Jesus is properly known as Santissimo Nome di Gesu, the Most Holy Name of Jesus. Its construction was started for the Jesuit Order near the last few years of the life of St. Ignatius of Loyola (who died in 1556), but eventually consecrated in 1584. Its initial simple and austere design was updated in the more artistic Baroque style from the 17th century. This church is to the Jesuits what Saint Peter's basilica is to most other Catholics.

PRECEDING PAGE. Albrecht Durer, 'St. Jerome seated near a pollard willow', drypoint, dated AD 1512. Saint Jerome, one of the early leading fathers of the Christian church, is shown as a desert hermit. He was born in AD 331 or 242 in Dalmatia of a wealthy family, and died in 420 and advocated fasting, celibacy and asceticism. The background scenery is based on quarries in the vicinity of Nuremberg. In other prints Durer depicted the Saint penitent and punishing himself, e.g. using a stone to beat his chest. In this image his guilt and search for salvation is palpable. The lion slouched at his feet represents the depressed Leo-based forces of courage within the heart.

Original

'Golden Sun', by Crispin Chetwynd. The alchemical relationship of gold to the Sun is indicated. As well as the visible outer material Sun, there are two inner Suns'. One of the inner Sun's represents the destiny of souls evolving throughout the solar system within a stream of karma and reincarnation, and the next innermost Sun conveys the cosmic spiritual natures of souls beyond the need to reincarnate. A lack of the inner solar quality in one's life imparts the state of depression, with its bleak and dark nature. This picture conveys the balance needed between the earthbound state and the elevation of the soul into the solar light.

Astrology

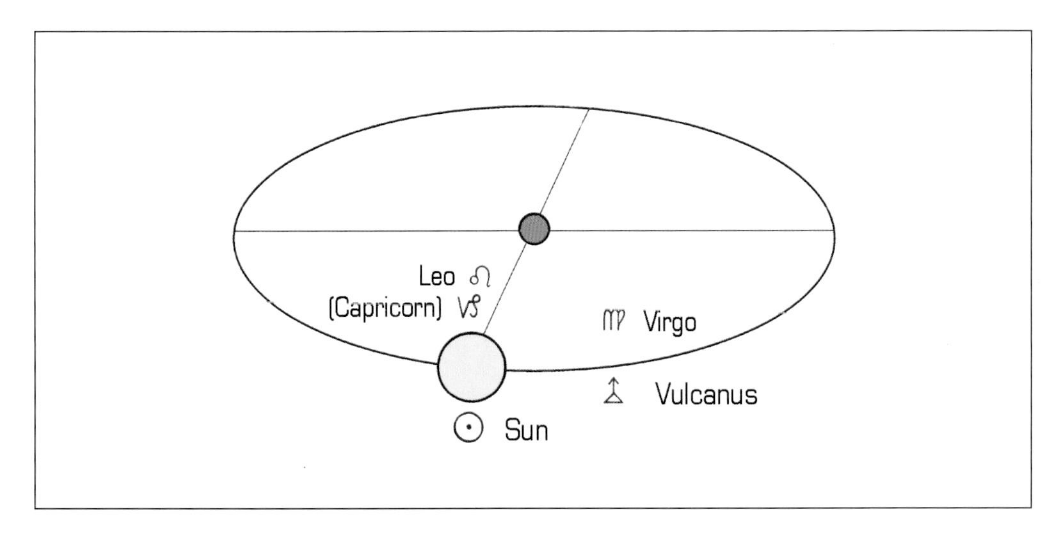

Sun within Leo (or Capricorn), with Vulcanus in Virgo.

Oriental

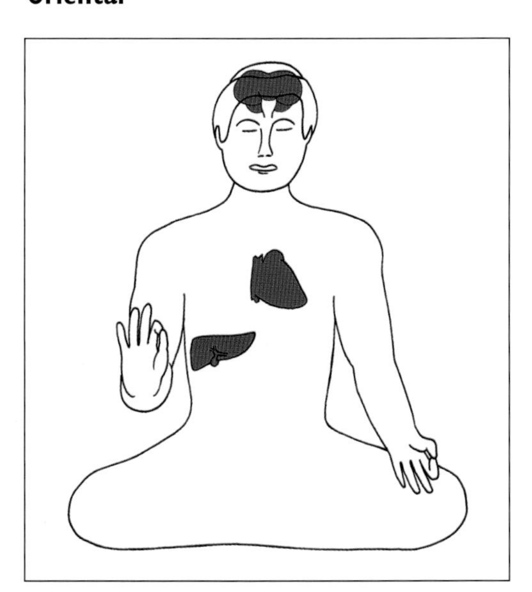

Blood and chi stagnation of brain, heart and liver.

Particulars

Normal heart, anterior-posterior section

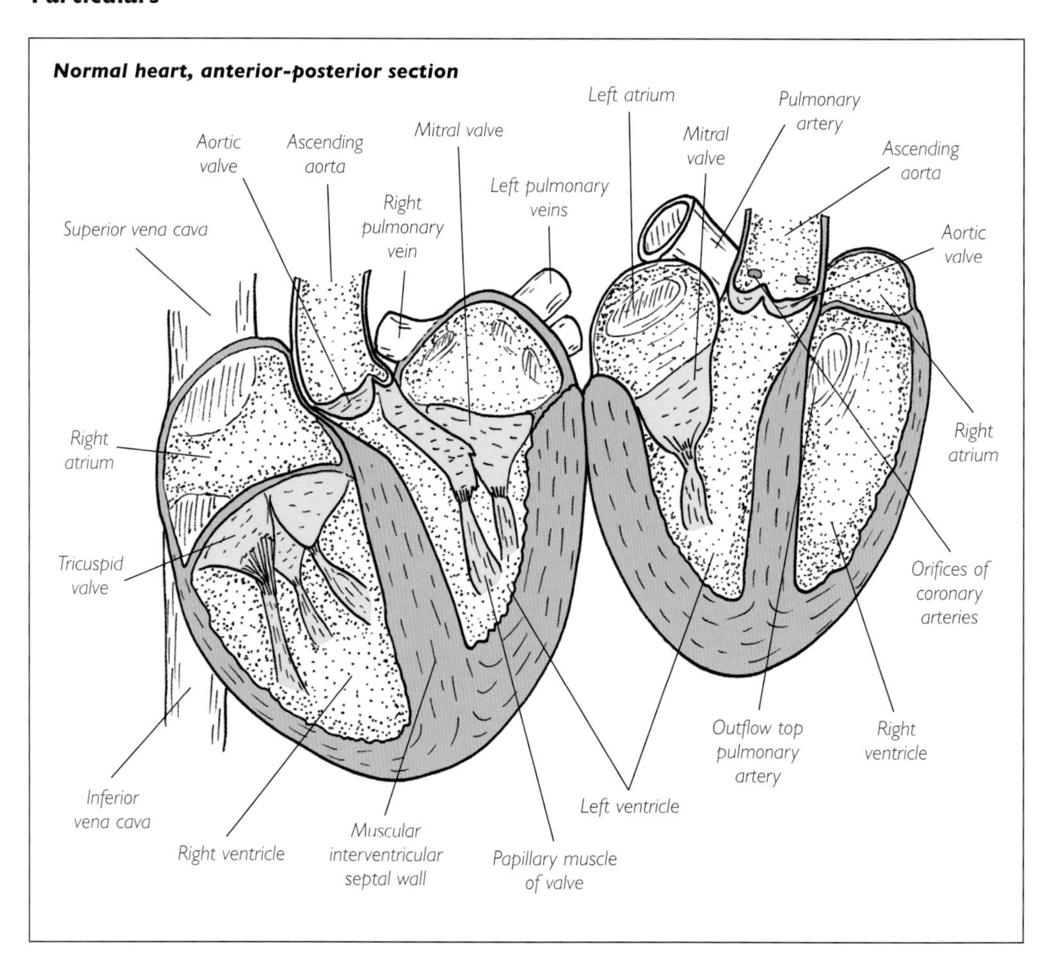

The heart consists of four chambers, two on each side. The right (pulmonary) side includes the right atrium and right ventricle. The right atrium receives deoxygenated blood from the superior and inferior vena cava (blood returning from the body) and pumps this at low pressure to the right ventricle through the 3-cusp tricuspid valve. The right ventricle then pumps this blood to the lungs via the pulmonary artery, where it passes through the pulmonary capillary network around the alveoli to take part in gaseous exchange. Thus oxygen enters and carbon dioxide exits the capillary blood. The left atrium receives this oxygenated blood via the pulmonary veins, and pumps this into the left ventricle through the 2-cusp bicuspid (mitral) valve. The left ventricle then pumps this blood into the ascending aorta at high pressure of about 120mmHg. It has a thicker muscle wall than the right ventricle. The heart valves are attached to the ventricles by papillary muscles and tendon-like chordae tendineae. There are valves also at the entrance of the pulmonary and aortic vessels to prevent regurgitation of blood into the ventricles during their resting phase. The atria pump simultaneously, followed by the two ventricles contracting simultaneously. The ventricular contraction phase is called systole, and the relaxation phase (with refilling of blood from their respective atria) is called diastole. The sino-atrial (SA) node is the primary pacemaker tissue sited at the entry point of the right atrium. This impulse is then passed to the atroventricular (AV) node at the upper septal wall and from here through conducting bundles or pathways into the ventricular muscle layers (conducting system not shown). The coronary arteries supply the heart with its own supply of oxygenated blood, and leave the aorta just distal to the aortic valve cusps.

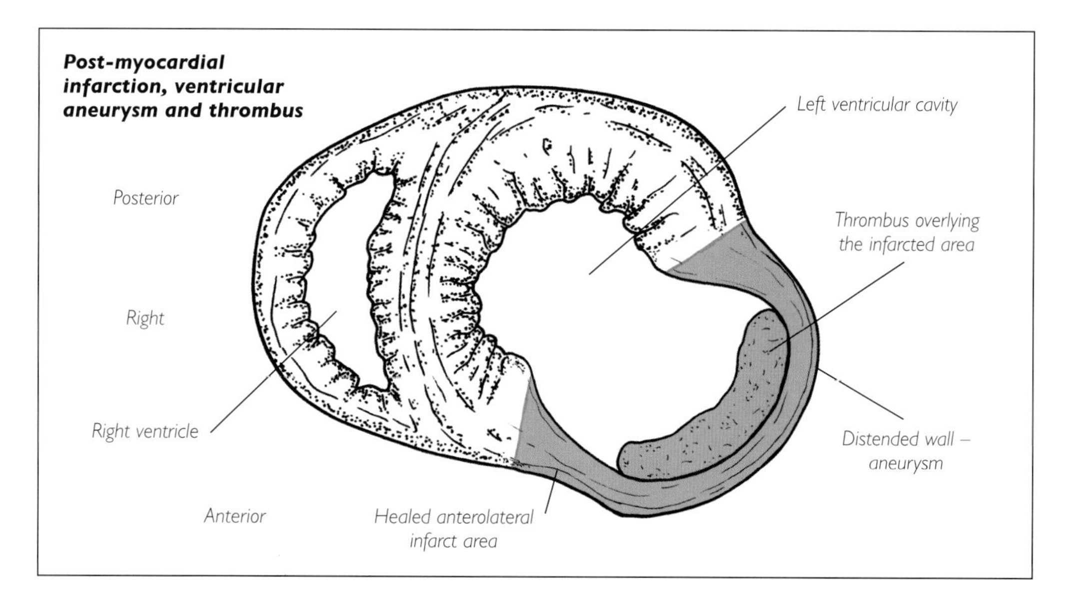

Left ventricular aneurysm is a late stage complication of a myocardial infarction. It can lead to heart failure, arrhythmias or systemic emboli (e.g. strokes). Part of the ventricle wall at the old infarct area has become distended and thinner, bulging outwards. It is common to find a large thrombus lying on the inner wall from the blood stasis at the site. The region bulging outwards is the anterolateral part of the left ventricle.

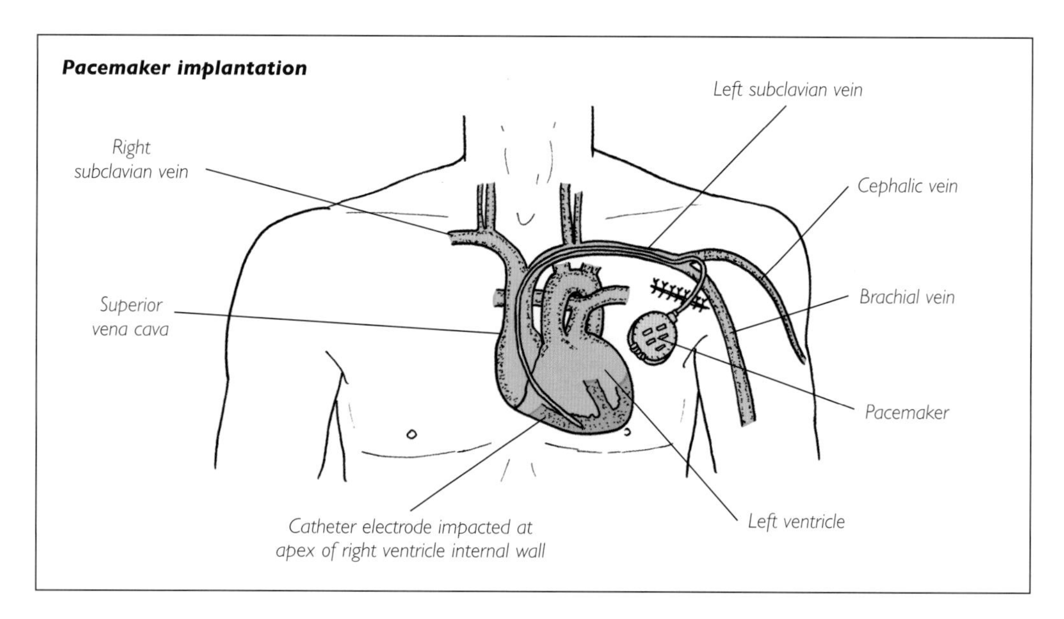

Pacemaker implantation is provided in certain heart rhythm disorders, such as complete heart block. In the example of a transvenous electrode pacemaker, insertion can be performed under local anaesthesia. There is a silastic tube containing the conducting metal coils and contact terminals. The catheter tip is impacted into the trabeculae muscle at the apex of the right ventricle, where the pacemaker generated electrical signals can be fed into the myocardium. Some pacemaker types are 'on demand', which may be set to fire on only if a 1-second or more gap period of absent heart beats develops. Alternatively it can be 'always-on' to drive the heart throughout.

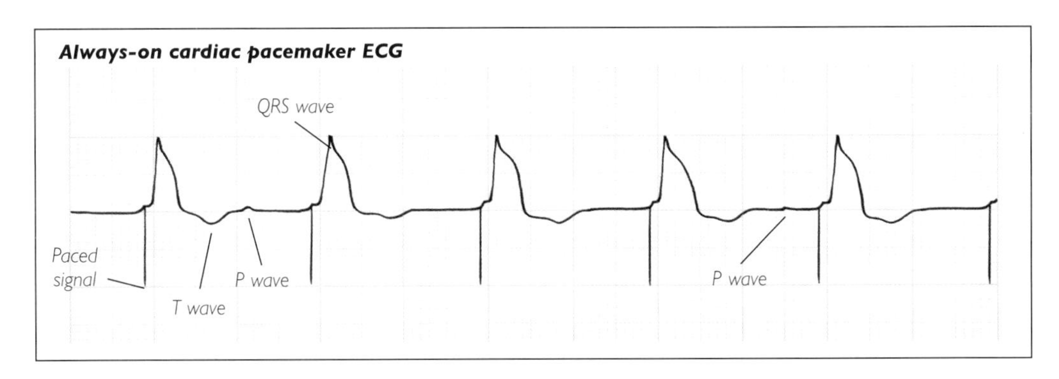

The tip of the pacing electrode catheter has been sited at the apex of the right ventricle. The thin vertical line represents the electrical impulse emitted by the pacemaker. Note there is no relationship between the P waves (atrial depolarisation) with the paced QRS waves, suggesting that before the pacing the patient had been in complete heart block (i.e. asynchronicity between the atrial and ventricular activity).

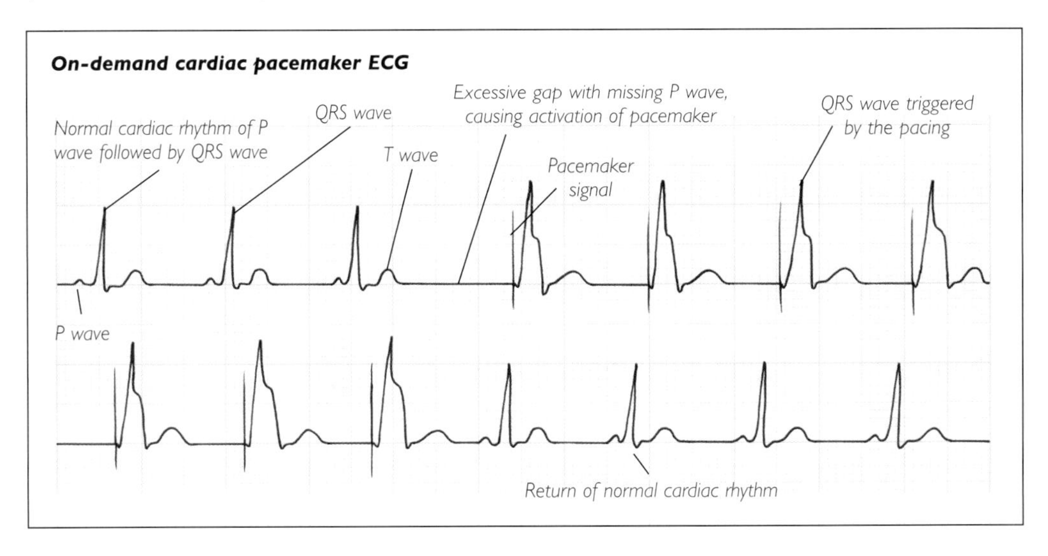

An 'on-demand' pacemaker will sense for normal cardiac activity (i.e. normal QRS or ventricular activity following the atrial P signal). The pacemaker inhibits itself in this situation to avoid competition of signals. However, if a pre-defined interval of time occurs with no P-QRS activity, the pacemaker discharges and creates a paced rhythm. If normal sinus rhythm returns the pacemaker then shuts itself off again.

Related Particulars

p.281 Bacterial endocarditis, p.519-520 Valvular heart disease
p.574 Hypertension & p.451 Myocardial infarction
p.299 Normal ECG & p.299 Atrial fibrillation ECG
p.314 Osteomyelitis & p.171 Osteoporosis
p.691 Paget's disease & p.687 Bone tumour
p.388 Nerve degeneration atrophy/injury & p.285 Cerebrovascular accident infarct
p.343 Multiple sclerosis, p.474 Sperm morphology
p.18 Parkinson's disease
p.17 Alzheimer's disease & p.55 Encephalitis

AYAHUASCA

Museum

The following three images are reproduced from 'Ayahuasca Visions: religious iconography of a Peruvian Shaman', by and © Luis Eduardo Luna and Pablo Amaringo (North Atlantic Books, Berkeley, California). 'Vegetalista' is the term used by shamans to describe themselves in relation to their use of power plants. Healing information is channelled through. Experience enables the shaman to understand the proper healing technique to use, as well as remain protected from the attacks of malefic sorcerers and evil spirits. A strict diet facilitates purification of the body prior to plant usage. 'Icaros' are power songs, especially potent when learnt during the visions and dreams produced by the psychotropic. Vegetalistas' are immensely important to the health and wellbeing of the local community, in rural areas of the Amazon they are the only help available. Illness is therein culturally accepted as due to factors such as invasion by pathogenic objects, spirits, entities, or as a consequence of loss of soul parts or breaking a taboo. There are also dangers to being a vegetalista, for example they may be prey to attacks by evil darts from evil magicians, stealing the soul of their patient's or sending animals to harm them. The images within the publication listed above, by the shaman artist Pablo Amaringo, are based on his experiences as a vegetalista. He possessed an almost photographic memory of the visions, later captured on canvas. There is much interesting iconography and symbology within Pablo's paintings, including Far Eastern/Oriental elements. These also stem from the visions, as Pablo was often shown other cultures across time and space, such as India, Egypt, Persia etc.

PRECEDING PAGE. 'Vision 3: Ayahuasca and Chacruna', © Pablo Amaringo & North Atlantic Books, California. The two essential ingredients of the Ayahuasca are shown. The Banisteriopsis caapi vine is on the right-side; out of this the shaman artist has clairvoyantly witnessed a large snake with yellow, orange and blue spots. The Psychotria viridis (chacruna) shrub is shown on the left-side, with red berries. Out of this flows a smaller more luminous snake, which is ejecting a violet and blue ray out of its mouth into the caapi-based snake. The two snakes penetrating each other thus create a circle, which leads to the consciousness-altering effect. To the left are also seen the four human figures of the teacher and his disciples during the Ayahuasca session. The thready depiction of the bodies represents their nervous systems, upon which the plant mix has had a stimulating effect, especially at the peripheries (fingers, toes, ears, lips, eyes and nose) which are shown in red. Branches of the vine especially link to their heads and pineal glands to indicate the development of their psychic senses. On the far upper left is a bird called rompe-mortajas, in the mid-left is a wise doctor queen and lower-left is a fairy. Just above the chacruna snake is a spirit of the stars/constellations. On the right, is a spirit gardener smoking a pipe – he is involved with the care of the plant. The cricket power animal works with him, and cries out whenever the plant is cut without proper praise or offering. The skulls on the right represent those who have died when using Ayahuasca without the proper care or preparation.

'Vision 28: Spiritual Heart Operation', © Pablo Amaringo & North Atlantic Books, California. The patient is Pablo Amaringo himself, receiving etheric surgery whilst under the influence of Ayahuasca, the people within the hut having appeared as clairvoyant visions. Pablo had suffered from a seemingly incurable and serious heart condition. The spirit doctor is dressed in a grey-violet suit and has opened the patient's chest wall from clavicle to lower left ribcage with a scapula and then broken open the ribs with a hammer. He has removed the heart onto a dish, where he proceeds to repair the coronary arteries using soft plastic tubular prostheses. Meanwhile the wife and daughter of the doctor (dressed in emerald-green costumes) to his left are providing nursing care, swabs and preparing the needle and thread for suturing the wound. Around the left perimeter of the hut the shaman artist sees seven 'Adonitas', these are guardians of sacred temples within outer space. On the upper left are two 'chaicunis', members of a secret tribe. On the far right are several types of beings, for example a medicine woman preparing medicinal herbs. There is a being in a red mantle radiating a yellow aura, this is a 'vegetalista', a particular type of Ayahusca spirit shaman. In the far background are three spaceships, with their extraterrestrials channelling wisdom to the plant-teachers.

'Vision 33: Campana Ayahuasca', © Pablo Amaringo & North Atlantic Books, California. A cleansing treatment is shown here. There is a vegetalista shaman on the lower left blowing onto the stomach of the supine patient, to cure his stomach disease. He is using the spirits of the tree behind him, Ayahúman (Couroupita guianensis, Cannonball tree). The fruits of this tree are shown as skull-like heads with red tongues being projected towards the patient's stomach in accordance with the vegetalista's treatment. At the lower centre is another patient having his aura and energy field cleansed by a vegetalista, who is using a rattle made from leaves of the Pariana plant. He is being assisted by a spirit queen (just above the vegetalista's head), who also has helpers dancing to the music of the icaros under the giant bell above. This bell represents the energy of the heart and of clairaudient hearing. It has been brought by guardian beings with red eyes (just above the bell) known as papulluses, they can be evil/vengeful or kind depending on the situation. The four-headed beings with swords at the centre are aquatic sylph-like elemental beings that reside within underwater cities. They have risen to protect the patient during the ceremony. The snakes to the right represent the powers of the Ayahuasca. The luminescent blue beings centre to the right are Venusians, note the lower half of their bodies is made of pure energy. They have arrived to teach medicine to the vegetalista. Above is a large spaceship. To the right and left of this are cities within the spiritual realm, abodes of masters and civilisations with great harmony.

Original

'Ayahuasca dimensional portals', by Iona Mackenzie. The jungle liana Banisteriopsis caapi is shown throughout the image, and the shaman on the left is vomiting under the effect of the Ayahuasca. An anaconda is grappling with a jaguar, whilst angelic beings gather around to assist in the healing journey triggered by the power plant. The astral plane is especially revealed to the user, thus snake-like and ghostly limbs reach out through these dimensional portals.

Astrology

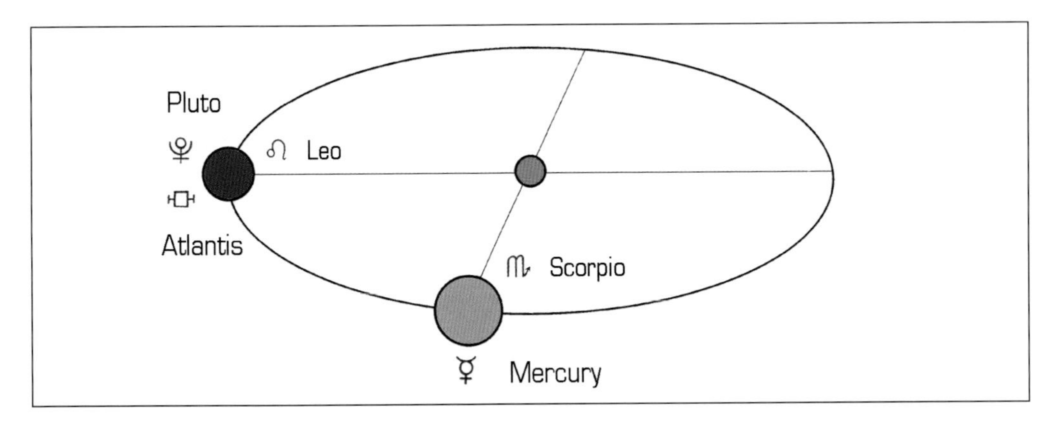

Pluto conjunct Atlantis within Leo, squared to Mercury within Scorpio.

Oriental

Exterior fire invasion of pericardium, with phlegm-fire harassing heart and brain, and also spleen phlegm/damp.

Related Particulars

p.81 Post myocardial infarction ventricular aneurysm & p.300 Cardiac failure, right-sided
p.299 Normal ECG & p.299 Atrial fibrillation ECG
p.91 Cardiac conduction block & p.383 Ventricular arrhythmia
p.82 Cardiac pacemaker ECG & p.640 Peripheral vascular disease
p.172 Osteomalacia & p.171 Osteoporosis
p.277 Motor neurone disease & p.375 Autoimmune disease
p.586 Muscle wasting & p.586-587 Poliomyelitis
p.514 Amniocentesis & p.513-515 Assisted reproduction techniques

BAPTISIA TINCTORIA

Original

'Baptisia and gut typhoid fever', by Yubraj Sharma. The plant is growing within the gut, the roots at the anus. To the lower right is the fruiting pod with the seeds falling out. The gut is inflamed with Salmonella typhimurium. This has led to an ulcerated bleeding rectum. The bacteria may persist within the gallbladder – this state is shown by eggs, suggesting the original chicken source of the Salmonella. The spleen governs the Peyers' patches, which are aggregates of white cells within the gut wall, shown as white lymph nodes. Specialised (as red and blue) white cells are attempting to control the gut bacteria.

experienced the Fall from grace. This third stage occurred during late Lemuria, with the creation of further duality and male and female forms. However, as shown here, the initial outer appearances were very infantile in development, analogous to the pre-pubescent phase of the modern human. The female's ovaries are being connected to the fertile forces Earth mother, whilst the male's testes are connecting to the more cosmic energy of new genetic encodements for the purposes of procreation. The Lemurians were horticultural and worked closely with the plant kingdom. Their influence is demonstrated by the majority of plants still having both male and female forms within their flowers, with the ability to self-pollinate a seed for the next generation.

Astrology

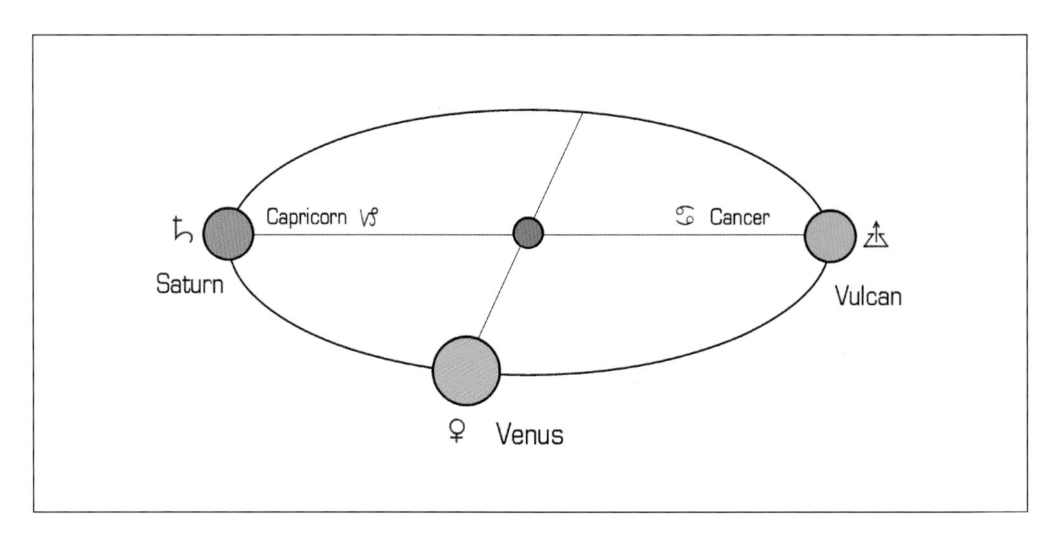

Hard aspects between Saturn and Vulcan (square or opposition), particularly where Vulcan lies within Cancer and Saturn in Capricorn. Venus squared to both.

Oriental

Kidney and brain essence deficiency, with muscle atrophy, spleen damp and lymph node/immunodeficiency.

Particulars

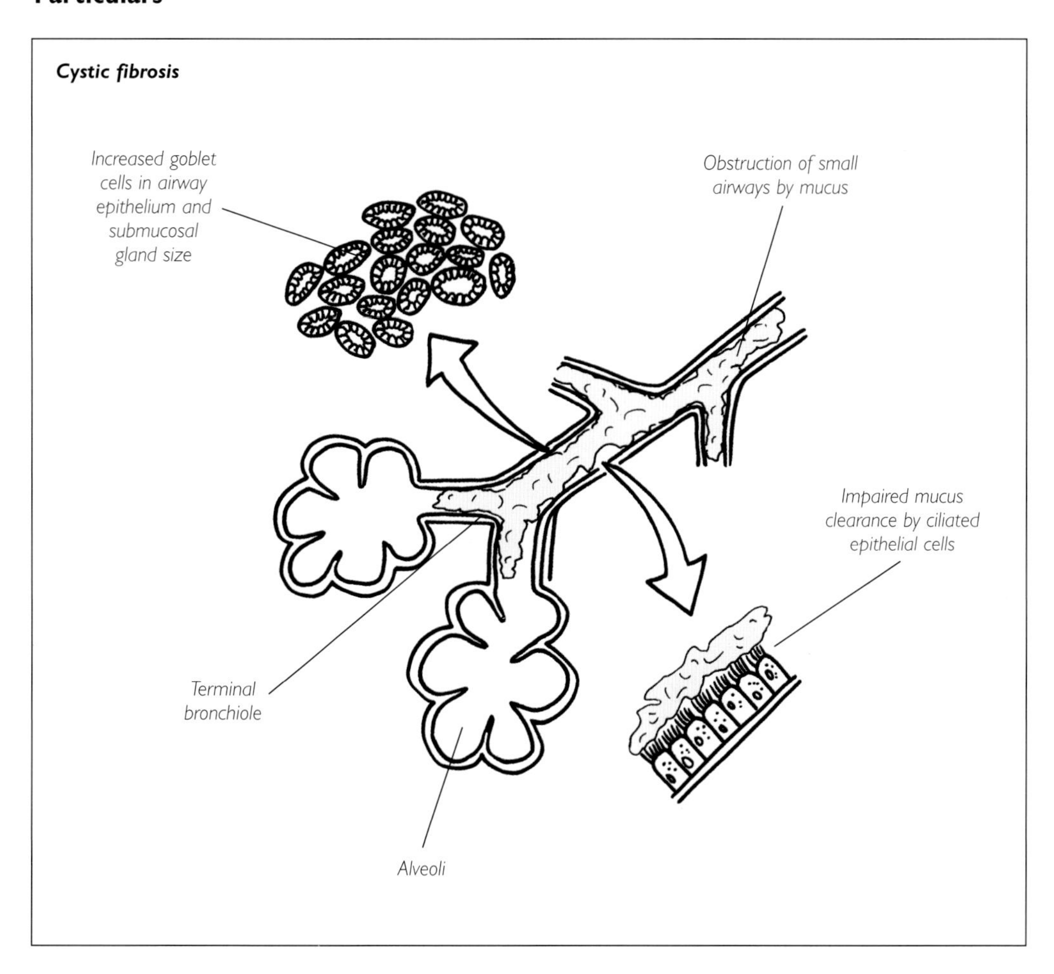

Cystic fibrosis is a common inherited genetic disease (4% of the population are carriers of the abnormal gene on chromosome 7). There is an imbalance of the transfer of chloride across cell membranes, affecting all the exocrine secretory glands to some degree, such as the pancreas, bronchi, bowel, bile ducts and testes. A viscid mucinous secretion is produced which obstructs the ducts of the organ affected, i.e. the bronchioles in this illustration. Recurrent infection (usually by the bacteria Pseudomonas aeruginosa) leads to further lung damage, with bronchiectasis and trapped mucus. Another key organ system treatable by Baryta carbonicum is the spleen and pancreas. In Oriental Medicine this pathology is equivalent to spleen yang deficiency with damp congestion. A state of mucus overload arises from the spleen's inability to transform and transport body fluids. Baryta is also a tonic to the pancreatic endocrine functions (insulin secretion), and exocrine functions (secretion of pancreatic enzyme and alkaline bicarbonate solution). Indeed, cystic fibrosis is the most common cause of exocrine pancreatic disease in childhood. The thick viscid secretions cause cystic dilation of the ducts within the pancreas, with eventual fibrosis or scarring. The lack of enzyme entry into the duodenum especially leads to fat malabsorption (with fat soluble vitamin deficiency), revealed as pale fatty stools (steatorrhoea).

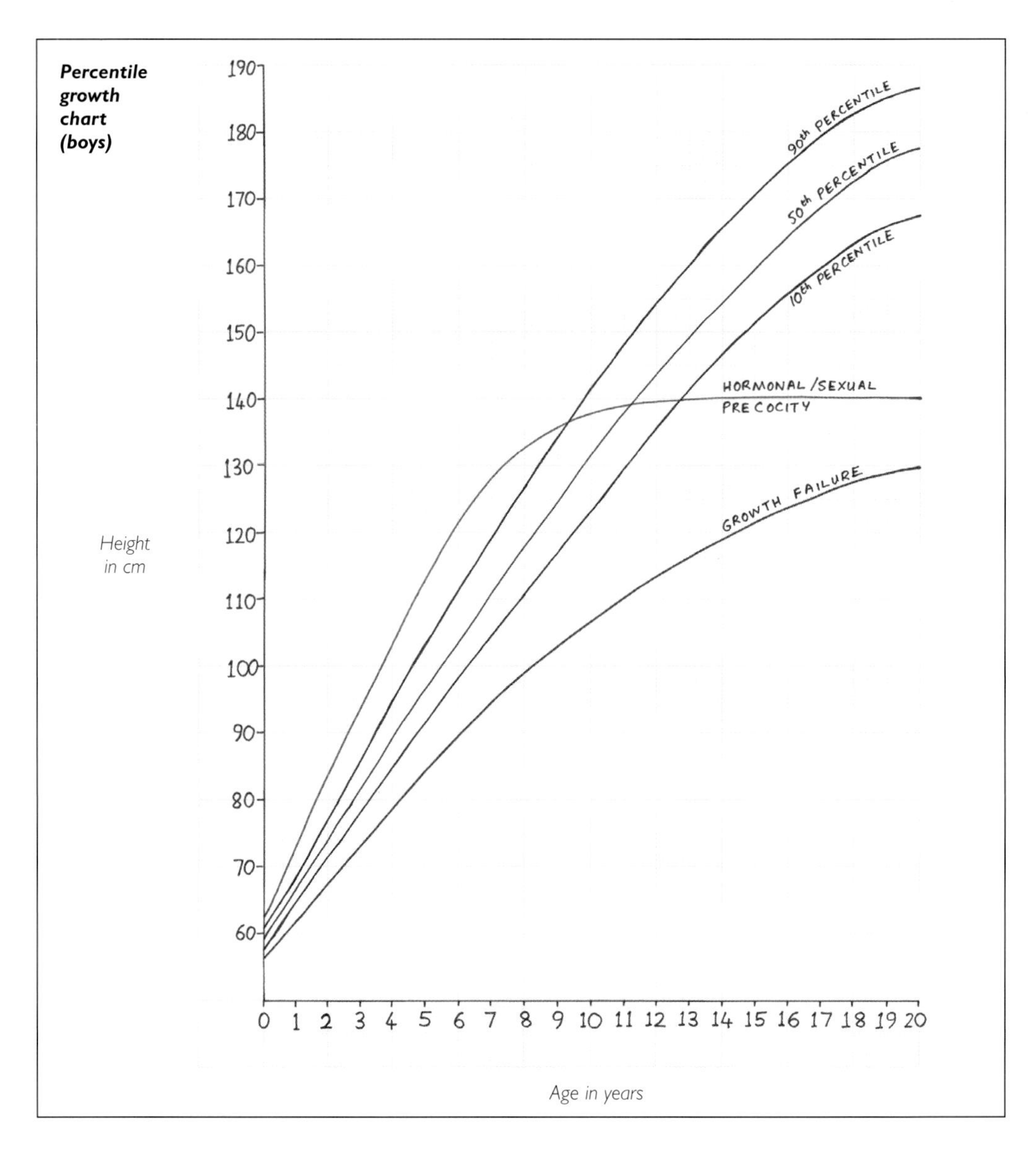

The final height reached after childhood is due to the rate of linear growth during childhood and the time when final epiphysial (growth bone plate) fusion takes place. Growth can be plotted on a cumulative percentile growth chart, as shown here. There is a standard distribution curve for height, compiled from the normal population of children over the age period. For example a 10 year old child at the 10th percentile would rank tenth in height amongst a theoretical population of 100 normal 10 year old children. The 50th percentile is the median height for that age period. The lower red curve depicts growth failure, where height is progressively falling below that of the normal population. There are many causes for this, including endocrine (e.g. hypothyroidism, hypopituitarism, growth hormone deficiency), bone disease (e.g. rickets, osteogenesis imperfecta), systemic disease (e.g. cystic fibrosis, congenital heart disease), genetic etc. The green curve shows a boy with sexual precocity, where excessive adrenal and testicular androgen hormones are secreted in the pre-pubescent period. This stimulates pubic hair growth, increase in testicular and penis size, and muscle mass growth prematurely. However, this growth acceleration then falls off later in the teens such that the boy often has a shorter final height than his peers.

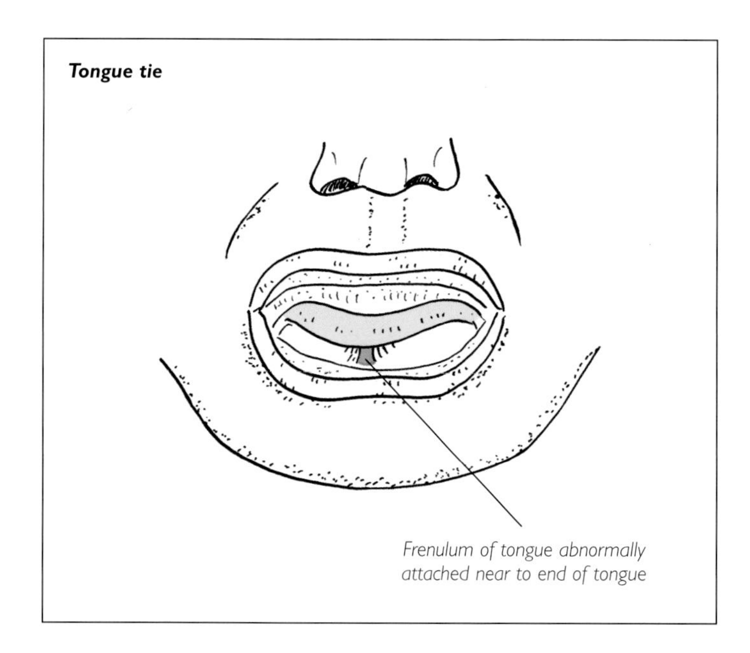

The tongue is a highly mobile muscular organ, comprising a root, body and tip. The root (its posterior part) is attached mostly to the floor of the mouth. The mouth part is freely movable, being loosely attached to the floor of the mouth by the lingual frenulum. When, however, (in the baby), this frenulum extends to the tip of the tongue there is restricted tongue protrusion out of the mouth. If the frenulum grows sufficiently during the first year of the baby's life then surgical correction can be avoided.

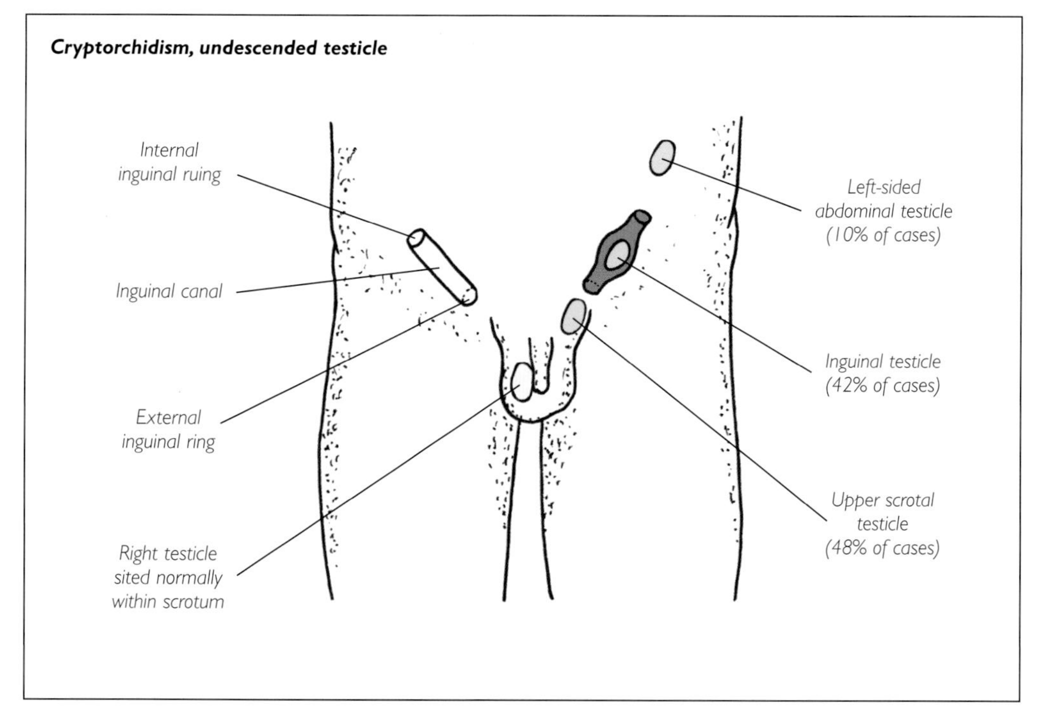

Cryptorchidism or undescended testis is a congenital abnormality where one or both testes are abnormally sited outside their normal position in the scrotum. In most infants the testicle will descend into the scrotum during the first year of life, after that refractory cases may become surgically treated. The descent of the testis may be arrested at any position from the abdominal cavity to the upper scrotum. In this diagram it is shown stopped at three possible sites: within the lower abdominal cavity, within the inguinal canal or at the entry point above the scrotum. An undescended testis is at risk of becoming a tumour, as well as being non-functioning.

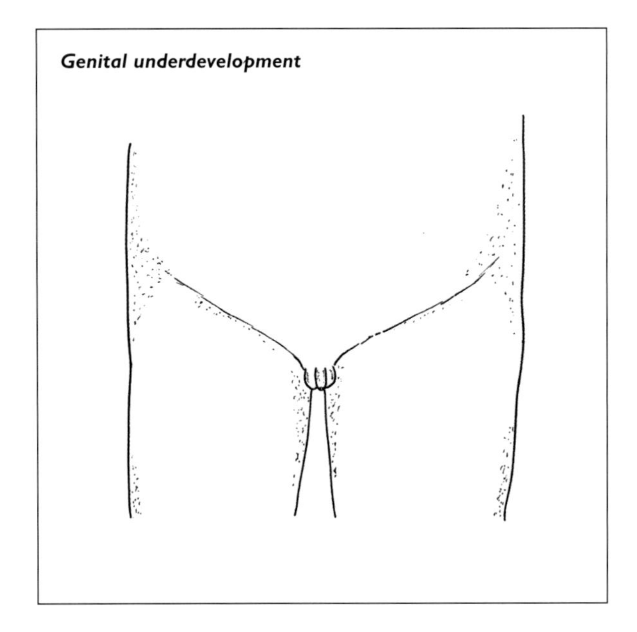

Genital underdevelopment

The primary event of sexual differentiation in the physical body is the establishing of the chromosomal sex, defined by the nature of the 23rd pair of chromosomes (there are normally 46 chromosomes which can be paired). Thus 46 XY is male and 46 XX is female.The embryos of both genders develop identically until about 40 days, and then the gonadal tissue differentiates into testis or ovary. Genes on the Y chromosome trigger the development of the testis; otherwise an ovary is the default pattern.The outer (phenotypic) sex is developed by the action of hormones from the foetal gonads onto the body tissues. There are primordial genital ducts (known as wolffian and mullerian) in the early embryo. The wolffian ducts become male internal genitalia (the epididymides, vas deferens and seminal vesicles) and the mullerian ducts become female internal genitalia (fallopian tubes, uterus and upper vagina). The external genitalia and urethra in both sexes develop from various folds and swellings in the genital tubercle and urogenital sinus regions (i.e. to develop into the penis and scrotum of the male; clitoris and labia of the female). There are many reasons for underdevelopment of the internal and/or external genitalia, in either gender (male shown in this diagram). One category of causation is chromosomal disorders. For example, Klinefelter's syndrome is characterised by small testes, lack of sperm production, gynaecomastia and is due to 47 chromosomes being present (with an extra X chromosome i.e. 47 XXY. In the XX male syndrome there is a genetic female (46 XX) but with absence of female internal genitalia, small testes and penis, lack of sperm and gynaecomastia. Another group of disease is due to disorders of the gonad formation despite normal chromosome genetics. The gonads may fail to develop (forming into a streak of tissue only) and a lack of development of internal and external genitalia. Another type is a disorder of hormone production, such as male pseudohermaphroditism with lack of androgen hormone (testosterone) production. Alternatively there may be 'normal' levels of androgens, but lack of response in the end-tissues to its stimulating action, e.g. due to a lack of cell receptors for testosterone.

Related images

p.103 Tonsillitis
p.501 Otitis media, glue ear
p.408 Sinusitis, nasal polyps

BELLADONNA

Museum

Melchior Haffner, after H.Z. Raidel. 'Poisonous qualities of Belladonna'. (1677), engraving. From a publication by Johann Mathias Faber, published in Angsburg by Goebel. © Wellcome Library, London. The illustration shows both cosmic/light and underworld/shadow influences upon the plant. Part of the zodiac is depicted in the sky (from right to left: Gemini, Cancer, Leo, Virgo, Libra, Scorpio, Sagittarius and Capricorn. Various planets are shown; Mercury in Gemini, Moon in Cancer, Sun in Leo, Mars in Sagittarius and Saturn in Scorpio – with an emphasis on the solar rays. These planets are instilling poisonous qualities into the belladonna plants growing in the shaded glade below, and some humans have become mad through eating them. The emaciated skeletal figure immediately to the right of the fruiting plant in the foreground appears to represent the Grim Reaper or Death. The black berries have ripened into their fully toxic stage and He is holding onto the plant with his right hand whilst harvesting a branch and monstrous half-human looking root in his left hand. Some of the victims almost appear to be sinking into the ground, as if being consumed by some underworld force.

Original

'Belladonna and the interplay of light and dark', by Iona Mackenzie. The plant is shown with its typically downward-drooping bell-shaped dusky purplish flowers. Light radiates downwards but is enveloped by shadow around the plant. Around the root are souls caught in some lower astral plane of existence, also representing aspects of phantom beings or repressed memories.

'Conscious mother and old crone', by Joanna Campion. The image can represent a woman in either the fertile period or within the menopausal phase of life. For a pregnancy the brow or third eye chakra is opening to receiving higher spiritual currents such as the biography of the incarnating soul. Meanwhile the sacral chakra is vitalising the embryonic tissues, preparing this new body for the soul's conscious entry at birth. For the purposes of a menopausal transformation, the third eye is receiving higher wisdom. The sacral chakra is clearing old patterns of behaviour (such as obsolete maternal instincts and physical procreative powers) whilst raising its focus upwards to vitalise the head centres. Belladonna assists this harmonious movement of energy, thus easing the discomfort of hot flushes during menopause.

Astrology

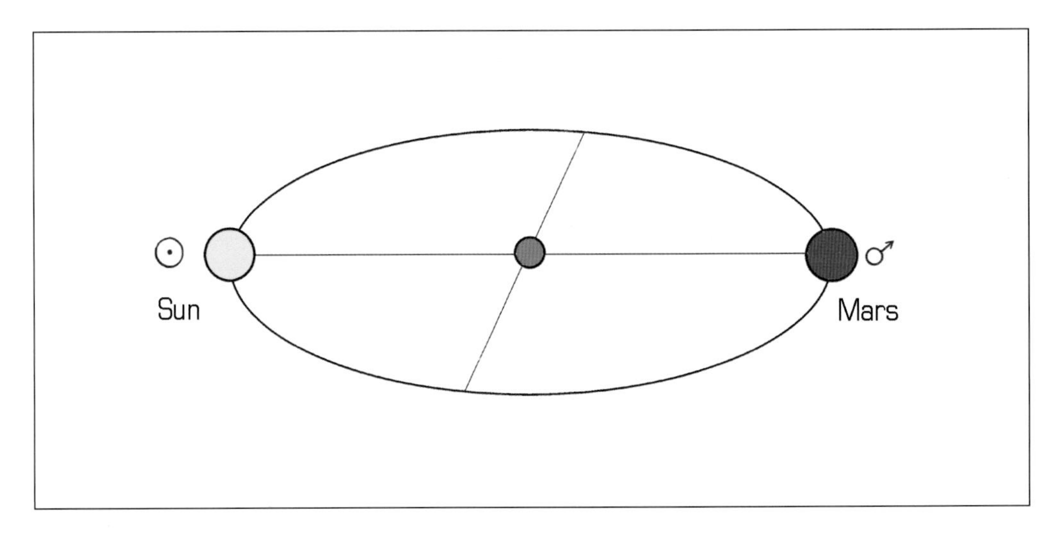

Sun opposite Mars.

Oriental

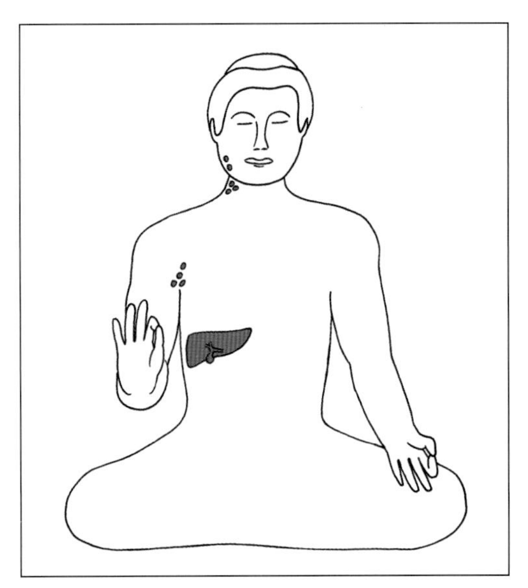

Liver full-heat with heat invasion in lymph nodes/defence layers.

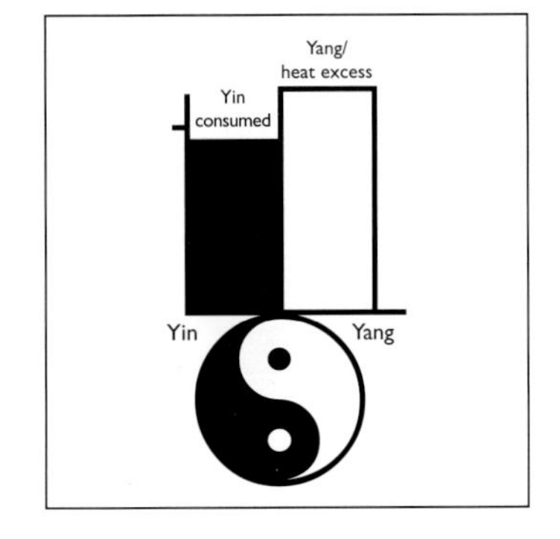

Particulars

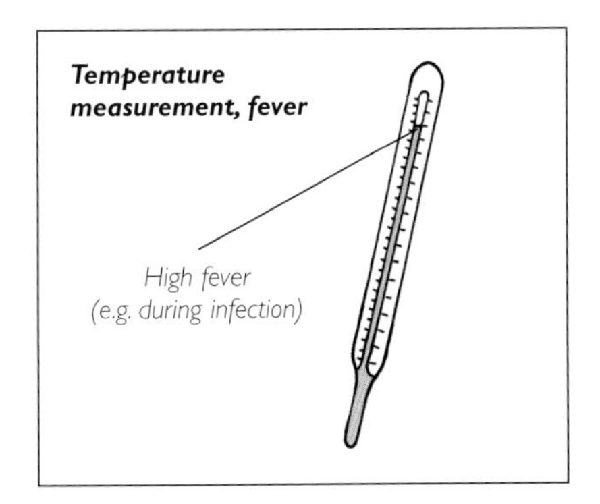

Body temperature is regulated by the anterior part of the hypothalamus at the floor of the third ventricle. This centre is sensitive to various inflammatory mediators released from the white cells when exposed to microbes or damaged tissue. Fever is produced as a positive reaction; every 1°C rise in temperature allows the metabolic rate to rise by 13%. Fever therefore increases the immune response.

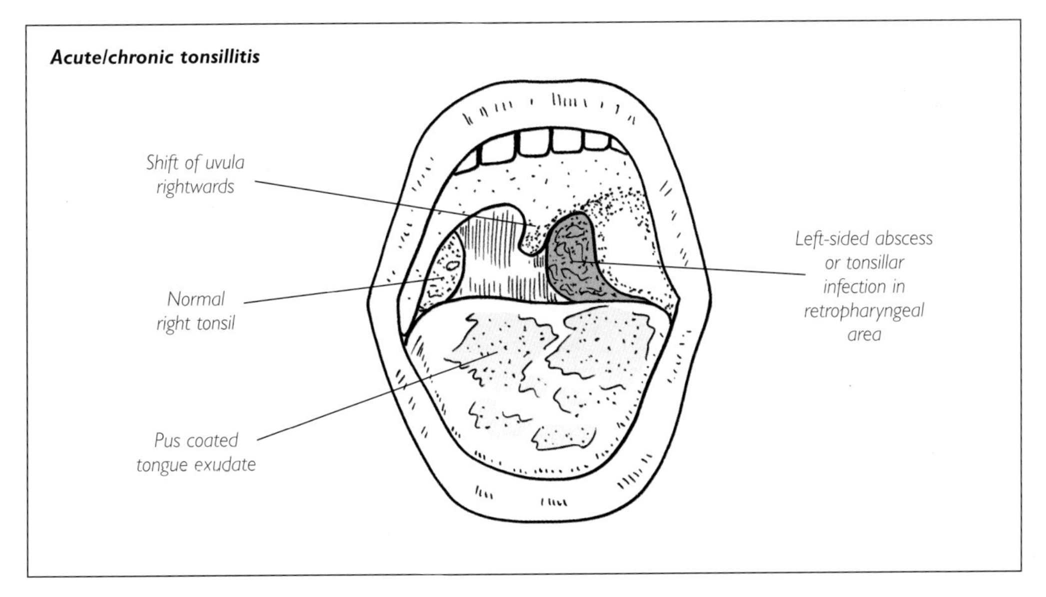

Tonsillitis is a common acute infection, in the past typically due to streptococcus bacteria, but now mostly viral since the widespread use of antibiotics. Initially there are swollen red tonsils with purulent exudates in the mouth. If it does not resolve, then it may progress to chronic tonsillitis and an abscess of trapped pus, as shown on the left side here.

Related images

p.233-234 Epilepsy
p.54 Meningitis
p.55 Encephalitis
p.574 Hypertension
p.37 Pyloric stenosis
p.335 Polycystic ovary

BELLIS PERENNIS

Museum

Gustave Doré (1833-1883), 'L'Enigme' (The Enigma). Paris, musée d'Orsay. © Photo RMN / © Jean Schormans. A sphinx is in a tender embrace with a winged angel and overlooking a scene of devastation from war. It seems strange to juxtapose a sphinx with the scene of a battle set during French history. Nonetheless, Doré may have based his imagery on a reported sighting of such a creature. Amongst other perspectives, the Sphinx has been taken as a guardian being, which could destroy as well as protect. The Egyptian Sphinx was benevolent, whereas the Theban Greek version ate people (preferring them raw). This she did if they could not answer her riddle: "What has one voice, and is four-footed, two-footed and three-footed?" This Greek type was conceived as the daughter of a female monster, either the Echidna or the Chimaera. Her father was the dog Orthos, her sister the Nemean lion. The Sphinx is variably shown as female, male, winged or unwinged, with or without a serpent's tail. The Oedipus myth is closely connected to the sphinx. This tragic Greek hero was the abandoned son of King Laius, who had driven a spike through the infant's ankles before exposing him to the wilderness to die or be eaten by wolves. In other versions he was born with deformed feet and exposed outside the city-state ('polis') to die, rather than to pollute the polis. The wounding of a hero is reminiscent of the chronic wound suffered by Chiron the centaur, or the long-suffering Prometheus. Even after healing, the wound remains at the psychic level. An earlier injury occurred through the child being wrenched away from his mother at birth by the 'evil' father. Yet he grew into a strong adult. Oedipus correctly answered the riddle of the sphinx on his way back from Delphi, stating it was 'Man' – after which the Sphinx committed suicide by leaping off the acropolis. It is noteworthy that Oedipus has therefore not killed the Sphinx with strength or sword, but through his intellect. Ultimately, the Sphinx has a relationship with the constellation Leo, representing the divine nature of the human heart. Free will, individuality and courage to be are related to the functioning of this star-system. The heart must bear true witness to the deeds of one's life, indicated by the weighing of the heart and soul within the Halls of Judgement in the afterlife journey of the Egyptian soul. Similarly, Oedipus is ultimately facing up to his karma without help from the gods. He 'unwittingly' kills his own father and then incestuously marries his own mother, without realising either of their true identities. It is as if he seeks to destroy the perceived source of his psychic pain (his father) and to return to the womb of his mother. He became leader of the polis, but was eventually expelled a second time. He discovered the truth of his crimes to his parents, symbolising the conscious mind realising what lurks within the subconscious. In his agony he blinds himself, taking out his own eyes as a symbol of retreat from the physical world into the inner realm. His mother commits suicide upon discovering she had married her own son. Yet he had exercised his free will in this sequence of actions, for even though the god Apollo had placed him where he was on the road from Delphi, it is Oedipus's own actions that are held to account. The story of Oedipus and the Sphinx combines both themes of how the universe works – chance/chaos and divine order from the gods/higher spiritual beings. Oedipus finds his own individual order within the chance of life; the gods are no longer there to assist him. He combines the two paradigms of being. Furthermore, Oedipus suffers a crippling mental complex leading to his tragic self-destruction. Initially he believes he is empowered and is therefore delusional, losing his connection with reality. This same state is experienced by many terrorists regarding themselves as heroes of a cause, but ultimately destroying the very thing they wish to safeguard. The Oedipus complex may be underpinning much of modern international conflict and war as well as at the individual level. These influences are unconscious and therefore not perceived by those suffering the state. With regard to the Egyptian sphinx, recent evidence has confirmed esoteric lore that the Giza sphinx actually dates back to at least 12,500 years ago, approximately 8000 years older than conventional theories in Egyptology. This would set its origin to the demise of Atlantis. Prophecy has suggested a hidden chamber under the sphinx, purported to be the Hall of Records storing the true history of the planet. The implication is that the sphinx may be able to heal the deep traumas lurking within the collective subconscious and unconscious of humanity from the karma and destruction of Atlantis (see Berlin wall p.119-120).

Original

'Bellis perennis and the scene of battle', by Caroline Hamilton. The daisy flowers are shown as the first population of plant growing amidst the remnants of a battle. Note the basal leaves and the typical disc and ray florets comprising the flowers. The destruction into wasteland with the decay of injured soldiers and the wreckage is clearly evident. Through this plant the Earth is able to heal the scars of war.

Astrology

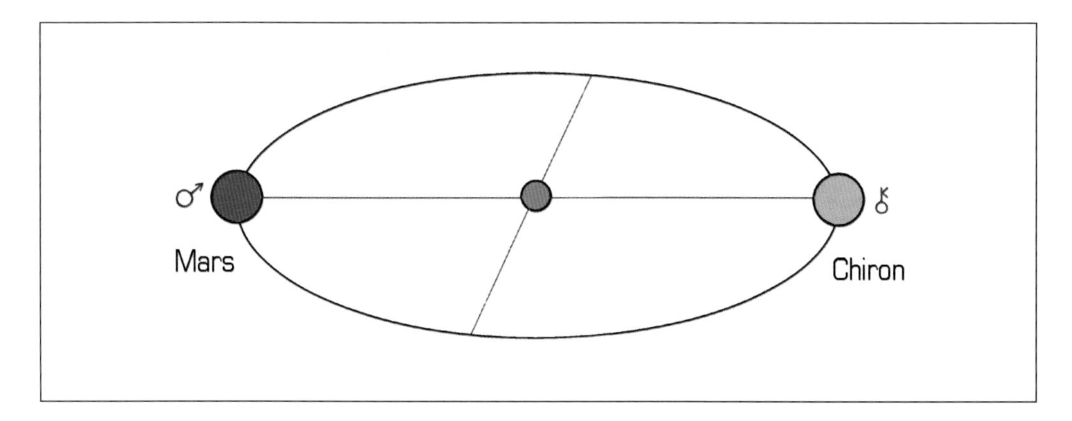

Mars opposite Chiron.

Oriental

Chi stagnation kidneys and blood stasis within lower burner, uterus, ovaries.

Related images

p.176 Cutaneous wound
p.177 Pressure skin sores
p.388 Coccygeal injury
p.461 Retroverted uterus during pregnancy
p.391 Epidural injection
p.339 Osteoarthritis
p.56 & p.340 Rheumatoid arthritis

BERBERIS VULGARIS

Museum

PRECEDING PAGE. Titian (1477/89-1576). 'Crowning with Thorns'. Munich, Alte Pinakothek © 1990, Photo Scala, Florence. This scene takes place after the interrogation of Christ by Pilate, who washes his hands and delivers Jesus over to the soldiers, who beat Him with whips stuck with lead and bone fragments. They then dressed Him in purple, gave Him a reed sceptre and placed a crown of thorns on His head. The soldiers are depicted in animated fashion encircling the central axis of Christ. The impression of dynamic movement is heightened by the sense that this axis is constantly rotating. Titian's brushstrokes are used with immense dramatic power, gradually dissolving into rapidly applied dabs of pigment as he seeks to convey his raw emotions in this tragic subject. Christ's pain and exhaustion is palpable, and the brutality of the soldiers' seems almost explosive. A creepy scene is suggested by the gloom of the background lit by smoky torches. At the front a young official urges the tormentors to continue.

Gustave Doré, 'Le Calvaire' (1833-1883), Strasbourg, musee des Beaux-Arts. © Photo RMN / © Jean Schormans. The crucifixion of Jesus Christ at Calvary/Golgotha, just outside the walls of Jerusalem, is shown in spectacular style by the artist. Within many esoteric teachings, Jesus is said to have received the Christ impulse at his Baptism at age 30, thus becoming Jesus of Christ. However, three years were to pass before the Christ energy could fully penetrate his physical body and enter the Earth, at the time of His crucifixion. It is especially pertinent to consider the role of the two Johns' (John the Baptist and John the Evangelist) in the mystery of Golgotha. Much of this information derives from the channelling of Rudolf Steiner, the philosopher and founder of anthroposophy. John the Baptist (see p.386) was the only person who saw, in the form of the dove, the descent of the Spirit-Self of Christ into Jesus of Nazareth at His Baptism. Steiner described in one of his last lecture cycles the series of incarnations of one of these John's, as Elijah–John the Baptist–Raphael–Novalis. The other John had begun as Lazarus and then transformed to John the Evangelist at his initiation in Bethany. John the Baptist continued to work from the spiritual realm after his death, in effect becoming a group-soul entity for the twelve apostles. Therefore he entered into Lazarus at his initiation in Bethany to bring the two John's into one. This evolved the consciousness of Lazarus greatly. Prior to this merger, Lazarus was only able to function to the level of the intellectual soul, which is the stage of soul development where the powers of the mental body must be evolved. The awakened Lazarus was to later write the Gospel of St. John.

The crucifixion occurred during the cultural phase known as the fourth post-Atlantean epoch or Greco-Roman period (the previous three epochs were the Ancient Indian, Persian and Egyptian), when the development of the intellectual capacity was only just beginning in the human race overall. By uniting with John the Baptist out of the spiritual world, Lazarus received certain capacities of the next soul stage (stages to come for the rest of humanity over the next few thousand years) known as consciousness-soul. With this, the spiritual body works more clearly into one's life on the physical plane. Thus, when Lazarus stood at Golgotha, he was a witness as a being encompassing the whole domain of earth, from its depths to the lofty heights of the world- and human-spirit.

Before the descent of Christ into physical incarnation, He resided within the Sun, as the light of the inner Sun. Ancient esoteric mystery schools recognised this phenomenon, hence initiations involved travel and communion of the initiate into this solar realm (during a three day death-like sleep which was repeated for Lazarus). Whilst within the Sun, the individual would experience life at the level of the solar system, no longer separated from the cosmic realm. However, before the Greco-Roman epoch, this could only be achieved by an initiation involving exit or travel out of the physical body. The twelve apostles had to go through this solar initiation during their training, thus becoming Sun heroes. Note the mythology of Hercules (see p.698-700) as the solar hero in ancient Greek culture by way of preparation. The apostles therefore were able to channel and receive these more ancient sun heroes after their initiation. This meant the power and influence of the inner Christed Sun could permeate humanity from henceforth, through the activities of the Apostles. Thus, at Golgotha, the being of Christ descended from the innermost Sun to the Earth through the physical body of Jesus on the Cross. This is also known as the Turning Point of Time. Lazarus, as witness, now knew that the Sun had once again begun to unite with the Earth, constituting the Turning Point in Time and the ascending arc of world and human ascension, i.e. the resurrection and redemption of the human race could now properly begin. A particular solar initiation was also received by Lazarus-John on Easter Sunday, as suggested in the Gospel of St. John (20:21-22). He is the first proper Christian initiate, and formed a bridging link between the realm of the Sun and Earth, thereby facilitating the descent of Christ from the Sun. Hence, just as John the Baptist functions as the witness to the initial beginning of Christ within Jesus at the Baptism, so Lazarus (see p.195) functions as witness to the conclusion to this process.

The reason why the Johns' could perceive the Christ impulse so clearly was due to the earlier incarnation as Elijah, who helped awaken the conscience of humanity and prepare for the entry of Christ into the world. Conscience is a particular attribute of the soul whereby it can judge the merits of its thoughts, actions and deeds. Usually such activity only fully unfold in a human being after physical death, when the soul can review the life just had. However, John the Baptist could activate the mass conscience of humanity after his death, within the spiritual realm, through his own highly developed conscience. This he transmitted also to Lazarus, thus activating the conscience of humanity at ground level at Golgotha. Indeed, the Gospels refer to the presence of Elijah at the crucifixion, after Jesus called out his last words on the Cross, some of the onlookers exclaimed: "He is calling for Elijah... Let us see whether Elijah will come to save him" (Matthew 27:47, 49). The awakening of conscience is evident in the consternation felt by those around (including the Roman centurions) when Jesus died.

There were four higher members of the spiritual body that were received by Lazarus whilst standing at Golgotha as witness to the crucifixion. Two of these were received from John the Baptist, i.e. the consciousness-soul and the Spirit-Self. Two other higher aspects were also received from other spiritual beings, these aspects being the Life-Spirit and Spirit-Man. Note that after leaving the physical body at death, the soul enters the spiritual realm and becomes aware to some degree of these higher members of its being. The soul initially meets its Spirit-Self, which enclothes the human soul during the period throughout Kamaloka and the astral plane. The Spirit-Self enables a human to become awake to the astral plane. When the soul enters the next level of the spiritual realm, Lower Devachan, it discovers (or becomes conscious of) and becomes enshrouded by its Life-Spirit. This awakens the soul to the heavenly plane. The soul has now shed its astral body; this no longer needed in Devachan. This state continues during its transition through Devachan. Although the Life-Spirit was present during the soul's passage through Kamaloka, it is unconscious to it. Yet, in Devachan, it can now look back on its experience within Kamaloka and realise a higher perspective from its Life-Spirit. A similar process is realised with the next higher member, Spirit-Man, which the soul only becomes conscious of when it enters Higher Devachan. All this pertains to the journey of an average human soul. For an initiate it is different. After his physical death, an initiate can experience the higher members of Spirit much earlier. He can feel the enshrouding by his Life-Spirit already at the actual moment of death and during the dissolution of the etheric body with its memories. He perceives the clothing of his Ego with the Life-Spirit during his passage through the soul or astral plane, and also become conscious of his Spirit-Man upon the initial entering into Devachan rather than later. The astral plane is cosmologically known as the Moon sphere, being regulated by lunar forces. Devachan is, however, an entry into the Sun sphere.

Lazarus, as stated earlier, also received the qualities of the Life-Spirit and Spirit-Man, aside from what he had received from John the Baptist as consciousness-soul and Spirit-Self. The Life-Spirit had to be received from a being residing within the Moon sphere at the time of his initiation in Bethany – this was alleged by Steiner to be the being formerly known as Zarathustra, who could therefore bring through the teachings of the second post-Atlantean epoch (the ancient Persian). During his initiations, Zarathustra had to sacrifice his lower bodies. He sacrificed his astral body to one of his students, who later would become Hermes Trismegistos. He then sacrificed his etheric body to another student, who later became Moses. By this means the whole Mediterranean region was prepared for the later coming of Christ. Zarathustra then reincarnated as one of the two Jesus children (see also p.456), the one depicted in the Gospel of St. Matthew. At age twelve he let go of his physical and etheric body to enter with his ego into the body of the other Jesus child, the Nathan child (that described in the Gospel of St. Luke). Zarathustra lived for 18 years within the body of this Jesus, during which time he imparted all the wisdom teachings of the Sun sphere that he had developed. Then, at the Baptism in the Jordan, Zarathustra left the Jesus man, having prepared the necessary sheaths for the Christ to descend from the inner Sun to replace him and inhabit Jesus. Zarathustra then travelled to dwell within the Moon sphere close to the Earth. During this time, he met again and merged with his former etheric body of the Solomon-Jesus child that had previously died (this was due to the power of attraction between them within the astral plane). This was the etheric body that he had himself prepared and thus contained his wisdom. A new physical body was formed out of this union. Zarathustra had no need to enter Devachan from the Kamaloka plane, because he had already achieved the necessary maturity of Devachan in his earlier incarnations. This union of the ego of Zarathustra with the etheric body of the Solomon-Jesus child could also occur due to the forces of the Life-Spirit that Zarathustra possessed. Also, due to the lack of need to enter Devachan, Zarathustra could and did reincarnate with much greater rapidity back into the physical world. He continued to therefore have earthly lives, with short phases between leaving the physical body and entering the next, thus being an influence at every century since Golgotha, in order to perpetuate the Christ influence on Earth.

Lazarus, at his initiation at Bethany, received an impulse from Zarathustra, in effect becoming Zarathustra's deputy during the phase of this being's residence at the Moon. In this way, Lazarus brought the entire second post-Atlantean epoch (which was founded by Zarathustra) into a resurrection of its Sun wisdom for the present epoch. In that ancient Persian culture, the Life-Spirit (also known as Buddhi) worked in the astral body, and this Life-Spirit was thereby imparted to Lazarus. It is pertinent to note the words Jesus spoke from the Cross to the watching Lazarus-John,

"Behold, thy mother!" This indicates the presence of the Mother as Sophia-Mary, the cosmic Mary and the presence of the ego of Zarathustra, who was the Solomon-Jesus child born to this mother. Jesus could direct these words to Lazarus as the latter had received this Zarathustra impulse.

A third individuality was also present at Lazarus's initiation, imparting to him the forces of Spirit-Man from the Sun sphere. When the event of Golgotha is perceived from this Sun sphere what is experienced is the departure of Christ from the Sun into the dying physical body of Jesus on the Cross. This sacrifice is a kind of cosmic death of Christ; i.e. He died to the Sun and came down to Earth. The solar beings, which included Archangel Michael, thereby noticed the aura of the Earth suddenly light up again from its previously darkened state. The Earth had become a new Sun. Rudolf Steiner especially points to the importance of the individuality known as Aristotle for this aspect of the event of Golgotha. The soul of Aristotle had developed a very clear and complete consciousness in the Sun sphere, and was thus a suitable witness from the Sun sphere for the Turning Point of Time. The Sun is the source of all intellectual life and Archangel Michael as Lord of cosmic intelligence oversees this function. During his life in the 4th century BC, Aristotle had translated practically the whole of the mystery-wisdom of the ancients into clear philosophical thoughts. He became the father of modern scientific and rational thinking. (Note that science has become excessively materialistic due to the added influence of the Academy of Gondhishapur through the Arab world). Plato, on the other hand, was still imbued with the imaginative thinking of the ancient mystery-schools. Plato could still perceive the workings of God and higher spiritual beings into earthly life, and considered the thinking of humanity was so feeble and unclear as to constitute the world of Maya or illusion. The being of Plato would not have been able to grasp the nature of the crucifixion, as he was not separated enough from the spiritual realm. Indeed, certain early Gnostic teachings even believed Christ had lived on Earth in an illusory body, and consequently experienced only an illusory or symbolic death. There is therefore no need for a doctrine of Resurrection from the physical and such teachings cannot comprehend the deeper mystery of the event. Only through Aristotelian thinking, with its separation of spirit and matter could Golgotha be rightly understood. Eventually such thinking will be able to fathom the underlying mystery of the event, i.e. the creation of the Body of Resurrection.

Aristotle took the development of thinking to a very high level. He sought to gain knowledge of every aspect of nature. He even created his 'Logic' as a means to analyse the laws of thinking itself. These principles are still valid today. Whereas Plato's knowledge was received as imaginations from out of Sun but reflected through the Moon sphere, Aristotle received his wisdom directly from the Sun - and this was thus abstract in nature. Aristotle was the first human being, using these Sun forces, to think through all the wisdom available to humanity at that time, including such wisdom beheld by initiates of the ancient mysteries. Through such activity, Aristotle created a spiritual-mental shell on Earth, which would receive the Michael impulses of cosmic-intellectual intelligence, particularly from the 8th century AD onward. Humanity is now able to thereby attain its freedom within the Aquarian age through the reception of such thinking.

Through such a life of receiving Sun wisdom, Aristotle was able to have a very clear existence in the Sun sphere after his physical death. Indeed, Aristotle had lived and thought on Earth as if he belonged to the community of Sun beings. The Sun was his true home. The aspect of Spirit-Man enables this Sun wisdom to be attained; it provides the clarity to develop the right ego-consciousness in the Sun sphere. Aristotle was able to more fully develop his Spirit-Man than any other prior human being; he could live intensely with this part of him. He thus made the Spirit-Man available to Lazarus at the Bethany initiation, at the same time as the channelling by Zarathustra of the force of Life-Spirit and John the Baptist of the Spirit-Self. Lazarus thereby stood before Jesus Christ like a pillar of fire connecting the depths of the Earth to the highest heavenly sphere of the Sun. By this means, Lazarus was to be the earthly witness to the Turning Point of Time, with the three spiritual individualities in his spiritual make-up being the super-conscious witnesses. This superconscious witnessing is all the more important when considering the path of descent of Christ from the Sun to the Earth at the Baptism. Christ would be required to leave His cosmic Spirit-Man behind on the Sun, and then leave His cosmic Life-Spirit behind in the Moon sphere surrounding the Earth, before entering with His Spirit-Self and Ego into the three auric sheaths of Jesus of Nazareth. It is of the nature of John the Baptist, Zarathustra and Aristotle to be able to follow this descent. It also indicates that John the Baptist has a particular affinity to the cosmic body of Christ's Spirit-Self, Zarathustra to His Life-Spirit on the Moon, and Aristotle to His Spirit-Man on the Sun. These three individualities will continue to be bearers of these aspects of Christ to future humanity and in their own future incarnations. John the Baptist re-incarnated as Raphael and Novalis, and will in further lives develop the Grail Mysteries - these will become fully developed teachings in the sixth cultural epoch. Zarathustra will bring to future humanity the peak of development of the forces of the Arthurian Knights, who at their time could perceive the influence of Christ's Life-Spirit in the Moon sphere. These teachings will be needed in the War of All against All in the seventh cultural epoch. Aristotle, as the thinker for all humanity, will transmit his impulses into the following great sixth earthly period, after the seventh post-Atlantean cultural epoch. At this great time there will be a total transformation of human consciousness.

Through Golgotha, Christ merged with humanity, brought His light to the world, and thus made it possible for every human to receive the same initiations as for Lazarus. The stage of Sun hero can now be attained without having to leave the physical body at death, and without having to lose consciousness of the material realm. The ultimate completion of this is the eventual merging once more of the Sun and Earth.

Gustave Moreau, 'Pietà' (1854), oil on canvas. Paris, musee du Louvre, D.A.G. (fonds Orsay) © Photo RMN / © Jean-Gilles Berizzi. Pietà refers to the Lamentation and also the Deposition of Christ after descent from the cross. Joseph of Arimathea obtained Pilate's permission to bury His body, and the closest people took Christ's body from the cross, washed it and buried Him in a new tomb not yet used for burial (being the eve of the Jewish Sabbath).

Original

'Berberis vulgaris and the crown of thorns', by Caroline Hamilton. The shrubby plant is shown coiled as a crown around the liver of Christ on the cross. Note the 3-pointed stem spines, the hanging flowers and berry-like red fruits. Through the liver puncture wound (created by a lance known as the Spear of Destiny) Jesus poured his Christ resurrection codes into the matrix of the planet. The descent of Christ from the cross, followed later by His Resurrection, Transfiguration and Ascension is shown as the vertical axis of the cross. Human blood similarly contains these resurrection codes. Iron within the blood flows between a polarity of earthbound heaviness and spiritualised buoyancy. If the individual is caught at one of these extremes it leads to the state of melancholy/depression or sanguine/mania respectively.

Astrology

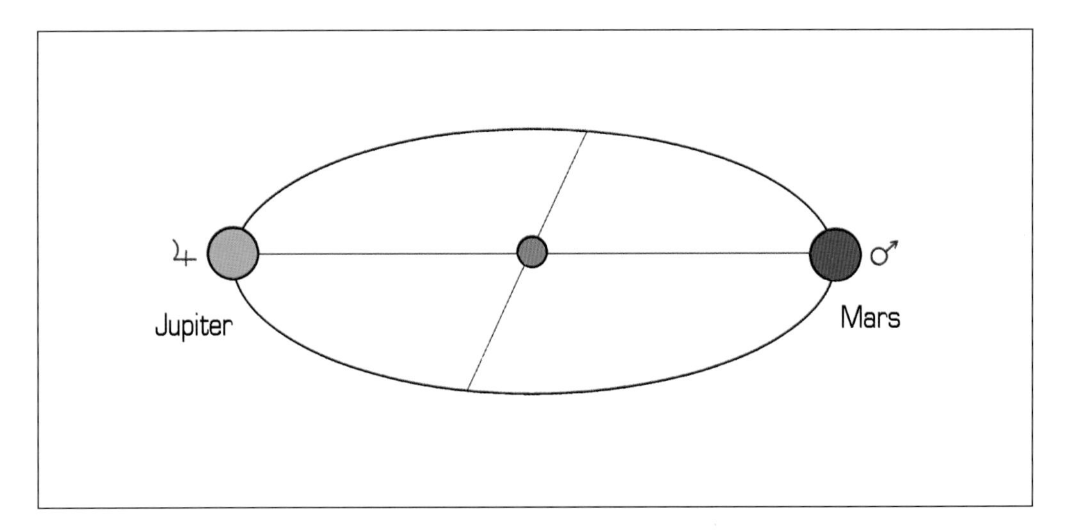

Mars opposite Jupiter.

Oriental

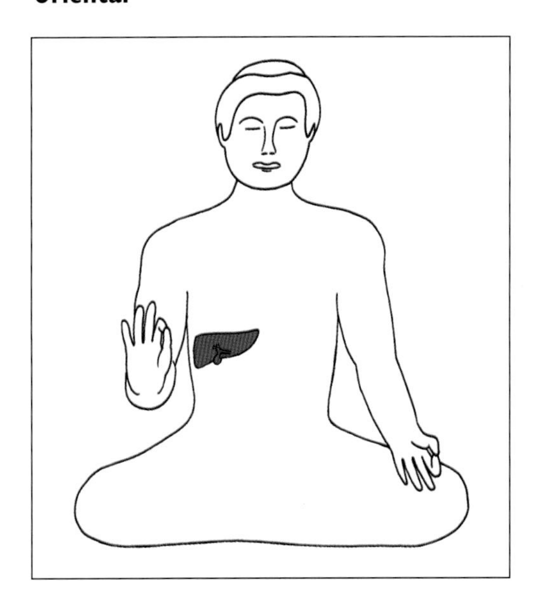

Chi stagnation of liver, gallbladder.

Particulars

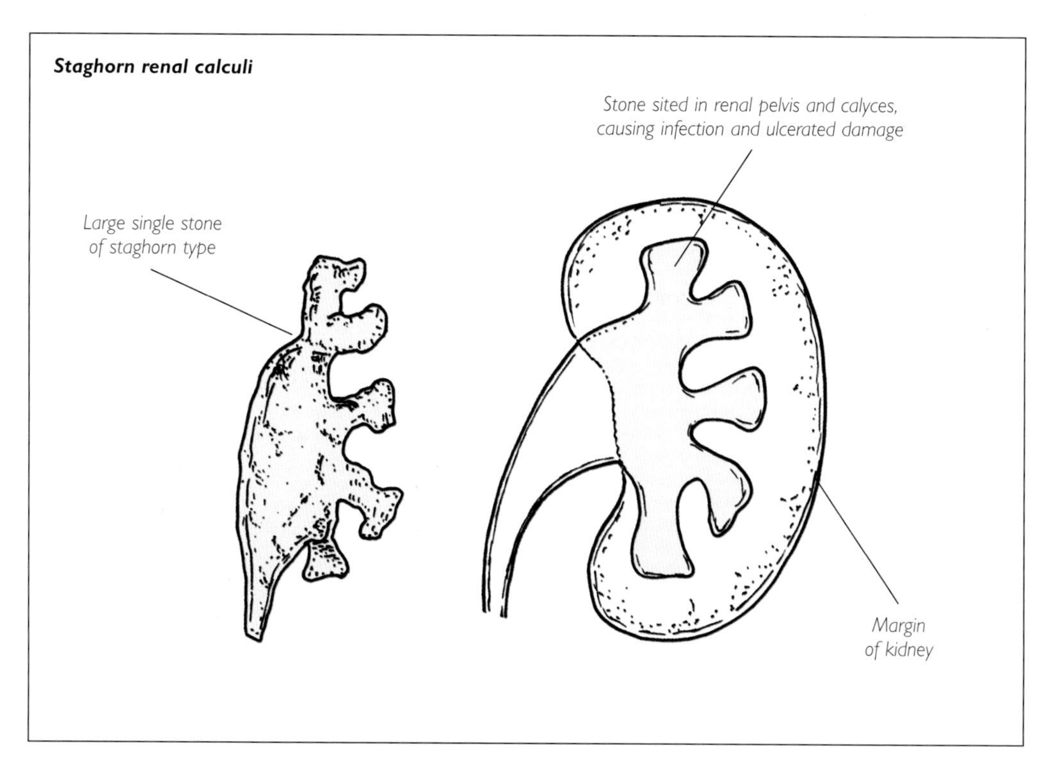

A staghorn calculus is possible after impaction of a large renal stone at the upper end of the ureter, with urinary stasis, hydronephrosis (dilated collecting ducts) and local infections. This encourages the formation of further stone formation on top of the seeding stone. In some cases there is a risk of cancer transformation.

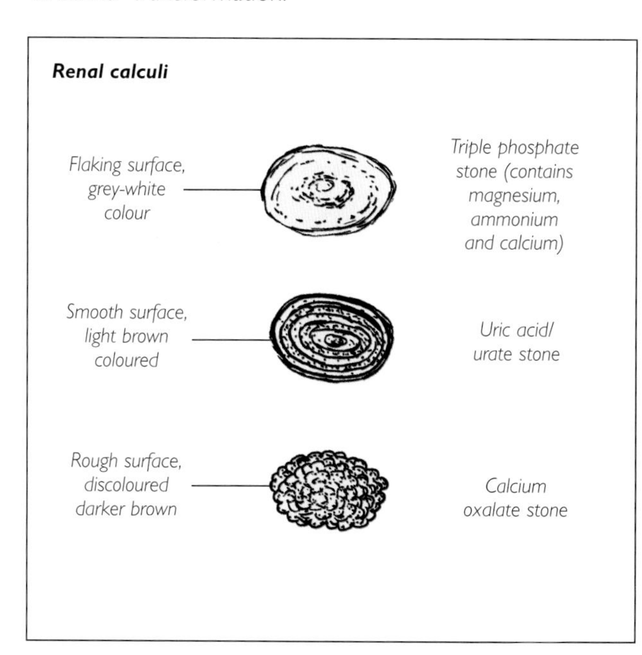

There are three basic types of kidney stones, and mixtures of these types may occur, e.g. urate stones can have a covering of calcium oxalate. Calculi generally form from excess excretion of the stone substance into the kidney tubules, with supersaturation and often bacterial superadded infection. Change of urinary pH, dehydration, any other causes of urinary stasis and other types of renal disease all increase the risk of stone formation. Passage of stones is painful with ureteric spasm and impaction of the stone leads to risk of kidney damage. The colicky pain is centred at the low back/loin area and radiating to the groin. There is painful urination with blood.

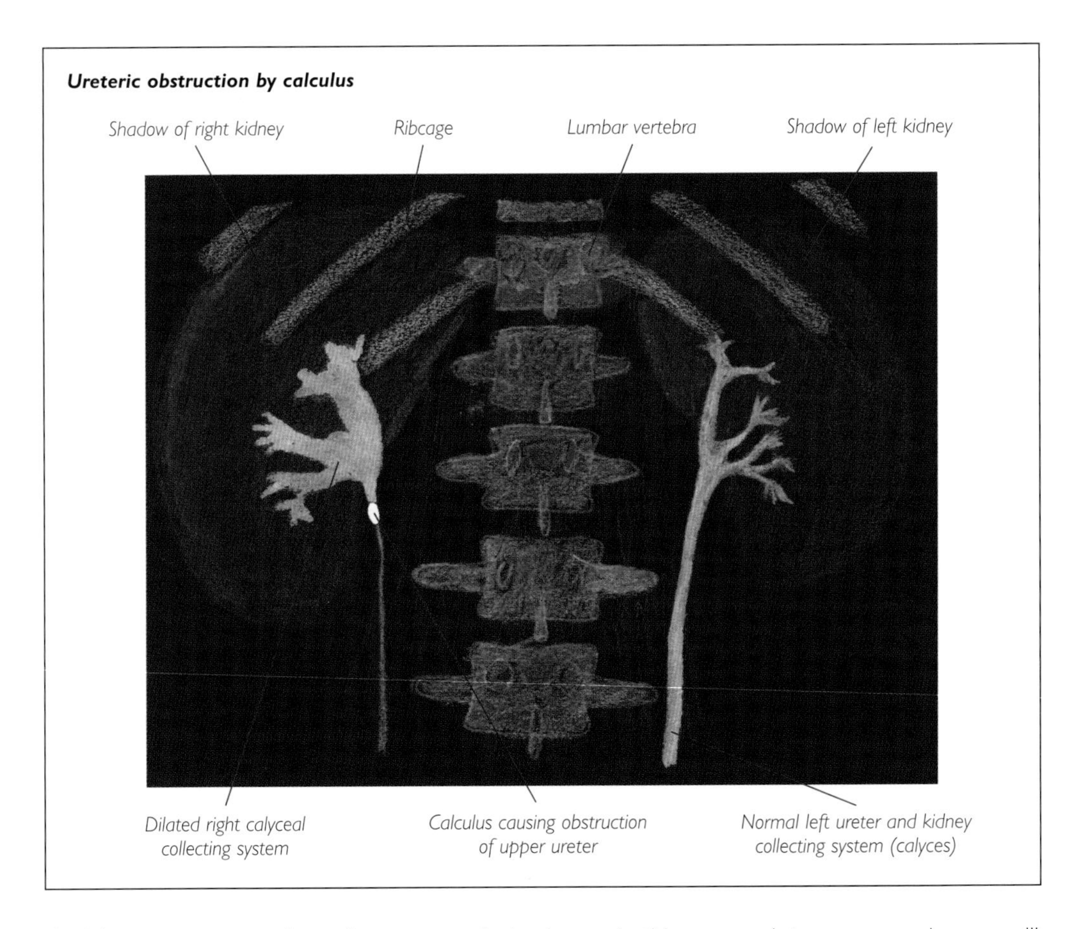

A plain x-ray may reveal a radio-opaque calculus but, as in this case, an intravenous pyelogram will highlight an obstruction in more cases (including those of a radiolucent stone). Most stones found obstructing the ureter were formed in the kidney, rather than in situ within the ureter. There is intense and severe pain of ureteric colic in the low back, radiating to the groin. There is a greater emergency if an infection also occurs proximal to the site of obstruction, or if there is already underlying kidney failure. Generally a smooth stone of less than 6mm diameter will pass through into the bladder, but a rough and/or larger stone tends to require prompt removal to avoid kidney damage.

Related images

p.223 Gallstones
p.222 Chronic cholecystitis
p.222 Fatty liver
p.561-562 Hepatitis
p.270 Gout
p.339 Osteoarthritis
p.56 & p.340 Rheumatoid arthritis

BERLIN WALL

Original

The Berlin wall was actually a complex system of walls, fences, barriers and watch-towers, such that by the end of the 1970s' it comprised of the following sections:

A – Border line on side of West Berlin, this region also known as the 'death strip'.
B – The last wall, known as the 'Wall'
C – Anti-vehicle trenches
D – Control track
E – Column track
F – Lighting system
G – Watch towers
H – Various types of barriers
I – Signal fence
J – Back-land wall with border area toward East Berlin

There were three checkpoints with crossing points across the Wall, which were also given phonetic alphabet names:

1 – Helmstedt (Alpha) checkpoint
2 – Dreilinden (Bravo) checkpoint
3 – Friedrichstrasse (Charlie) checkpoint, the first one set up in August 23, 1961.

The whole border area (and thus West Berlin) lay within the territory of East Germany/East Berlin.

FOLLOWING PAGE. 'Berlin wall and the Scream', by Katherine Mynott. The sentry guards, watchtower and barbed wire covered Wall loom threateningly in the background, consuming the huddled dejected individuals at the base. Note an entity possessing one of them. The depiction of the Scream (in the style of Edvard Munch) in the foreground captures the horror of all that the Wall represented. There are etheric holes and tears in this creature's etheric field to represent its lack of auric boundaries.

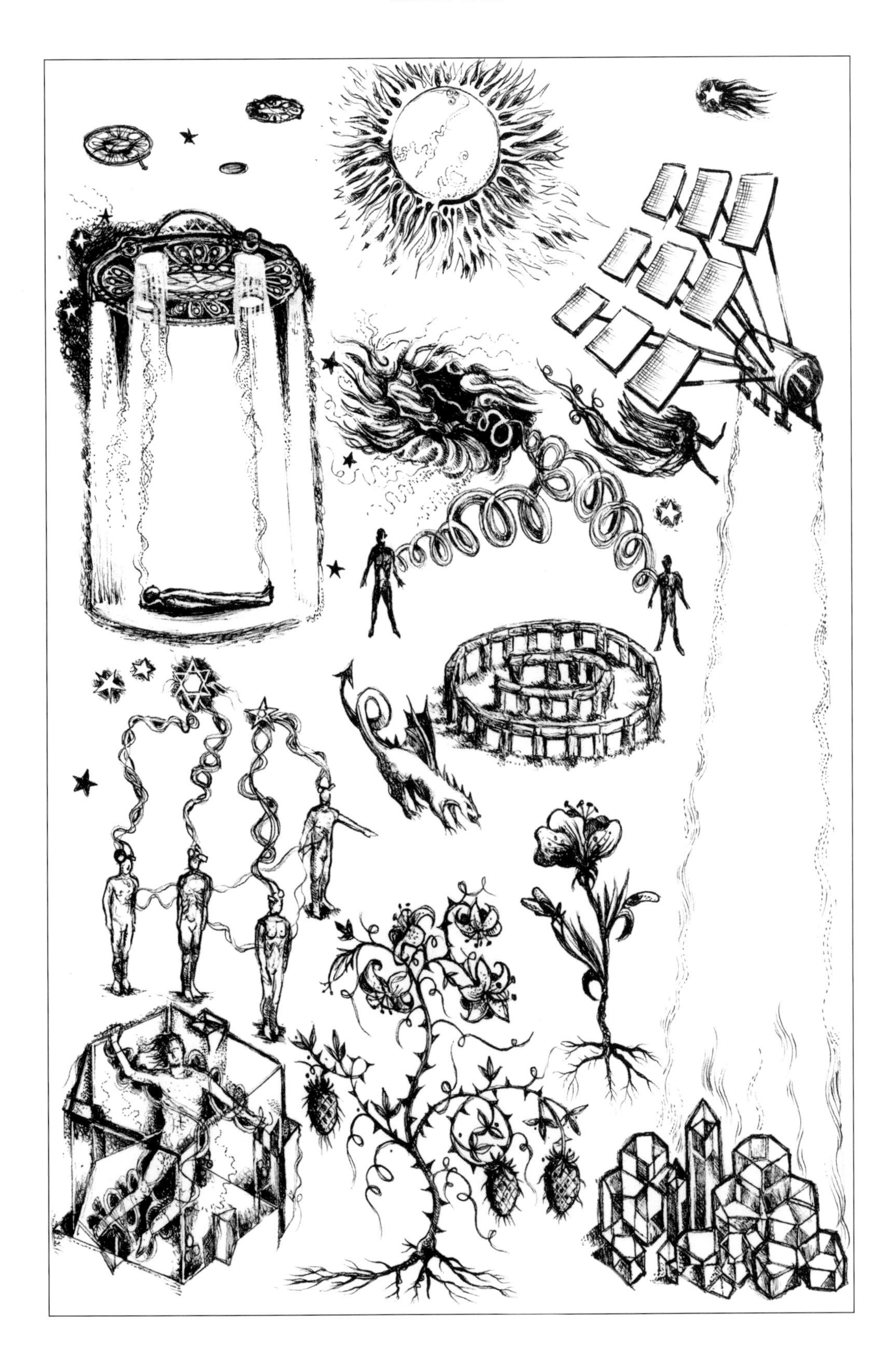

PRECEDING PAGE. 'Atlantean root race', by Katherine Mynott. Various aspects of Atlantis are depicted. This civilisation existed on a land mass previously existing in the region of the Atlantic Ocean. The predominant subtle body undergoing development within the Atlantean root race was the astral. The Atlanteans needed to suppress the sacral chakra arising out of the previous root race of Lemuria – the reason being that, in comparison to the typical human incarnation, the Lemurians were still functioning like a pubescent child of about twelve years old. The emotional life had scarcely been realised. The next chakra to harness was the solar plexus, which became the Atlantean centre of emotional expression and perception. However, this emotional development required humans to experience emotional negativity as well as the positive. The solar plexus became much more connected to the astral plane and what to us is now the subconscious and subterranean realm.

Towards the lower left side several humans are shown interconnected with karmic cords through their solar plexus. Entrapment and domination-victimisation patterns could thereby be played out. Cancer is a special problem derived from Atlantis and is a disease of emotional suppression leading to stagnation. Base emotions, such as guilt, anger, fear and resentment were buried and suppressed within the Atlantean psyche as they attempted to purify the astral body with the higher emotional attributes e.g. love, grace and forgiveness. The astral body is a body of sensations, desires and emotions. However the Atlanteans also utilised other astral powers, which to modern humanity would be magical and supernatural. Their dream-like reality enabled them to flow quickly between coordinates in time and space, including traveling forward and backward in time. Two Atlanteans are being projected into such an astral plane vortex in the upper centre image. Psychic faculties were the norm, such as shapeshifting, teleportation, telepathy and clairvoyance.

A variety of extraterrestrial influences occurred (such as Sirian, Pleidian, Orion, Lyran, Annunaki, Zeta), some of it negative. In the upper left corner there is channeling of such alien energy. The race made use of crystal technology, Earth energies and starlight to assist their culture. Thus, by the latter days of Atlantis, their emotional bodies contained much by way of negativity. Souls had karmic experiences with each other, with control issues, power struggles and victimization. There was intense paranoia and delusion by this stage. The chief karmic problem in Atlantis derived from theft. Stealing became rife, and the levels of fear and vulnerability reached an all-time high. Souls committed theft of other soul parts, and such disembodied fragments of others were kept imprisoned in devices, amulets and dark crystals. The victim invariably felt scattered, confused and lost – and opened to control by various dark regimes. Such a pseudo-crystal (specially designed for this purpose) housing a stolen soul fragment is shown in the lower left image.

There was inappropriate use of Earth's resources, by way of technologies for harnessing solar (as shown by the solar panels in deep space at the upper right-hand corner) and wind power – but to drive machines of destruction and control. The relationship between humanity and the spiritual beings residing within the inner Sun was thereby deranged. There was inappropriate genetic research, including hybridisation across species and kingdoms, cloning and assisted fertilisation techniques (genetically modified plants are shown in the lower middle section). The destruction of Atlantis is described with an image on p.436. During the midpoint of the Atlantean race the world had reached its densest possible state, most separated from the laws of the spiritual plane. However, the blueprints of redemption and resurrection were not able to penetrate the world during Atlantis, hence Christ did not incarnate during this epoch – but only into the next (or current) epoch of humanity. Such Atlantean circumstances were recreated within the 20th century, particularly during the phase of the Berlin wall and cold war.

Astrology

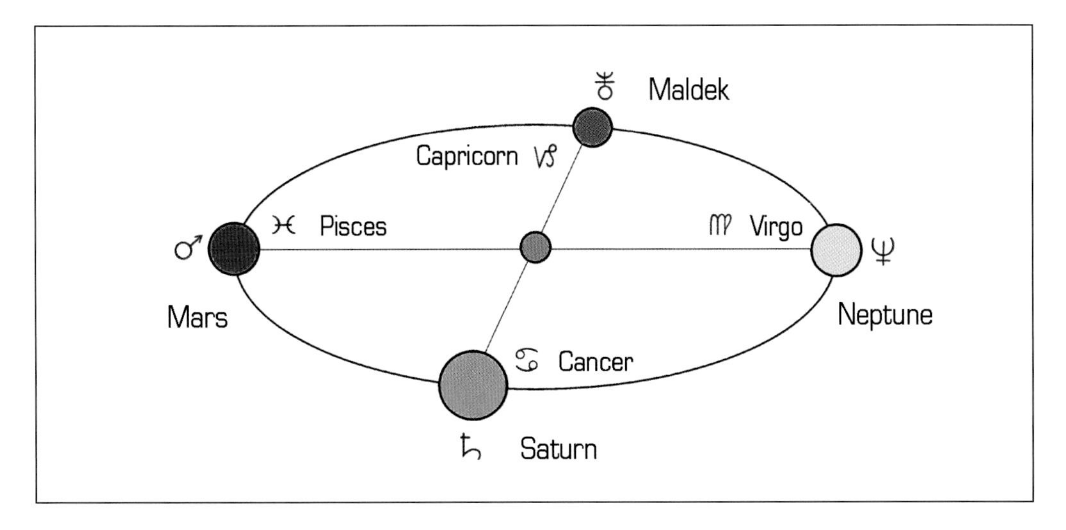

Grand cross, Mars in Pisces opposite Neptune in Virgo, and Saturn in Gemini opposite Maldek in Sagittarius. Saturn in Gemini leads to restriction or suppression in communication issues and blockage of the throat chakra. Maldek in Sagittarius leads to karmic control and oppression in the life of will and personal freedom.

Oriental

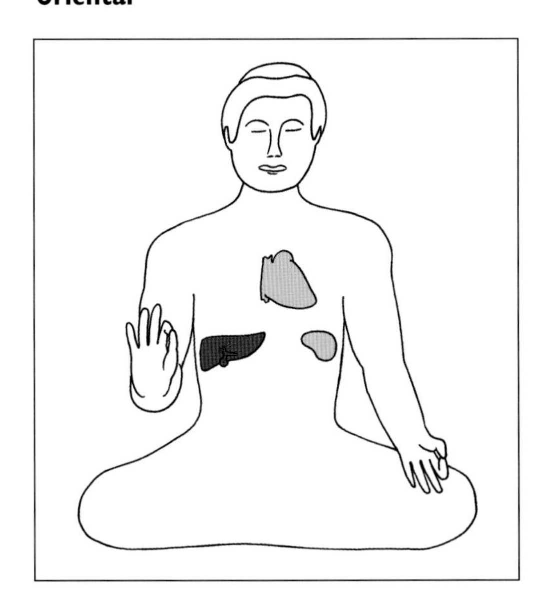

Liver chi stagnation, with heart and spleen phlegm-damp.

Related images

p.606-612 Properties and effects of radiation
p.376 Bone marrow immunosuppression
p.512-515 Artificial and assisted reproduction
p.296 Kidney transplantation
p.285-286 Cerebrovascular accident
p.17 Alzheimer's disease
p.17 Investigation of higher cortical function
p.389 Stereotactic brain surgery
p.389 Lumbar puncture procedure
p.391 Epidural injection
p.206-210 Cancer and malignancy
p.528 Migraine visual aura
p.656 Cataract
p.319 Glaucoma
p.730-732 Thyroid disease
p.28 Supplementary oxygen therapy
p.451 Myocardial infarction
p.133 Liver failure and ascites
p.164 Scoliosis
p.340 Rheumatoid arthritis late stage
p.657 Ankylosing spondylitis

BLATTA ORIENTALIS

Original

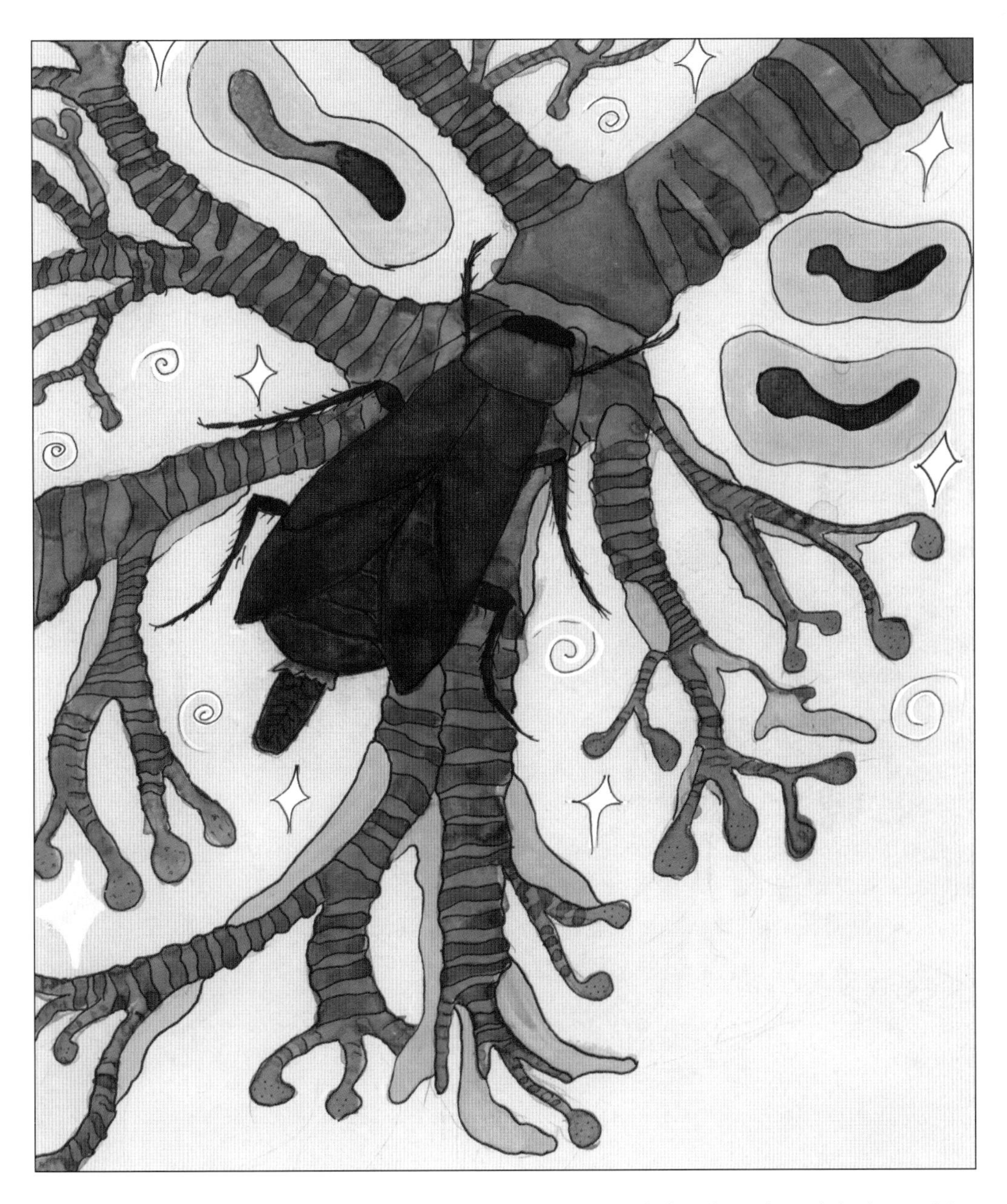

'Blatta orientalis at the bronchial airways', by Nadine Kardesler. A female cockroach is shown flying within the lungs, with an egg case attached to her rear. There are neutrophil white cells within the connective tissue space and mucus attached to the cartilage lined bronchial tubes. The stars and spiral galaxies in the background symbolise that the astral body (known to the ancients as the sidereal or starry body) must normally have a rhythmic flow into and out of the lungs to facilitate the breathing process. Cramping of this astral body is the basis behind the bronchospasm of asthma.

Astrology

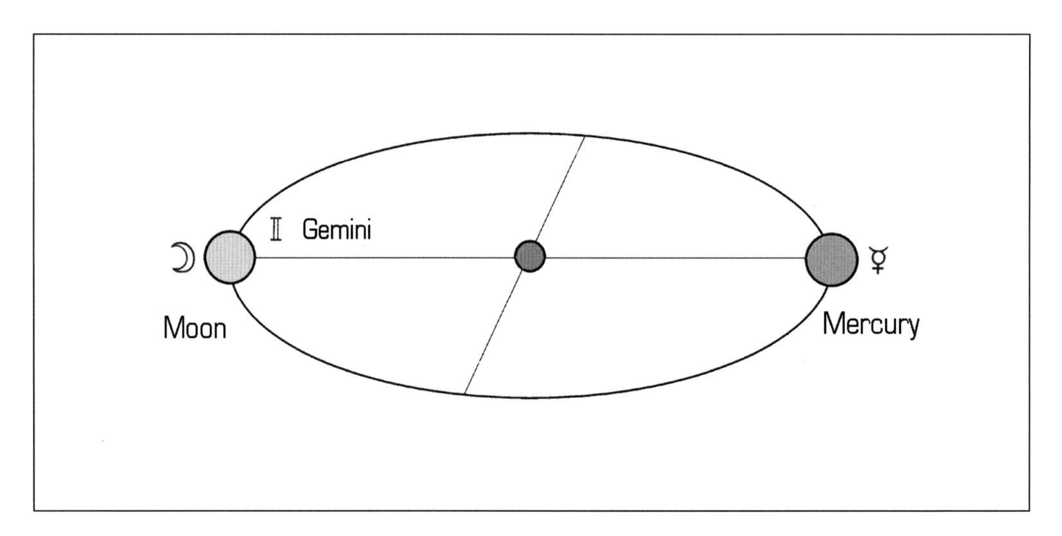

Moon in Gemini opposite Mercury.

Oriental

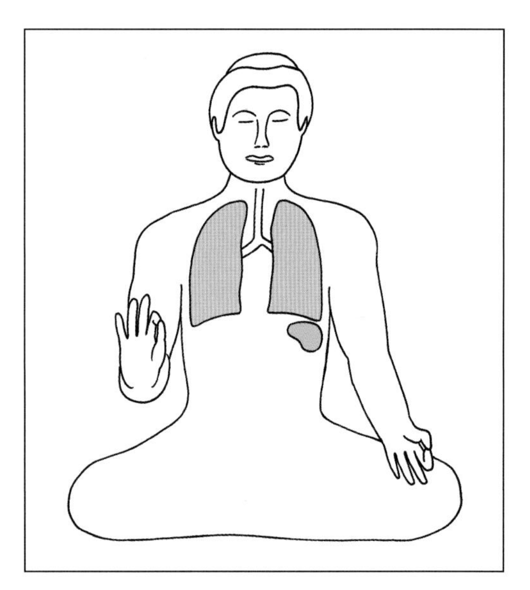

Spleen yang deficiency, with lung phlegm-damp.

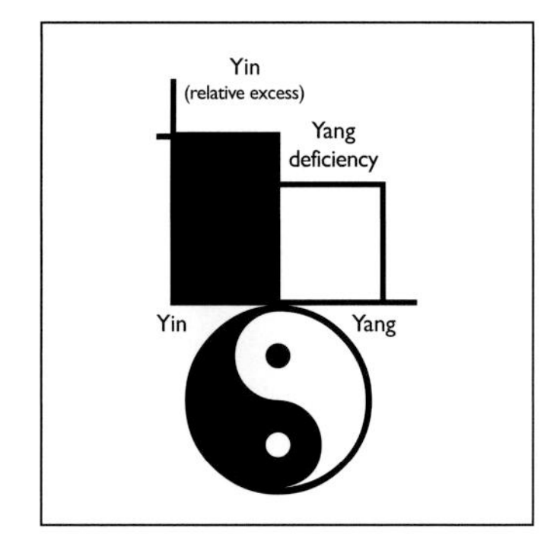

Particulars

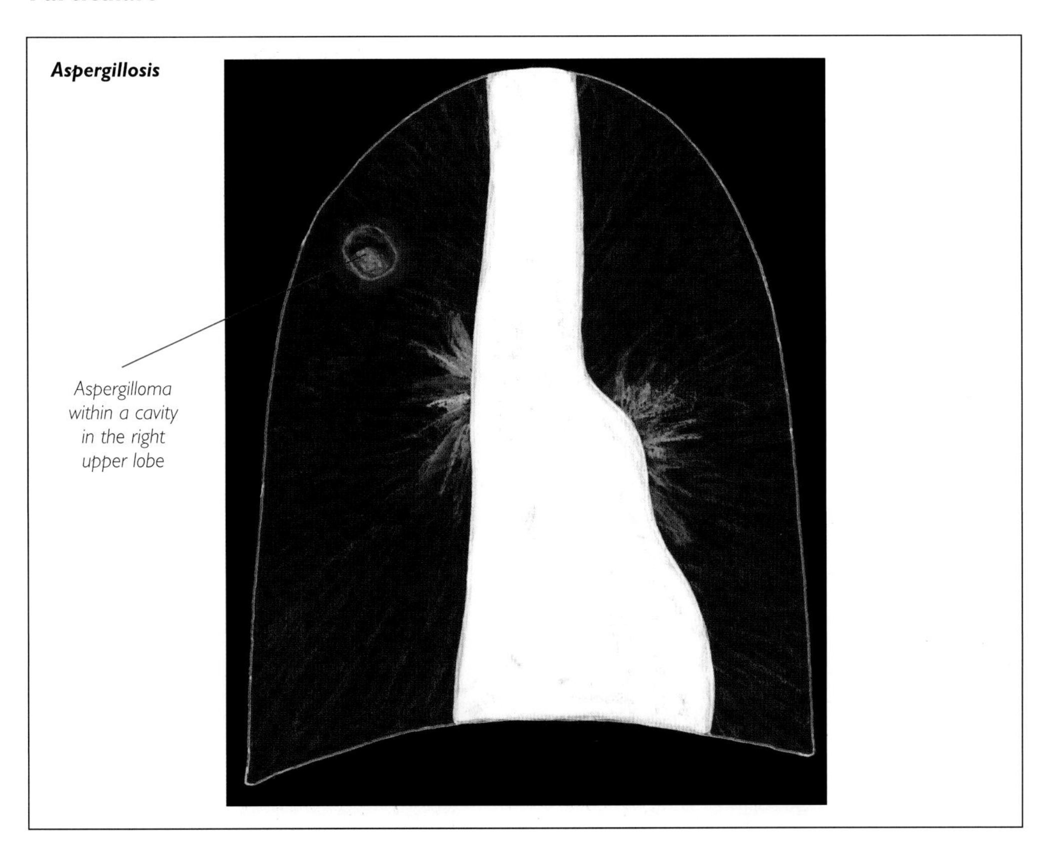

Aspergillosis

Aspergillosis is a fungal infection and often colonises a pre-existing lung cavity, to form a fungus ball within this space. The cavity may have developed from earlier tuberculosis, lung abscess, cancer, emphysema, sarcoidosis or bronchiectasis etc. Typically such cavities are in the upper lung lobes. The chest x-ray reveals the rounded mass of fungus surrounded by a meniscus of air and capped by a faint lining. The mass may be shown to move within the cavity upon moving the body position and repeating the x-ray. Other chest x-ray appearances of aspergillosis, however, include widespread pulmonary infiltrations with shadows, or lung collapse from airways obstruction.

Related images

p.72 Asthma
p.504 Chronic bronchitis
p.198 Emphysema
p.306 Bronchiectasis
p.28 Supplementary oxygen therapy

BRYONIA ALBA

Original

'Bryonia dioica rooted within the cerebral brain', by Lorraine Spiro. The plant is shown with its typically creeping stems, lobed leaves and spiralling tendrils off the stems. There are small white-greenish flowers and black berries. The large rootstock is growing within a brain-like earth surface, to symbolise the effect of the remedy within the nerve-sensory system and meningeal linings. Beams of light descend upon the cerebrum to represent the penetration of higher thought-forms into the brain substance.

FOLLOWING PAGE. 'Bryonia and the Worm at the Gate', by Tasvi Shah. This image is styled on one of the engravings by William Blake from his 'Gates of Paradise' (of which two versions exist, the first version of 1793 especially for children). The worm overlooks a human baby-headed caterpillar resting or gestating upon the leaf. Blake had arranged the images of this collection into the theme title of 'Ideas of Good and Evil' and to follow the life of human from birth to death. The inscription written by Blake for this image was "What is Man. The Sun's Light when he unfolds it depends on the Organ that beholds it".

The worm is a feature of various esoteric creation myths, usually preceding the more fiery serpent or dragon forces that later facilitate the activity of creation. The worm represents the shaping forces needed to mould matter into a form ready to receive spiritual blueprints. An important spiritual doctrine is that everything outside, within nature, is reflecting an attribute within the human body. The worm process is especially found within the brain. Hence the transformation of a caterpillar worm into a butterfly symbolises the liberation of beautiful creative thoughts out of the activity of the amorphous plastic-like brain substance.

Astrology

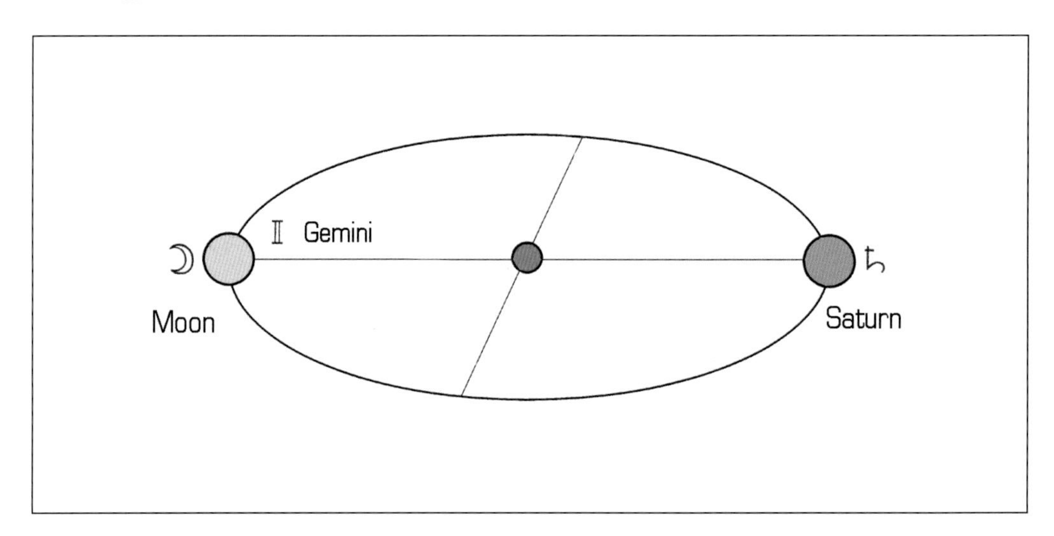

Moon in Gemini opposite Saturn.

Oriental

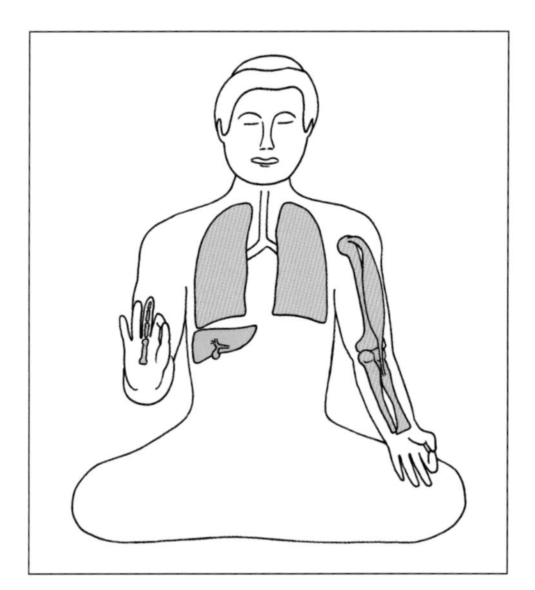

Liver interior wind, with lung wind-damp and damp-based painful obstruction syndrome of joints/muscles.

Particulars

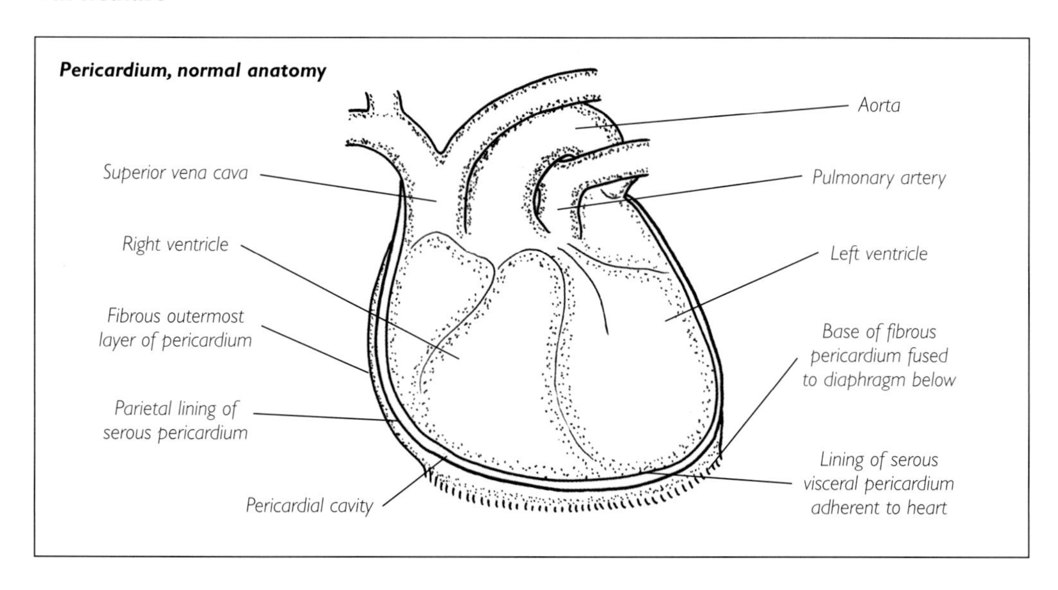

The pericardium consists of an external sac, the tough fibrous pericardium, and an internal double layered sac called the serous pericardium. The outer fibrous pericardium protects the heart and is also fused with the diaphragm. The serous pericardium consist of two further layers, the visceral layer is part of the epicardial or external layer of the heart wall. The parietal layer is attached to the internal surface of the fibrous pericardium. The space between the visceral and parietal layers is called the pericardial cavity and normally contains a thin film of fluid to enable the heart to beat without friction.

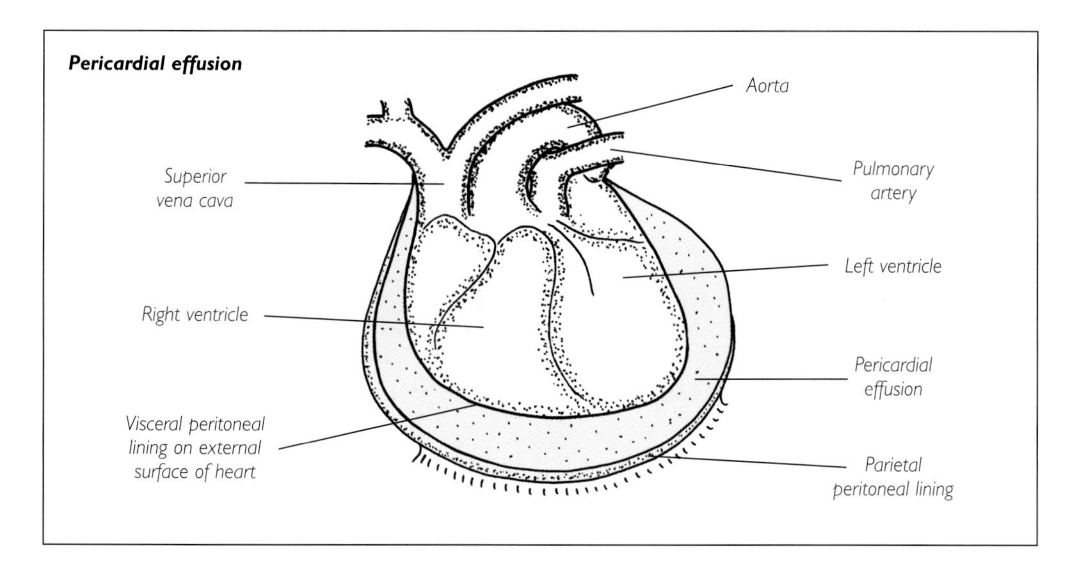

Pericardial effusion can occur subsequent to acute or chronic pericarditis. The fluid collects in the closed pericardial space around the heart. When the pericardium is distended to maximum capacity then heart compression prevents filling of the ventricles by blood to cause potential collapse. Causes of the initial pericarditis include infection by virus, bacteria (especially tuberculosis), malignant invasion, secondary to renal failure and after a myocardial infarction. In an emergency the effusion is tapped and drained to relieve pressure on the heart.

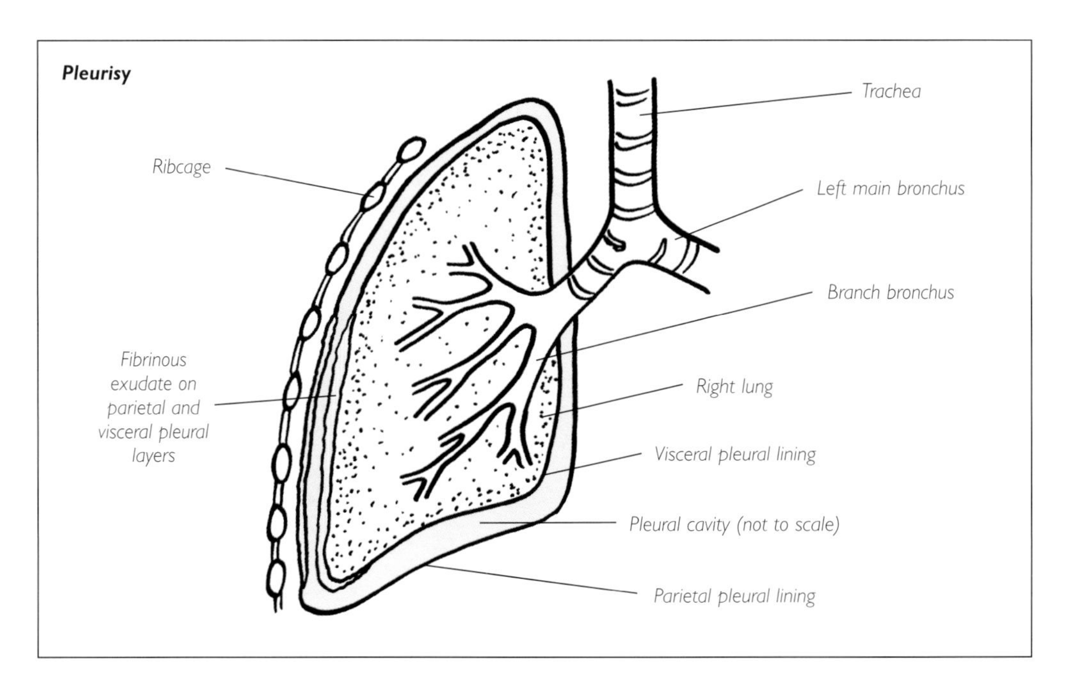

Pleurisy is inflammation of the pleural linings. There are several causes, e.g. infection (such as from pneumonia or tuberculosis), after a penetrating injury, autoimmune attack (such as rheumatoid arthritis) or overlying a pulmonary infarct. A fibrinous inflamed exudate or fluid occurs on the inner visceral and outer parietal layers. This causes sharp pleuritic chest pain worse on movement and breathing. In some cases the exudate is absorbed and then develops pleural adhesions as the two layers stick together. In other cases a build-up of fluid in the pleural cavity causes a pleural effusion.

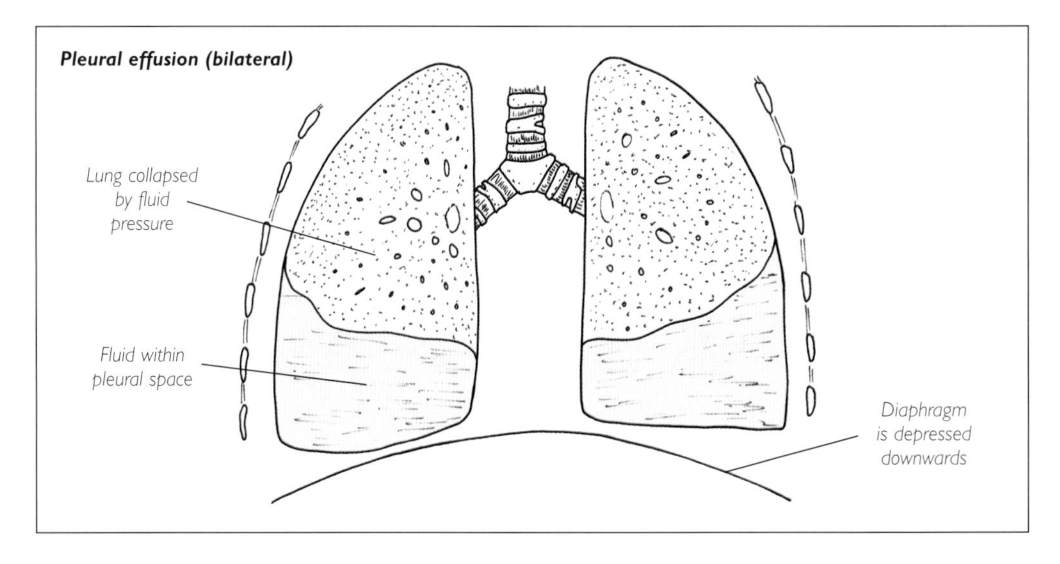

Pleural effusion is characterised by the accumulation of fluid within the pleural space around the lungs, and is a form of local odema. It can be due to heart failure, spreading infection with pleurisy, certain autoimmune diseases of connective or joint tissue (e.g. rheumatoid arthritis) or cancer invasion of the pleural lining. The symptoms include breathlessness from underlying lung compression, and possibly local chest wall pain.

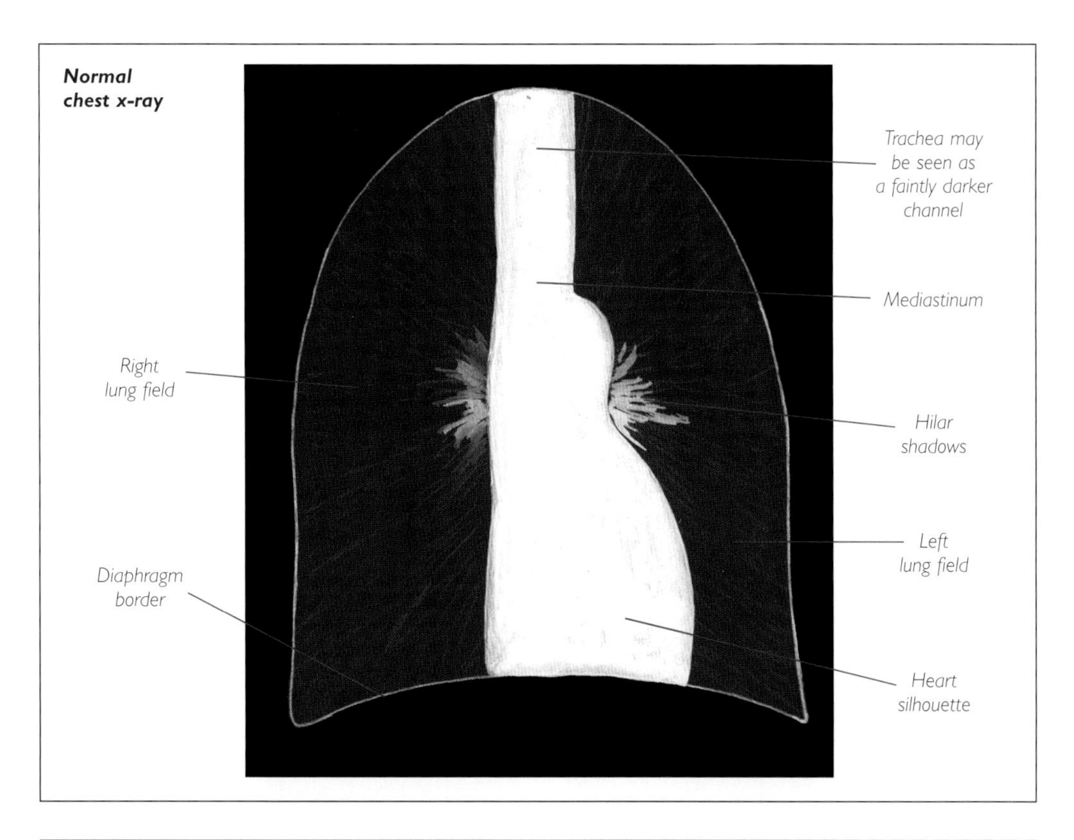
Normal
chest x-ray
Trachea may
be seen as
a faintly darker
channel
Mediastinum
Right
lung field
Hilar
shadows
Left
lung field
Diaphragm
border
Heart
silhouette

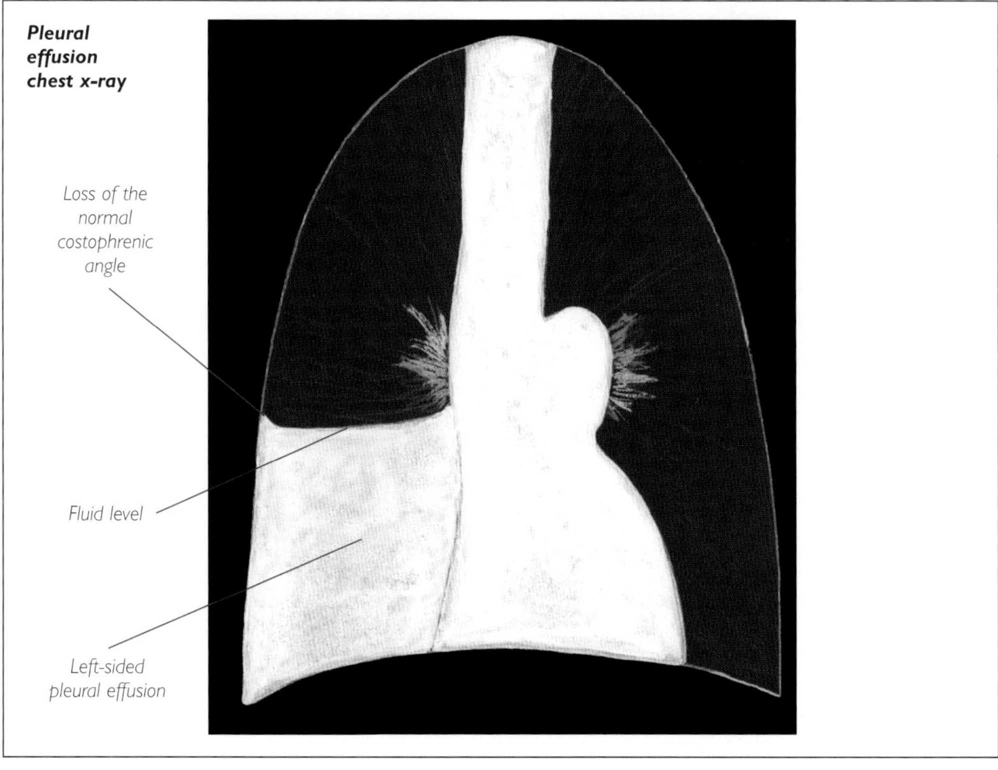
Pleural
effusion
chest x-ray
Loss of the
normal
costophrenic
angle
Fluid level
Left-sided
pleural effusion

PRECEDING PAGE. An adequate chest x-ray is properly centred, with good penetration of the x-rays through the lungs. A postero-anterior (PA) view is the routine way of taking the film, where the detecting plate is placed on the front of the chest and the x-ray beam travels from behind the patient. Observations are made of the bony structure and shape of the chest wall. The trachea and mediastinum should be central. The diaphragm should be even, neither elevated nor flattened. The heart size (horizontally) should be somewhat less than half the width of the thoracic cavity and of the right silhouette shape. The central hilar shadows should have the normal size and shape, indicating normal pulmonary blood vessels and mediastinal lymph nodes. There should be faint, evenly distributed, vascular markings throughout the lung fields, with adequate aeration all over. Note that in all the artistic depictions of chest x-rays in this book there are no ribs, clavicles or other bony structures, so as to enable clarification of the lung features only.

A pleural effusion is an accumulation of fluid within the pleural space. There are several causes. One type, due to transudation of fluid, is caused by, e.g. heart failure, kidney failure and hypothyroidism. Exudates are of another type and tend to contain higher protein content, being caused by, e.g. bacterial pneumonia, lung cancer, tuberculosis, connective tissue (autoimmune) disease, mesothelioma etc. If caused by a malignancy, the effusion will tend to reoccur after drainage. Symptoms of an effusion can be breathlessness (e.g. from lung compression) as well as the features of the underlying disease.

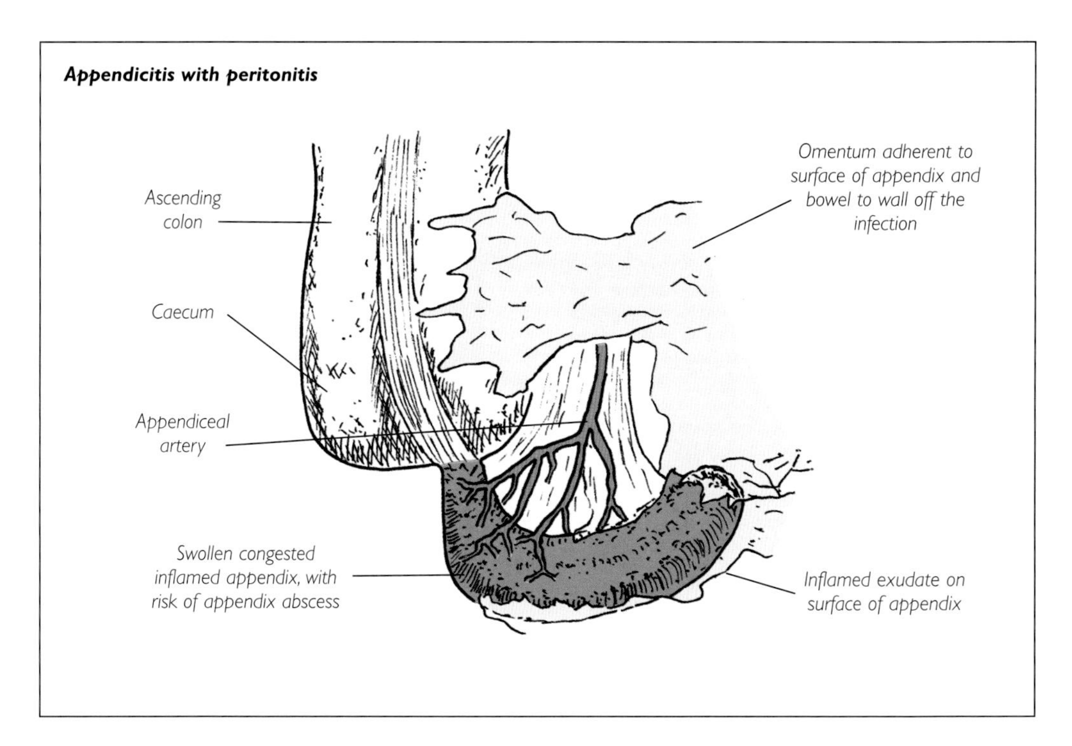

Appendicitis usually occurs after obstruction of the appendix by viral infection or impacted faeces. This inflames and ulcerates the appendix wall, which can rapidly develop gangrene and perforate (especially in children). An appendix abscess and peritonitis can then result. The omentum often adheres to the surface of the appendix to help prevent spread of inflammation throughout the peritoneal cavity. The initial symptoms are vague colicky central abdominal pain, which then radiates and localises to the right lower abdomen. There is mild-moderate fever and sometimes associated bowel symptoms of constipation, nausea and breath odour. Peritonitis presents with generalised severe abdominal pain, with board-like rigidity of the abdominal muscles and loss of bowel sounds.

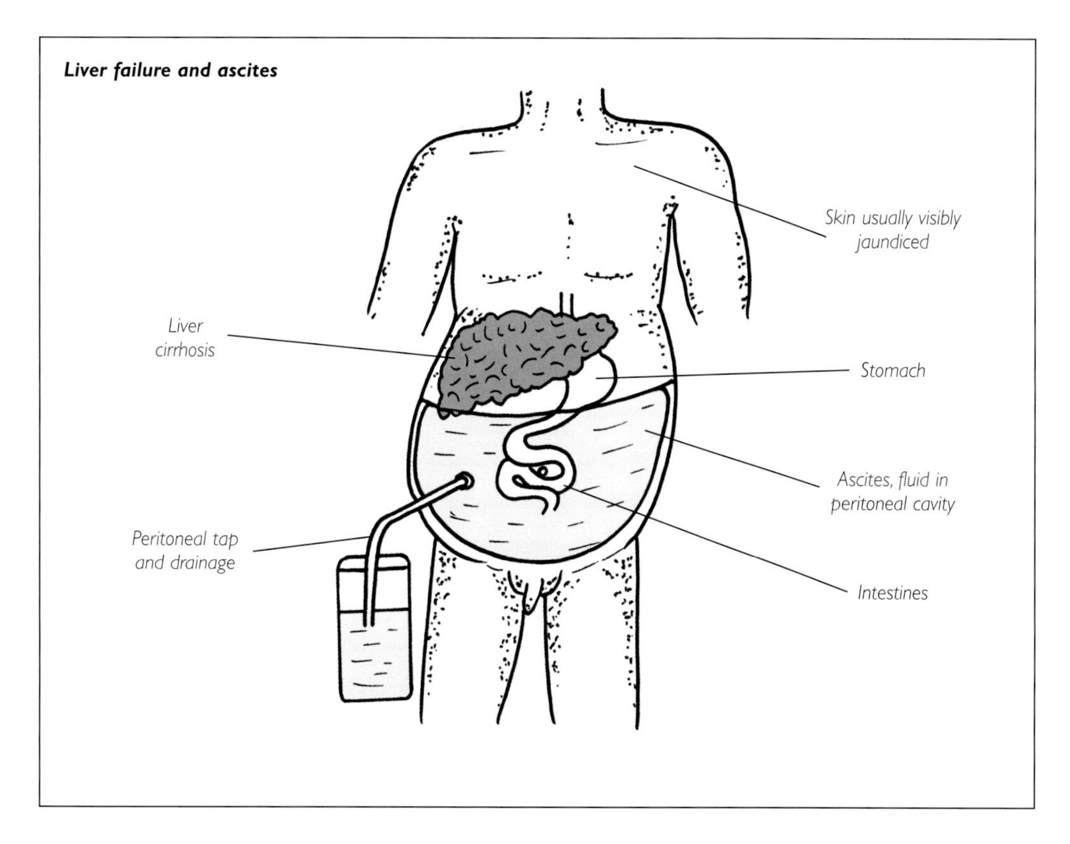

Liver (hepatic) failure can be an acute consequence of e.g. poisoning or acute hepatitis, or slowly progressive from chronic hepatitis. Cirrhosis is the end stage of many chronic liver diseases, and is characterised by fibrosis and abnormal nodules altering the architecture of the liver. The liver cells die, but regeneration is irregular and with continued inflammation. Alcohol is a particular cause. This causes obstruction to the blood vessels within the liver. Dilation of the anastomatic or other connection vessels between the portal blood circulation and systemic veins leads to bypassing of blood away from the liver. This further deteriorates liver function. The signs are jaundice from the high bilirubin levels, encephalopathy (confusion of mind), ascites (fluid accumulation in the peritoneal cavity), bleeding tendencies, and hypoglycaemia. Note that ascites can occur from other causes, such as ovarian tumours, cancers invading the peritoneum, heart or kidney failure.

Related images

p.527 Headache
p.528 Migraine visual aura
p.622 Cervical spondylitis
p.621 Bursitis
p.621 Capsulitis, frozen shoulder
p.56 Rheumatoid arthritis acute stage
p.57 Ovarian inflammation acute and chronic
p.335 & p.427 Ovarian cysts

BUFO RANA

Museum

'A toad is better than a sinner'. Engraving with etching on paper, published by Rob. Walton, London. © Wellcome Library, London. The lettering states: 'A toad better than a sinner. Heaven; the sinners seat; hell. What more loathsome can be to mortal eye than this most ugly toad which is hard by. Although a toad I be and object of mans hate yet better am I than any reprobate.' A Stuart gentleman is standing before Whitehall, which is entitled 'Sinner's seat' and in front of which is depicted hell as a man-eating monster (on the right lower corner). He is contemplating the toad before him, and above this creature heaven is shown as a cloud with righteous souls. It is an allegory of vice and virtue.

FOLLOWING PAGE. 'Toad and the portal to the underworld', by Tessa Gaynn. For most toad species, after mating, the fertilised eggs are released in their 1000's into water (covered by a jelly-like protective membrane). The female usually returns to shore, whilst the male may remain in the water for the rest of the breeding season. An example of the distinctive male midwife toad (Alytes obstetricans) is shown in the central image. The eggs were laid on land by the female, as a double string or chain, and then fertilised. The male pulls them off the female's hind legs and entwines these around his own thighs and hips, where they remain for several days. The eggs are occasionally dipped into the water to prevent dehydration. When ready to hatch they are deposited into a vacant pond. The lower images symbolise the use of toads by witches during history to engage with underworld forces. The burning of human parts in the cauldrons represent transformation of soul parts (karmic unresolved aspects of the soul) – but ultimately for the higher good. This scene is based on part of the detail on 'Gluttony' from the painting 'Last Judgement' by Hieronymus Bosch. Historical records suggest that human (including sacrificial) blood, parts of corpses and toad flesh were ingredients in various witchcraft potions. The effect of toadskin combined with solanaceous plants (e.g. belladonna, hyoscyamus or mandragora) is especially hallucinogenic. Wise women could utilise their 'familiars' (power animals), such as toads, to journey into other dimensions of reality and the sphere of the Moon, such astral travel being depicted in the upper images.

Original

'The toad-guru', by Rishav Shah. In Chinese and Japanese legend and culture, the toad is a creature presiding over magic and the secrets of immortality. An example of a toad-guru or Kosensei (also known as gama sennin) is shown in this illustration, and is based on an 18th century painting of the Japanese Edo period. A mountain hermit, he was an ugly man with warty pimpled skin, and his sole companion was a giant three-legged toad. This toad he had found sick and nursed it back to help, in return for which the toad taught the hermit magical secrets. He could even turn himself into a toad, and was depicted when in human form sitting or standing beside, on or under his toad. On the other hand, the toad was also regarded as an ally of demonic forces. Thus a dualistic philosophy pertains to toad stories. For example there is the demon-toad 'O Gama' of Suwo in Japan that consumed snakes and destroyed by spitting its poison. The toad was a companion to the Woman of the Three Road River, a Japanese equivalent of the Greek River Styx, the river en route to the underworld for souls journeying after physical death. The toad is often featured as residing within the Moon, and feeding off pills of immortality. Sometimes it would swallow the Moon, which would cause an eclipse.

CACTUS GRANDIFLORUS

Museum

Robert John Thornton, 'Night-blooming Cereus: Temple of Flora' (1812). © The Provost & Fellows of Eton College. Dr. Thornton's publication the Temple of Flora is a famous tribute to the Swedish botanist Linnaeus, and is considered by many to be the most magnificent botanical work ever produced. The images, by a number of artists, are bold and unique, with classical landscapes behind the plants. He spared no expense in producing a limited number of lavish and extravagant editions.

Original

'Cactus grandiflorus amidst the desert', by Caroline Hamilton. Note the spiny stems and the trumpet-like showy white flowers with numerous stamens in the plant at the foreground. The Sun is setting, a time for this blossoming process to proceed and continue only during the night. A non-flowering cactus is also shown in the right-side background.

Throughout mythology and religious symbology, the wilderness and desert has represented the state of humanity's separation from spirit. The heart centre is thereby veiled or walled off from perceiving the higher reality of soul-spiritual unconditional love. The individual is caught within a conditional set of emotional attachments and desires, and an inner emotional state at odds with the environment. Nonetheless, the human race had to fall into this wilderness (as indicated by the Fall from Grace by Adam and Eve) in order to evolve a self-centredness during the redemption back to wholeness. When the armour around the heart begins to dissolve, the individual may experience uncomfortable transitional symptoms, as found in the profile of this remedy. These include chest tightness, pain and angina. A heart-breaking life experience also propels the sufferer into his individual desert of the dark night of the soul, but ultimately to reconnect to the joy of his/her soul-spirit.

Astrology

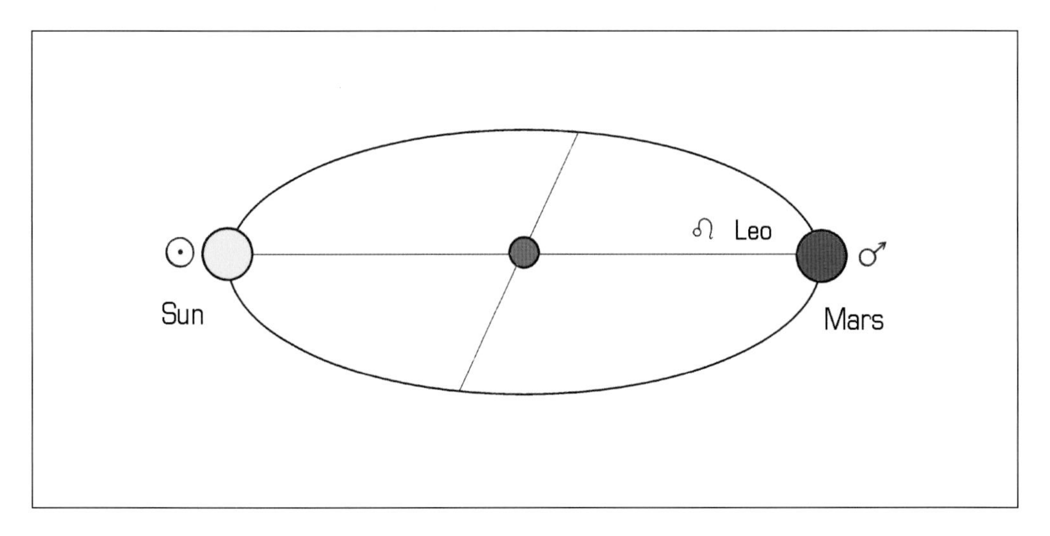

Sun opposite Mars in Leo.

Oriental

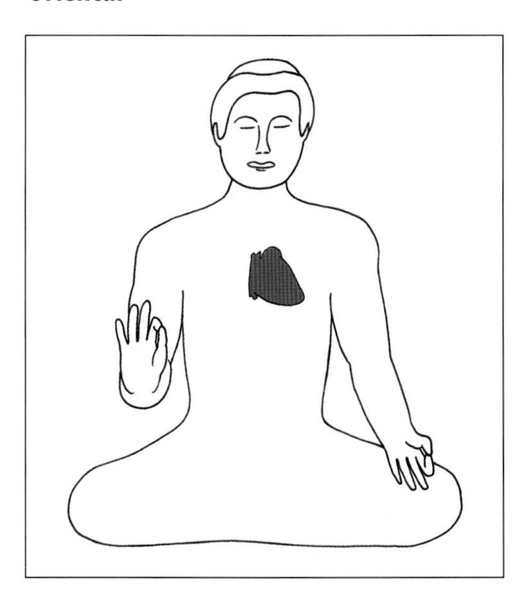

Chi stagnation/constraint of heart.

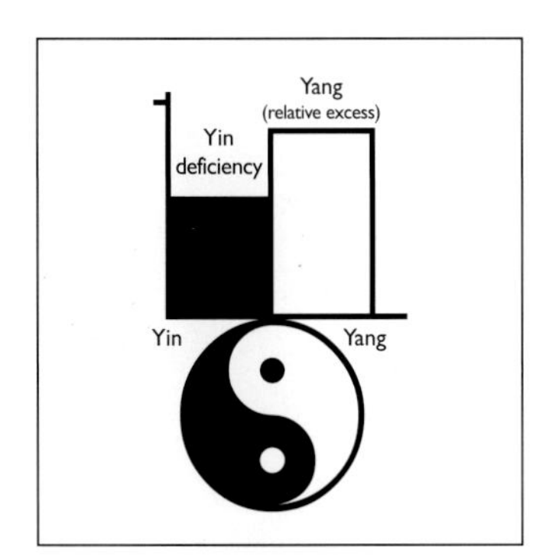

Particulars

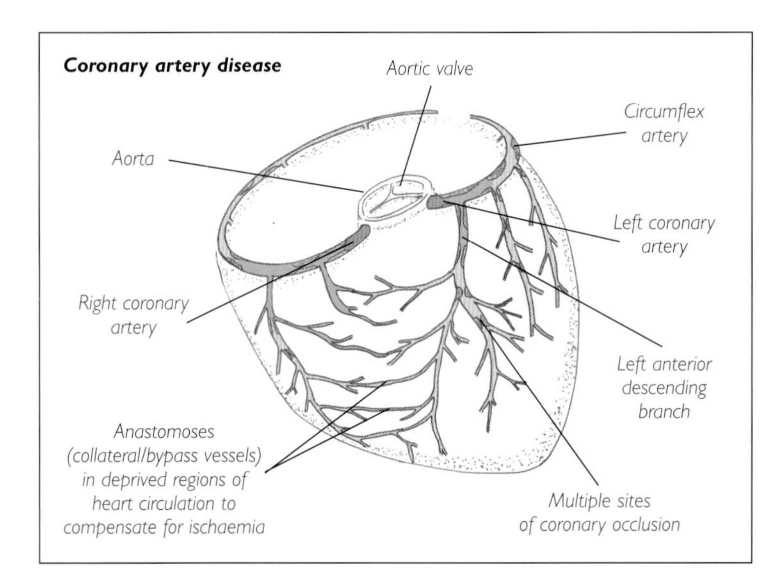

Sites of atheromatous plaques within the coronary arteries may be a few to many, with ischaemia at the muscle distribution areas of the arteries. Significant disease increases the risk of myocardial infarction.

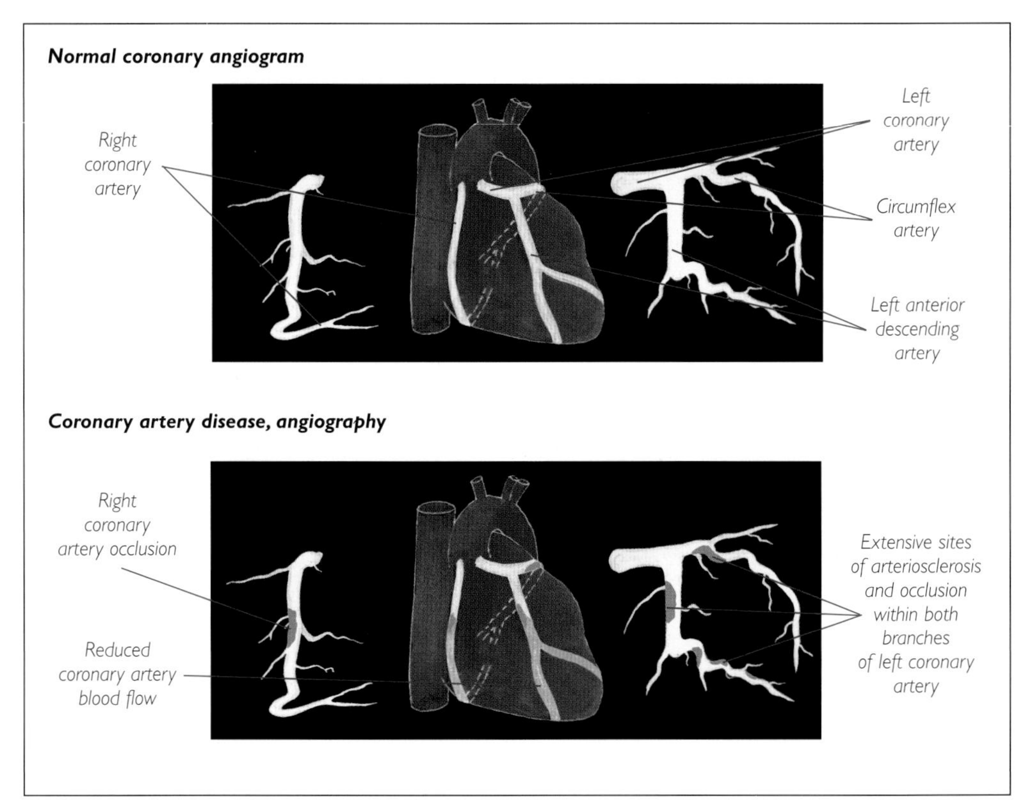

Normal coronary angiography appearances are shown in the upper image where there are no filling defects. Coronary artery disease in the lower image is revealed by lesions with narrowing of the lumen and reduced blood flow from the stenosis. Severe disease is indicated by long lengths of thrombosis, irregular borders to the lesions and ulcerated patterns.

CADMIUM SULPHURICUM

Original

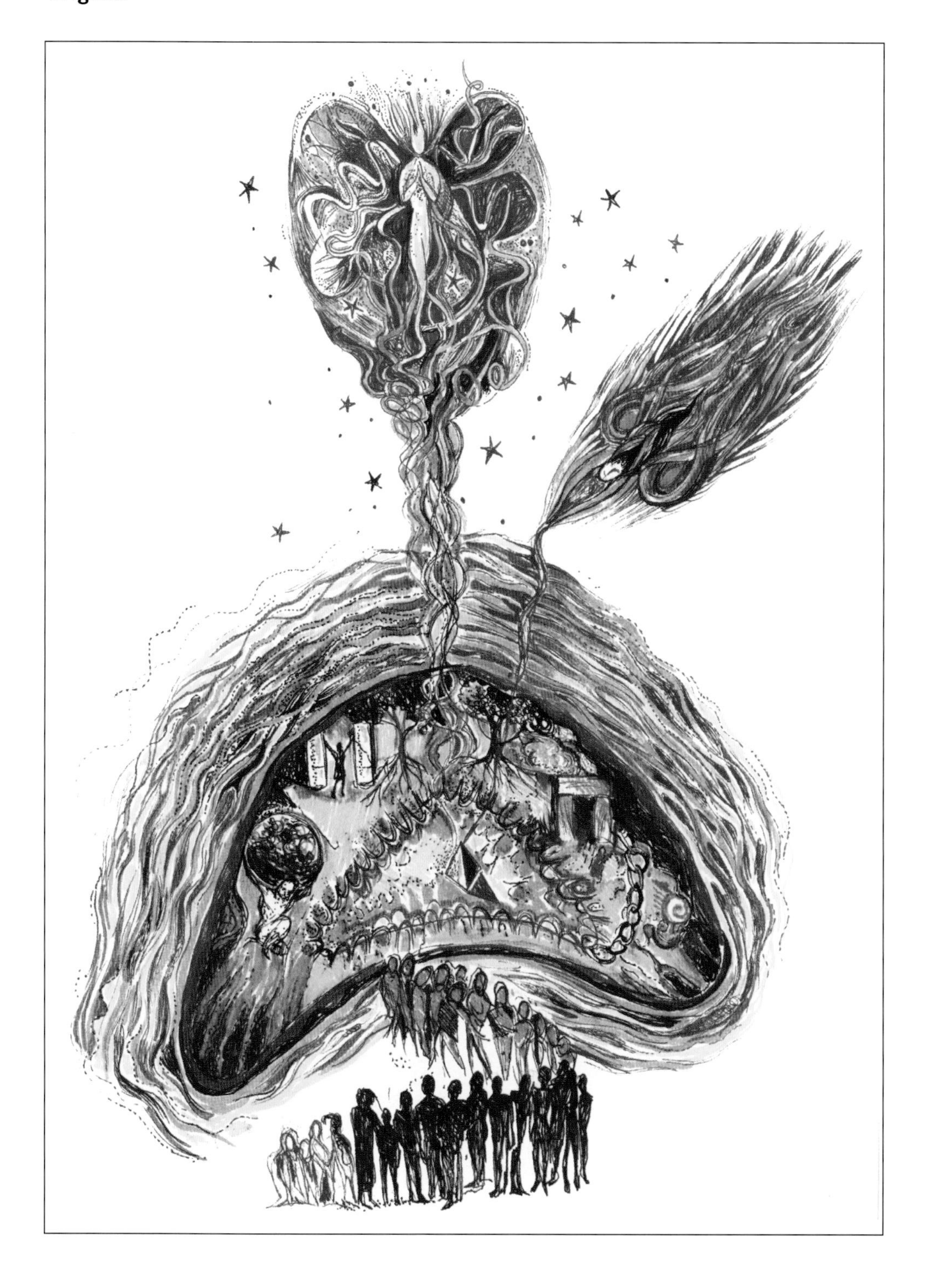

PRECEDING PAGE. 'Cadmium sulphuricum and astral incarnation into the adrenals', by Katherine Mynott. Various aspects of the esoteric physiology of the adrenal glands are shown. The warm glowing fire surrounding the helmet-shaped adrenal gland symbolises its pertaining to Kidney-Yang, the more dynamic fiery aspect of kidney chi. Deficient adrenal states can therefore cause chilliness and lack of metabolic vitality. The purple entity flying into the adrenal gland from the right-hand side represents the astral body. This enters through the element of air via the throat and lungs, to become grounded within the physical-etheric body by the kidney-adrenal system. The glowing orange-red zone within the centre of the adrenals represents the central medulla zone, where the adrenaline hormone and sympathetic nerve impulse is most active. This is the region of greatest catabolic astral activity, and enables the drive and force of the astral body to engage and overcome any stress the organism may face. Such stressors are symbolised by the chain (such as blocks in life), the Atlas-like human holding the earth (e.g. carrying of life burdens) and Samson-like human holding apart two megalith stones in the background. A weak astral impulse here would create symptoms of apathy, fatigue and hypotension (as shown by the Cadmium remedy). The green colouration within the rest of the adrenal represents its cortex region, where the glucocorticoid, mineralocorticoid and androgen hormones are produced. From here there is a vitalising astral impulse which penetrates the rest of the etheric body, symbolised by the turquoise coloured entity rising along the central axis. In this way the catabolic intense astral impulse has been converted into a softer anabolic impulse working into the physical-etheric body, where it can have shaping, artistic and transformative effects. Loss of this transformation can cause a shapeless or poorly defined body, as found in Calcarea carbonicum children. There is then a lack of emotional force penetrating the physical sphere of life. In the lower aspect of the illustration the row of beings represents the biography of the soul's past lives and the ancestral souls, i.e. the kidney-adrenal system forms the basis to the constitutional or inherited life-force.

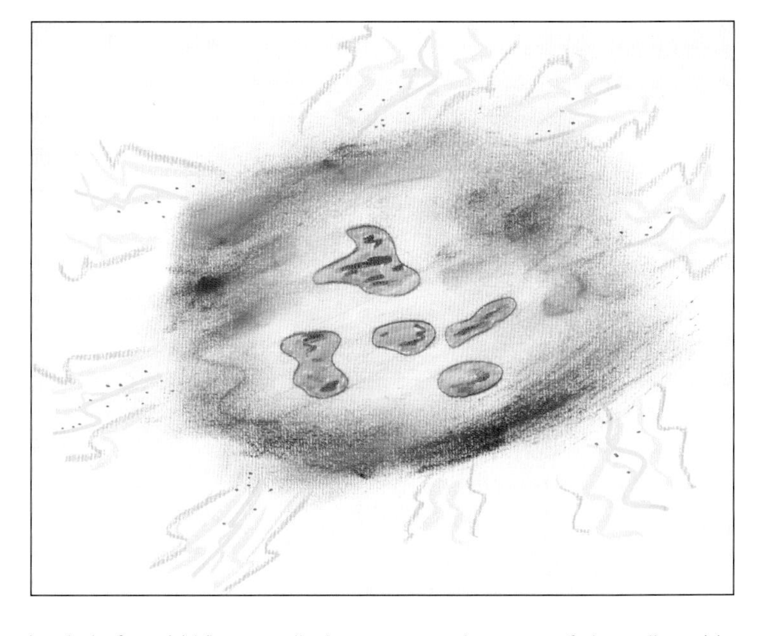

RIGHT. 'Veiling and suppression of malignant cells after chemotherapy', by Yubraj Sharma. Chemotherapy induces heavy metal toxicity and the related miasm, causing progressive kidney failure as well as toxic buildup within the liver metabolism. Chronic mucus and the toxic precipitation veil the cancer source, as shown by the grey-brown discolouration and clouded mucus around the central tumour cells. In Oriental medicine, a diagnosis of Kidney chi toxicosis is found. Where radiotherapy was also part of the allopathic treatment, then depletion of yin and secondary soft tissue fibrosis around the cancer also seals the malignant cells into their sanctuary site. Vibrational remedies, such as the indicated homoeopathic remedies, then find it difficult (if not impossible) to penetrate into the region - as shown by the blocked light transmissions in the periphery. Cadmium sulphuricum may sufficiently remove the toxicity around the cancer to enable access to the anti-tumour remedies.

Astrology

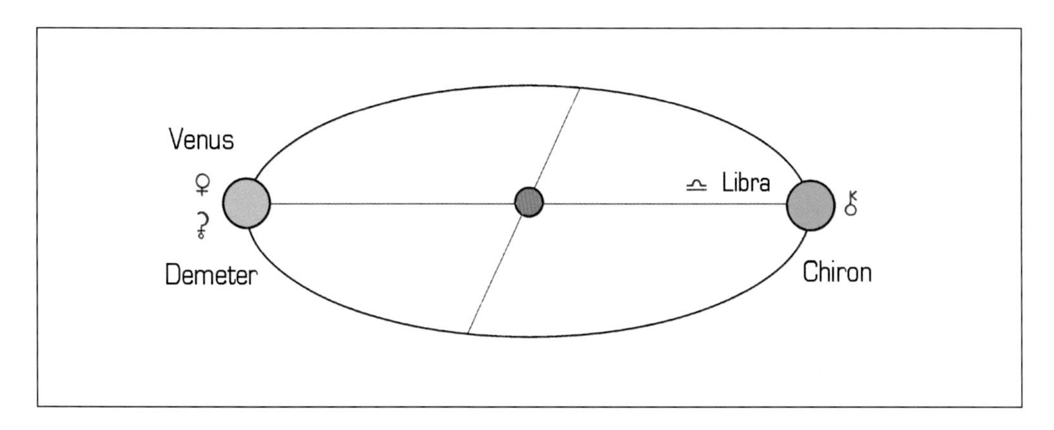

Venus conjunct Demeter opposite to Chiron in Libra.

Oriental

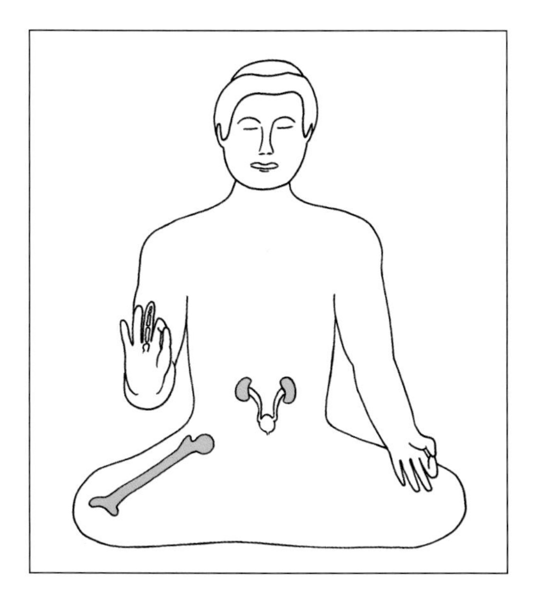

Kidney yang deficiency, with yang/chi deficiency of marrow and bones.

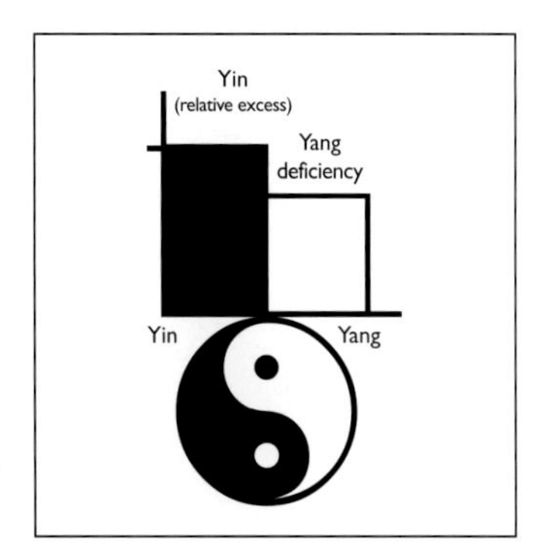

Related images

p.582 Infectious gastroenteritis
p.470 Prostate, normal and benign enlargement
p.471 Prostate cancer
p.207 Cancer growth and detection chart
p.248 & p.250 Renal failure and dialysis
p.300 Pulmonary odema x-ray
p.199-200 Lung function tests

CALCAREA CARBONICUM

Original

CALCAREA FLUORICA

Original

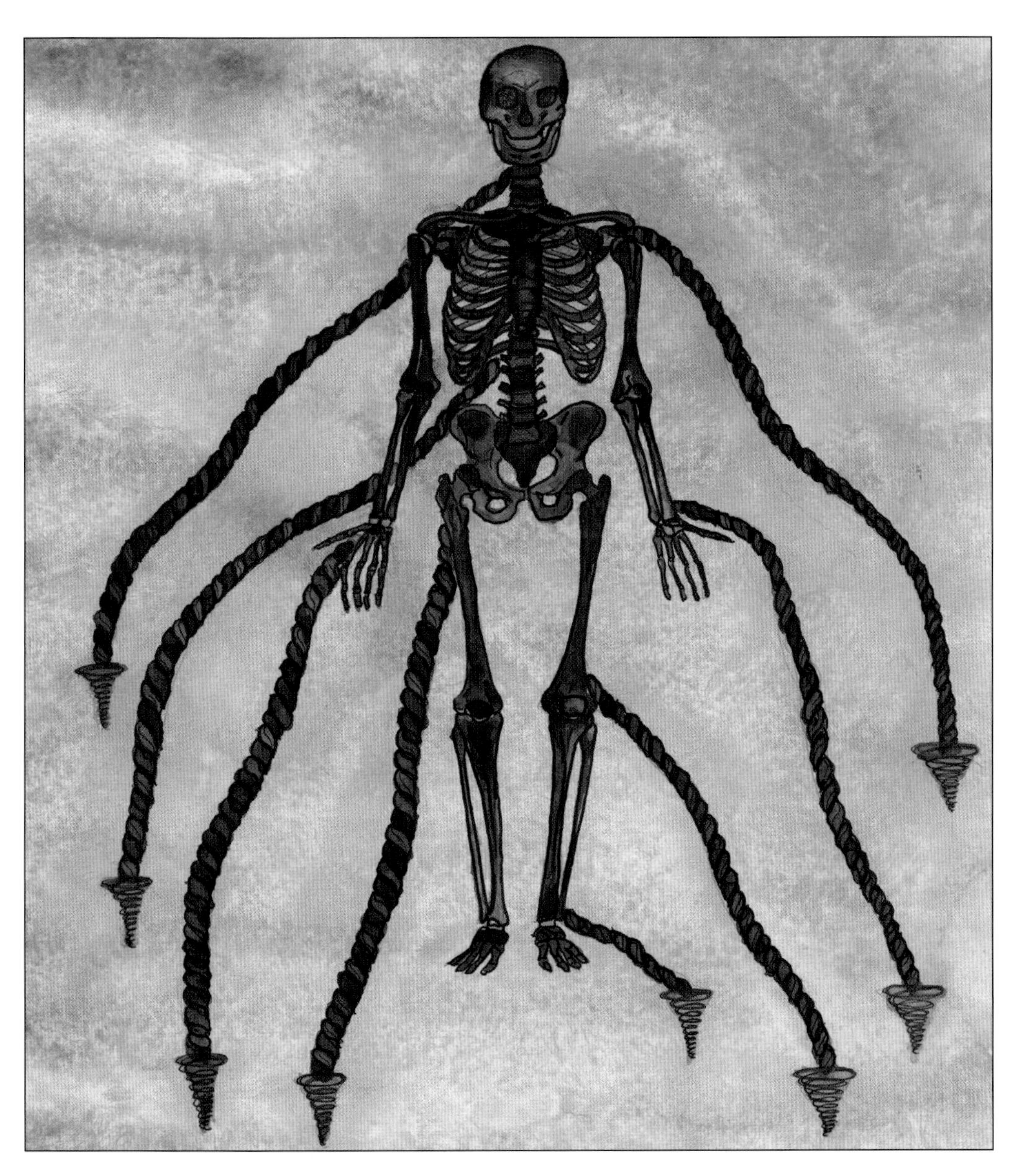

'Calcarea fluorica and bone breathing', by Nadine Kardesler. Creative impulses or formative principles underlie the skeleton. Such impulses are hidden behind the outer manifestation, and therefore grasped by spiritual sight. The skeleton changes as the human being anchors his/her spirit-self into the physical structure, and this involves greater flexibility and strength. The skeleton experiences both the forces of gravity and Earth connection with those of weightlessness and buoyancy. The skeleton of the newly formed embryo is made of cartilage or fibrous connective tissue which become suitably moulded to final shape. Gradually bone is laid down to replace this softer tissue (ossification). This recapitulates the initial stages of humanity when the body was softer, watery during the Old Moon age and Lemurian age. Later, during Atlantis and into the present Earth phase, the mineral kingdom developed and Spirit became more deeply penetrated into the material realm. Thus the body became harder or more mineralised. It is possible to breath in cosmic and star energy into the bones. All forms of life on the planet depend on this cosmic energy (not only sunlight) for nourishment. Compressing this energy into the bones eliminates marrow fat. Healthy bones contain more red marrow (red, white cell and platelet-making marrow) than yellow fat. Fat increases in ageing, pushing the red marrow to the peripheries of the bone, which then becomes much less efficient. The crystalline properties of the bones develops through adequate chi circulation, generating energetic fields around and through them. The prior image illustrates the clearing of obsolete blueprints from the skeleton, a process best accomplished during the growth years of childhood. These descend into Earth for recycling. The below image reveals the reception of cosmic currents into the skeleton; sacred geometrical codes are also shown within the bone.

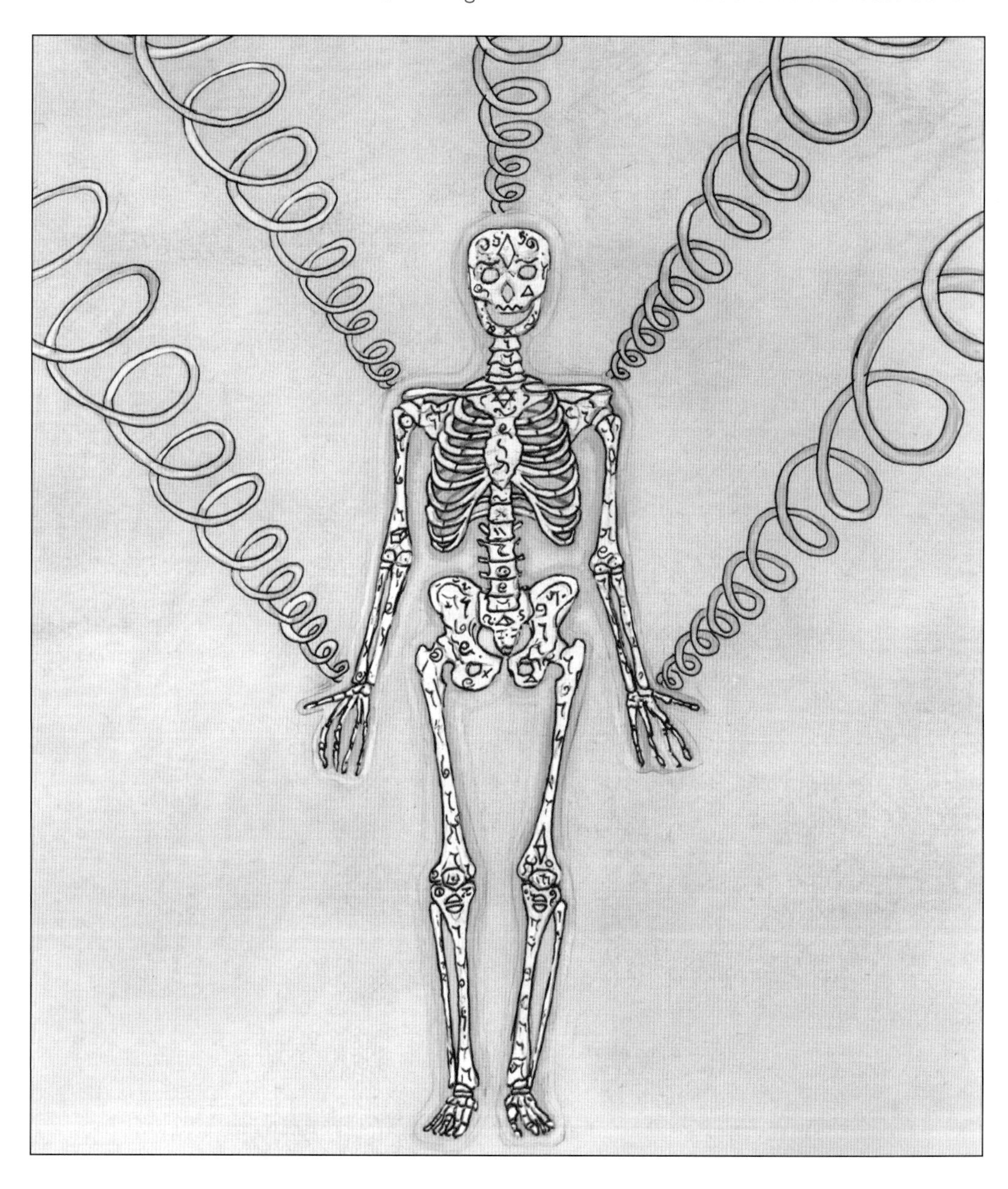

Astrology

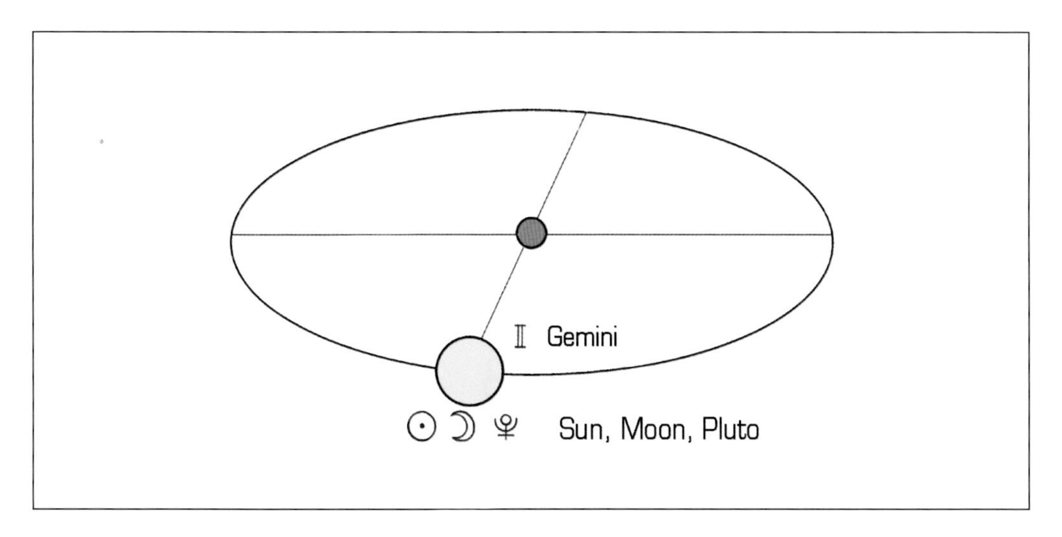

Sun, Moon and Pluto conjunct within Gemini.

Oriental

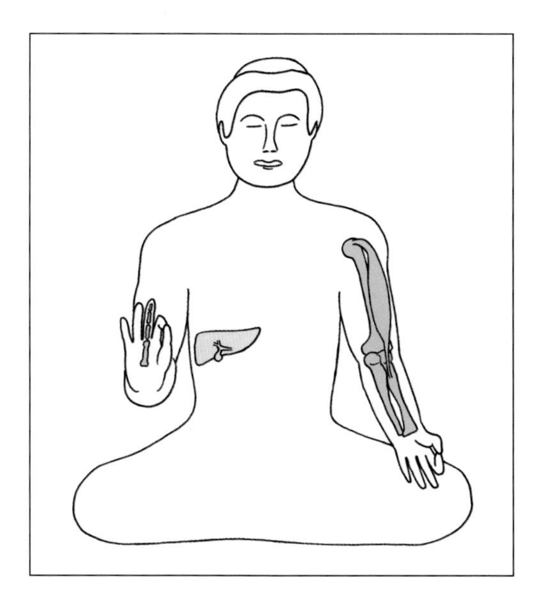

Liver blood deficiency, with wind invasion and painful obstruction syndrome of joints/muscles.

Particulars

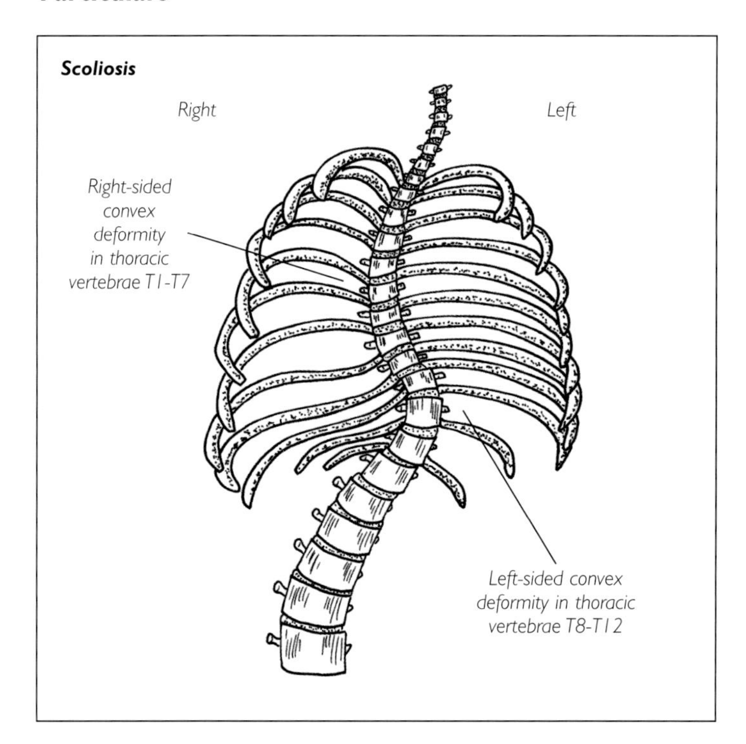

Scoliosis is characterised by a lateral deviation/ curvature of the vertebral column and often occurs alongside kyphosis (anterior-posterior deviation) as kyphoscoliosis. Causes include congenital disease of the vertebrae, early onset tuberculosis or osteomalacia and poliomyelitis. There is deformity also in the rib cage and therefore chest movements are restricted. Severe cases can lead to later stage lung failure.

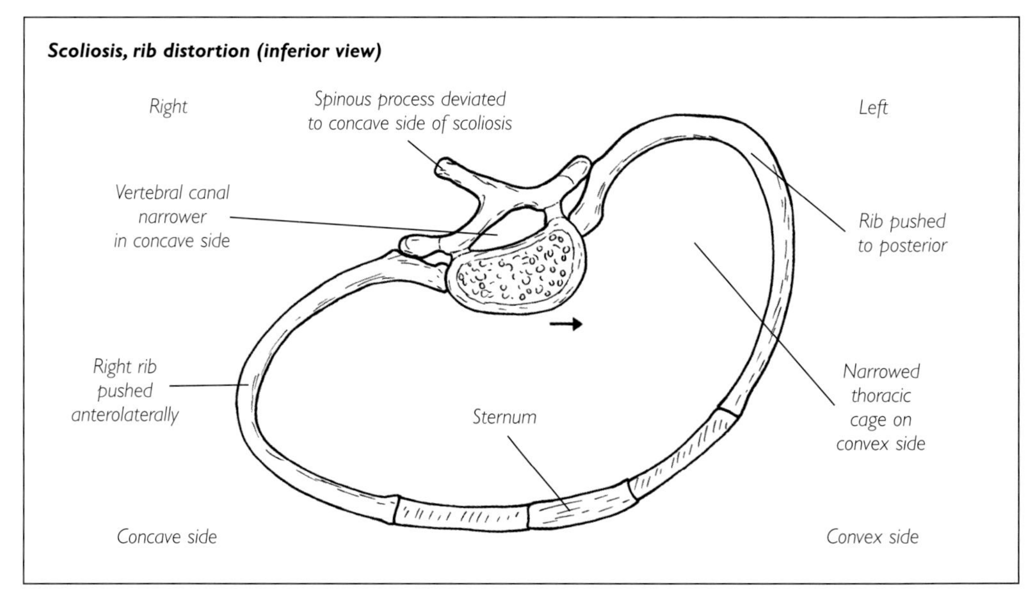

The characteristic distortion of the vertebral and rib cage is shown in cross section for a thoracic vertebral body and rib pair. The ribs on the convex side of the scoliosis are severely deformed with marked restriction of heart-lung function (when the curve exceeds 60°). The ribs pushed toward the back or the convex side thereby form a hump. The torso tilts to the convex side. There is also compression of the vertebral canal on the concave side, which can lead to nerve root and spinal cord compression syndromes.

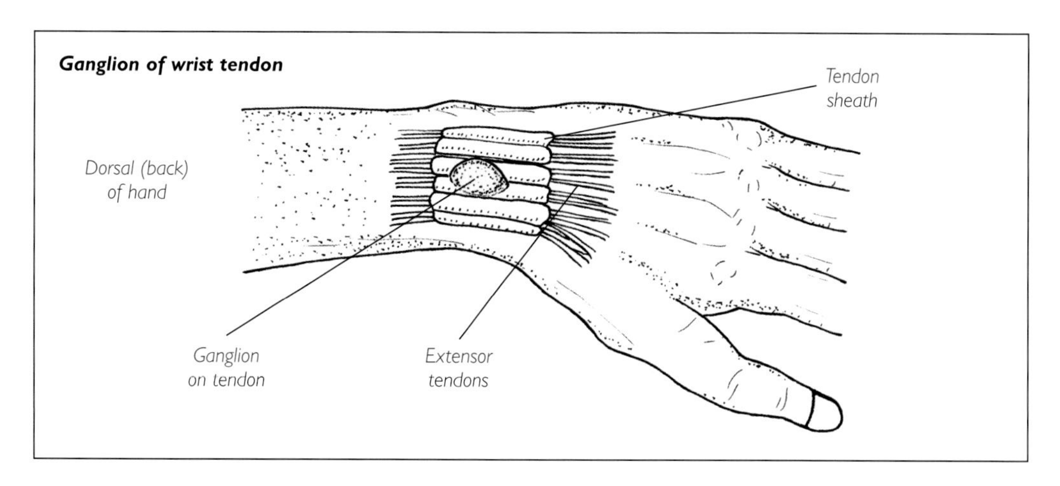

A ganglion is a cyst attached to a joint capsule or tendon sheath, especially found in the hand and wrist (at the dorsum or back of the hand). The ganglion is composed of an outer fibrous lining, an inner synovial membrane lining and contains clear colourless fluid. It occurs from cystic degeneration of the connective tissue near the joint or tendon sheath. Other than being unsightly, sometimes there is aching pain and weakness in the area.

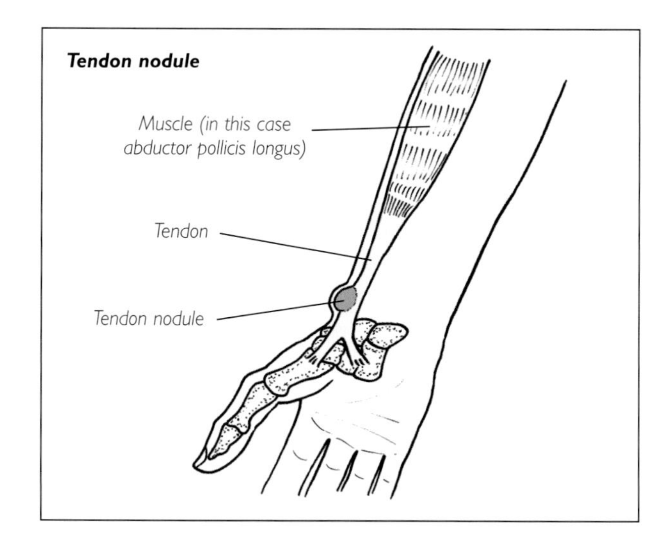

A cystic nodule can develop on a tendon, usually on the back of the wrist or hand, typically the size of a grape. Wrist flexion may cause the swelling to enlarge; whilst extension reduces its size. Such nodules are called ganglions, and may be in communication with the synovial sheaths around the tendons of the extensor muscles. Occasionally nodular deposits form around or on the joints, tendons, ligaments and bursa composed of calcium hydroxyapatite. This is bone mineral which has abnormally become deposited in soft tissues.

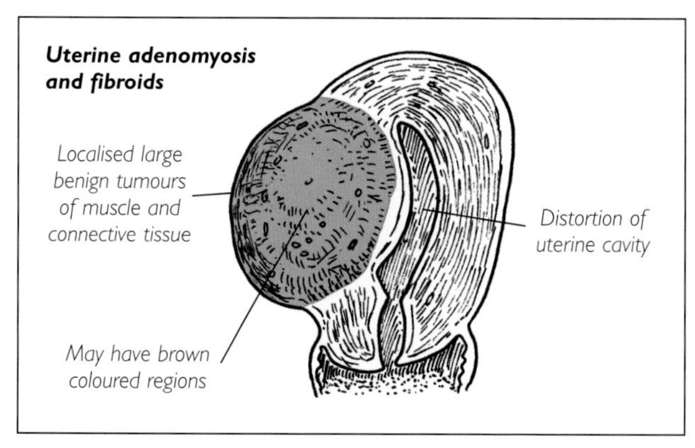

Uterine adenomyosis is a condition of ectopic inner endometrial deposits within the myometrium (the outer muscle layer of the uterus). There are typically brown coloured deposits. A fibroid, on the other hand, is a hard, white tumour of overgrown muscle tissue. The symptoms include heavy menstrual bleeding, palpable lumps and infertility.

Ligament injury (ankle)

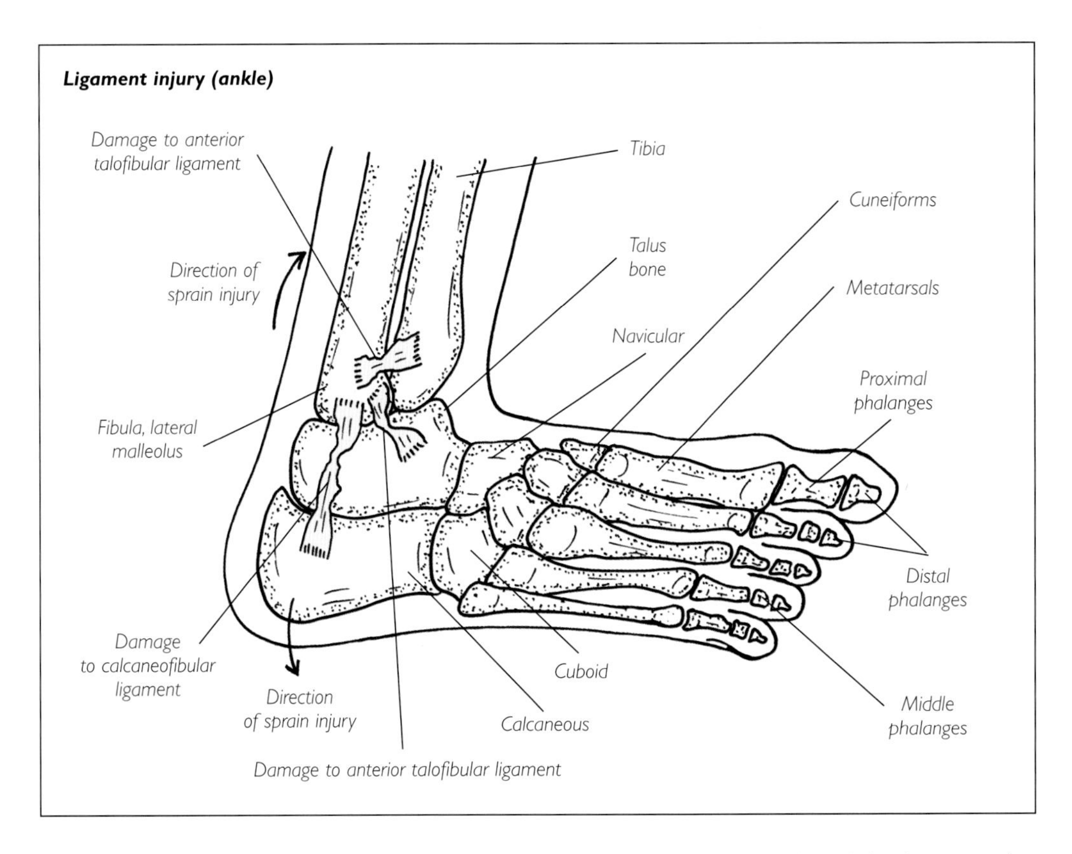

The foot is a mobile weight bearing mechanism, whereby the ankle is a hinge joint between the tibia, fibula and talus. This forms a mortise joint, allowing flexion (plantar flexion) and extension (dorsiflexion). With excessive rotation of this joint, as shown by the arrows, fractures and/or torn ligaments can occur. The foot can adjust to motion on tilted and irregular surfaces due to the subtalar (talocalcaneal) and transverse tarsal (talocalcanonavicular and calcaneocuboid) joints. At these sites a degree of inversion and eversion (side to side twisting) can occur. The ankle also has strong medial ligaments, but weaker lateral ligaments. Therefore, the lateral ligaments are more often damaged (by inversion sprains or a twist of the foot inwards).

Related images

p.233 Squint
p.528 Migraine visual aura
p.343 Multiple sclerosis
p.171 Dentition crowding, delayed
p.503 & p.265 Toothache and abscess
p.339 Osteoarthritis
p.623-624 Rheumatoid arthritis deforming
p.691 Paget's disease
p.758 Varicose veins
p.528 Breast fibroadenoma
p.209 Breast adenocarcinoma
p.730 Thyroid multinodular goitre

CALCAREA PHOSPHORICUM

Museum

PRECEDING PAGE. Leonardo da Vinci, 'Virgin and Child with St. Anne and St. John the Baptist' (circa 1495), charcoal, heightened with white, on cardboard. © National Gallery, London. The original sketches are now lost, and this one is known as the Burlington House Cartoon. Despite being preparatory for a oil-painting (which was never done) it has been as highly regarded as one of his finest works. The infant Christ is shown blessing the young St. John during a meeting in the desert. Christ is on the knee of the Virgin Mother, who is herself seated on St Anne's lap. Thus a stream of life flows through these three generations. The painting is used to illustrate the theme of incarnation of light into the body and therapeutically assisting the incarnation of the soul into its embryonic and newborn physical body. The birth of John heralds the birth of Jesus. Subsequently the Christ energy could be brought into Jesus (at 30 years) in the Jordan through John's Proclamation and Baptism. Both the forces of light and dark are portrayed in the calendar of the birth of these two children. Thus, Mary received the Annunciation in Spring. On the day of the summer solstice (the height of the solar forces) John the Baptist was born, and it was in the deepest point of darkness around the winter solstice that Jesus was born. Furthermore, the souls of the two children communicated to each other whilst in gestation. Mary visited the elderly Elizabeth, both with child, an episode known as the Visitation. A light flashed between the two embryos' to interweave their destinies –Elizabeth feeling her child leap within her womb when Mary came near, as if to jubilantly greet the other unborn child. The Jesus embryo represented the most youthful possible state of humanity, i.e. the highest Adam soul from a paradisical state of Heaven before the Fall from Grace. On the other hand, John the Baptist represented the oldest possible state of soul, an individual that matured through the immensity of human incarnations and multiple destinies. The meeting of the two would therefore reflect the union of phosphoric light with heavy calcific earth.

For a different interpretation of the painting, note that there are several esoteric and non-Gospel sources indicating the presence of two Jesus children (see p.456), for example, the Testament of the Twelve Patriarchs (of which Greek and Hebraic versions circulated throughout Europe at least until the 15th century). One Jesus was of the priestly line, the other of a royal kingship. Furthermore, the Gospel of Luke describes a more earthly nativity scene, where Jesus is lain upon the ground within a stable and adored by shepherds. Matthew's Gospel, on the other hand, describes a kingly Jesus sitting upon Mary's lap (thus not touching the Earth soil) and receiving the Adoration of the Magi or Kings. Note how the two children are depicted in this painting, one standing on the ground to reveal His earthly connection, the other in Mary's lap to indicate His more regal position. It was a popular theme throughout Renaissance art to show the Child Jesus with the Giovannino (the youthful John the Baptist). This may, however, actually have been a veiled attempt to represent the Two Jesus children without the charge of heresy levied by the Church and its terrorist arm the Inquisition. In many paintings the Giovannino was identifiable by his wearing a fur garment, holding an Agnus scroll and a long cross. The scroll represented the Proclamation (John's statement regarding Jesus): 'behold the Lamb of God'. Sometimes he would be held by his aged mother, Elizabeth. The standing child does not display any of these attributes, suggesting he may not be John the Baptist at all – but the second Jesus child.

FOLLOWING PAGE. 'Calcarea phosphoricum and bone light', by Nadine Kardesler. The femur or thighbone is depicted; indeed it can be seen as a bony image of the whole person. It is the longest, heaviest and strongest bone in the body. Its upper (proximal) aspect is a compact head and forms a joint with the hipbone. Its lower (distal) aspect forms a joint with the tibia and patella in the knee. A skeletal polarity can be seen with the relatively round, enclosing and concentrated head pole (this is linked to the nerve-sense system) and the linear mobile radiating less dense lower limb poles (linked to the metabolic-limb system). In the middle is the equivalent region of the thorax (the rhythmic system) which has elements of both poles, i.e. it is enclosing but less than the skull, and is mobile but less so than the limbs. Each long bone in the body has a similar relationship with the whole organism. Furthermore, centres of ossification and where a nutrient artery enters the bone are minor chakra sites. The illustration shows the descending spiritual-cosmic light entering the bone from above (the phosphorus process), a cut-out section of this head region is shown. The light spirals through the midshaft, to ground into the Earth grid of energy (relating to the calcium process).

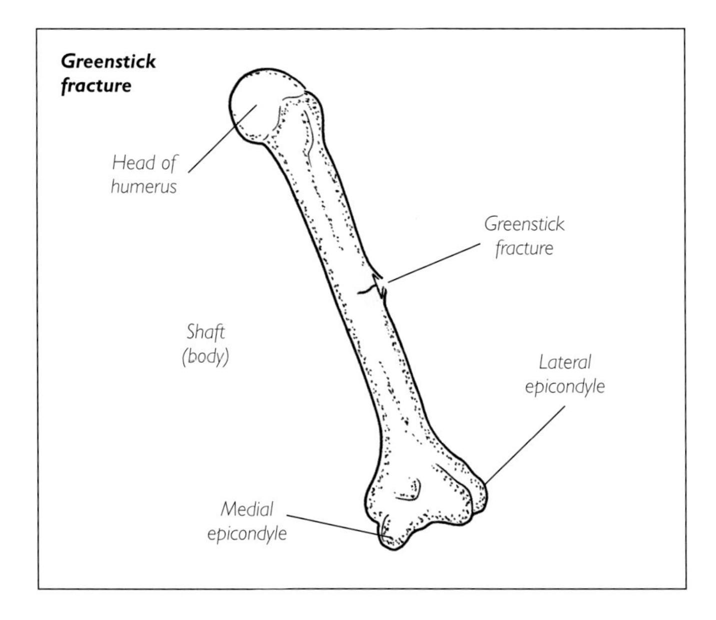

Fractures in normal bones are more common in children due to the more slender bones, many of these are hairline breaks, known as green-stick fractures. The bone breaks like a willow bough, and also heals more rapidly. There is a small tear in the periosteal lining rather than through the whole thickness of the bone, and this will rapidly repair. The child will have local pain or swelling at the bone, but without deformity or abnormal bone movement.

Related images

p.96 Growth chart
p.164 Scoliosis
p.527 Headache
p.622 Cervical spondylitis
p.689 Bone fracture healing
p.687 Bone tumour
p.691 Paget's disease
p.690 Fracture non-union
p.339 Osteoarthritis

CALENDULA OFFICINALIS

Original

'Calendula officinalis and the decay of tissue', by Caroline Hamilton. The plants are growing out of rotting, putrefying vegetation, so as to assist their recycling process. The orange flowers, as shown in this sample, have been regarded as more medically potent than the yellow flowered type. Wispy vapours are released into the atmosphere, including sulphur gases – to represent the dematerialisation of matter taking place. A few angels are visible above the scene, such beings assisting the Earth elementals in the regulation of the etheric realm of the planet. The elementals comprise those of the gnomes of the earth, undines of the water, sylphs of air and salamanders of the fire element. The activity of these beings can be imagined in various aspects of this illustration. If this imagery is then projected into the situation of a putrid or poorly healing wound, then the recycling and regeneration activity of the plant can be appreciated.

Astrology

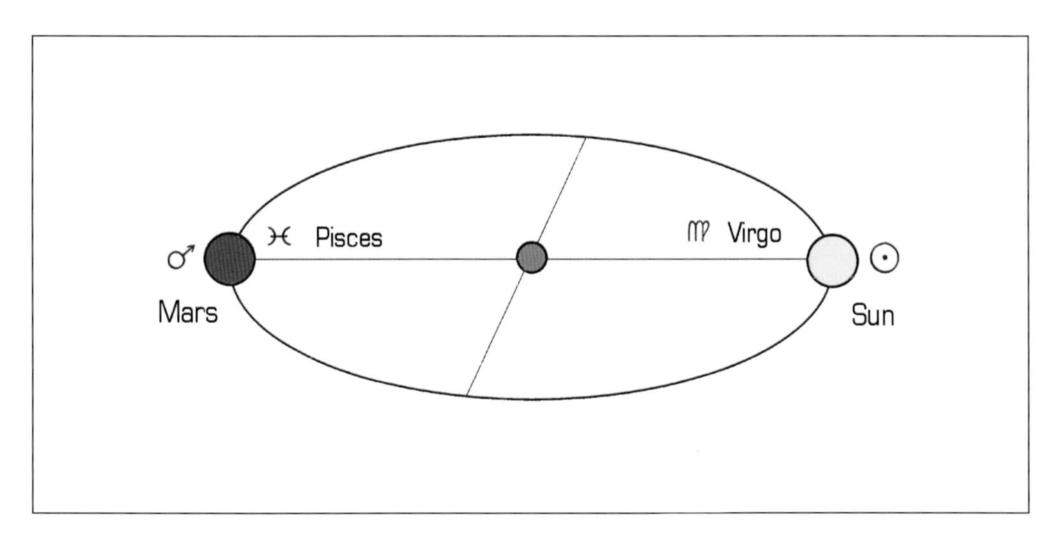

Sun in Virgo opposite Mars in Pisces.

Oriental

Damp-heat invasion of kidneys, bladder, uterus, lower burner and defence chi/lymph nodes.

Particulars

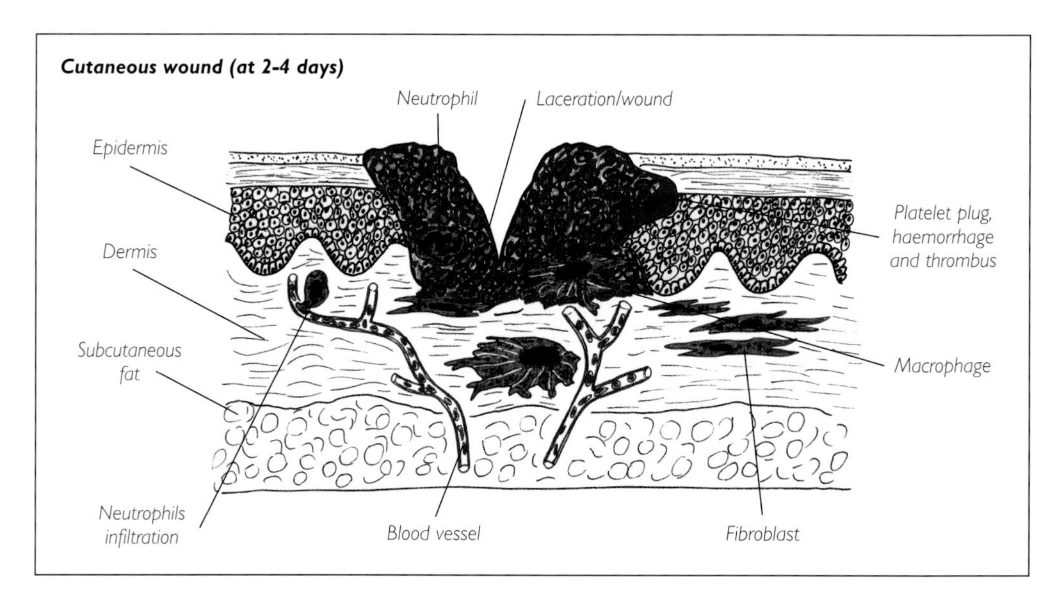

The initial response to tissue injury is inflammation, followed by repair and regeneration. A thrombus (clot) stops the bleeding and upon drying out forms a barrier to the wounded skin, preventing further microbial invasion, as well as preventing the loss of tissue fluid. The thrombus is formed from fibrin (out of the blood plasma) and platelets. Later the thrombus will be 'digested' by proteolysis to allow for the growth of new epithelium. Also, initially, an acute infiltration of neutrophils from the blood circulation helps to scavenge the necrotic tissue. Macrophages are then attracted into the region and continue this role. Growth factors are released that stimulate collagen secretion and new blood capillary growth. Granulation tissue is the transient repair tissue, and predominantly is a mixture of fibroblasts, capillaries and monocyte/macrophage white cells. The fibroblasts secrete collagen into the tissue.

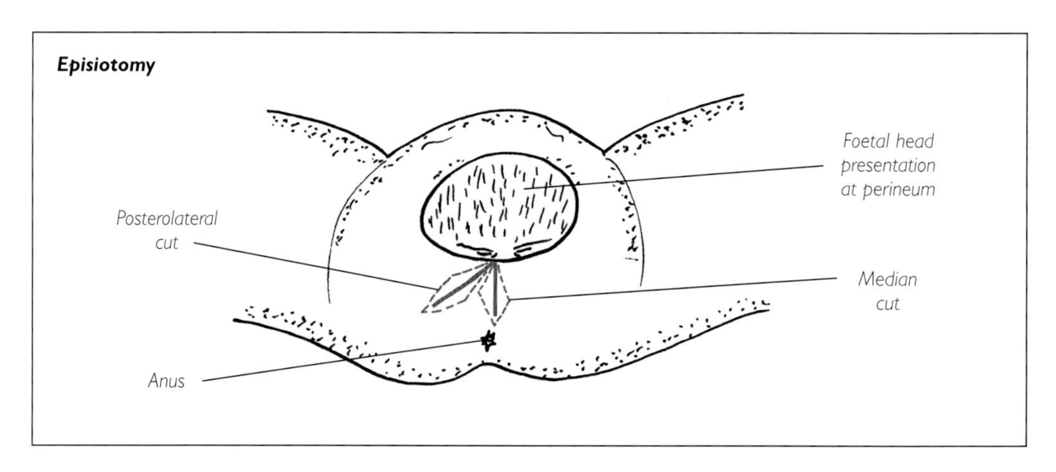

Episiotomy involves an incision in the perineal body at the time of delivery. It is used in order to prevent undue stretching and tearing of the perineum and muscles (with the risk of the tear involving the anal sphincter) and to protect the foetus if it is premature and/or pushed against an inflexible perineum. The median incision is usually the easiest to perform and repair, but has the risk of extending by a tear into the anal sphincter. The posterolateral incision is more difficult to repair, but does protect the anal sphincter.

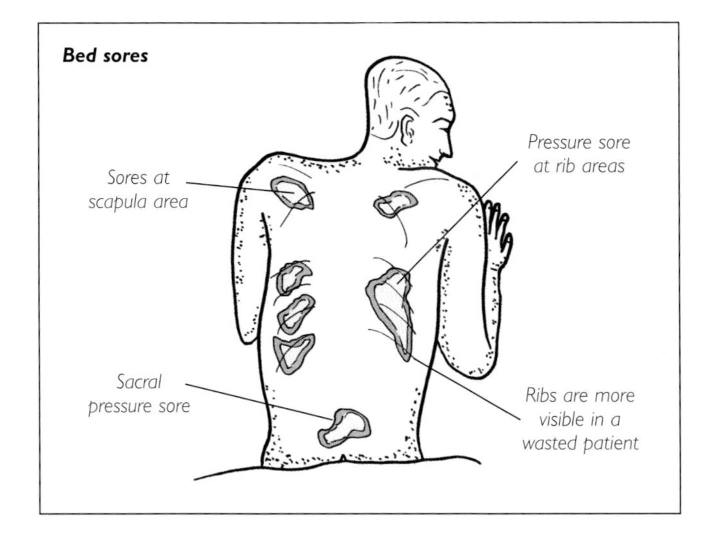

Bed sores are the result of neglect in a debilitated or wasted patient; muscle wasting and soft tissue wasting causing some exposure of the ribcage and bones. Whilst lying on his back, pressure especially occurs at the sacrum, trochanters (hip area), femurs, heels, malleoli of ankles and rib cage. If the early signs of skin redness are missed then the skin breaks into an open sore, which can be difficult to heal. Frequent mobilisation of the patient by nursing staff can be preventative.

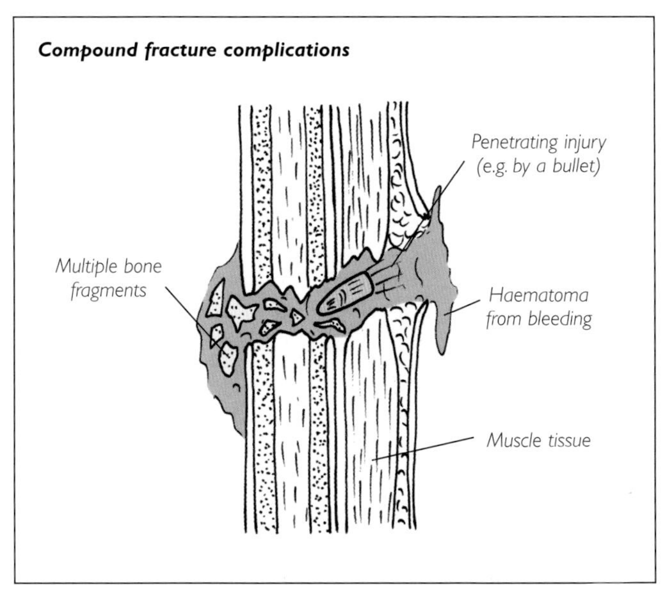

The risk of serious infection is high in this example, due to a penetrating injury occurring from the outside environment (allowing the invasion of bacteria), the multiple shattered bone fragments and severe soft tissue/muscle damage being around the fracture site.

Related images

p.339 Keloid scar
p.454 Puncture wound with lymphangitis
p.186 Burn chart
p.185 Burns
p.215 Electric burn
p.543 Haemorrhoids
p.758 Varicose veins
p.758 Venous ulcer
p.239-243 Problems during labour and miscarriage

CAMPHORA

Original

'Camphora officinalis and activation of metabolic heat', by Tessa Gaynn. The shrubby tree and magnified views of leaves and flower are shown growing within a grid of fiery warmth. Surrounding the tree is the kidney system to symbolise the relationship of this organ to the base chakra (alongside the adrenal glands – not shown in this image). The overall effect is the grounding of the warmth forces of the Ego/Self into the physical-etheric body.

Astrology

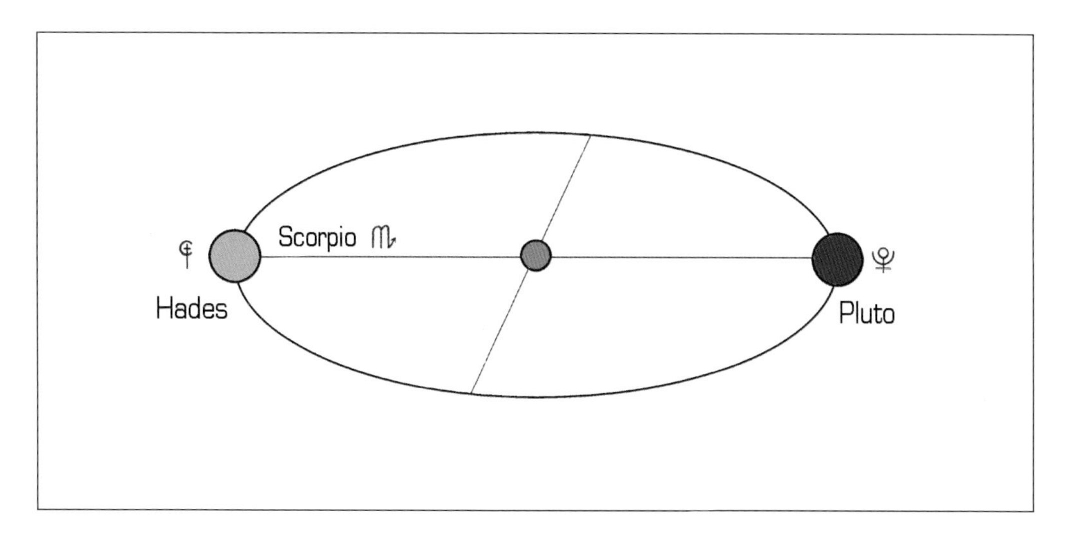

Pluto opposite Hades in Scorpio.

Oriental

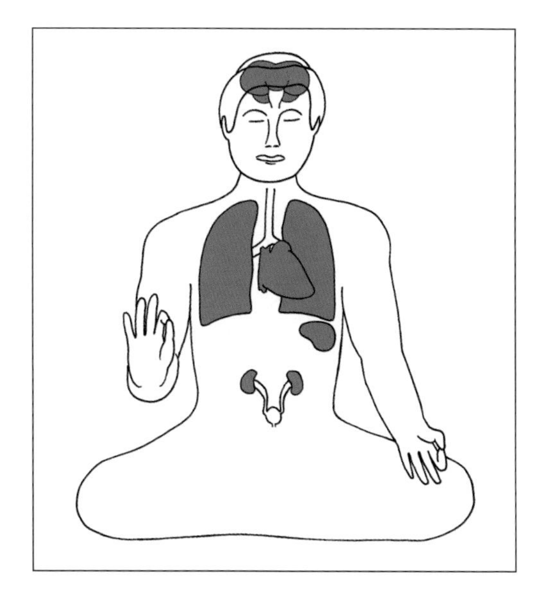

Collapse of yang of heart, lungs, spleen kidneys and brain.

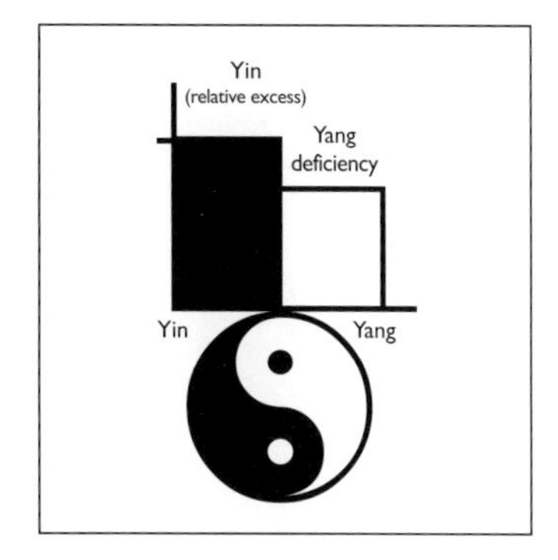

Particulars

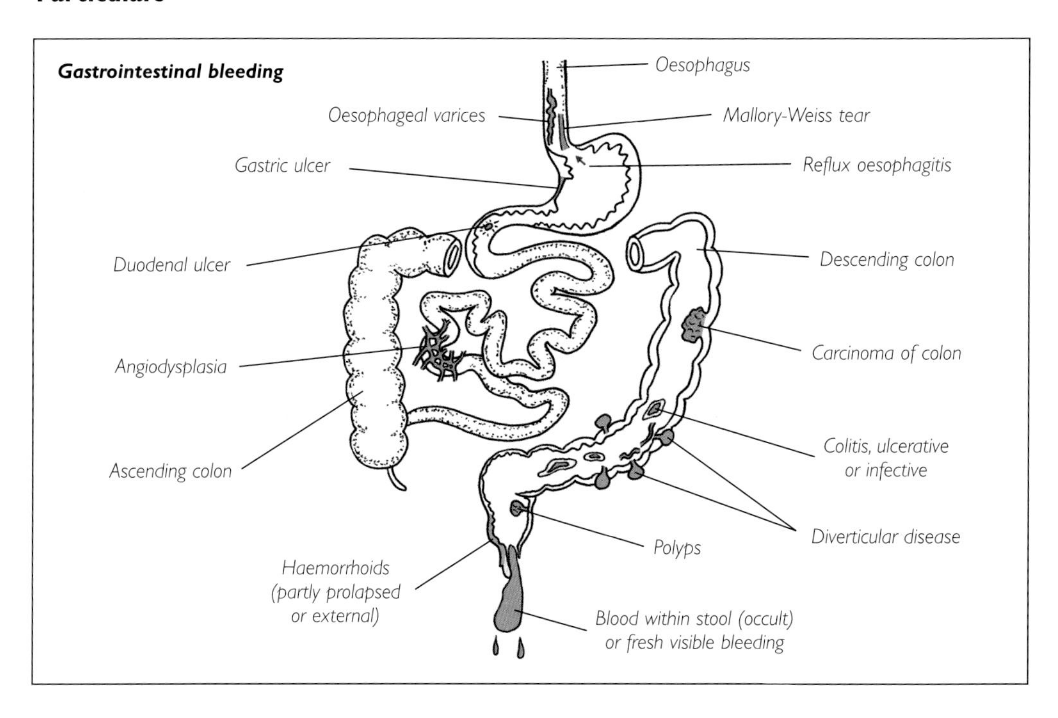

Bleeding is categorised into upper or lower gastrointestinal in origin. The vomiting of blood is known as haematemesis. Melaena is the passage of black tarry stools (the black colour is due to altered or digested blood). Sometimes fresh bleeding is witnessed per-rectally if acute bleeding from a lower site has occurred. Causes of upper gut bleeding are illustrated. The most common is chronic gastric or duodenal ulceration (about 50% of cases). Drugs such as aspirin and other non-steroidal anti-inflammatory drugs particularly causes gastritis and ulceration. Varices are dilated veins, occurring especially at the lower end of the oesophagus. Mallory-Weiss syndrome is a tearing at the oesophageal-gastric junction area with bleeding. Less commonly a gastric cancer is a cause of bleeding. Causes of lower gut bleeding are also shown. Angiodysplasia is a rare cause, due to a deranged blood capillary network at the site. Diverticulae are weak points of herniation in the colon wall. Colitis or inflammation can be an autoimmune disease (as in ulcerative colitis) or infective, e.g. typhoid fever, with ulceration of the colon wall. Cancer of the colon may particularly present with anaemia of unknown cause in the elderly, due to occult or non-visible but long-term bleeding.

Related images

p.233-234 Epilepsy & p.454 Tetanus
p.133 Liver failure and ascites & p.470 Pancreatic failure
p.248 & p.250 Renal failure and dialysis
p.50 Sleep apnoea, respiratory failure
p.300 Heart failure, right-sided
p.451 & p.145 Myocardial infarction
p.383 Ventricular arrhythmia ECG
p.504 Chronic bronchitis & p.198 Emphysema
p.281 Supplementary oxygen therapy
p.582 Infectious gastroenteritis

CANNABIS INDICA

Original

'Cannabis indica and breathing out the astral body', by Crispin Chetwynd. The marijuana plants are growing around the central yogi figure, note the long lanceolate 5-part leaves. Smokers are exhaling out their astral bodies into a pooled astral entity hovering above, amidst the mountainous backdrop. Aspects of the individual astral bodies are linked to other astral plane spiritual beings, such as the angel on the left and extraterrestrial to the right. The flightiness experienced by the user is symbolised by the birds.

Astrology

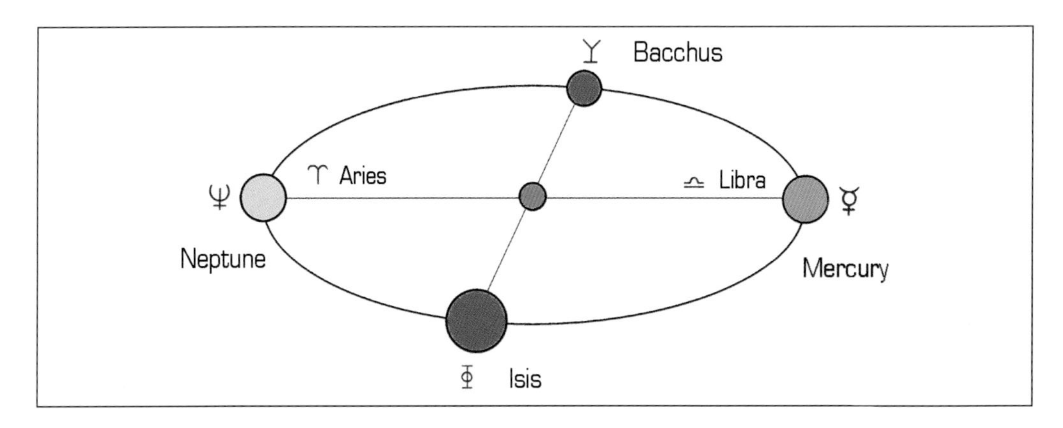

Grand cross, Mercury in Libra opposite Neptune in Aries, and Isis opposite Bacchus.

Oriental

Kidney yin deficiency with heart chi constraint/stagnation.

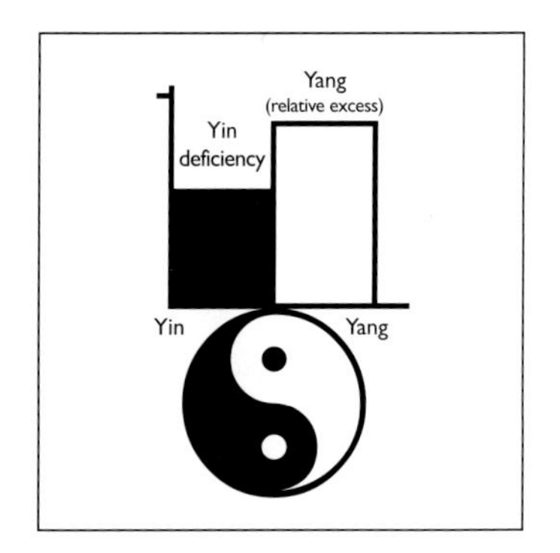

Related images

p.593 Adrenal atrophy
p.489 Gonococcal abscess vulva
p.488 Gonorrhoea and urethritis

CANTHARIS VESICATORIA

Original

'Cantharis and sacral chakra cords of sexual relationships', by Loolie Habgood. The two lovers are modelled on the sculpture 'The Kiss' by Auguste Rodin. These two are locked in an infinite embrace with emotional force and vitality. Their soft curves are contrasted with the gross representation of the insect. However, in many cases, the sexual energy from previous relationships (even those from other incarnations) is not sufficiently cleared and so can plague the sacral chakra function during the current relationship. Furthermore this contaminating astral-etheric energy may precipitate into the physical body as a sexually transmitted disease, cystitis or kidney inflammation.

Burns chart

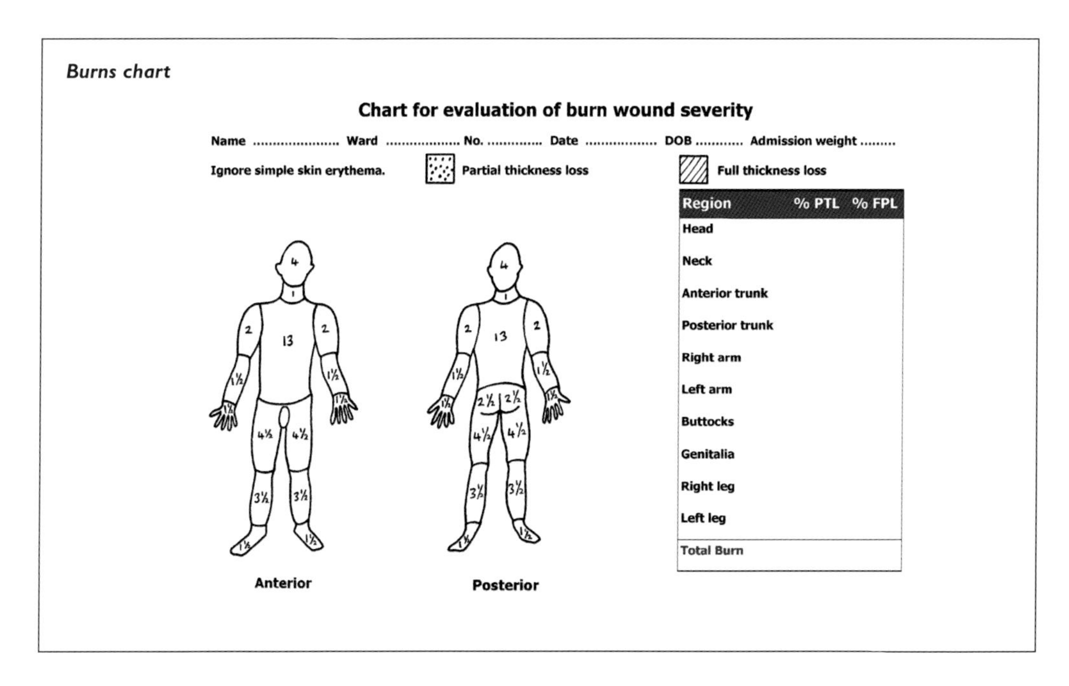

The extent of tissue damage from a burn is related to the temperature and duration of time of the burn. The treatment plan must include a fluid rehydration plan, unless there is mild (first degree) non-extensive burn. There are greater fluid requirements for greater surface areas of burn. A method of calculating surface are is based on summating the percentages allocated to discrete surface area regions of the body, as shown on the chart, for front and back of the body. Thus a burn involving the whole of one arm (anterior and posterior) would involve 10% of the skin in total. A full-thickness burn extends through the whole depth of the skin (note it will not be painful and will appear like dried parchment). A partial thickness burn is anywhere between the extremes of mild superficial redness and full thickness burn. Most burns can be managed on an outpatient basis. However, partial thickness burns over 15% in surface area (or over 10% in children and the elderly) and full thickness burns require hospitalisation, possibly into a specialist burns unit. Indeed a formula has been devised, whereby if age + %burn is greater than 100, then there is a very poor chance of survival.

Trichomonas vaginalis

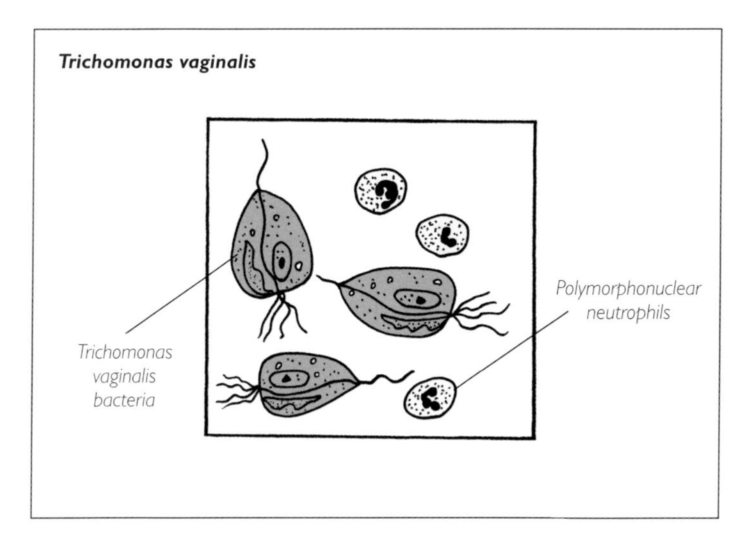

This image is a microscopy of the vaginal discharge where infection is by the flagellated protozoon, Trichomonas vaginalis (see also p.188). This can invade the genital region from the bowel; it is a common infection after coitus in the female. The discharge is profuse, thin, yellow-green to grey in colour, with a fish-like odour, often frothy with small bubbles. It infects the cervix and vagina, which become red and sore.

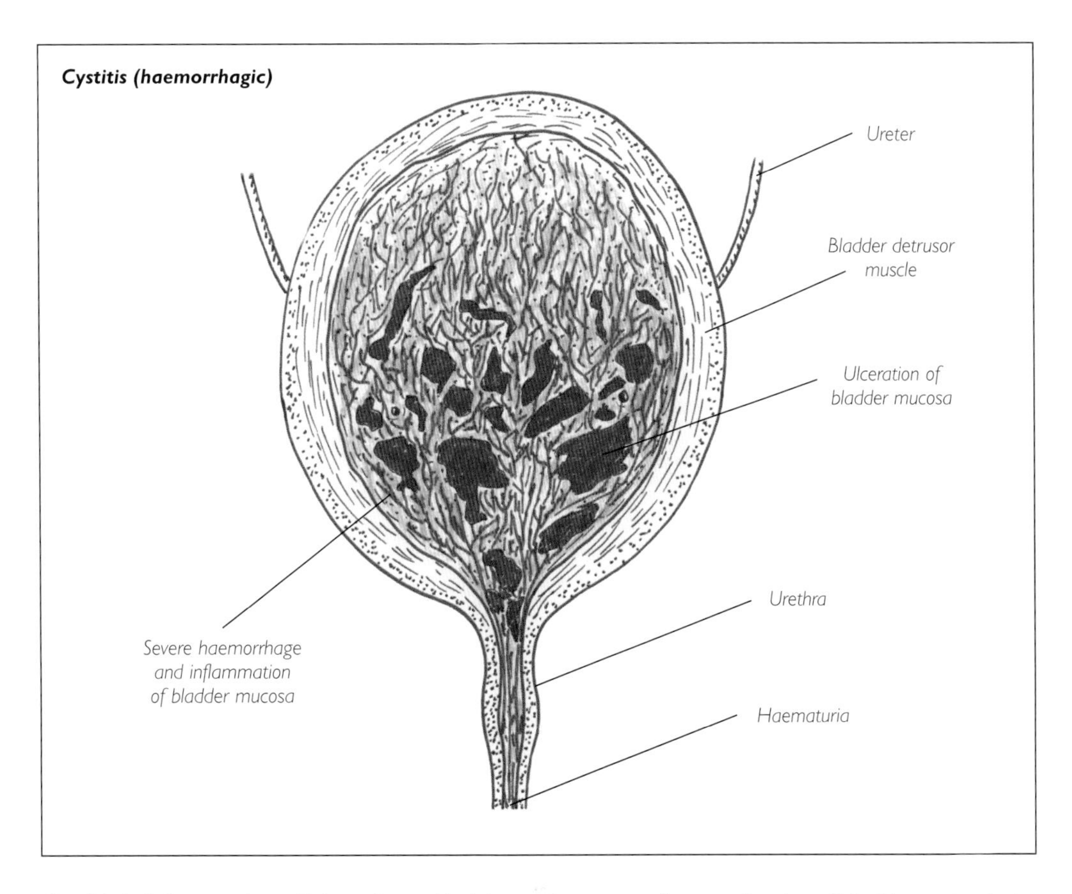

Cystitis is inflammation of the urinary bladder, and can vary from a simple self-limiting episode to uncommonly a severe attack that extends to the kidneys to cause acute kidney failure. Cystitis particularly starts from an ascending infection of the urethra, especially in the female. Sometimes it occurs from an infection descending from the kidneys, e.g. tuberculosis. If cystitis occurs in the adult male or in children (of either gender) this may be sign of an underlying anatomical abnormality – which should be investigated for. The symptoms of acute cystitis are painful and frequent urination, and occasionally haematuria (blood in urine). Ulcerative and haemorrhagic cystitis are severe forms from e.g. massive infection, or damage by certain types of toxins, such as chemotherapy drugs (especially cyclophosphamide).

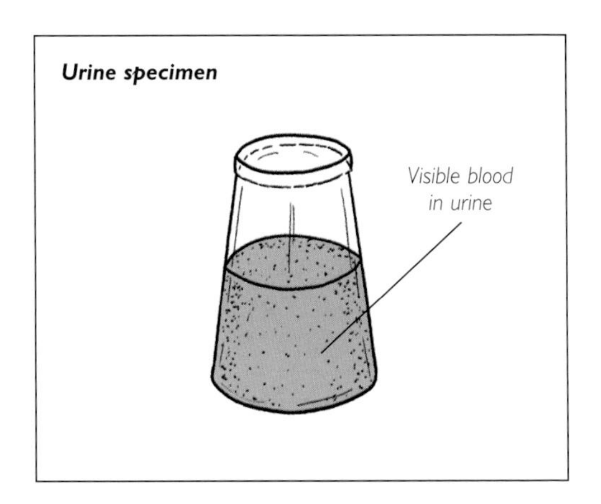

Haematuria or blood within the urine may be visible or microscopic and found only on chemical testing (whereby test strips inserted into the urine undergo a colour change). Causes of haematuria include kidney trauma, stones, nephritis, cancer anywhere in the urinary tract, infections (e.g. tuberculosis, parasites such as schistosomiasis, bacterial).

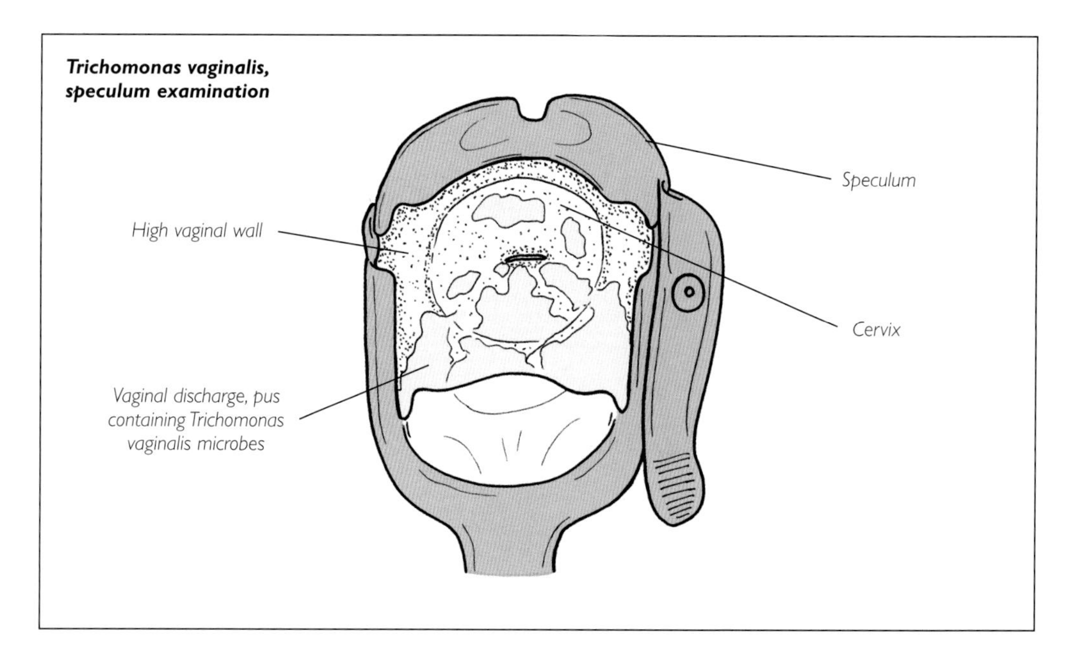

Trichomonas vaginalis (see also p.186) is a protozoan microbe, possessing four flagella and a flexible cell membrane providing motility. It exists in the female urethra & vagina, and male urethra & prostate. It is a sexually transmitted disease; a few episodes occurring through fomite (object) contact, such as via clothing or toilet surfaces, or by passage through the birth canal (in the baby). There is usually a scanty watery odious (fish-like) vaginal discharge, sometimes with severe erosion and inflammation of the vaginal lining – with much itching, burning pain and painful urination.

Related images

p.295 Polycystic kidney
p.115 Renal calculi
p.582 Infectious gastroenteritis
p.488 Gonococcus
p.488 Urethritis
p.490 Pelvic inflammatory disease
p.335 Ovarian cysts
p.619 Shingles

CAPSICUM ANNUUM

Original

'Capsicum annuum and the fiery metabolism', by Nadine Kardesler. The cayenne pepper fruit and leafy twig is surrounded by a matrix of warmth activity. This is shown symbolically functioning as a harmonious whole, of Ego forces, into the metabolism (which is seated within the realm of the etheric body).

Astrology

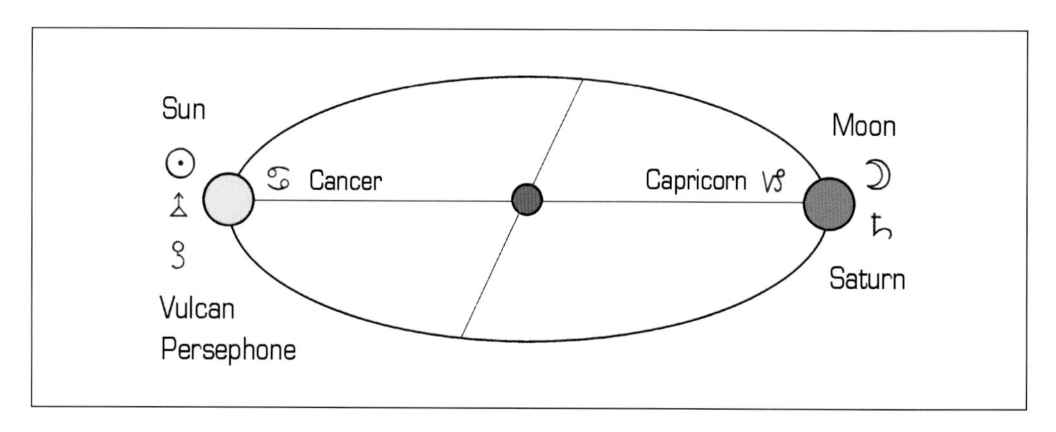

Sun conjunct Vulcan and Persephone within Cancer, opposite Moon conjunct Saturn within Capricorn.

Oriental

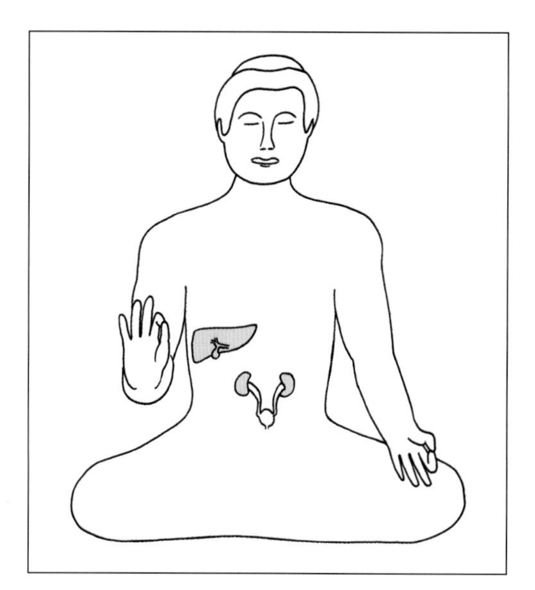

Yin and blood deficiency of kidneys and liver.

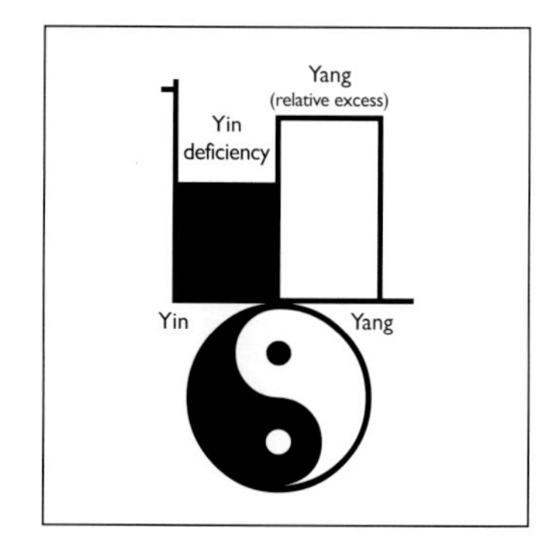

Related images

p.730-731 Diffuse thyroid goitre
p.4 Croup
p.130 Pleurisy
p.718 Pyelonephritis
p.582 Infectious gastroenteritis

CARBO ANIMALIS

Original

'Carbo animalis and transmutation of the lower astral plane', by Jemma Hone. The fumes rising from the animal hide burning within the lower (material) plane are shown drifting into the greyish middle zone, which represents the lower astral plane. Images of graveyards and ghosts symbolise the stagnation of souls caught within this realm after physical death. Parts of the soul and its astral body may also stagnate here during physical incarnation, e.g. upon chronic disease and organ failure. The angelic realm in the upper zone represents the higher astral plane, reached by the soul after successful review and processing within the lower astral plane.

CARBO VEGETABILIS

Museum

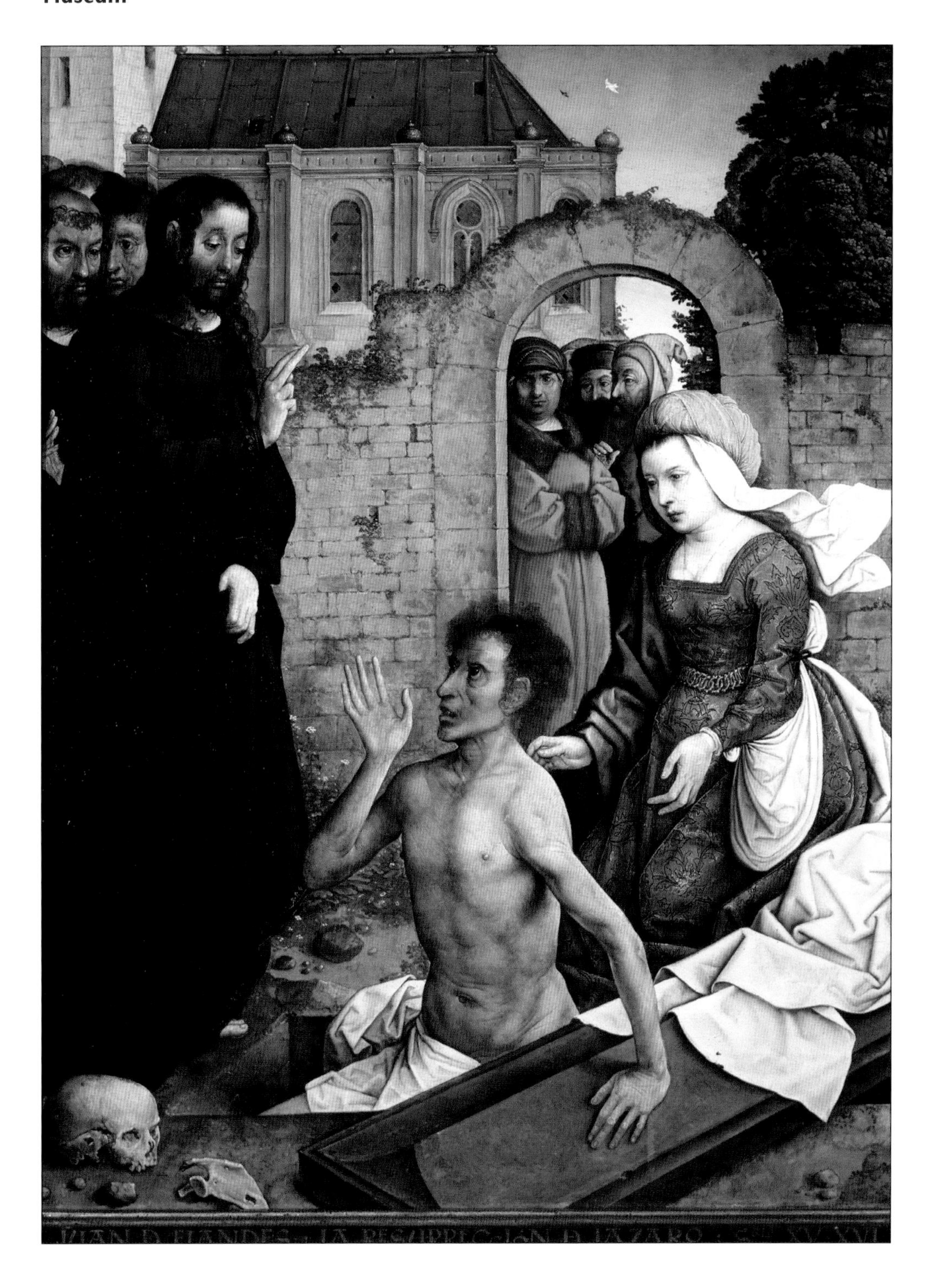

PRECEDING PAGE. Juan de Flandes, 'Resurrection of Lazarus' (around 1500), Derechos Reservados (all rights reserved) © Museo Nacional del Prado, Madrid. According to the Gospel of John (11.1), Lazarus was miraculously resurrected from the dead. Lazarus lived in the town of Bethany, his sisters were Mary and Martha, the former sister having anointed Christ with perfumed oil and dried his feet with her hair. The sisters subsequently asked for Jesus to come to heal their sick brother, but Jesus tarried where he was – with the result that Lazarus was already dead and buried for four days upon his arrival. Martha reproached Jesus for his delay, but Christ assured her that Lazarus would rise again. She took this to mean on the day of resurrection, at which Jesus replied "I am the resurrection and the life; whoever believes in me, even if he dies, will live, and everyone who lives and believes in me will never die." Lazarus was buried in a cave – Jesus had the sealing stone rolled away and bid Lazarus to come out, which he did, still wrapped in his grave-cloths. It was after this event that many people believed in Jesus. In this painting, a tomb is depicted, and in keeping with the near eastern custom of embalming of the dead, Lazarus is wrapped in linen. Christ's hand is raised in the traditional gesture of authority. Further details on Lazarus and his role in the drama of Jesus Christ may be found in Berberis p.108-112.

Some perspective on the nature of death and resurrection is pertinent for this image and the remedy Carbo vegetabilis. Death was only really experienced by the human race after the Fall from Grace (expulsion from paradise). This occurred during the Lemurian root race. Although this was a discrete event the circumstances of the Fall unfolded over a long timeframe. Linear time cannot easily catalogue such rounds of world evolution, but it would be extremely ancient (at least 1 billion years ago) and prior to Atlantis. By mid to late Lemuria humanity was established in the material plane, although with bodies still in a soft gel-like state. Up till early-mid Lemuria and during the two previous root races (Polarean and Hyperborean) humanity largely resided within the spiritual world and therefore had no need for death as a means of returning to this higher realm. However, with the partaking of the fruit of the Tree of Knowledge, Adam and Eve could wake to their material senses and be propelled to Earth matter. This is part of the reason behind safeguarding the Tree of Life (the other Tree forbidden by Jehovah) within the Garden of Eden, so that primordial humanity could not take their immortality with them into the descent. Death was subsequently required in order for souls to reincarnate, enabling the experience of multiple lives with a gap within the spiritual realm. Without death the soul would remain bound to its karma on the Earth plane. Jesus Christ brought the resurrection and redemption codes from that pristine Adamic state back to humanity and the world. He therefore reversed the need for death. As this shift is progressively received by the race, then a future stage of humanity will be able to come and go between the spiritual and material realms at will, without the need for disease or death to leave the material state. Lazarus therefore pre-empts a future faculty.

He is a shadowy figure in the Bible, and is only mentioned in the Gospel of John. After his resurrection by Christ, Lazarus seems to disappear from the story and yet is known to have become a close companion of Jesus right up to the crucifixion. This is because, in esoteric lore, Lazarus is none other than the Apostle John himself. His initiation at Bethany represented a contemporary version of the 3-day death sleep of the ancient Mystery schools (such as ancient Egypt and Greece). The disciple would enter a temple sarcophagus, his physical body would become icy-cold as if dead, with barely enough etheric body attachment to maintain life. His/her astral body and soul would fly free into the spiritual world. The rest of the etheric body was also liberated from the binds of the physical flesh, enabling it to receive the imprints of the cosmos relayed by the astral and Ego, as well as being permeated by world etheric forces. Thus, when Lazarus is called back to life by Jesus, it is not a ghostly emaciated figure that walked out of the tomb, but a radiant transfigured being. The words 'I Am the Resurrection and the Life' can therefore be understood, as a reconnection to the paradisical state but with the addition of the Tree of Life.

Original

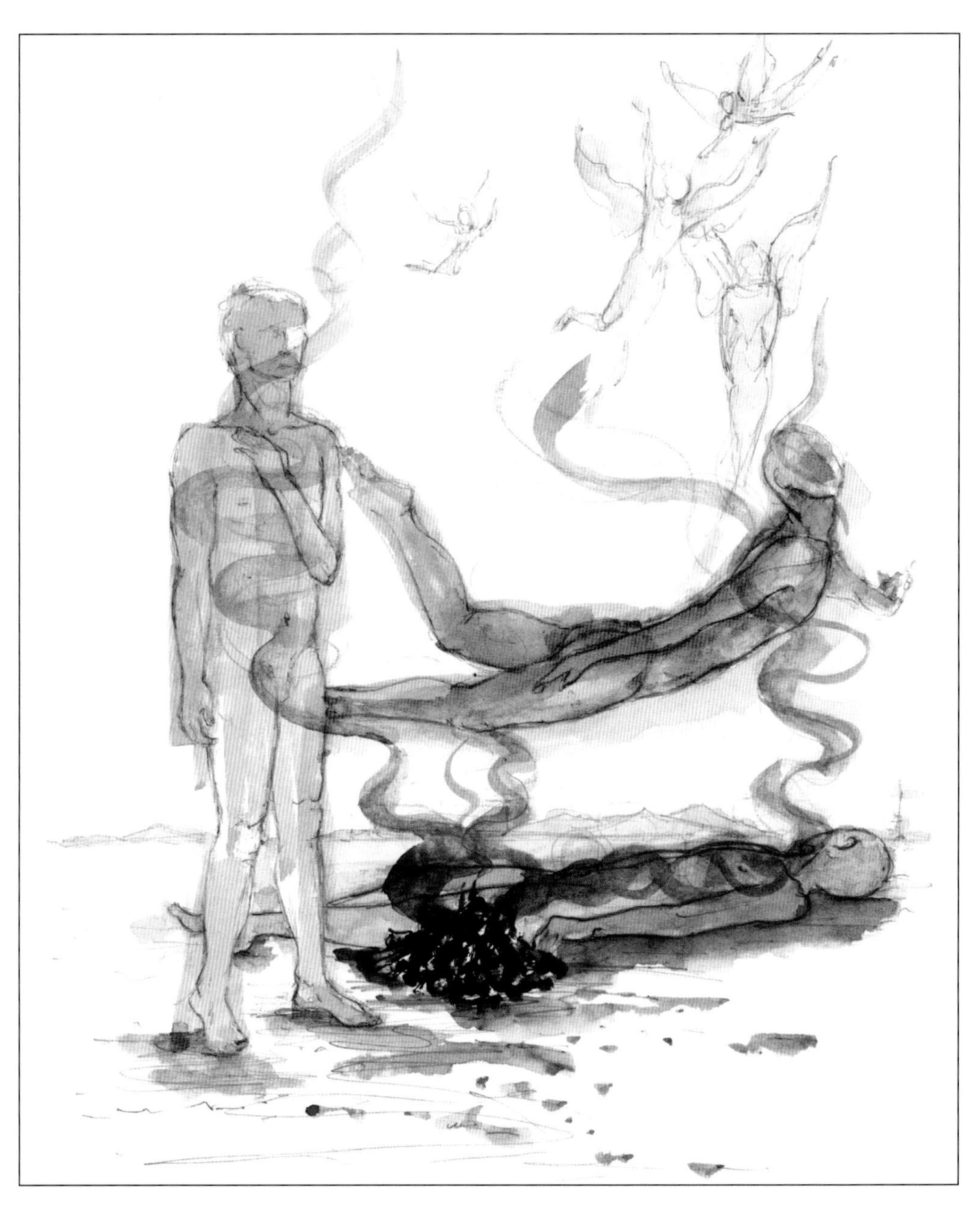

'Carbo vegetabilis and aeration of the physical body', by Esther Lane. Various stages in the relationship between the air-related astral body and the physical body are shown. The bluish body lying prone next to the fire is indicative of either the sleep state, or the stage after physical death. There is release of the astral body as a spiralling movement through the kidney radiation and lung system. The astral body partially exhales for the purposes of sleep, but completely separates from the physical body upon death. It is then shown flying upward, to reach the astral plane above (shown populated with yellowish angelic figures). The standing figure represents normal waking consciousness, with rhythmic movement of the astral body into the physical body, as a partial inhalation and exhalation through the lung-kidney systems.

Astrology

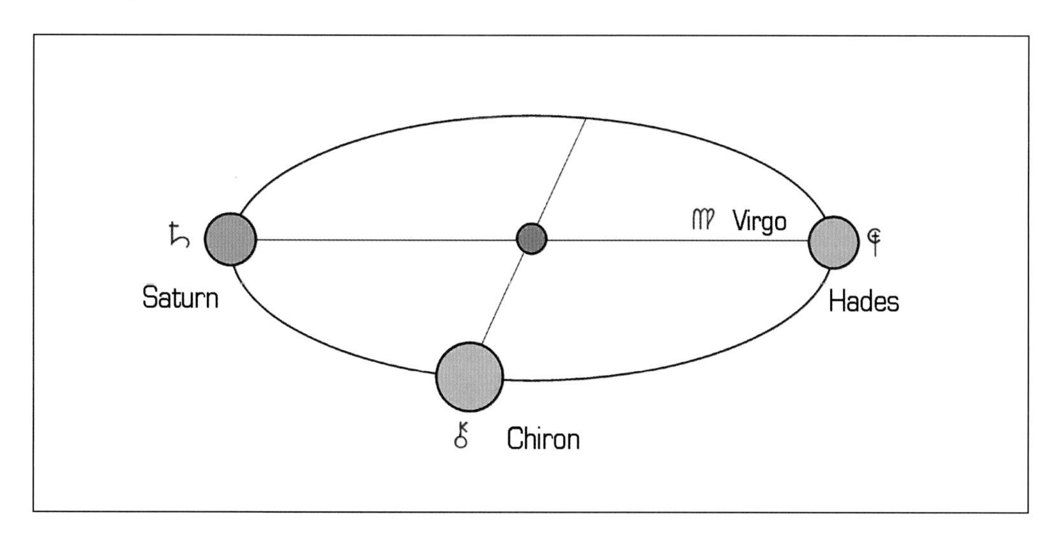

Saturn opposite Hades in Virgo, squared by Chiron.

Oriental

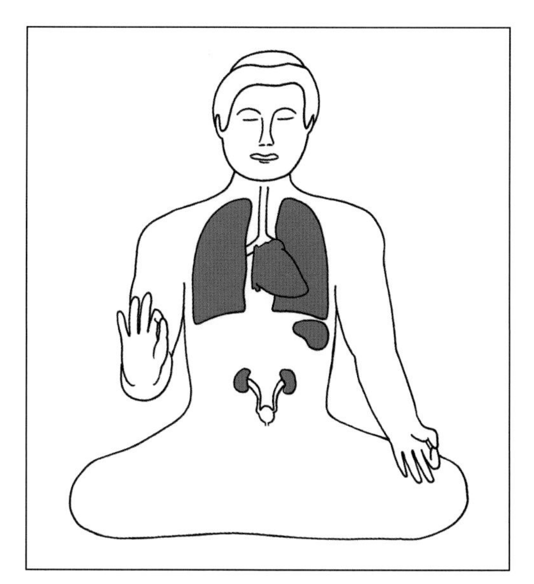

Yang collapse of heart, lungs, spleen and kidneys.

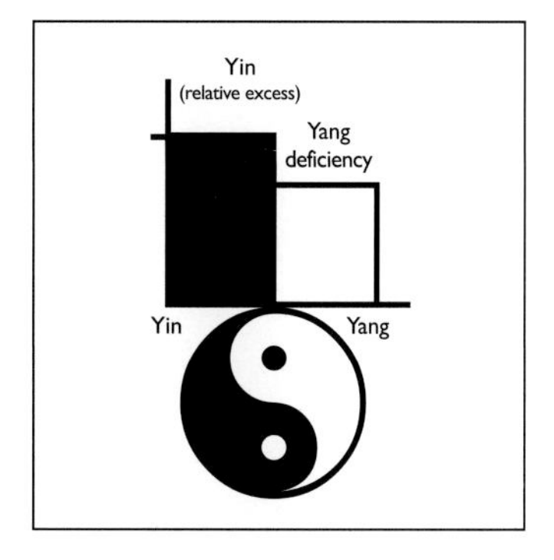

Particulars

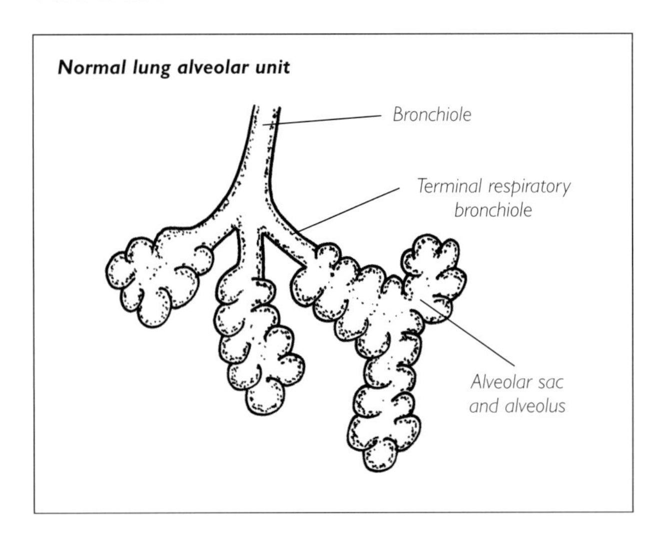

Within the lungs, the segmental bronchus branches into several bronchiole airways of less than 1mm in diameter. At this stage the cartilage lining of the airway is replaced by smooth muscle (which enables broncho-dilatation or constriction as needed). The terminal bronchioles finally divide into a few respiratory bronchioles, which end as the alveolar sacs – the site for gas exchange with the capillary blood.

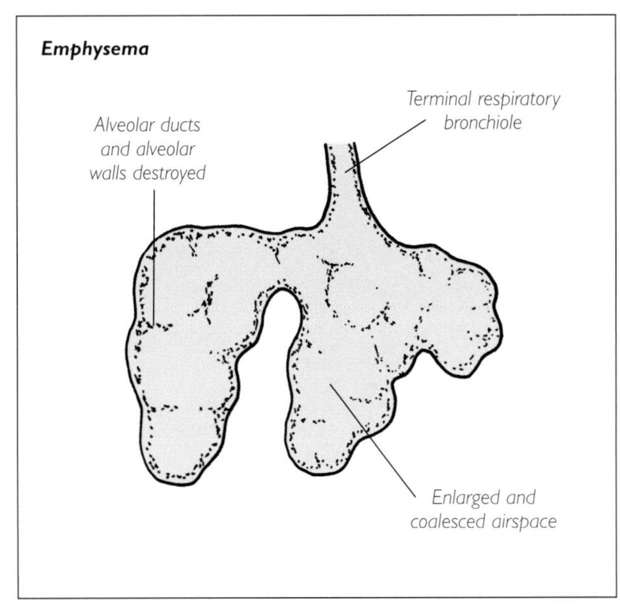

Emphysema is characterised by enlargement of the airspaces distal to the terminal bronchioles with destruction of their walls. The most important cause is cigarette smoking; this habit increases the neutrophils and elastase/protease enzymes in the alveoli – which appear to destroy the alveolar tissues. Emphysema can be localised in the lung, sometimes forming a very large single (or a few) dilated areas called bullae. Or it can affect most or all the lung. The enlarged airspaces are inefficient for gas exchange, causing breathlessness and reduced exercise tolerance, also hyper-inflated lungs (with a barrel shaped chest).

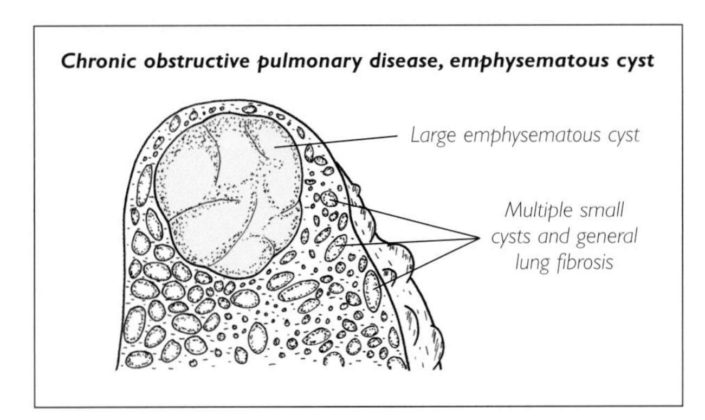

Chronic obstructive pulmonary disease with predominance of emphysema is characterised by generalised damage of alveolar integrity and areas of fibrosis. The bullous or large airspaces progressively enlarge and cause inefficiency of gas exchange. The symptoms of breathlessness deteriorate. Sometimes a few or single very large cystic cavities develop, as shown here.

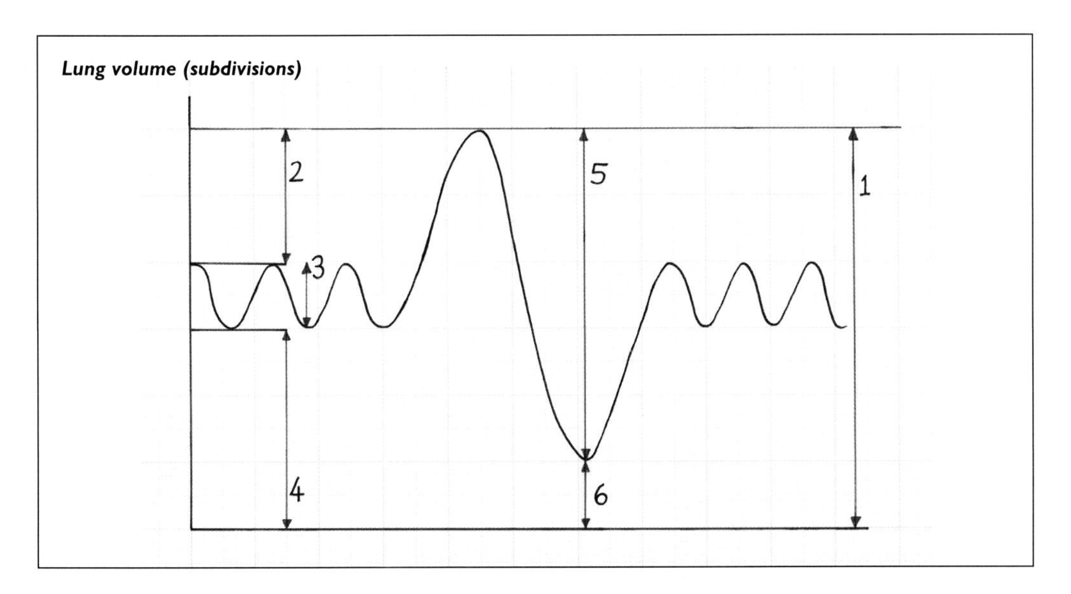

1 – Total lung capacity. 2 – Inspiratory reserve capacity. 3 – Tidal volume. 4 – Functional residual capacity. 5 – Vital capacity. 6 – Residual volume.

The subdivisions of the lung volume are shown.

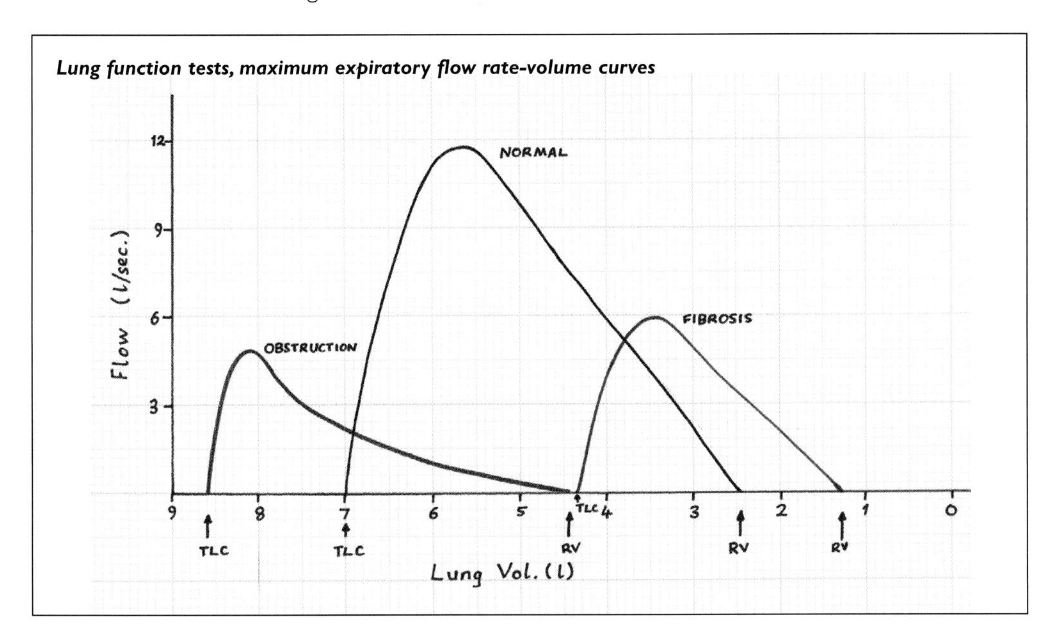

The residual volume (RV) and total lung capacity (TLC) are measured by means other than a spirometer (e.g. by measuring how much helium gas from a reservoir must be used to fill the lungs completely). The total lung capacity is a measure of the volume of air required through inhalation to fully fill the lung airways and alveoli. The residual volume is a measure of how much air has been left within the airways and alveoli after full exhalation. In airways obstruction there is a marked increase in residual volume, i.e. 4.5 litres in this example. The TLC is measured at approx. 8.5 litres, but this is due to the larger volumes of air retained in the lung, the tidal volume is actually lower than suggested by this reading. In fibrosis or restrictive lung disorders, all lungs volumes are reduced.

Lung function tests, spirometry

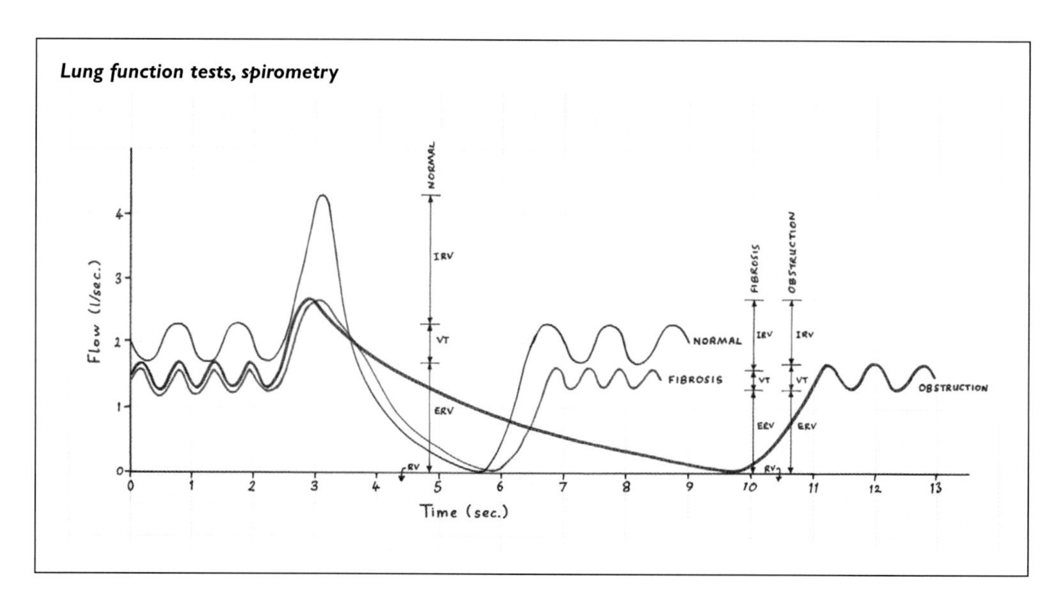

VT – tidal volume (in litres). IRV – inspiratory reserve volume. ERV – expiratory reserve volume.

The spirometer measures the tidal volume and vital capacity of the lungs, with measurement of FEV1 and FVC. The FEV1 is a measure of the air flow during expiration (exhalation). Normally, during exhalation, the pressure within the alveoli and pleural cavity must rise in order to remain open (i.e. so as to not collapse the airspaces). This left hand section of the graph is reflective of normal (tidal) breathing. In chronic obstructive airways disease the tidal flow falls, and is a sign of the reduced exhalation of air (shown in red in the left hand section of the growth by VT, i.e. the height of the sinus waves of breathing). Lung fibrosis has also caused reduced air flow (shown in green on the left hand section) due to the reduced elastic recoil of the lungs and reduced lung movements. The patient is then asked to make a forced maximal inhalation, which for normal lungs has exceeded 4 litres/second of flow. Both in the fibrosed and obstructed lungs it can barely exceed 2.5 litres/second in this example. This is a measurement of the IRV, i.e. the capacity for inhaling beyond the normal tidal volume (VT). The patient is then asked to make a forced expiration. In obstruction it takes far longer to exhale air down to the baseline and the reserve capacity is reduced as well (i.e. lower ERV). Patients with pulmonary fibrosis have therefore increased elastic work of breathing. They breathe shallowly and rigidly. Patients with airways obstruction include those with chronic bronchitis and emphysema. The rate of outflow out of the lungs during the rapid forced and complete exhalation (from total lung capacity, i.e. after a full maximal inhalation) to the residual volume (i.e. to the point where no more exhalation is possible) is a measure of the flow-resistance out of the lungs. In practice, the volume exhaled during the first second of this forced exhalation is measured, and is called FEV1. The FEV1 is much lower in obstructive airways disease and usually lower for fibrosis.

Bronchoscopy view of lung cancer

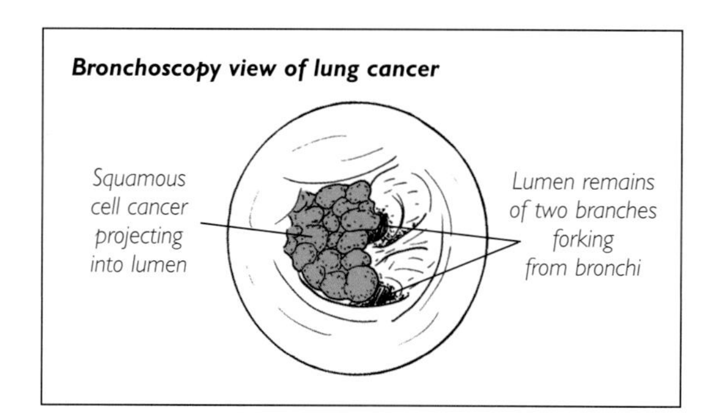

Diagnosis of the particular lung cancer type requires histological examination of biopsy material or sputum cytology. Investigation therefore includes performing a bronchoscopy (using a flexible telescopic fibre-optic tube through the nose, pharynx, larynx, trachea and thence into the bronchi). Biopsy material and bronchial washings can be then be collected. The view of a tumour is shown as through a bronchoscope.

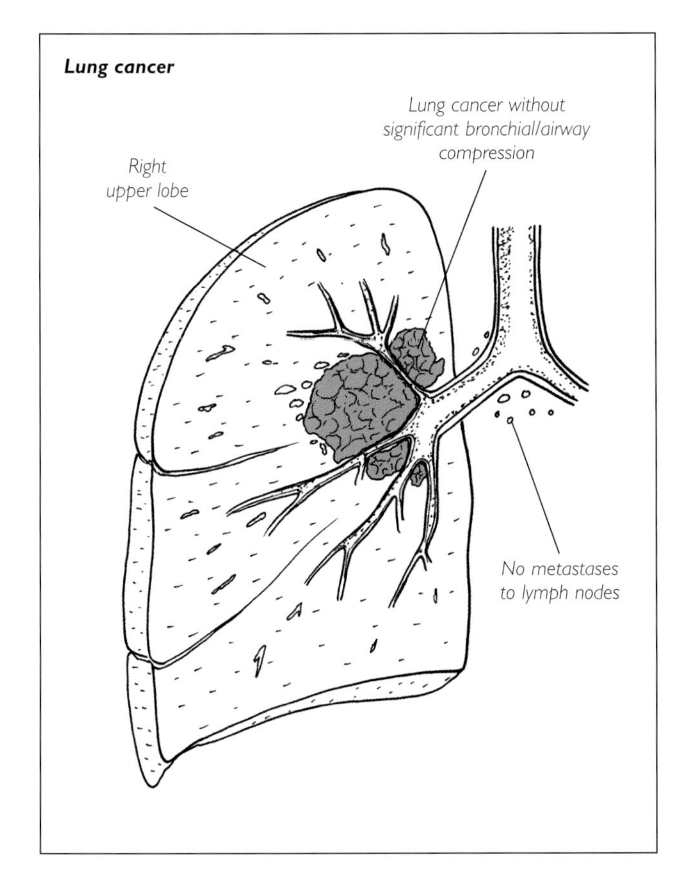

Bronchogenic or lung cancer is a very common cancer, especially in smokers and certain occupational settings (e.g. asbestos, chromium or nickel workers). The most common pathological type is squamous cell carcinoma; others are large cell anaplastic, small cell anaplastic and adenocarcinoma. The symptoms of lung cancer may be cough and sputum, haemoptysis (blood within sputum or expectorate), chest pain, breathlessness, wheezing and/or secondary infection. Often the airways are obstructed, leading to collapse of the supplied lung region – as shown for the right upper lobe in the example below. Such bronchial obstruction particularly occurs for the small cell anaplastic cancer type. The cancer may metastasise or spread through the lymphatics to the draining local lymph nodes, to the pleura and chest wall (e.g. ribs) or through the blood to distant organs (e.g. liver, bone or brain).

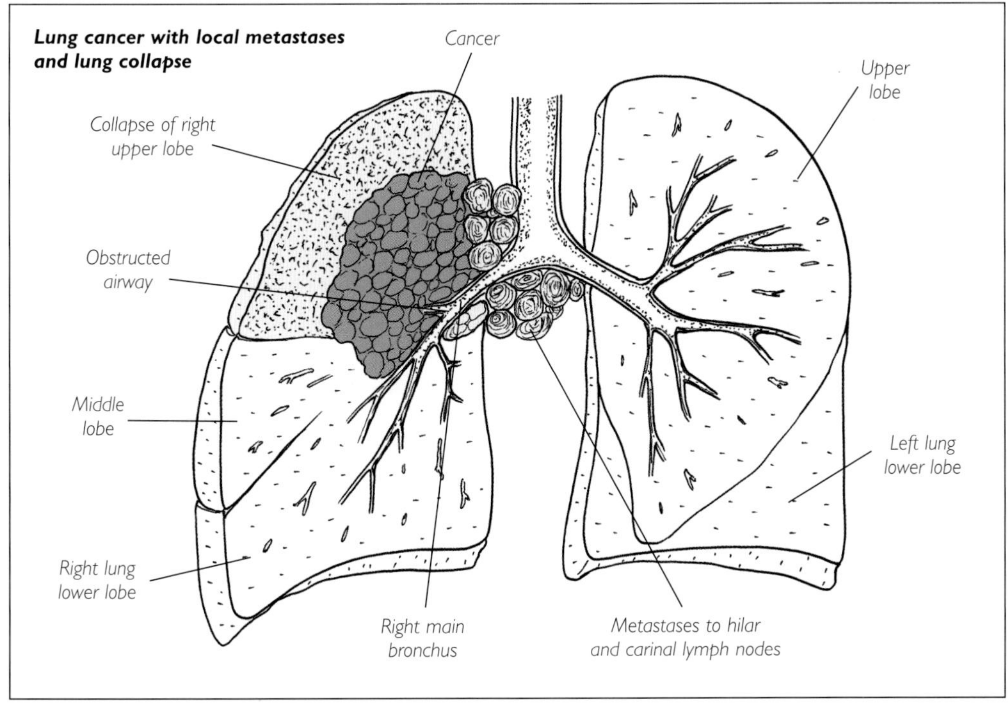

Lung cancer, chest x-ray

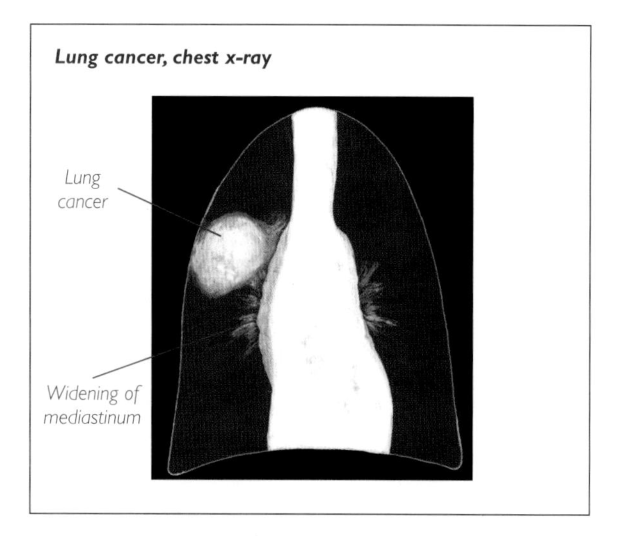

A chest x-ray will not necessarily distinguish between a benign or a malignant tumour within the lungs. The tumour may be sited centrally within the lungs (e.g. bronchogenic, arising from a main bronchus), close to the mediastinum, or it may be positioned peripherally closer to the pleural surface. Hilar and mediastinal lymph node spread may be visible as widening at that region. Other complications of a cancer may be visible, such as a pathological rib fracture, or collapse of a lung lobe. Diagnosis otherwise depends on direct histology/cytology from sputum samples and/or bronchoscope washings and biopsy.

Lung metastases, cannonball type, chest x-ray

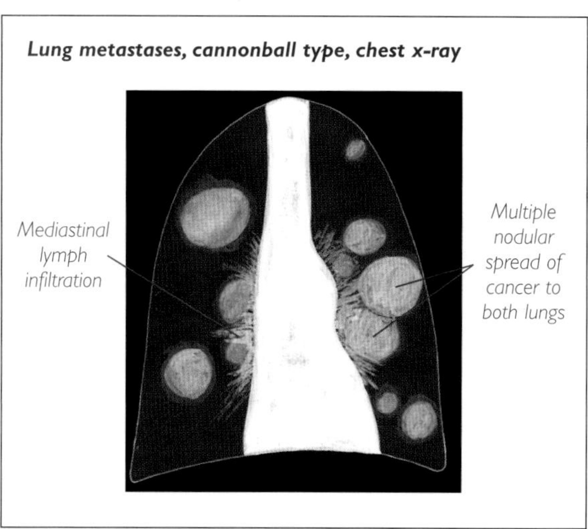

Cancer metastases to the lung are a common progression of malignancy, occurring in about 30% of all cases. There are many patterns of presentation of such secondaries on the chest x-ray. It could be a solitary nodule, but are more often multiple deposits. These can be of a cannonball pattern with many variable-sized nodules. Another pattern is like a 'snow-storm', from a fine patchy alveolar infiltration, or from numerous tiny nodules of cancer. Primary sources of cancer that particularly cause cannonball lung metastases are kidney, testes, colon, breast and salivary gland.

Glasgow coma scale

Eye response	Score
Eyes open	
- spontaneously	4
- to speech	3
- to pain	2
- never	1

Best motor response	Score
- obeys commands	6
- localises pain	5
- flexion withdrawal	4
- decerebrate flexion	3
- decerebrate extension	2
- no response	1

Best verbal response	Score
- orientated	5
- confused	4
- inappropriate words	3
- incomprehensible sounds	2
- silent	1

The Glasgow coma scale is accepted as the international standard for measuring the neurological state of a patient with regard to loss of consciousness. The best eye opening, motor response and verbal response is allocated a score – the sum of which is between 3 and 15. Coma is defined as an overall score of less than 8.

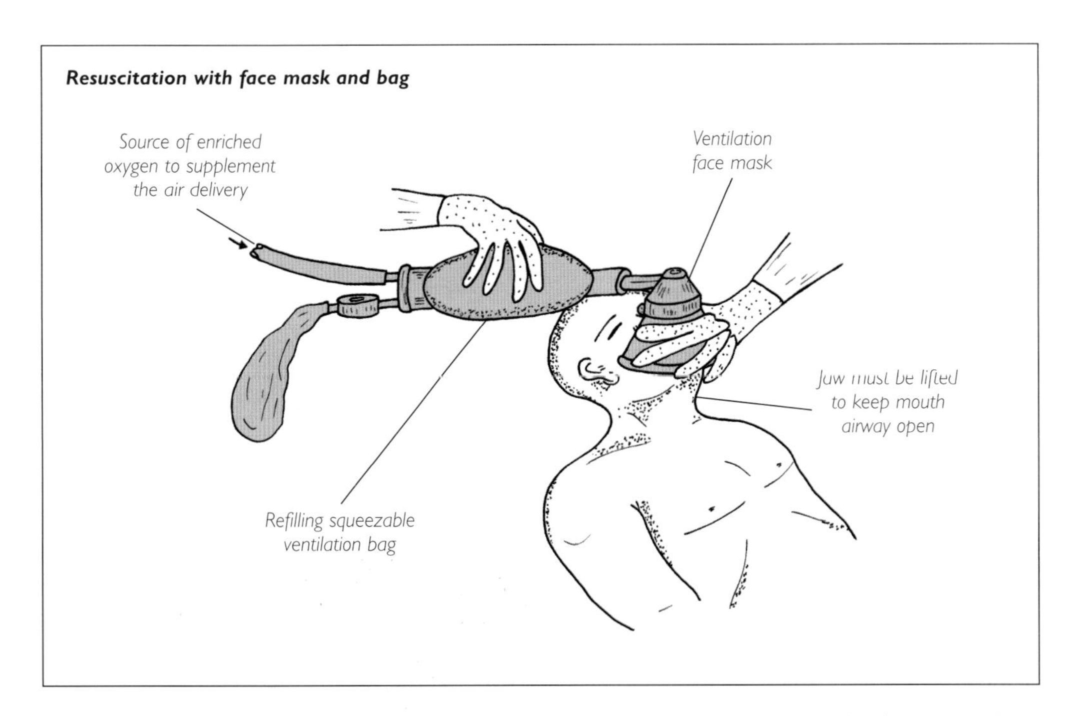

Resuscitation with face mask and bag

Emergency resuscitation in the basic setting (cardiopulmonary resuscitation CPR) is centred on the delivery of expired air respiration and external chest compression (e.g. in a situation of cardiac arrest). For more advanced purposes resuscitation airway devices may be used to maintain airways opening, improve breathing or add artificial ventilation. Ventilation masks offer protection to the rescuer as well as provide direct contact with the patient. Typically it is used with a non-rebreathing mask when using expired air resuscitation (whereby the rescuer breathes into the ventilation mask and thence into the patient's mask). A self-refilling bag can be attached to the mask to delivery air, and this can be enriched with oxygen if a source of compressed oxygen is also attached to it. The mask must be held with the jaw lifted by one hand, whilst the other hand is squeezing the bag. Ventilation must be continued until the patient's condition is stable. Obviously this must be in conjunction with any necessary heart support (e.g. external chest compression if no heartbeat is present).

Related images

p.50 Respiratory failure and sleep apnoea
p.504 Chronic bronchitis
p.95 Cystic fibrosis
p.72 Asthma
p.300 Heart failure, right-sided
p.299 Atrial fibrillation
p.383 Ventricular arrhythmia
p.36 Hiatus hernia
p.541 Peptic ulcer
p.133 Liver failure and ascites

CARCINOSIN

Original

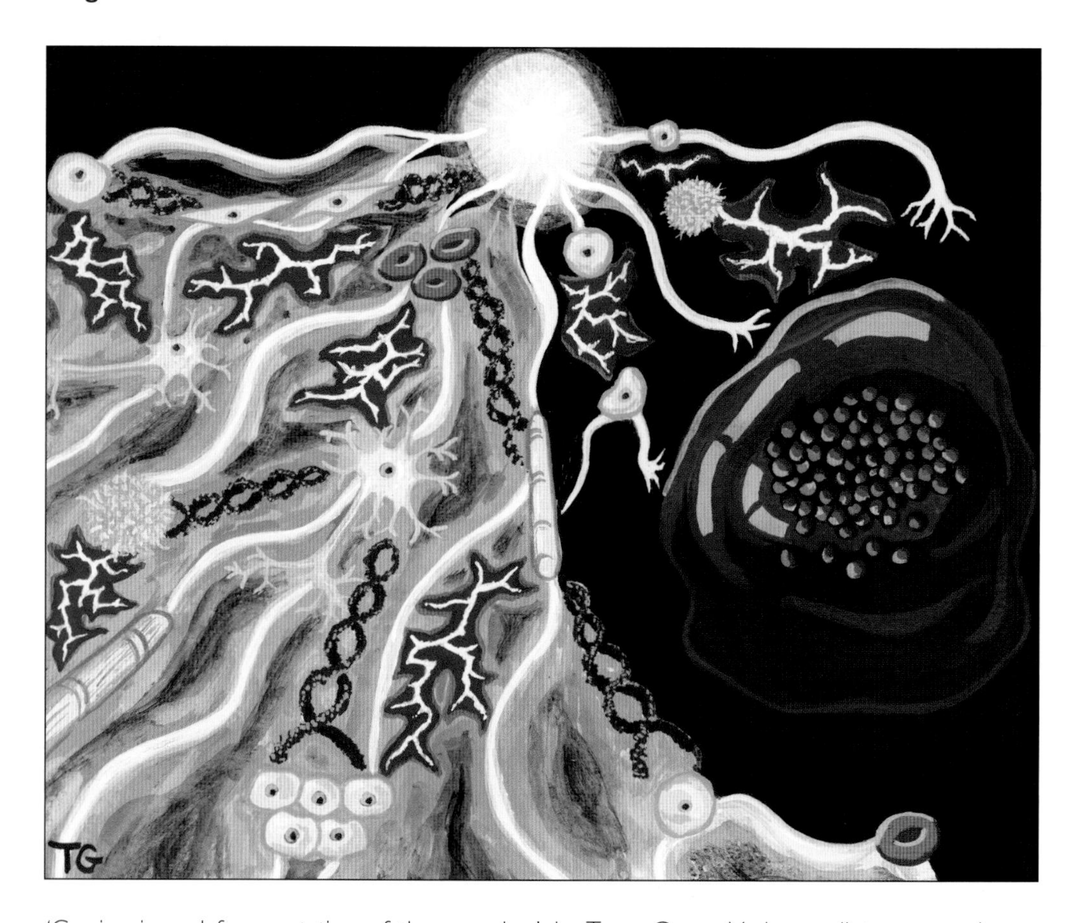

'Carcinosin and fragmentation of the organism', by Tessa Gaynn. Various cell types are shown on the left-side, such as red blood cells, neurones, muscle and epithelial. They are all interconnected by filaments of light and spirals of DNA. Their sense of identity (of Ego) is derived from a common source, which is the star symbolising the Higher Self above. In this manner all the cells perceive their part in the whole and act in a synchronised fashion. Differentiation is provided from the Ego; therefore cells from a pluripotent stem cell only develop into the right cell type for that tissue. However, to the right is a region of disconnected or separatist cells, with a sickly green colour – this is suggestive of liver chi stagnation and is a site for cancer development. This region has become walled off and may even develop its own blood circulation independent of the rest of the organism. Sometimes toxic material (including chemical carcinogenic materials) becomes precipitated into crystalline deposits within the cancer. Nerve endings close to the tumour also appear irritated, which causes pain within the physical body from the emotional issues behind the cancer.

Astrology

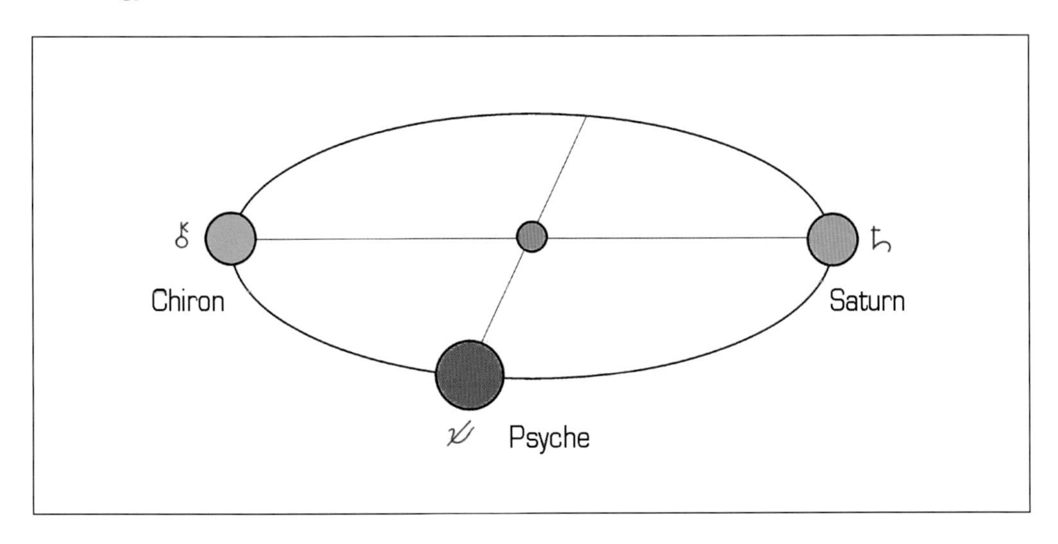

Saturn opposite Chiron, squared by Psyche.

Oriental

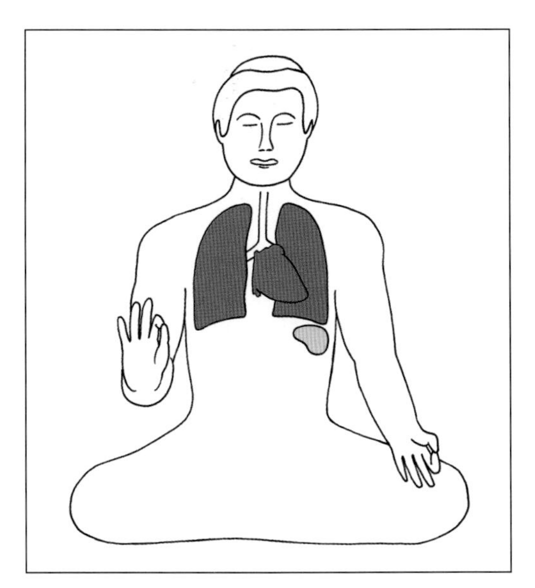

Spleen damp-phlegm with stagnation (chi and phlegm-damp) of heart and lungs.

Particulars

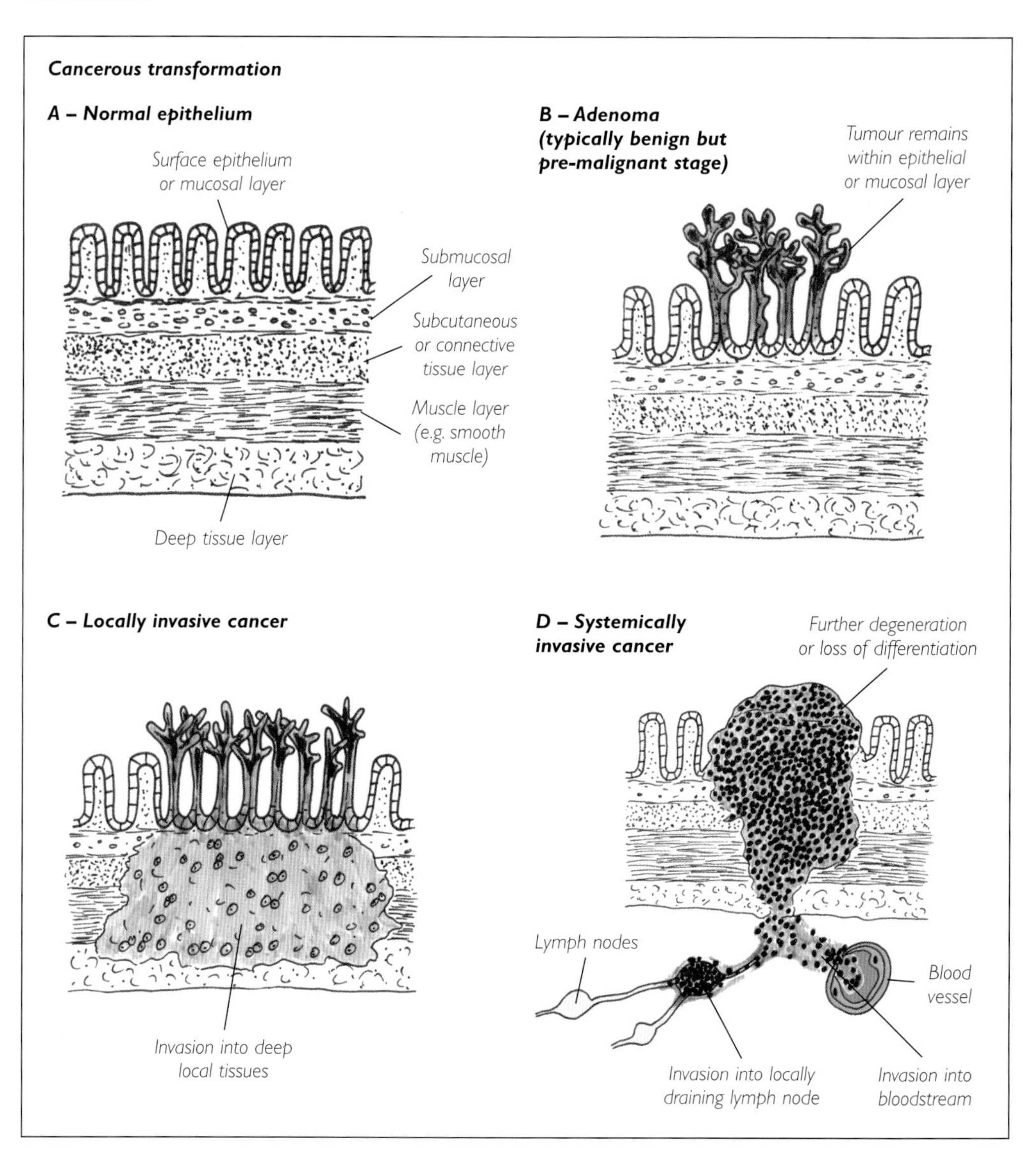

There are several stages along the development of malignancy/cancer. The normal tissue (A) is often initially triggered into the formation of a benign tumour (B), e.g. an adenoma. This is more or less associated with genetic inheritance, dietary, viral or other risk factors. Some types of benign tumours are especially known to transform into cancer, e.g. polyposis coli of the bowel, or cervical polyps of the cervix. There may at this stage be carcinoma-in-situ, or intra-epithelial dysplasia (abnormal cells), whereby the suspicious cells can be found microscopically and are not yet definitive of cancer. Eventually a malignant change can occur and begin invasion locally (C). If sufficient deeper tissue penetration has occurred then systemic spread through the circulation of blood or lymph can occur (D), with local lymph nodes becoming hard, matted and indurated. At each stage there is the potential for control of the situation, with earlier stages (B and early in C) reverting to normal. However, by the time D has occurred distant sites will become seeded with metastatic cancer.

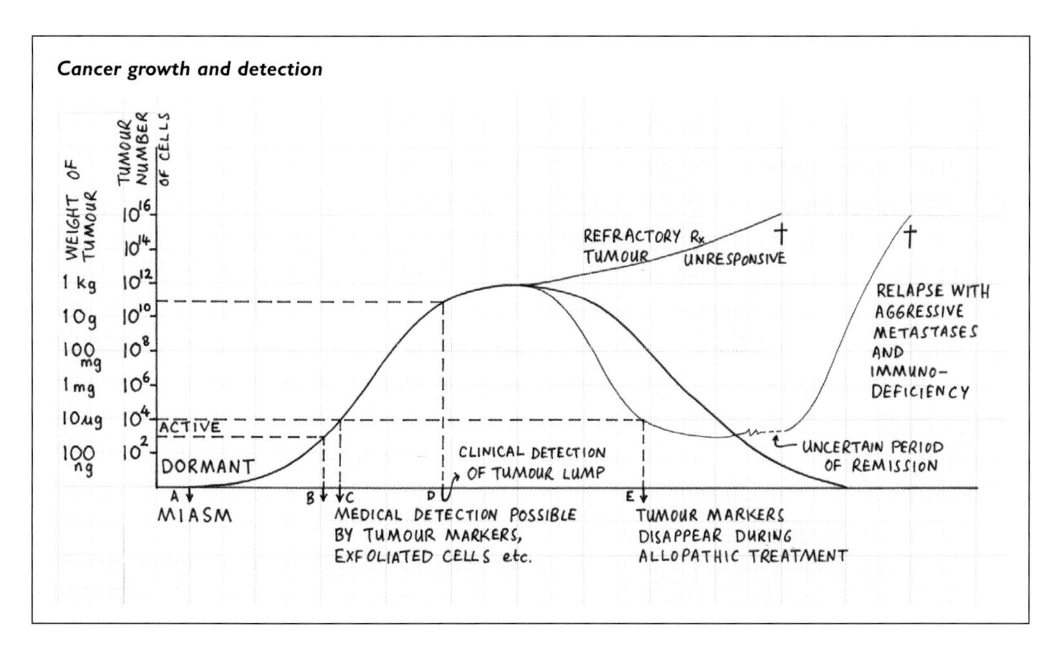

The growth of a cancer can be studied in terms of the number of tumour cell, and the total weight of the tumour – as depicted by the two vertical axis lines on the left. The cancer tends to only become clinically detectable (e.g. a palpable/visible lump, or signs of bleeding etc.) when its cell population has reached between 10^{10} to 10^{12} cells, i.e. at point D on the horizontal timeline axis. Until then there is the possibility of early medical detection by screening methods (e.g. blood tumour markers, scans, endoscopy etc.), from point C. Before this point the cancer will be medically undetectable (at cell count 10^4 onwards). It can be said therefore to exist at a dormant miasmatic level before this point (from A), and revert to an active cancerous miasm at point B when it approaches a medically detectable point. The slope of the growth curve of cancers is extremely variable, depending on the doubling time of the tumour. A rapid doubling time will become a very aggressive cancer with a rapid downhill course to the disease. With appropriate treatment the tumour cell count will fall back to zero. However, the red curve indicates an initial response to treatment with a fall in cell count, followed by relapse of the cancer (e.g. with metastases) after a variable period of dormant disease. On the other hand, the cancer may not be responsive to the initial treatment at all, as revealed by the green curve extending from the peak of the bell curve.

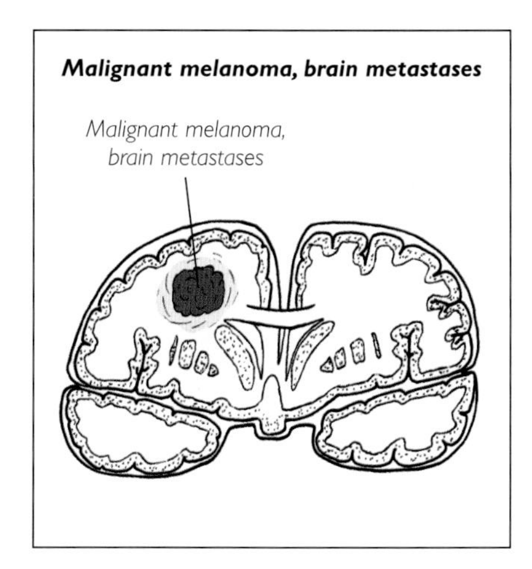

Metastasis or spread of a cancer to the brain represents a particularly serious and devastating stage in progressive cancer. Tumours that commonly spread to the brain include lung, breast, kidney and in this example a skin malignant melanoma. The tumour spreads through the bloodstream and usually grows at the border between the grey and white matter of the brain. There may be multiple or a single metastasis. They are usually solid, but may become cystic with fluid or internally bleed. There are focal neurological symptoms depending on the region of the brain that has become damaged (e.g. weakness down one side of the body or speech deficits). Other, more general features are headaches, blurred vision and vomiting from raised intracranial pressure and fits from irritation to the brain tissue.

Café-au-lait patches are pale brown flat patches/macules (1-20mm) in diameter on the skin. Isolated or single patches are common in 'normal' persons, but more than five patches indicates the underlying disease of neurofibromatosis (von Recklinghausen's disease). This disease is characterised by multiple skin neurofibromas (tumours of superficial nerves) and pigmentation. There may be many such nerve tumours – appearing as soft subcutaneous lumps. Neural tumours can also arise within the deeper body nerves, spinal cord and brainstem.

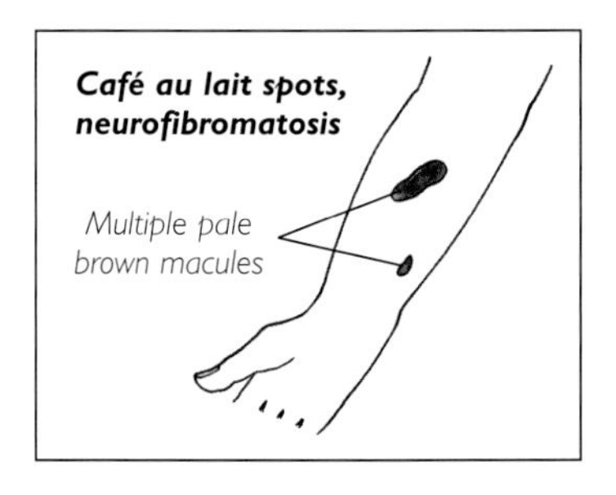

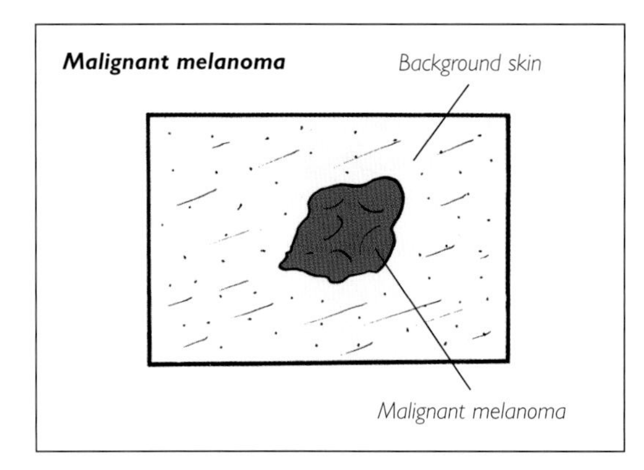

Any new mole, or a prior mole which has changed its character should be considered malignant until proven otherwise. Exposure to sunlight (the ultraviolet component) is a causative factor. A superficial melanoma begins as a slightly elevated irregular brown or black patch. It may form a nodule, a sign of rapid vertical invasion. Other warning signs are change of shape, bleeding, burning sensations, ulceration. The prognosis depends on the depth of the skin invasion; if beyond 3mm below the skin (i.e. past the dermis) then there is a worse outcome.

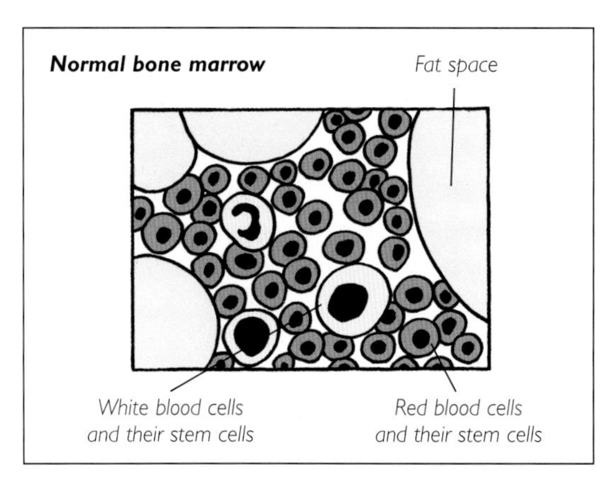

In normal bone marrow there is a balance in cell numbers, with new cells being produced (red cells, white cells and platelets) from their respective stem cells – balanced equally with the same classes of cells being destroyed in the body. Fat spaces also exist within the marrow.

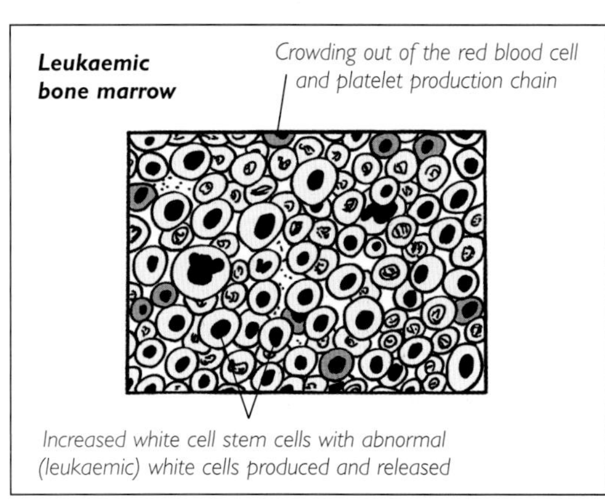

Leukaemic bone marrow is characterised by the proliferation of new and immature white blood cells in the bone marrow combined with ineffective destruction of these abnormal cells in the rest of the body. This leads to a raised white cell count within the peripheral blood. Total marrow cellularity is increased, causing loss of fat spaces and crowding out of other cell lines. This results in anaemia and thrombocytopenia (reduced blood platelet count). The symptoms of leukaemia therefore include easy bleeding or bruising, pallor or fatigue and susceptibility to infections.

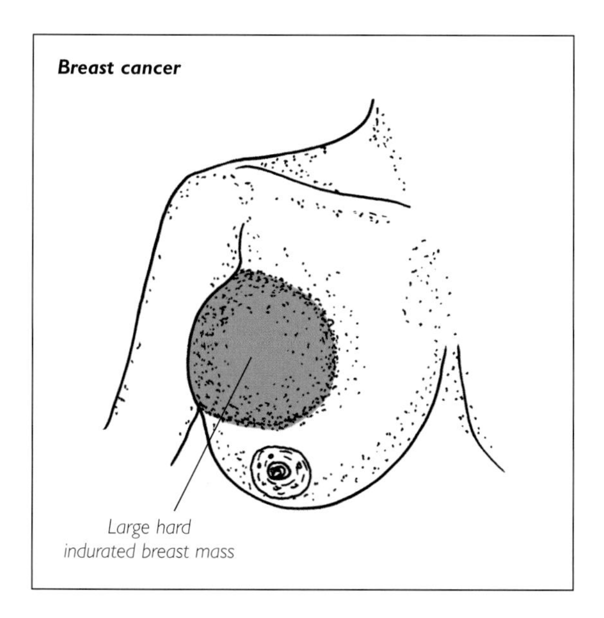

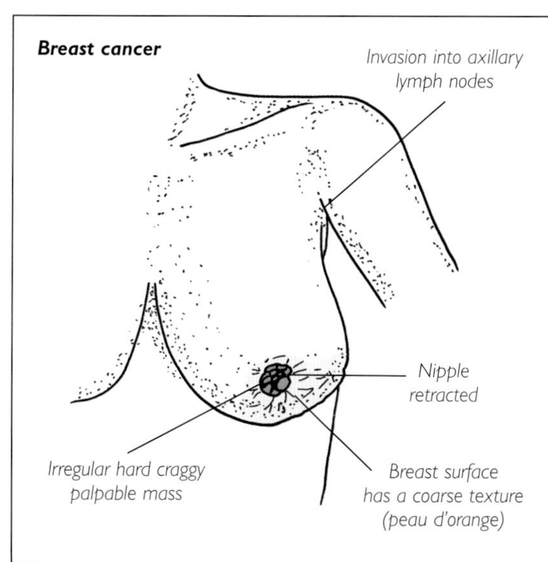

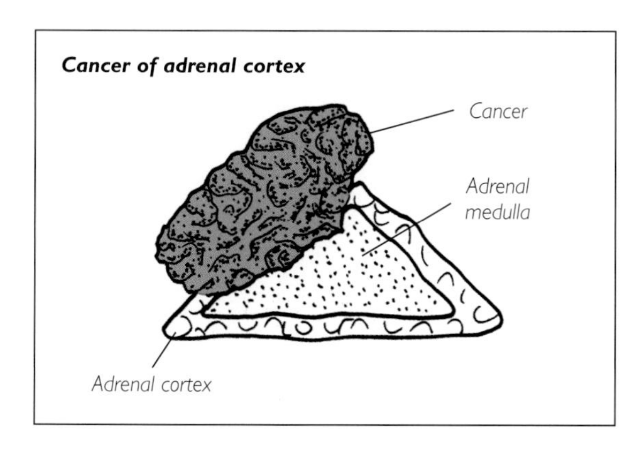

Breast cancer is the commonest malignancy in the female. There is a strong genetic familial association. Breastfeeding reduces the risk of cancer. They are usually slow-growing, and thus tumour size is proportional to the duration of its presence. In the advanced type there usually is a firm hard lump, craggy and irregular in shape. There are then strands of fibrous infiltrated tissue around the tumour. If present in the ductal region the nipple can become retracted or pulled inwards. Although usually internal, in late stages cancer can penetrate into and ulcerate the skin. The skin may then show a rough texture known as peau d'orange. Metastatic spread is via the lymphatics (to axillary nodes and through the thoracic internal mammary lymphatics) and via the bloodstream. Late stage metastases can then develop, particularly to the liver, lung and bone. Lumps less than 1 cm rarely metastasise. The first image shows a large mass, which is more likely to involve local lymph nodes, the skin, chest wall and distant organs. The second image shows general breast infiltration with nipple retraction. Small or localised lumps are often surgically resected, e.g. lumpectomy, quadrantectomy or even total mastectomy. Some tumour cells are oestrogen receptor positive, i.e. this hormone may stimulate its growth. This is, however, indicative of the strong etheric building up processes without sufficient astralising forces of differentiation from progesterone activity. Nonetheless, the allopathic treatment in such cases is usually hormonal suppression by anti-oestrogens (different drugs being used depending on the menopausal state of the woman). Advanced disease is generally treated with chemotherapy regimens (and possibly bone marrow stem cell support if high doses are used).

Carcinoma at the adrenal cortex can also lead to Cushing's syndrome, with the same features as for a hyperfunctioning adenoma (a benign tumour). However, such cancers are highly aggressive and with a poorer prognosis. They also tend to rapidly metastasise locally and to distant sites.

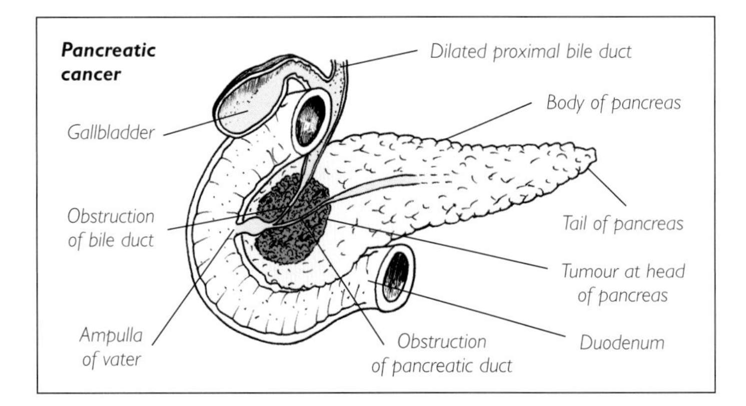

Pancreatic cancer most commonly occurs at the head of the pancreas (70% of cases) as opposed to body or tail of the pancreas. Progressive jaundice results from bile obstruction, and digestion is impaired by the reduced pancreatic enzyme secretion (especially fat digestion to cause steatorrhoea or pale-coloured fatty stools).

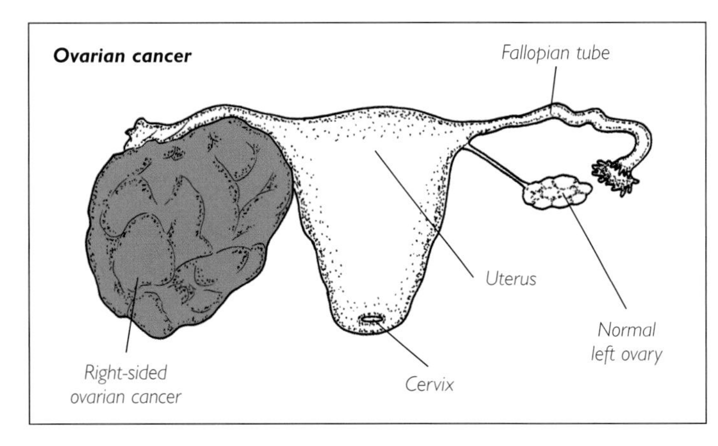

Ovarian cancer comprises 5% of all female cancers and one-quarter of genital tract cancers. Ovarian tumours can be benign or malignant, and there are many subtypes of both. For example, there are cancers derived from clonal proliferation of ovarian surface epithelium (e.g. clear cell adenocarcinoma), from specialised connective tissue cells (e.g. theca cell tumour) or from germ/egg cells (e.g. teratomas). Also secondary metastases may deposit in the ovary from cancer elsewhere (e.g. from the uterus, cervix, breast or colon). The early symptoms may be vague, such as aching pains in the lower abdomen, painful intercourse, abdominal distension and menstrual disturbance. In this diagram the tumour has massively enlarged and begun to spread into surrounding tubal and uterine tissues. The ovarian cancer is likely to spread when beyond 8-10cm in size (the normal ovary is usually less than 4cm in size). Spread is thereby commonly to the fallopian tubes, uterus, peritoneum, lymph nodes, bladder, colon, pelvic wall, liver and diaphragm.

Related images

p.375 Autoimmune disease
p.193 Cancer of tongue
p.420 Cancer of vulva
p.421 Cancer of cervix
p.528 Breast fibroadenoma
p.612 Radiotherapy
p.719 Cancer of bladder
p.722 Cancer of colon
p.721 Cancer of testes
p.228 Pernicious anaemia
p.247 Inherited disease
p.520 Congenital heart disease

CAUSTICUM

Museum

Eugène Delacroix (1798-1863), 'Liberty leading the people, 28 July 1830', (1830). Paris, musée du Louvre © Photo RMN / © Hervé Lewandowski. To quote from Lamartine, Histoire des Girondins: "The impartiality of history is not that of the mirror which reflects only objects... Annals are not history: to merit its name history has to have a conscience, because that conscience later becomes the conscience of the human race." The Romantic ideal in art and human consciousness is very much born with the French Revolution. The tragic outcome with the death of the hope of social happiness and the reaction of the Royalists nonetheless instilled courage and passion into the search for enlightenment. The subject of the painting is the bloody insurgency of 1830, triggered by the constitutional violation by King Charles X, who tried to reinstate an absolute monarchy. The people, in rage, are storming towards the viewer over the dead and wounded and through a barricade of stones and missiles. There is the dust of gunpowder and firearms. The crowd is led by the allegorical figure of Liberty, who is dressed somewhat as a Parisian market-woman. The people are thus fired up through her enthusiasm, igniting the dormant dignity within their souls. The painter has portrayed himself as the intellectual revolutionary, wearing the hat off-centre to the left and, unlike the others, gazing thoughtfully into the distance and holding his rifle with control.

Original

Causticum and the flow of etheric forces', by Iona Mackenzie. The individual is shown standing next to a flowing river amidst a lush landscape – to represent the flow of etheric and vegetative (plant-like anabolic) energy within the body metabolism. An erupting volcano symbolises the warming influence of the Ego forces into the etheric body (especially focused at the liver), without this heat the metabolism would become too cold and stagnant. Nonetheless, the figure appears devitalised and permeated by an aura of grey heavy life-force, to indicate the negative aspect of the remedy of liver stagnation, melancholy and irritability.

Astrology

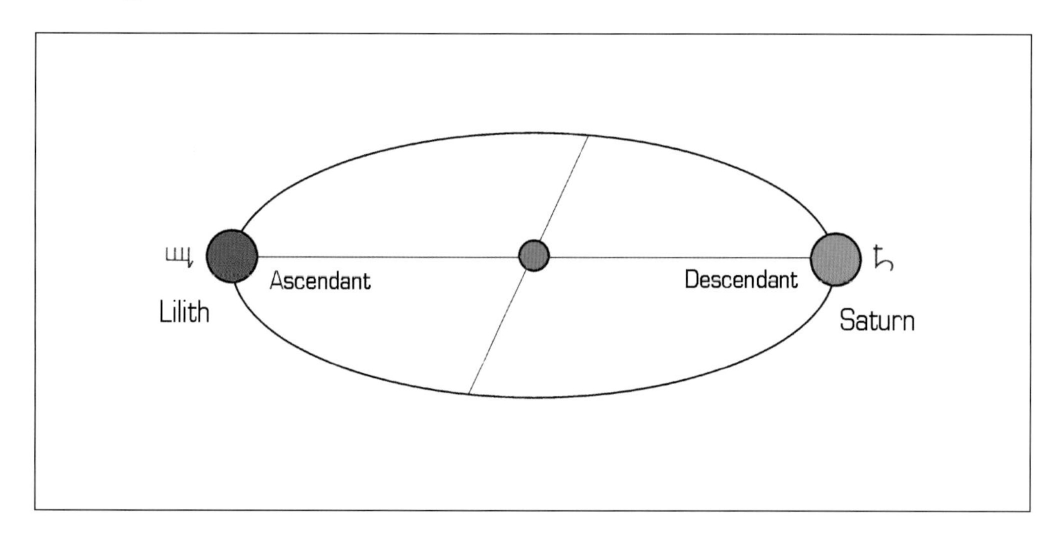

Saturn at Descendant opposite Lilith at Ascendant.

Oriental

Kidney and liver yin deficiency, with wind-stroke of brain and muscle.

CHAMOMILLA MATRICARIA

Museum

J. E. Chaponniere, 'Revolt at a maternity ward', colour lithograph, with red wash, published by E. Scheffer, Paris. © Wellcome Library, London. Babies at a maternity ward of the hospital are refusing to breastfeed until the Houses of Parliament are dissolved, being in political rebellion.

Nonetheless, there are several events in the newborn's life that may precipitate a similar rebellious mood, including the allopathic treatments often unnecessarily given. For example, the vitamin K injection provided at birth induces liver production of clotting proteins, ensuring no undue haemorrhage occurs from birth trauma. However the incarnation of the soul does not proceed all at once, but in stages. The blood of a newborn needs to be sufficiently light and permeable for these Ego forces. If the blood is made to coagulate too readily, it is literally blocked from receiving the forces of self. The child thereby develops liver chi stagnation and its astral body cramps in an effort to incarnate. The symptoms include abdominal colic and irritability – a symptom profile matching Chamomilla. Vaccinations, antipyretic drugs and antibiotics are all other examples of drug distortion to the child's incarnation.

Original

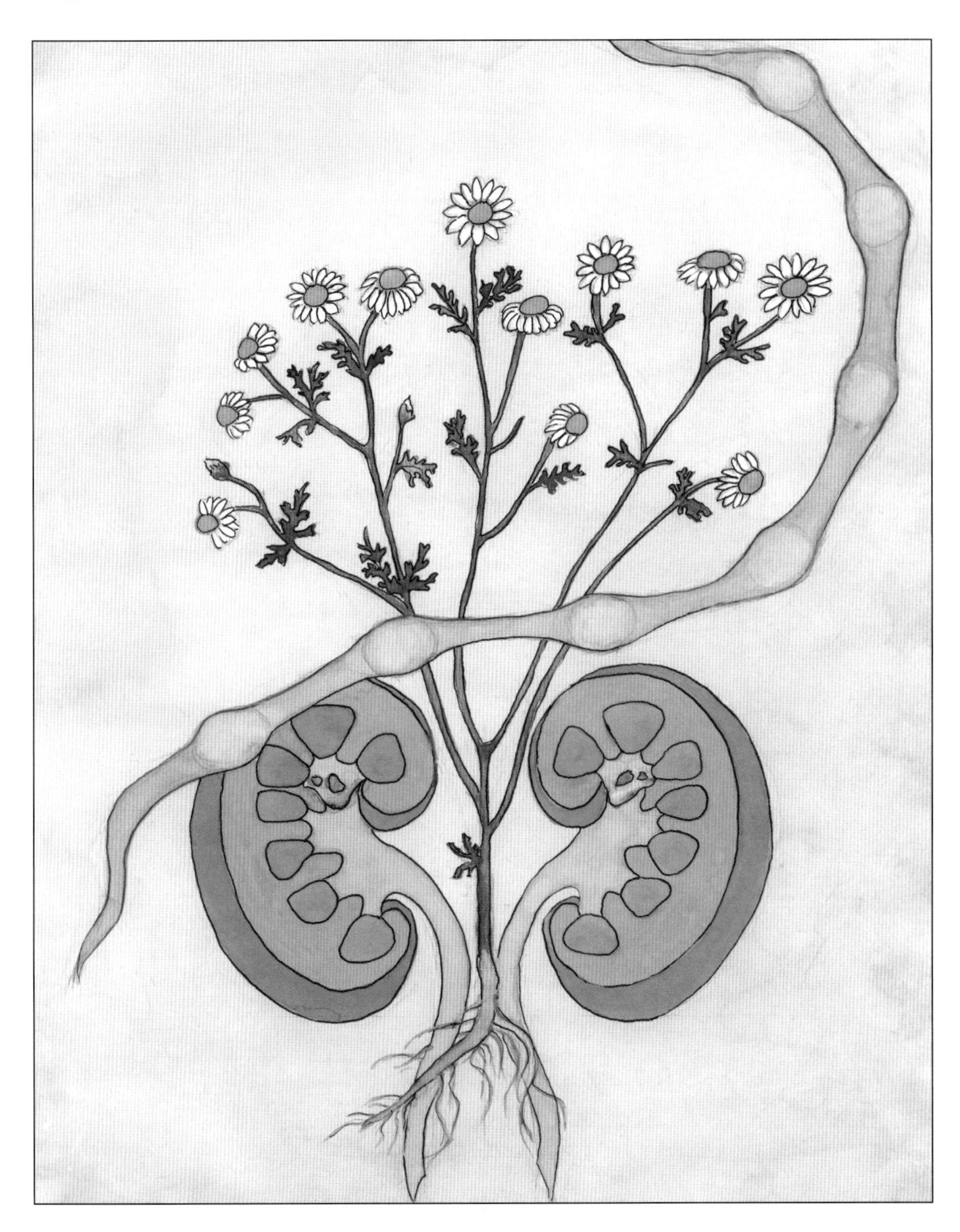

'Chamomilla, the sympathetic nervous system and kidney physiology', by Nadine Kardesler. The plant is growing between the two kidney organs to indicate the therapeutic effect on this system, its root at the level of the ureters. The astral body is guided into the kidney (and adrenal) system, thus relaxing any cramping or spasmodic pathology from a weak 'incarnation'. The sympathetic nervous system is portrayed by the chain of nerve ganglia (which normally lie laterally to the spinal cord). The nodes of this chain contain collections of the neurone cells, from which stream the sympathetic nerve axon fibres.

Astrology

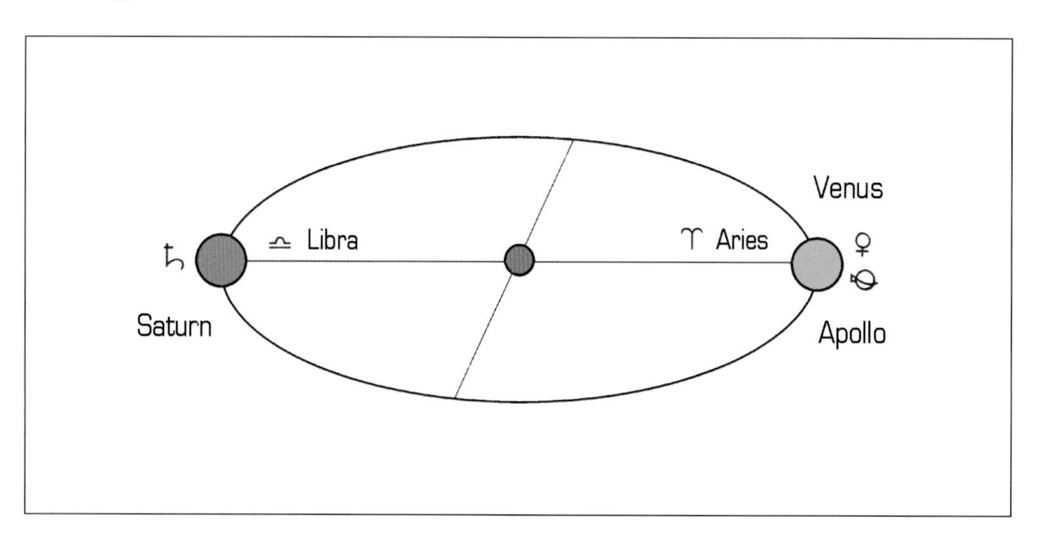

Venus conjunct Apollo at Aries, opposite Saturn at Libra.

Oriental

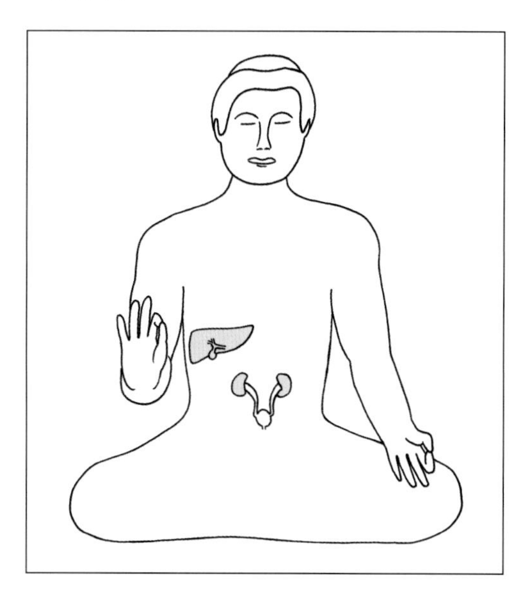

Kidney and liver yin deficiency.

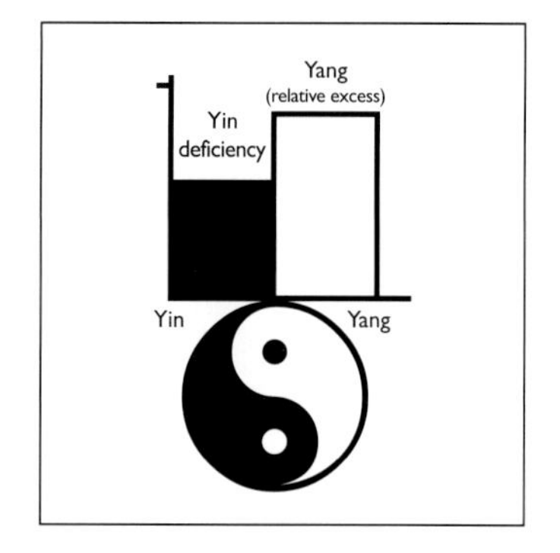

Particulars

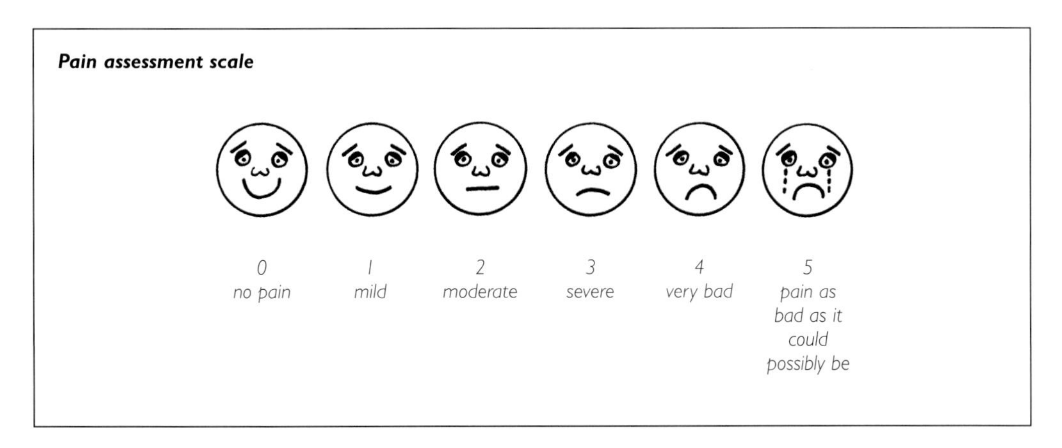

This image is an example of a visual rating scale for pain assessment in children of age group 3-6, known as the Wong-Baker scale. Children this young would usually find it difficult to verbalise or describe their level of pain without such visual and intuitive aids. It is a helpful measure when treating children with chronic disease, such as juvenile rheumatoid arthritis. The child allocates the appropriate face to their pain, and a quantitative measure is then allocated to this spectrum (from 0 – no pain to 5 – the worst possible pain).

Related images

p.3 Trigeminal neuralgia
p.368 Otitis externa
p.501 Otitis media, glue ear
p.503 Teeth circulation and nervous supply
p.265 & p.503 Toothache and abscess
p.264 Supraventricular tachycardia

CHELIDONIUM MAJUS

Original

'Chelidonium majus, Ego warmth and the liver iron process', by Caroline Hamilton. The plant is growing within a fluid, representing the liver watery etheric forces. The fiery Ego forces from above have a warming action on this fluid. Iron, the metal of incarnation, (within the bile and gallbladder) is stimulated, as indicated by the descending forces to the Earth iron core. The darker colouration of the surrounding atmosphere above indicates the potential for dark depression should there be a lack of this iron or warmth.

Astrology

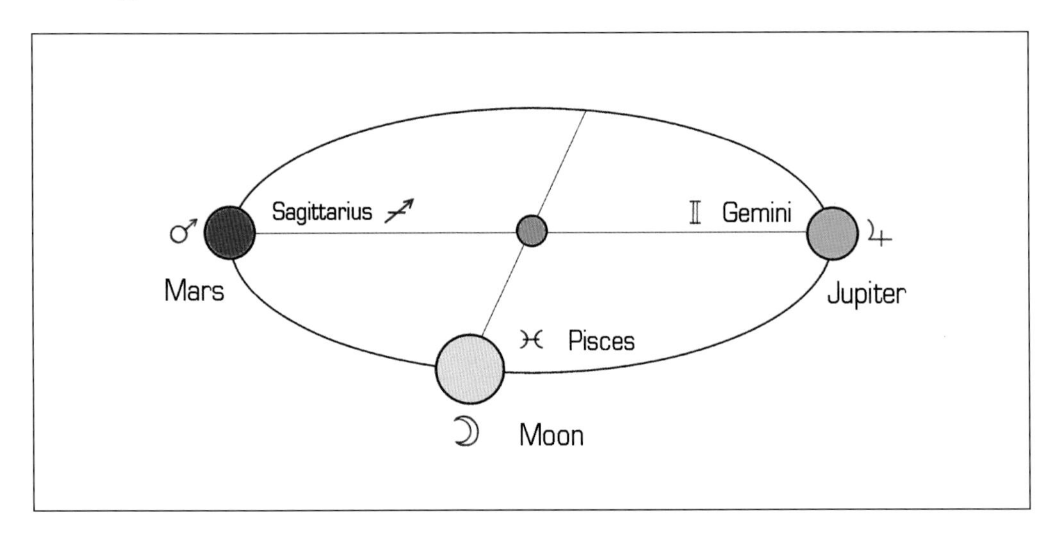

Mars in Sagittarius opposite Jupiter in Gemini, squared by Moon in Pisces.

Oriental

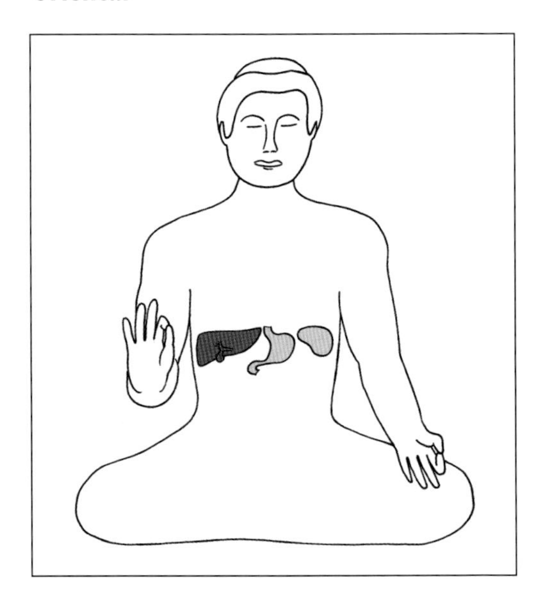

Liver chi stagnation/constraint, with rebellious chi of stomach and spleen.

Particulars

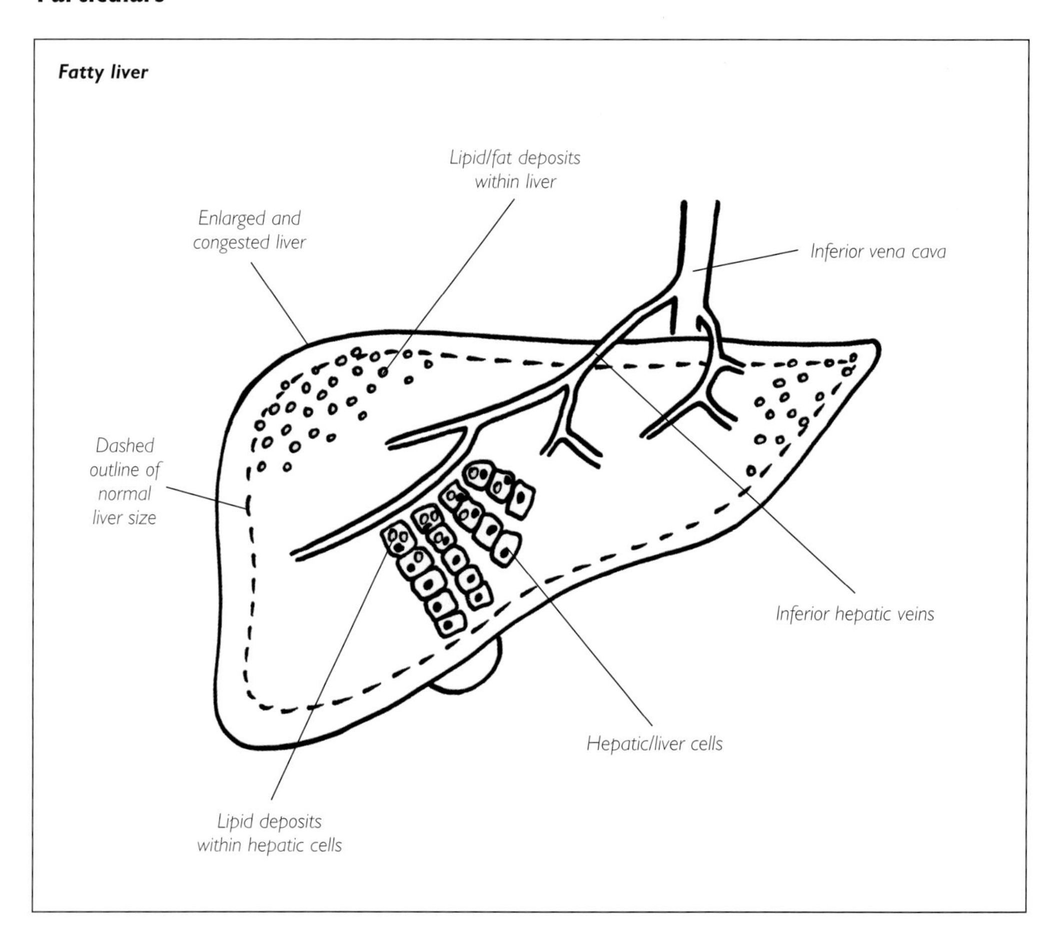

Fatty liver is a pathology occurring in various chronic metabolic disorders of the liver, but particularly after excess alcohol intake. Fat accumulates in the hepatic/liver cells due to deranged fat and carbohydrate metabolism from the alcohol. It can lead to alcoholic induced hepatitis, and then liver cirrhosis if severe – which may be irreversible. Nonetheless, fatty change is reversible even when extensive, unless a significant degree of hepatitis with cell death has occurred.

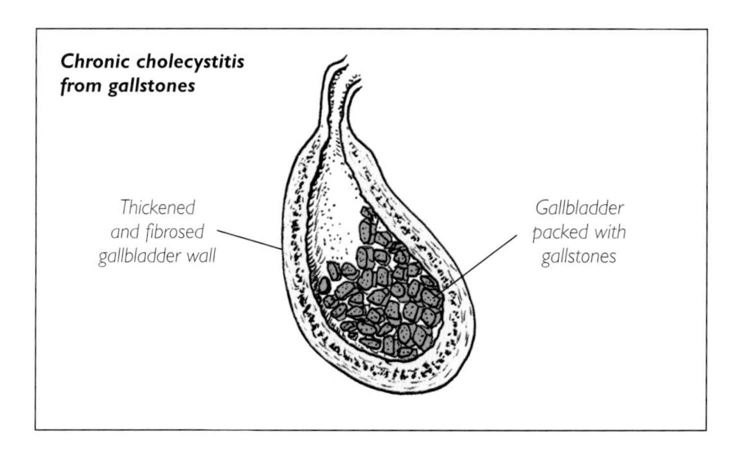

Chronic cholecystitis usually features a history of acute attacks of cholecystitis, or a chronic situation may develop with only a history of vague indigestion to fatty foods. There is chronic inflammation of the gallbladder wall with a hypertrophied muscle layer. The symptoms are also often vague, including indigestion and abdominal bloating after food.

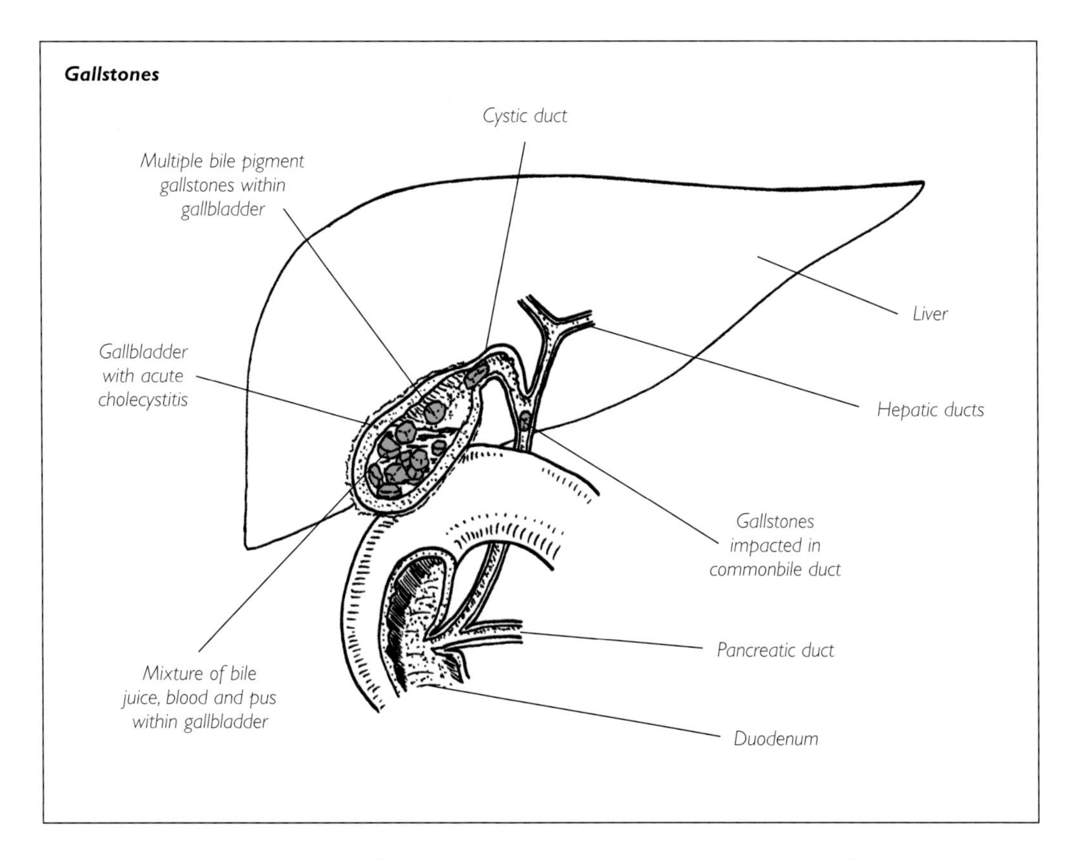

There are three main types of gallstones: cholesterol stones (usually large and solitary, coloured pale yellow), bile pigment stones (always multiple, usually small, black and irregularly shaped) and mixed stones of cholesterol, bile pigment and calcium salts. There is the risk of acute cholecystitis with inflammation of the gallbladder. Symptoms include acute upper abdominal pain with fever. Bile obstruction occurs if stones impact within the common bile duct, to cause episodes of jaundice and digestive disturbance (especially of fat malabsorption).

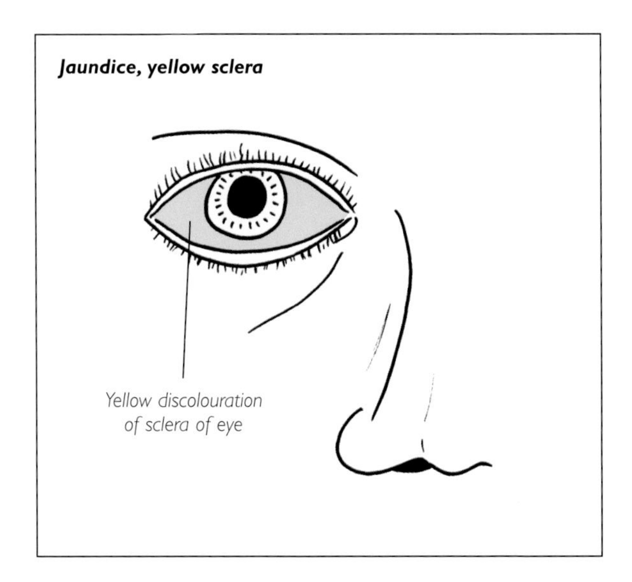

Jaundice occurs if the serum bilirubin level exceeds 34 micromoles/litre. Bilirubin is produced from the breakdown of red blood cells (which normally have a limited lifespan of about 120 days) by macrophages – mainly within the spleen. These by-products are then bound to glucuronic acid within the liver and secreted into the bile. Jaundice can then occur if there is much increased red blood cell destruction (e.g. haemolytic anaemia), or from liver cell damage/failure (e.g. hepatitis) or from obstruction of the bile ducts out of the liver (e.g. by gallstones or pancreatic cancer). Yellowing of the white sclera of the eye is the easiest first sign of jaundice to observe.

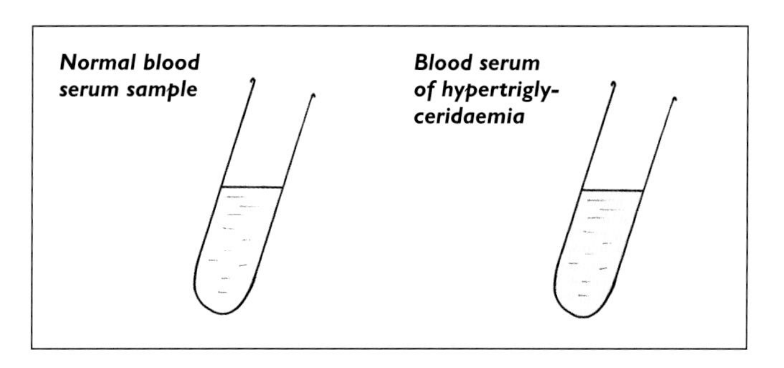

Hypertriglyceridaemia, or raised levels of lipids in the blood plasma will appear as a creamy-white serum (after spinning out the blood cells). There are several types of hyper-lipidaemia, e.g. due to diabetes, chronic liver disease, congenital disorders of metabolism, chronic pancreatitis and so on.

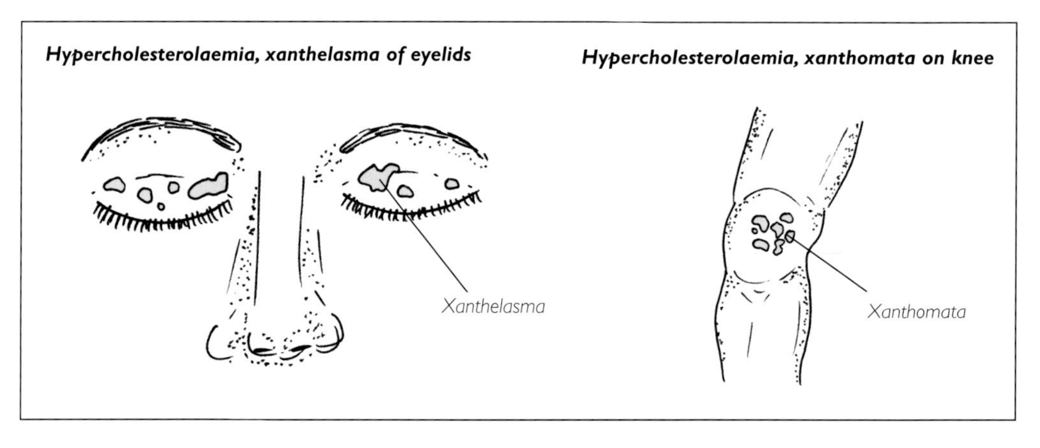

A raised blood cholesterol (hypercholesterolaemia) can occur from inherited disorders of the metabolism, diabetes, chronic liver disease (e.g. biliary cirrhosis) etc. Cholesterol deposits occur at various body sites, especially the cornea (causing an arcus or white ring visible around the iris), on the eyelids (xanthelasma), on the elbows, knees or buttocks (xanthomata). A high cholesterol may or may not also occur with raised blood lipids/fatty acids, and conversely so for hyperlipidaemia.

Related images

p.370 Pneumonia and lung abscess
p.90 Subdiaphragmatic abscess
p.561-562 Hepatitis
p.491 Gonococcal perihepatitis
p.133 Liver failure and ascites
p.470 Pancreatic failure
p.227 & p.229 Malaria
p.656 Cataract
p.527 Headache
p.528 Migraine visual aura
p.56 Rheumatoid arthritis
p.621 Capsulitis, frozen shoulder

CHINA OFFICINALIS

Original

'China with malaria-infected bloodstream', by Loolie Habgood. The tree and a flowering stem is shown against the background of the icy Andean Mountains. Flowing toward the foreground are blood vessels with mature red blood cells. The ring forms within some of these cells are the asexual phase of the malaria parasites (particularly of the Plasmodium vivax subtype in this example). Other subtypes have differing appearances, such as oval shapes for P. ovale, crescenteric for P. falciparum. At the front, two red cells have haemolysed or ruptured, releasing the merozoite stage into the blood. The patient will become infective again during this period. At some point these will transform into the sexual phase.

Astrology

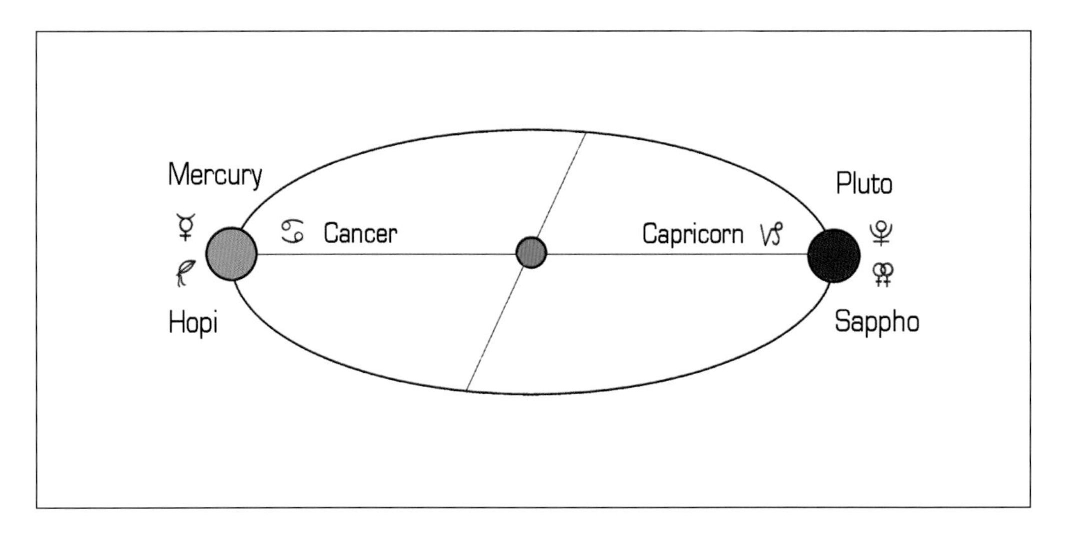

Mercury conjunct Hopi within Cancer, opposite Pluto conjunct Sappho within Capricorn.

Oriental

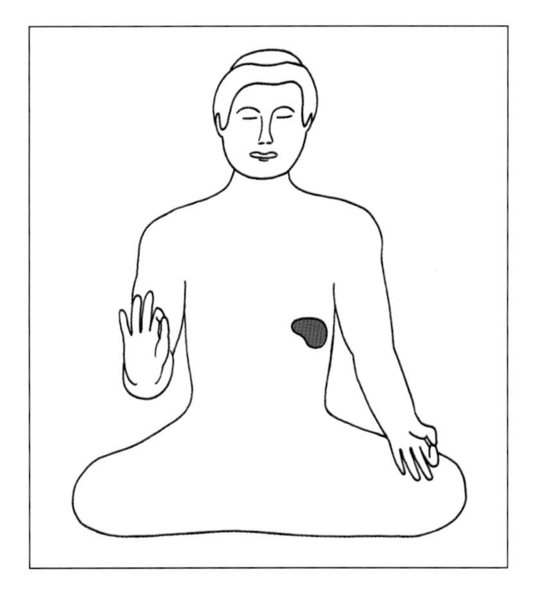

Spleen blood and chi deficiency.

Particulars

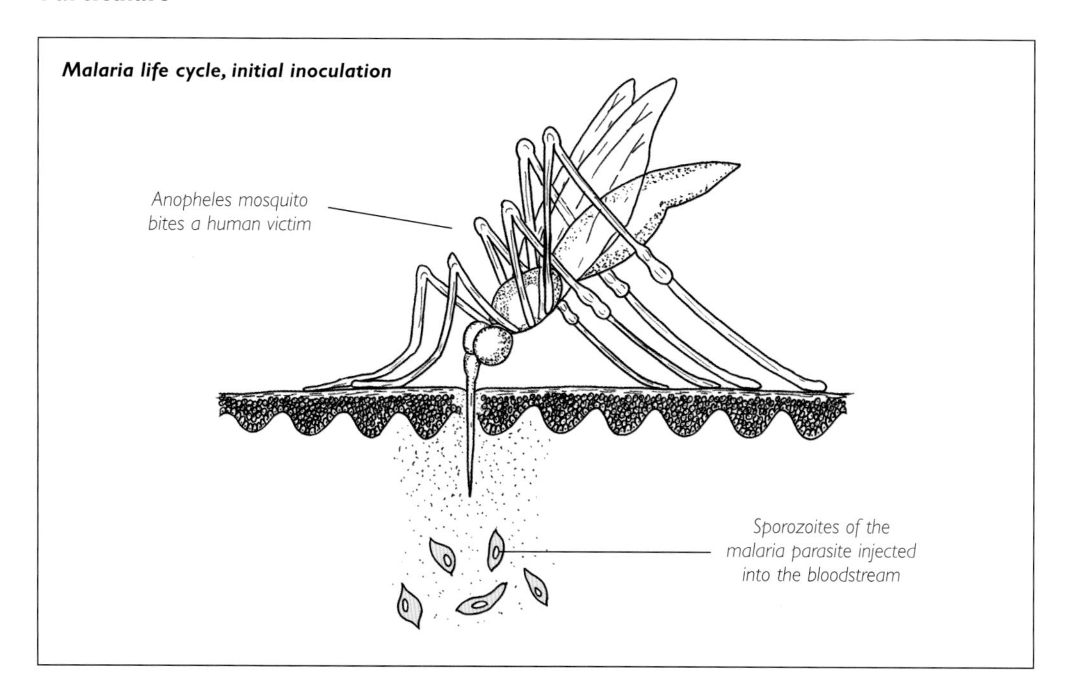

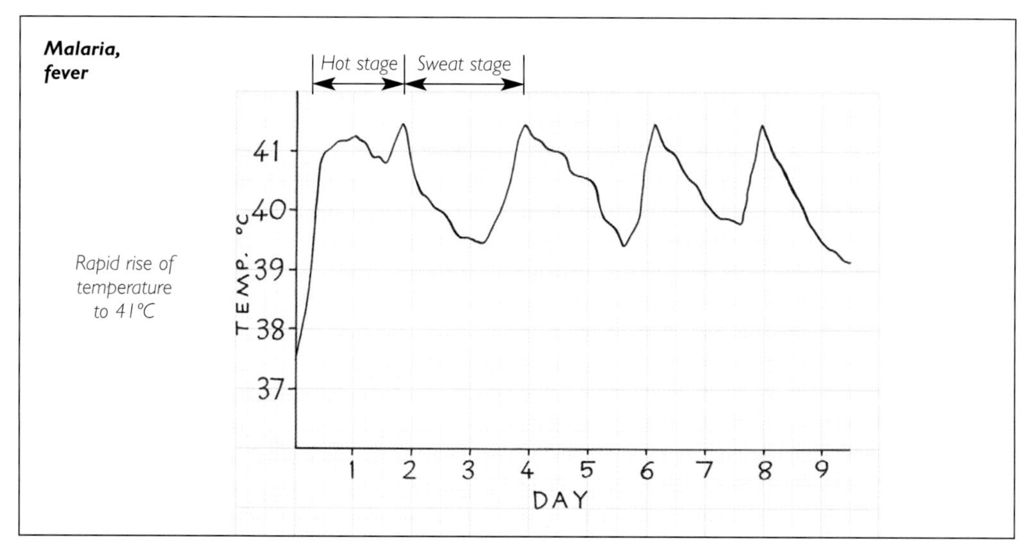

Human malarial infection (see also p.229) is caused by one of four species of the Plasmodium parasite: P. vivax, P. ovale, P. falciparum and P. malariae. The incubation period varies, being 18 days to 6 weeks in P. malariae, and 10-14 days in the rest. Symptoms then develop, i.e. fevers, anaemia, spleen and liver enlargement. Of the fever there is a chilly phase, then a rapid rise of temperature up to 41°C. The hot stage then lasts several hours, often with delirium, followed by a sweating stage. The fever is due to rupture of the red blood cells by the schizonts stage of the parasite. In P. vivax and P. ovale established disease occurs every other day, as shown in this case. In P. malariae the fever is more chronic without the same spiking pattern. P. falciparum is the most severe form of malaria with more tissue and organ destruction throughout the body. The fever follows no particular pattern.

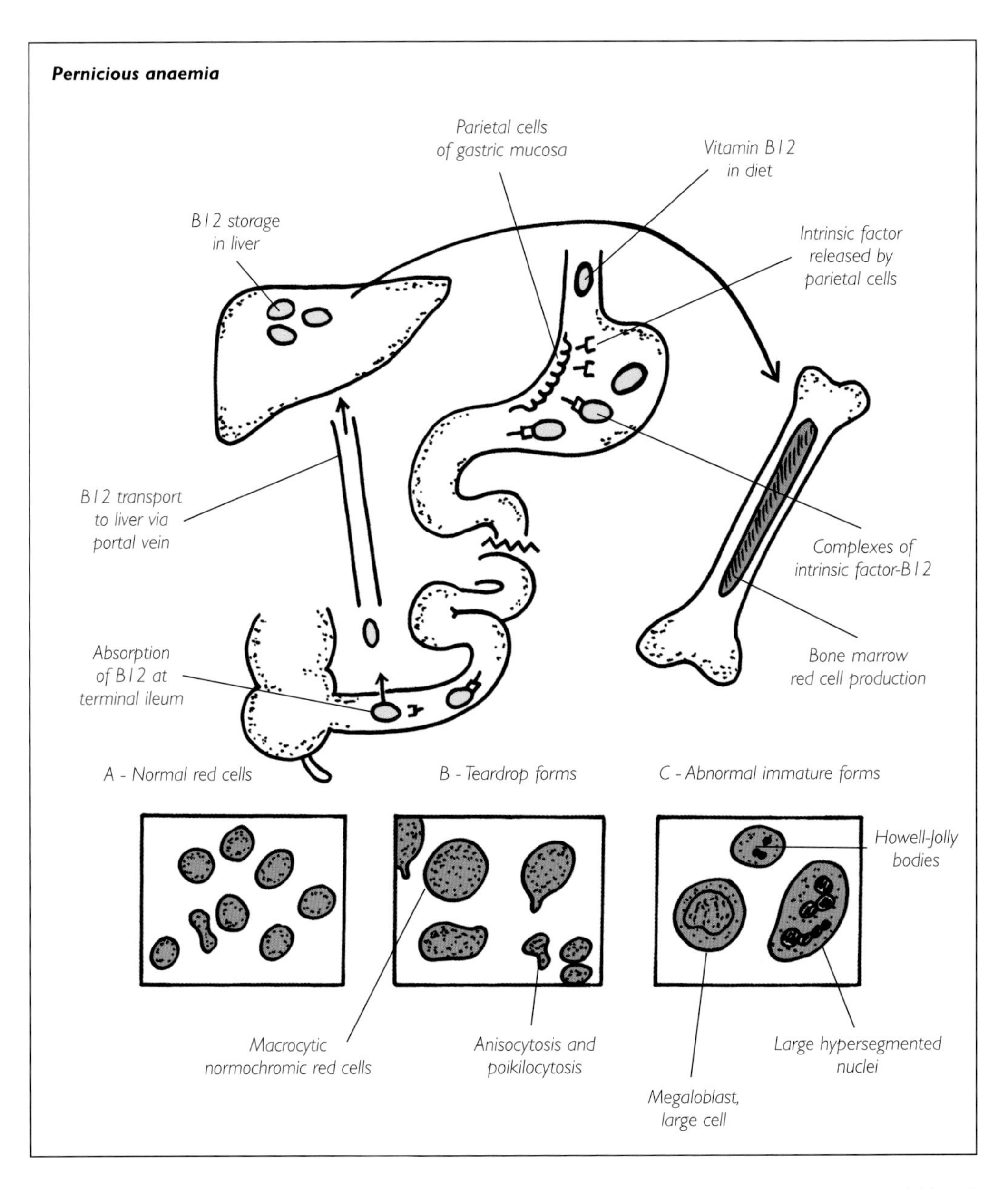

Pernicious anaemia is due to vitamin B12 deficiency, which is a required component for red blood cell production in the bone marrow. There is always reduced gastric hydrochloric acid production and atrophy of the gastric mucosal lining. Vitamin B12 is especially present in animal products (meat, eggs, dairy products etc.). Its absorption requires the secretion of a binding agent called intrinsic factor, by the parietal cells of the gastric mucosal wall. This attaches to the B12, and then releases it at the terminal ileum for absorption and thence storage in the liver (up to 10 years supply can be stored here). In pernicious anaemia there is auto-antibody attached to the gastric parietal cells, preventing release of the intrinsic factor. The blood changes to B12 deficiency include pancytopenia (reduced numbers of all cell types – red cells, white cells and platelets). The red blood cells are larger than normal (macrocytic) and abnormally shaped, as shown by B. Abnormal immature cell types are released, as shown in image C. There is also serious degeneration in the nervous system, particularly the spinal cord, with the risk of ataxic incoordination and spastic paralysis.

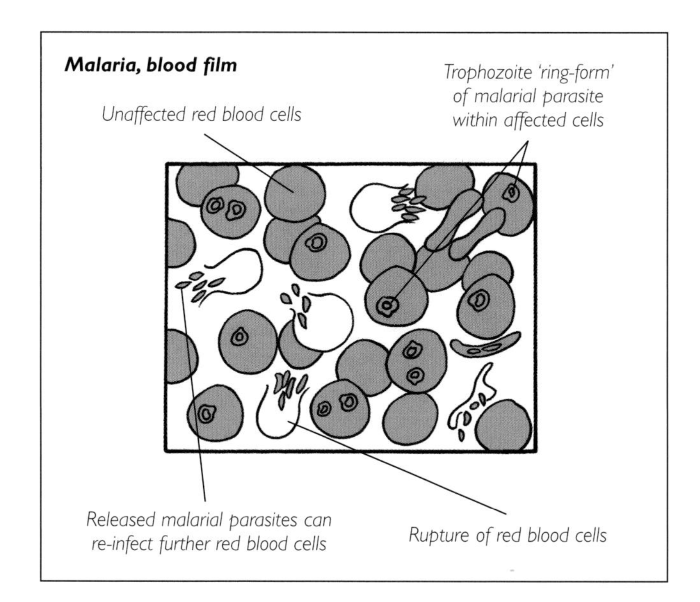

Malaria (see also p.227) is an endemic disease prevalent in parts of Africa, Asia, South & Central America, with a mortality rate of at least 1% of victims. The parasites are originally introduced into the skin by the bite of an infected mosquito. They then invade and mature within the liver (forming schizonts), and then spread into the blood (as merozoites) upon rupturing the liver cells. There is then a trophozoite stage appearing as 'rings' within the red blood cells (RBCs'). When the RBCs' rupture there arises a high fever, haemolytic anaemia and jaundice depending on severity.

Related images

p.180 Gastrointestinal bleeding
p.737 Tubercular type fever
p.156 Worm gut infestation
p.527 Headache
p.528 Migraine visual aura
p.300 Heart failure, right-sided
p.133 Liver failure and ascites
p.470 Pancreatic failure
p.222-223 Gallstones
p.222 Fatty liver
p.223 Jaundice
p.504 Chronic bronchitis

CICUTA VIROSA

Original

'Cicuta virosa and astrality within the central nervous system', by Nadine Kardesler. The plant's leafy region is aligned with the chest to symbolise its relationship to the rhythmic system (heart & lung function). The umbel flowers lie alongside the brain. Rhythmic movement of the astral body is promoted, cramping disorders of this within the CNS are thus released. The nerve-sensory pole connects to the spiritual realm (shown by stars), whilst the metabolic pole connect to the material Earth realm below (shown by the grid).

Astrology

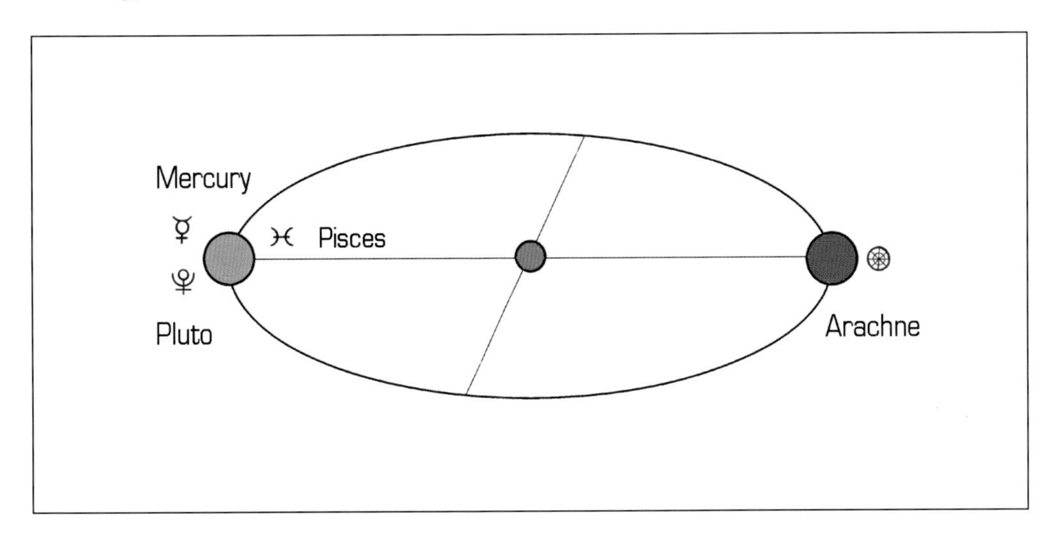

Mercury conjunct Pluto within Pisces, opposite Arachne.

Oriental

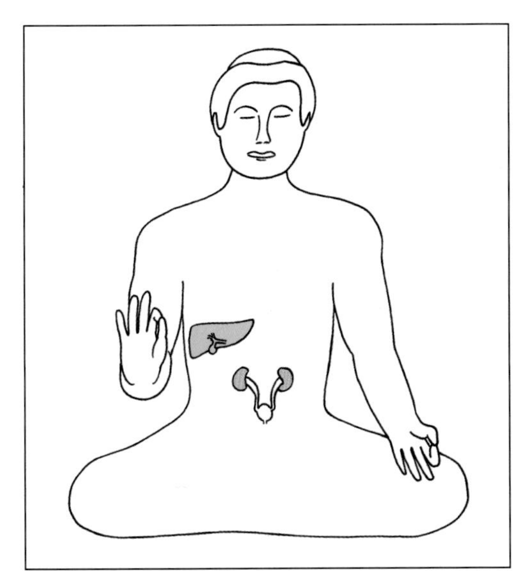

Kidney essence deficiency with liver interior wind.

Particulars

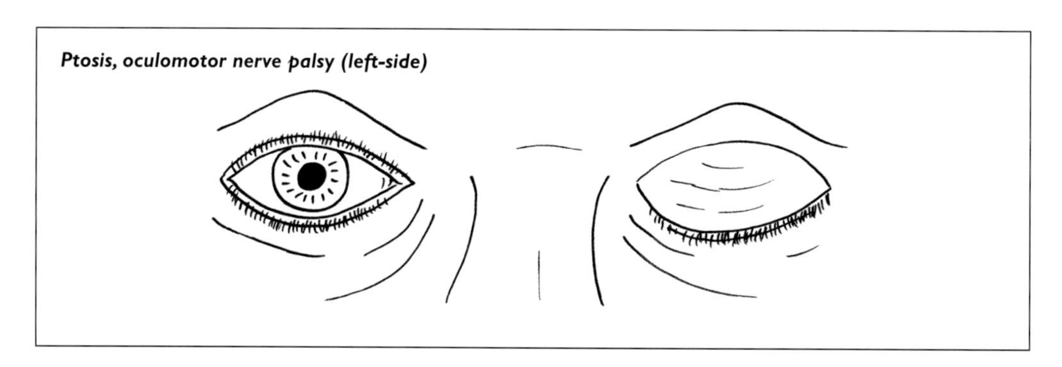

The oculomotor nerve (3rd cranial nerve) controls the extraocular muscles for eye movements, alongside the 4th and 5th cranial nerves. Complete damage to the oculomotor nerve will cause a complete ptosis (dropped or closed eyelid) on that side, with the eye under the eyelid facing downward and outward, with loss of pupil reflexes to light. Causes can include a tumour compressing the nerve in the midbrain region of the brainstem, pressure from an arterial aneurysm and diabetes.

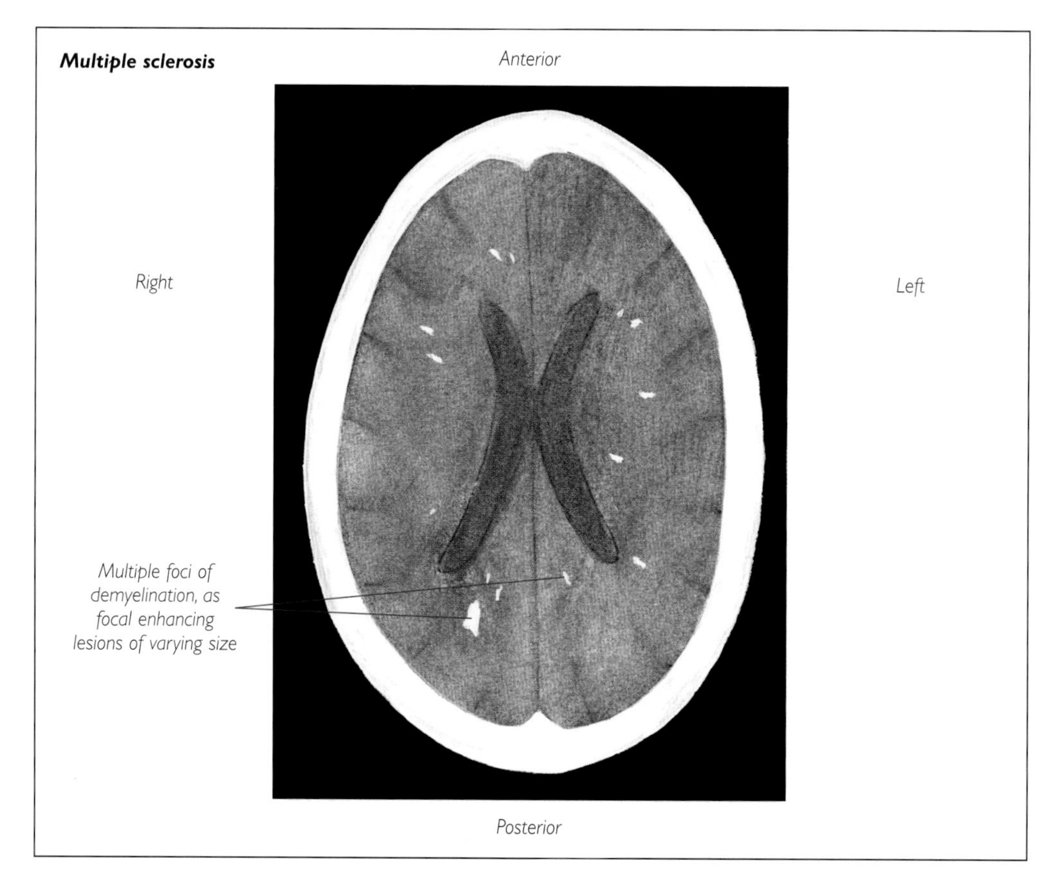

The CT brain scan investigation of multiple sclerosis requires the injection of contrast medium. This reveals the areas of nerve demyelination as focal enhancing lesions of variable size, and situated mostly in the white matter (inside of the outer cortical rim of the brain).

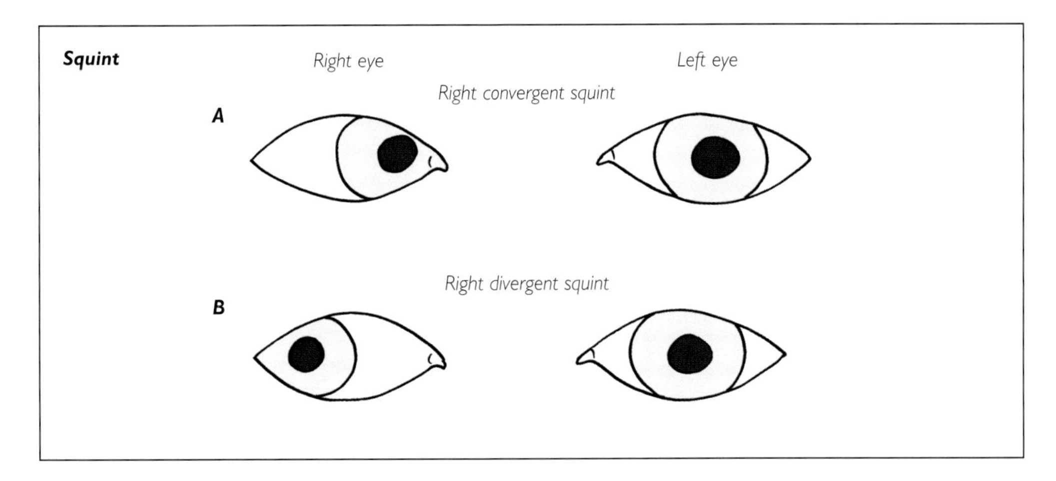

A squint is characterised by one eye drifting inward (convergent) or outwards (divergent) in relation to the other. Most childhood squints are convergent in nature, and occur before the age of 4 (some occurring from birth). Paradoxically, the child does not usually report double vision because the image from the squinting eye is suppressed by the brain – and leads to that eye being amblyopic or 'lazy'. In most squints there is an underlying genetic factor with failure of the central nerves to control smooth binocular single vision.

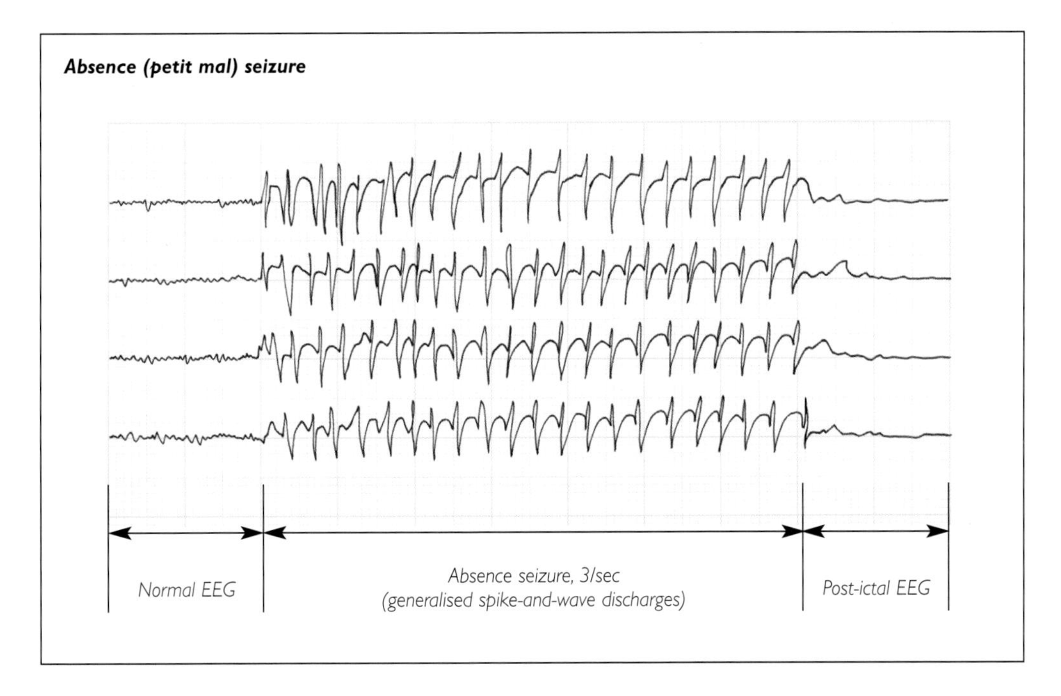

Absence (petit mal) seizures are a milder form of epilepsy than grand-mal, and occur mostly in children. An episode usually last 5-10 seconds, during when the child loses awareness of his surroundings, is unresponsive and interrupt/cease motor activities. There is a black stare and sometimes upward deviation of the eyes with mild twitching of the face or limbs. Occasionally there are chewing, lip smacking or mouthing movements. Attacks can occur quite frequently during the day. The electroencephalogram (EEG) shows spike-and-wave discharges, 3 per second, over the two cerebral hemispheres, and is diagnostic.

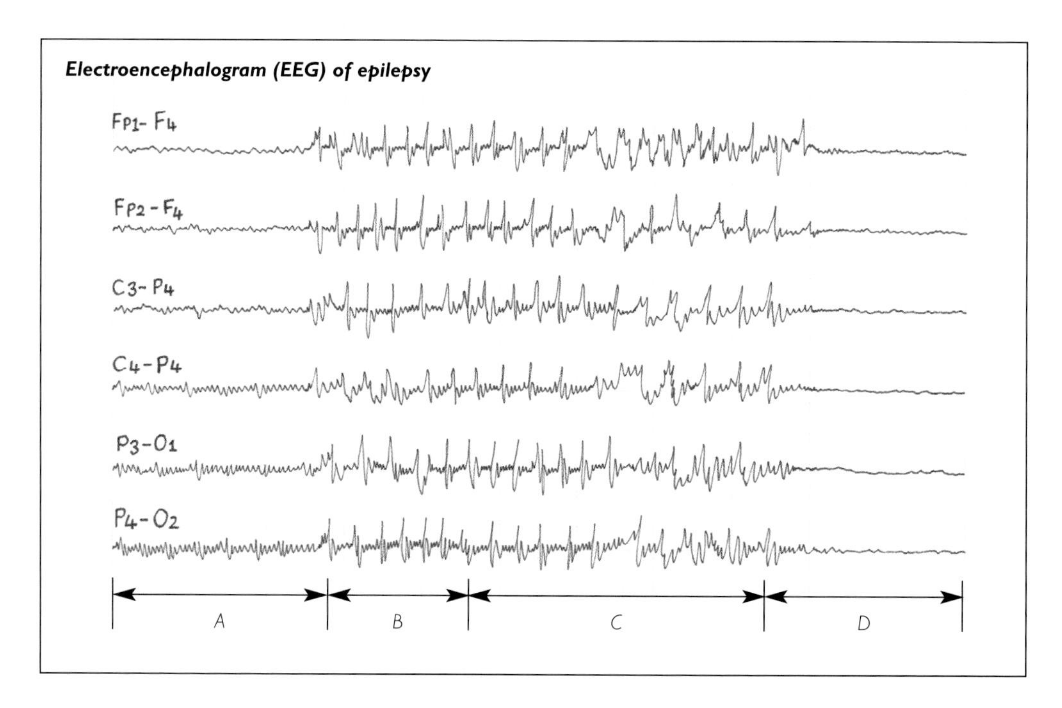

Electroencephalogram (EEG) of epilepsy

An epileptic seizure is a transient disturbance of cerebral brain function with an excessive abnormal electrical discharge of a collection of neurones. The diagram shows an EEG during a generalised grand mal (tonic-clonic) seizure, with sudden loss of consciousness and generalised tonic stiffening of the body with muscle contraction. (A) shows the EEG during normal wakefulness before the fit. (B) shows the seizure activity. The patient may bite his tongue, salivate and have urinary incontinence during this phase. During the tonic phase the EEG shows fast repetitive generalised spikes. This is followed by diffuse trembling of the body and a clonic phase of bilateral synchronous jerking of the body (C). During this phase there are spike-and-wave- discharges. During the post-ictal phased (D) following the seizure, the patient is limp, drowsy and remains confused for some time. This phase shows slow wave activity

Related images

p.454 Tetanus
p.479-480 Rabies infection
p.54 Meningitis
p.156 Worm gut infestation
p.159 Impetigo
p.71 Eczema
p.411 Acne vulgaris
p.138 Gum hypertrophy

CIMICIFUGA RACEMOSA

Museum

LIBER QVARTVS.

DE VARIETATIBVS NON NATURALIS partus, & earundem curis.

Quan-

PRECEDING PAGE. 'Childbirth', by Jost Amman. © Philadelphia Museum of Art: Smith, Kline and French (now Smith Kline Beecham) Laboratories Collection, 1949 (1949-97-12a). It was formerly thought the term caesarean section derived from the birth of Julius Caesar, the Roman political and military leader. The manner of his birth by this means is, however, now contentious. The name 'Caesar' is actually a cognomen (Roman nickname) borne by descendants or clan members as a kind of surname. The original Caesar is, indeed, not known. A legend by Pliny recounted the first Caesar was named thus due to his being cut from the womb of his mother, and the term has been used ever since to refer to surgical delivery through the abdominal wall and uterus as opposed to normal vaginal birth. The first caesarean section in mythology was performed by Apollo on his lover Coronis (who he had himself killed with his arrow in jealous love), to successfully deliver his son Asclepios. This child went on to become a god-like healer, able to resurrect dead souls back to life. Another etymological or origination of the word could be from the Latin verb cauder, which means 'to cut'. Furthermore, Roman law prescribed surgical delivery at the end of a pregnancy if a woman were dying, so as to save the life of the baby. This was known as lex caesarea. This is regarded as further evidence against this being the manner of Julius Caesar's birth, as his mother lived to a long life after the delivery. The procedure tended to result in death of the mother, until techniques improved from the end of the 19th century.

Historically, Cimicifuga was used extensively alongside other herbs such as Aristolochia (Birthwort), Caullophyllum (Blue Cohosh), Capsella bursa-pastoris (Shepherd's purse) by midwives to heal and repair any surgical or traumatic wounds during childbirth. Much of this herbal lore was temporarily lost through such problems as the witch-hunt trials and the pharmaceutical shift of the medical profession. Much female power has become subjugated by a male-dominated perspective of childbirth. For example during a spiritually-focused gestation the woman should become suitably prepared for a gratifying labour and birth process. If the mood of the fertile goddess were adopted (see the Immaculate Conception in p.456) then certain spiritual forces are already at play, which provide rhythmic and harmonious contractions of the uterus and cervical opening. The incarnating soul must ideally incarnate into a physical body perfectly suited to fulfil its life purpose or destiny on Earth. If a divine channel of light were visualised by mother and midwife alike, then the soul descends from the spiritual plane into its physical body without the sense of trauma or forgetfulness as to its true nature. Arguably such spiritual shifts in perspective towards childbirth would reduce complications such as episiotomy wounds, or the need for analgesics.

FOLLOWING PAGE. 'Cimicifuga racemosa and embryo gestation', by Lorraine Spiro. The plant can be imagined growing within the ground of the ancient Earth-Moon, when the lunar influence strongly permeated the planet. Note the 3-lobed leaves and rocket-like flower raceme. Fertile reproductive forces are stimulated, symbolised by the linking chromosome pairs around it. The horizontal whitish lines between these chromosomes are the spindle fibres (which appear in the later stages of cell division). The lowest pair is the 23rd chromosome pair, defining the genetic gender, the short or stunted 'Y' chromosome (right-side) and the normal length 'X' chromosome (left-side). A human embryo is developing around the root region, its long umbilical cord originating from the Earth below and wrapping round the root as it enters the body.

The sheath of the embryo (largely comprising its amniotic sac) provides a protective and cushioning layer around its physical and etheric body – rifts in this sac can lead to persistent weakness in the aura after birth, with holes in the etheric body. During Old Moon and Lemuria, the human being did not have a sufficiently independent sense of self to be able to separate itself from the environment. It would become so permeated by the world's physical and etheric forces that the body literally moulded or shape-shifted rapidly to suit the prevailing circumstances of the environment. For example it would dehydrate if the surroundings were too dry. Such plasticity of the body is a faculty of the embryo, thus the human would in effect be an embryo all its life. A reversion to this state can occur in certain pathologies, such as cancer.

Original

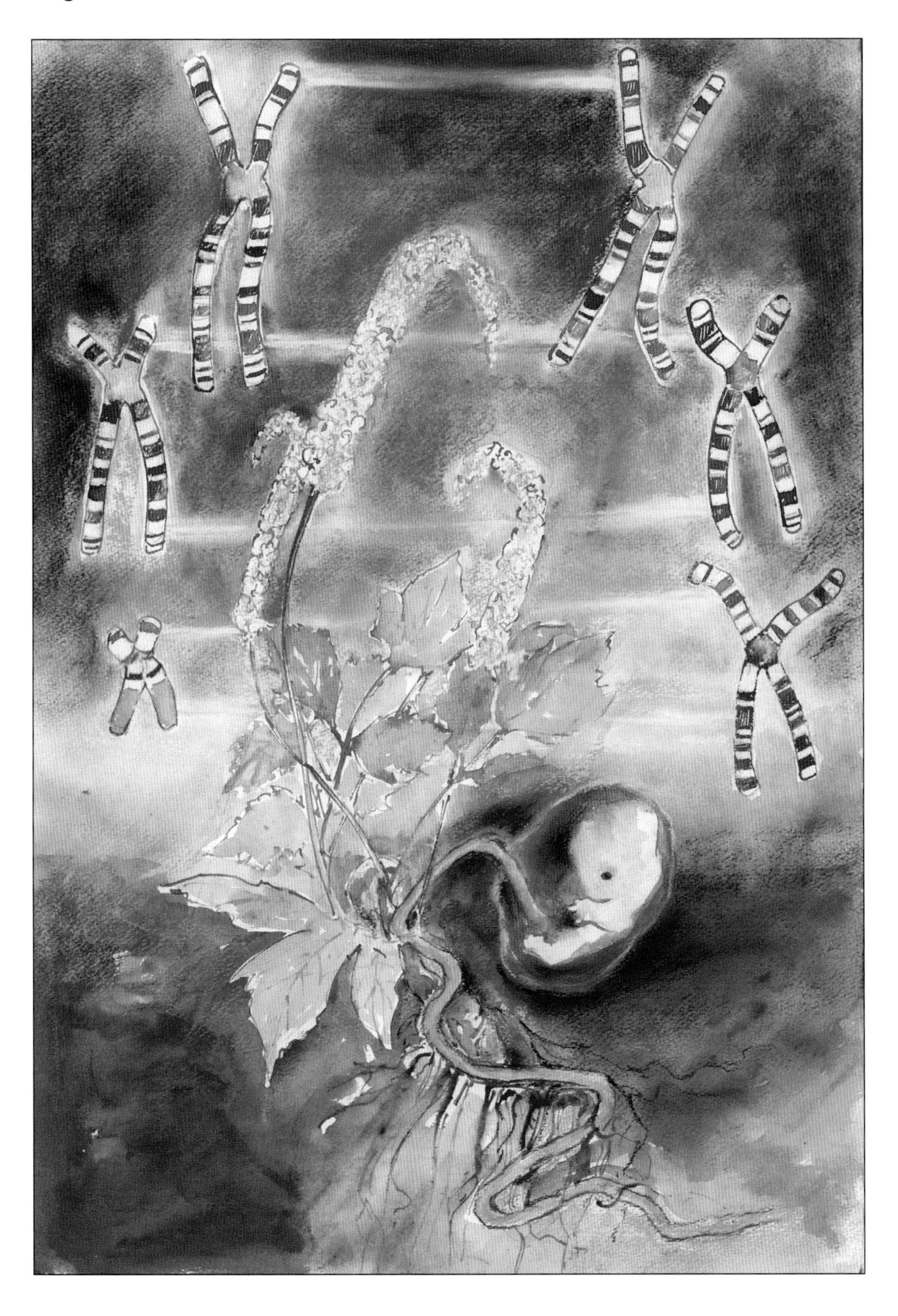

Astrology

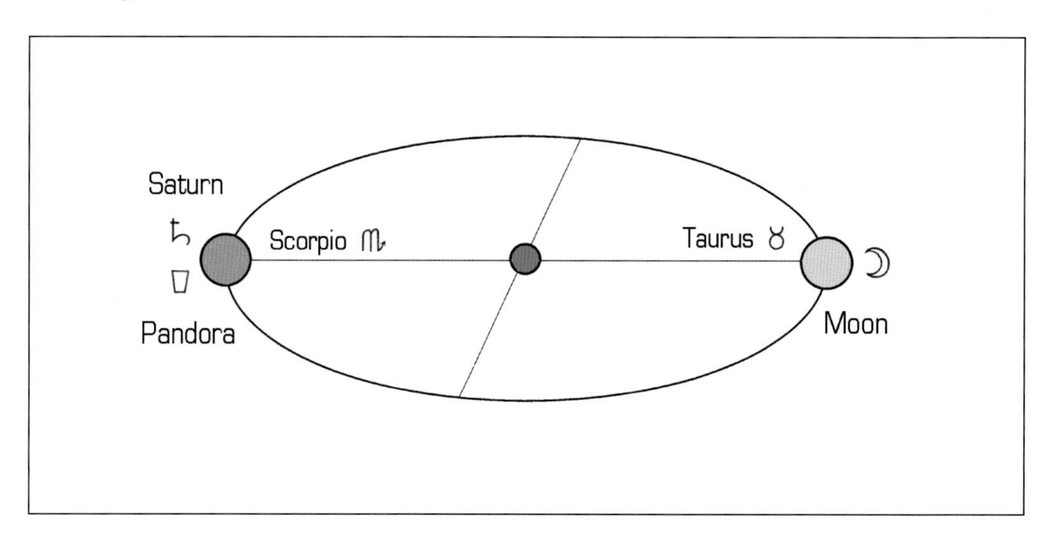

Moon in Taurus opposite Saturn conjunct Pandora within Scorpio.

Oriental

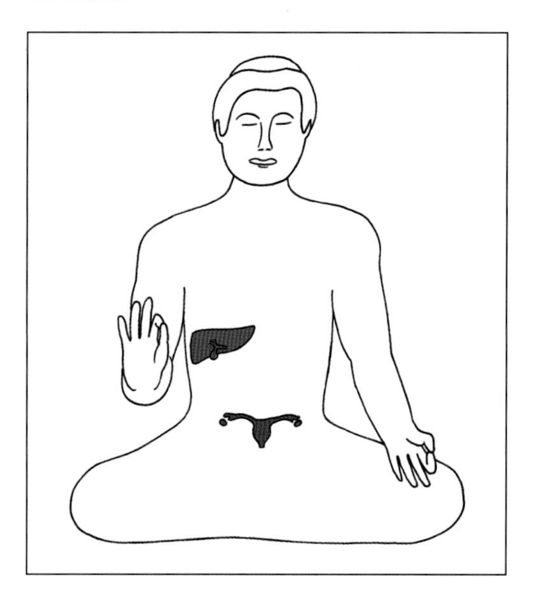

Liver chi stagnation with uterus/ovarian blood stagnation/stasis.

Particulars

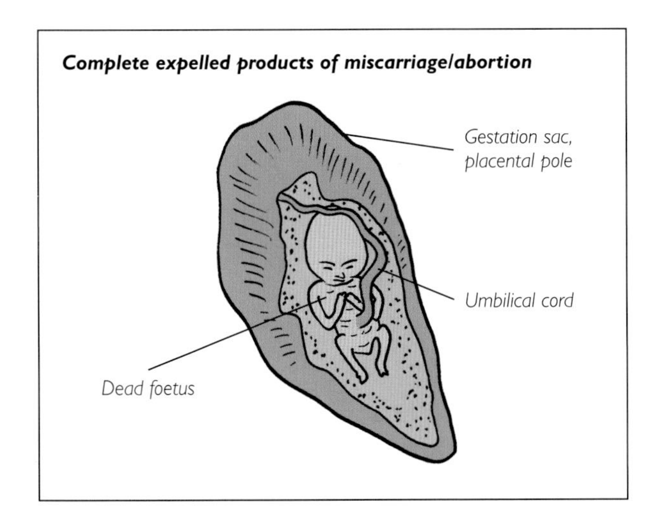

Miscarriage or abortion leads to the expulsion of the conceptus during the gestation; technically miscarriage is defined as occurring before 24 weeks of gestation. Up to 12 weeks there is likely to be complete expulsion, but between the 12th and 24th weeks the gestation sac is liable to rupture, causing the expulsion of the foetus but retention of the placenta. This may then need further surgical methods to complete the miscarriage (dilatation and curettage).

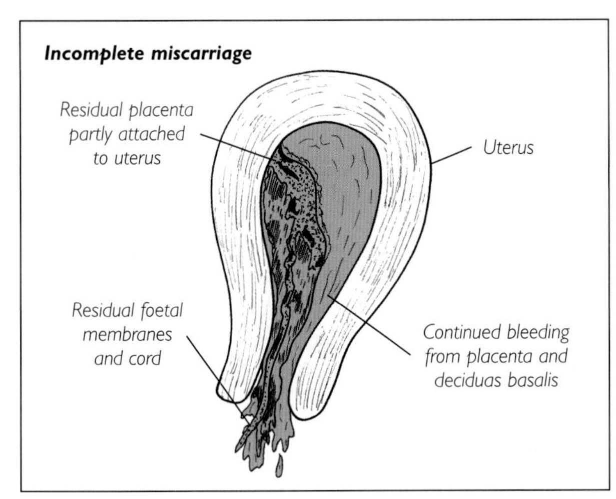

An incomplete miscarriage occurs where only the foetus and some membranes are expelled, despite the uterine contractions and cervical dilatation. The placenta remains partly attached and heavy bleeding continues. Usually an intramuscular injection of ergometrine is given to control the bleeding and surgical evacuation (dilatation and curettage) performed to complete the miscarriage.

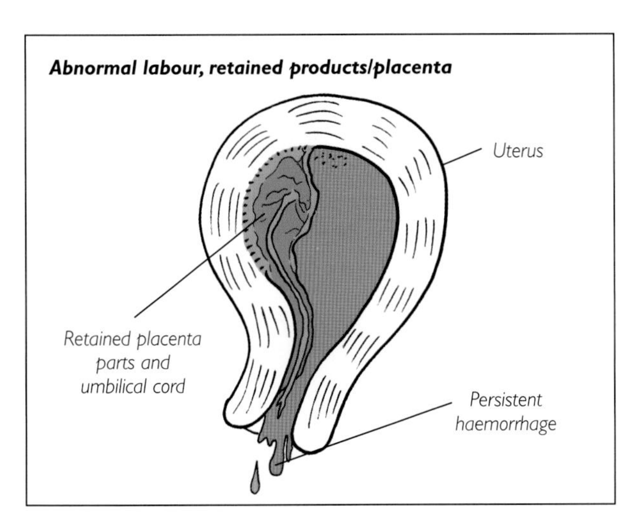

The third stage of labour is defined as the period after delivery of the baby until the final expulsion of the placenta. Normally the placenta separates from the uterus within a few minutes of the delivery of the baby; certainly it should have become released by 20 minutes later. Causes of a retained placenta include failure of full separation from the uterine wall, and rarely an abnormal attachment of the placenta to the uterine muscle. If only partial separation has occurred there is likely to also be bleeding, which can become severe.

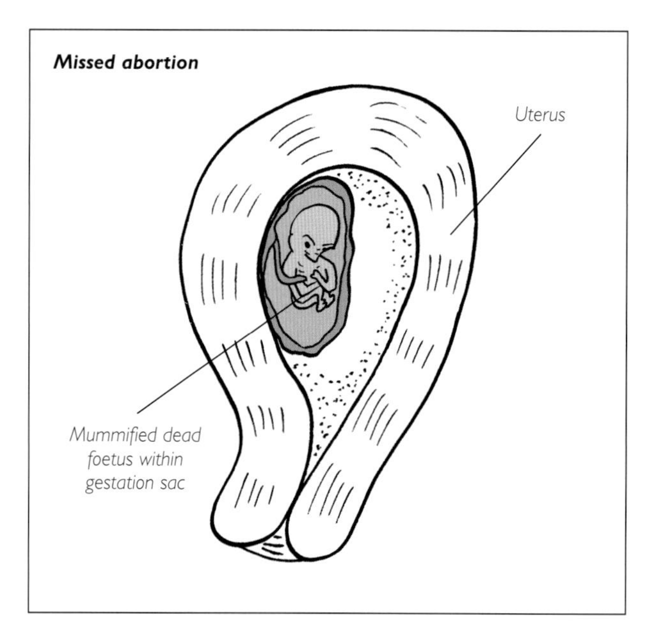

A missed miscarriage occurs where there is retention of a foetus, after its death, within the uterus for a number of weeks (or longer). The death of the foetus has become unnoticed (e.g. there may have been little or no vaginal bleeding). The symptoms of the pregnancy, however, disappear, so the uterus shrinks and the amniotic fluid is reabsorbed. Usually the foetus and sac will eventually become expelled spontaneously, without surgical treatment. But if this does occur, the tissues within the gestation sac can degenerate into a mixture of blood clot and dead tissue. Mummification and calcification are also rare but possible outcomes.

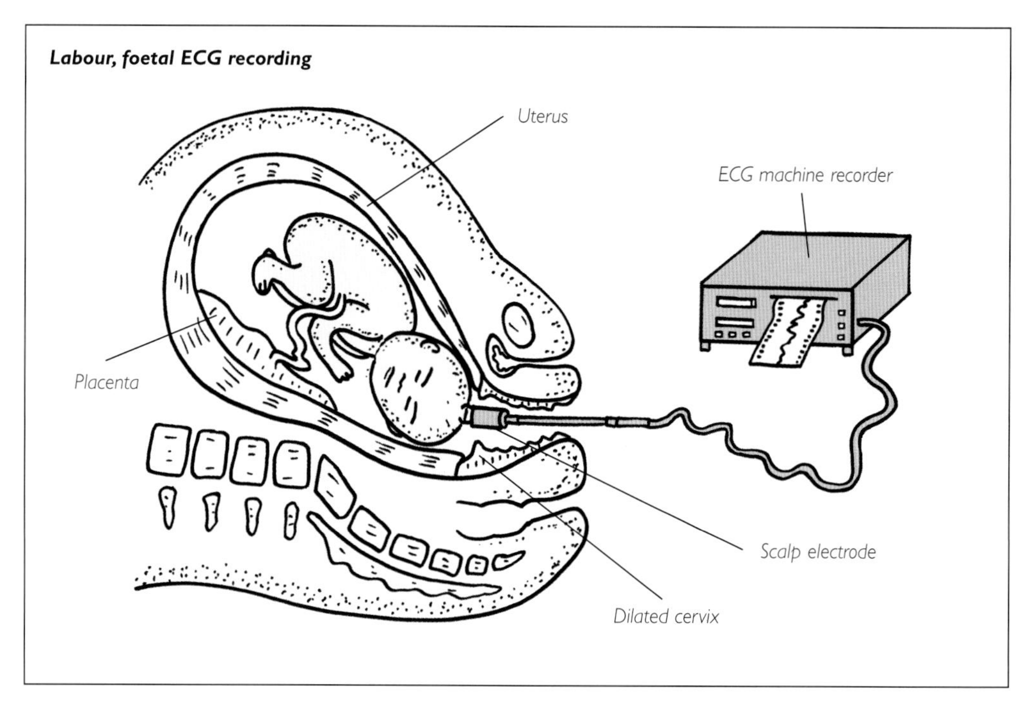

A key assessment of the baby's condition during labour is measurement of the foetal heart rate, which can be done manually by a pinard stethoscope, or by a foetal monitor through a surface ultrasonic transducer. Shown here is a more invasive method, with a sensing electrode attached to the foetal scalp through the birth canal. An ECG can then be obtained. However, it requires that the membranes must be ruptured and the foetal head is accessible. Also it should not be performed if there is a risk of transmitting any viral infection from the mother to the foetus (e.g. hepatitis B, C or HIV). The average baseline foetal heart rate should be 120-160 beats per minute. If faster or slower then it can indicate foetal distress.

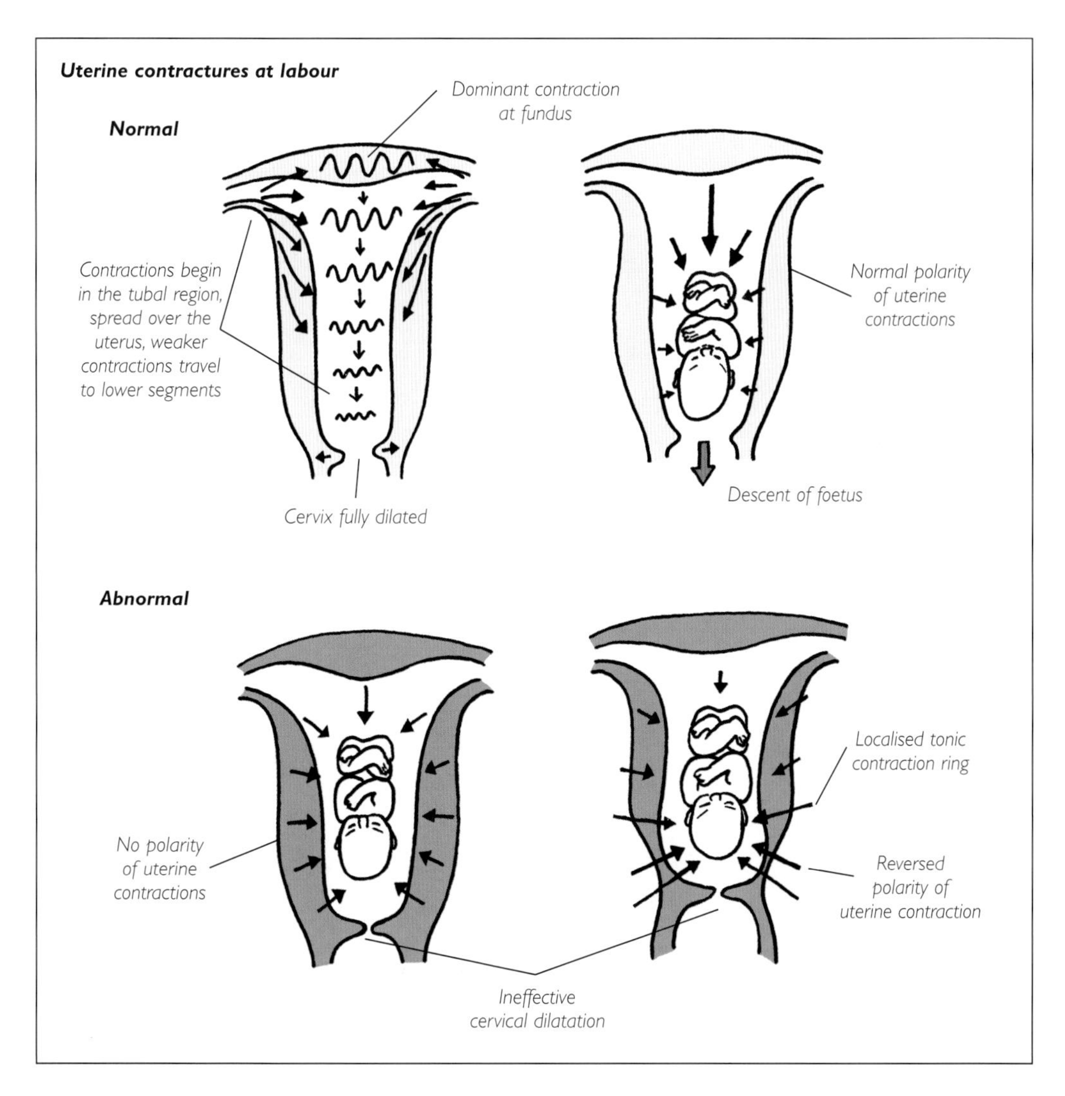

Normal uterine contractions at labour create a polarity of intra-uterine pressure, which guides the foetus downwards through the dilated cervix and dilated vaginal birth canal. Each contraction is begun at the junction of the fallopian tubes and uterus, thereby spreading over the uterus with a gradient pattern of dominant contractions at the upper pole. The lower uterus wall thins as the upper uterus wall thickens. The cervix dilates fully, aiding the foetal head to be well-fitting at the lower uterine segment. Various abnormalities can, however, arise. A normal polarity of uterine contractions may be present, but these may be too weak or too strong. Weak and/or infrequent contractions (hypotonia) lead to slow progress in labour. Excessively strong contractions, however, may cause foetal distress due to the persistent pressure on the placenta and the forced rapid moulding of the foetal head. If the foetus is also malpresented in any way then both foetal damage and./or uterine rupture could occur. Where polarity is abnormal then there could be various possibilities. An incoordination of uterine contractions, with no harmonious spectrum of strength will tend to manifest as painful labour contractions but with no effect, leading to slow or no progress in labour. If the lower uterine segments are hypertonic and/or local tonic contraction rings develop, then there is non-descent of the foetus, and often foetal distress. The cervix may also be rigid, either from scarring damage (e.g. from prior trauma or surgery) or having lost its normal elasticity. Labour will not progress therefore; and there is a strong risk of uterine rupture.

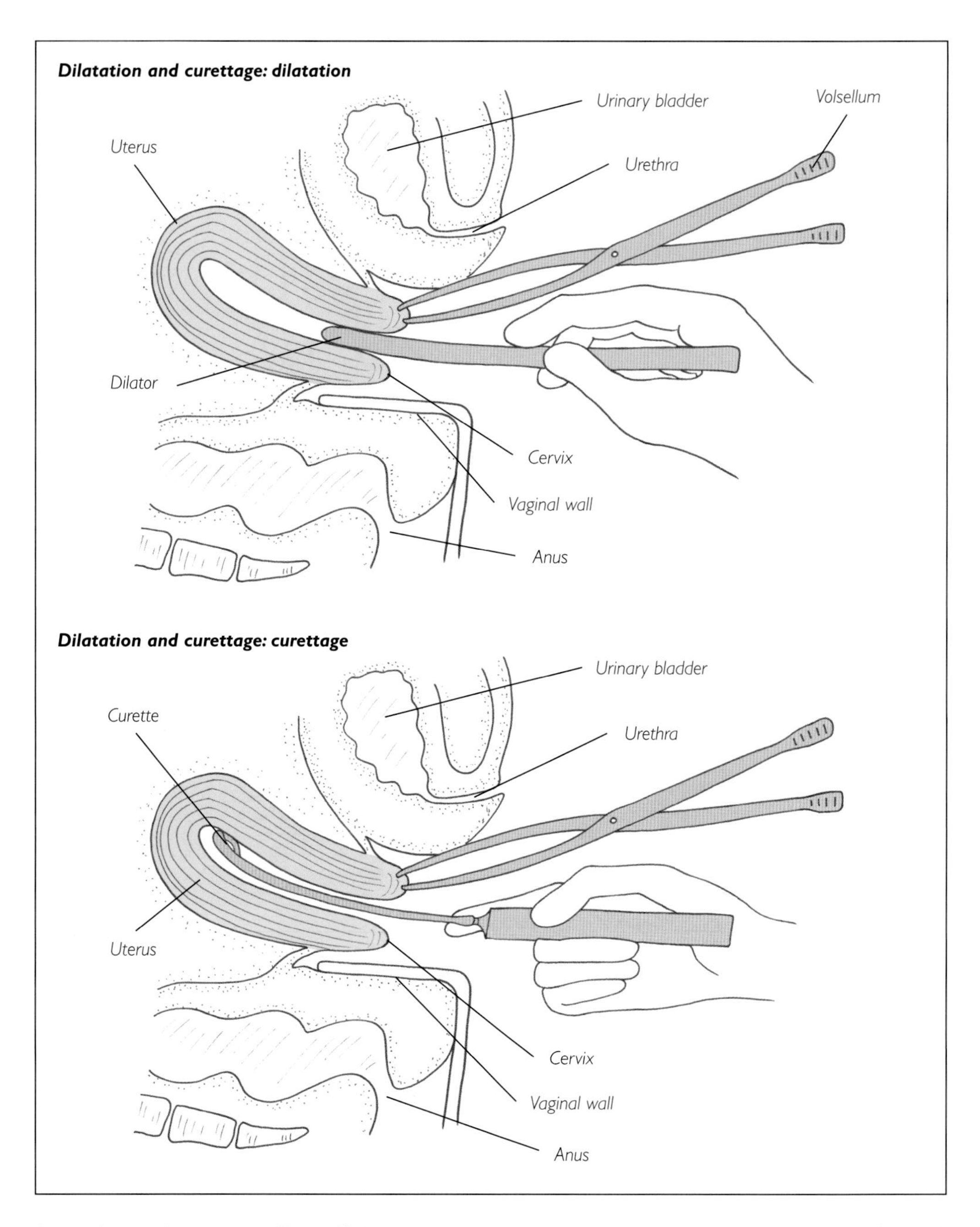

Dilatation and curettage (D & C) is a very common gynaecological procedure. It is performed under anaesthesia and in a sterile environment. The bladder is emptied by catheterisation. The cervix is held steady by a volsellum and the endocervical canal dilated to 8mm using several dilators in progressively wider sizes. Excessive penetration of the uterus by the dilator must be avoided to prevent perforation of the uterus. The curette is then introduced and the endometrial surface (inner lining of the uterus) systemically scraped. Indications for the procedure include treatment of heavy menstrual bleeding, removal of an early pregnancy in termination, to remove retained products after a spontaneous abortion, removal of intrauterine polyps, lost contraceptive devices or a retained placenta after childbirth.

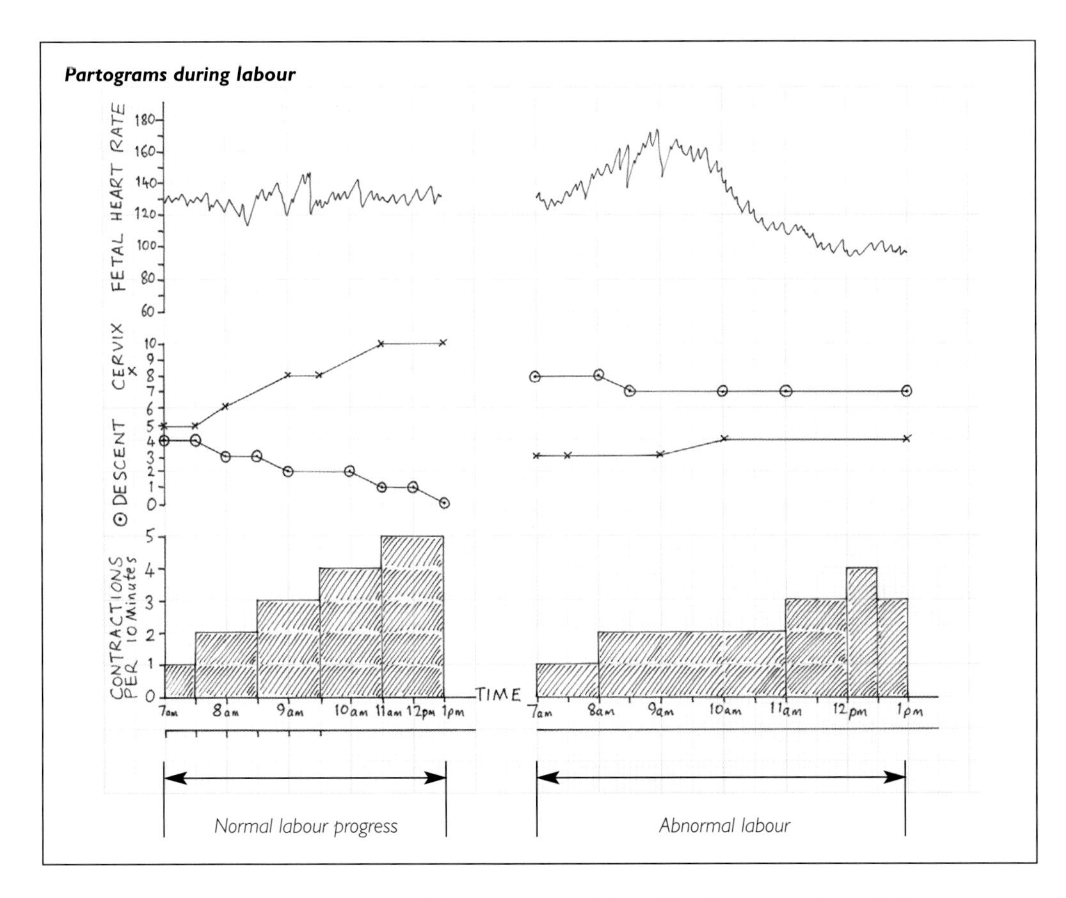

Partograms during labour

The partogram is a graphic display of the progress in labour. The lower portion of this partogram shows the number of contractions (per 10 minutes) each hour. Next is shown the descent of the baby, 0 indicating the emergence of the baby out of the vaginal birth canal. The cervical dilatation is then shown; to the maximum of 10cm. Above is the foetal heart rate, where this is being monitored. Usually cervical dilatation goes through a latent phase, from the onset of labour up to a dilatation of 3-4cm. thereafter, the active phase begins, with progressive cervical dilatation at approximately 1cm per hour to full opening. An example of normal labour is shown on the left hand side. On the right is an example of abnormal, with weak and ineffective uterine contractions, poor descent of the baby, insufficient cervical opening and then foetal distress (i.e. a falling foetal heart rate from time 10am).

Related images

p.642 Placenta abruption
p.642 Placenta infarction
p.640 Threatened miscarriage
p.650 Cervical incompetence
p.622 Cervical spondylitis
p.621 Capsulitis, frozen shoulder
p.619-620 Tendonitis
p.347 Polymyalgia rheumatica, temporal arteritis
p.56 & p.340 Rheumatoid arthritis

CLAY

Museum

William Blake (1757-1827), 'Elohim creating Adam', 1795/circa 1805, colour print finished in ink and watercolour on paper. © Tate, London 2006. This image relates to the Book of Genesis, where Elohim is a Hebrew name for God. 'And the Lord God formed man of the dust of the ground'. Elohim is depicted with some earth in his left hand, with Adam thereby shown growing out of the Earth. Blake believed that the Fall of humanity occurred at the time of creation, as shown here (i.e. not within the Garden of Eden), when man was made material from out of the spiritual world. He considered the God of the Old Testament to be a false god. Furthermore, the very nature of morality derived out of the separation of good and evil, upon God placing Adam and Eve within the middle of the earthly paradise. Note in Genesis 1:26, 'And God said, Let us make man in our image after our likeness…', whereas in Genesis 1:27, 'So God created man in his own image, in the image of God created he him….' And in Genesis 1:29, 'And God said, Behold, I have given you every herb…' These statements appear to be contradictory, for initially there is a pluralistic God, or more than one being, but thereafter there is some sort of individual God. This dilemma has been the subject of much theological debate. The Elohim are also a reference in Hebrew lore of divine creator-gods as a step lower than the universal creator. This would also be in keeping with dualistic beliefs in Gnostic Christianity and Catharism, that the world and human race were fashioned by fallen gods. Adam is a root word which also signifies 'man' or 'mankind' in various Semitic, Phoenician and Sabean languages. Genesis also seems to relate the word 'Adam' to 'ha-adamah', which means 'ground'. It can also mean 'to be red'. This creation of Adam myth reveals the formation of the human before even that of the plants and animals. The earth is still depicted as a lifeless barren place, and man has been formed out of the dust, which Yahweh/Elohim animates by breathing into his nostrils. In the other Genesis account, Adam is formed in the sixth day, after the animals. These apparently divergent views are actually compatible when considering the notion that the human soul is present from the very beginning of the world. The collective human spirit as Adam is organised as multiple souls who are to consequently experience individualisation and a karmic journey in the world. But these humans lie within the spiritual realm, as soul-spiritual seeds that would eventually descend into physical bodies prepared for them. Such physical bodies would first require the development of plant and animal life-forms, from which biological tissue is made available to create an animalised human body for spiritual descent. Since the Elohim makes Adam in his own likeness, then each human has within him/her the divine blueprints of the image and similitude (resemblance) of God, i.e. there is a spark of God within each and all.

Original

'Clay and the primordial descent of reptilian-Venusian genetic codes', by Jonathan Krantz. The planet Venus is shown radiating light packets of genetic information from the upper right-hand corner. These are received by the desolate clay base of the Earth below, symbolised by the slab with etched code. The serpents wrapped around this slab provide the necessary EL-shift to cause the information to 'Fall'. The constellations shown at the upper left corner are from above downward: Ursa major (Great Bear/Plough), Draco, Ursa major and Cassiopeia (being the 'W' shaped constellation). These are some of the circumpolar stars in the current time epoch, the Pole star being Polaris within Ursa minor. However, the ultimate source of the human blueprint remains the cosmos in its entirety.

Astrology

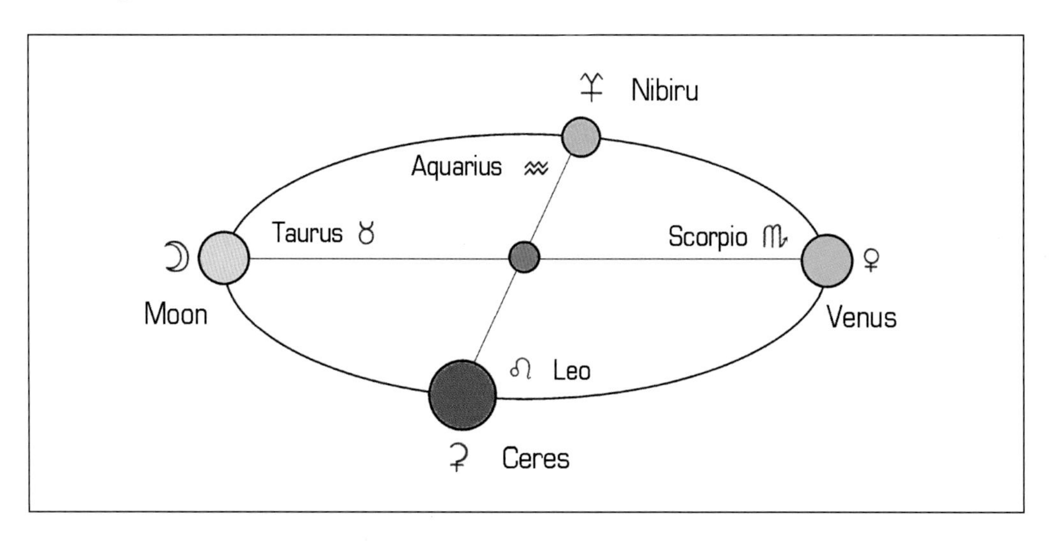

Grand cross, Moon in Taurus opposite Venus in Scorpio, and Ceres in Leo opposite Nibiru in Aquarius.

Oriental

Kidney and spleen yang deficiency, with phlegm-damp retention in muscles.

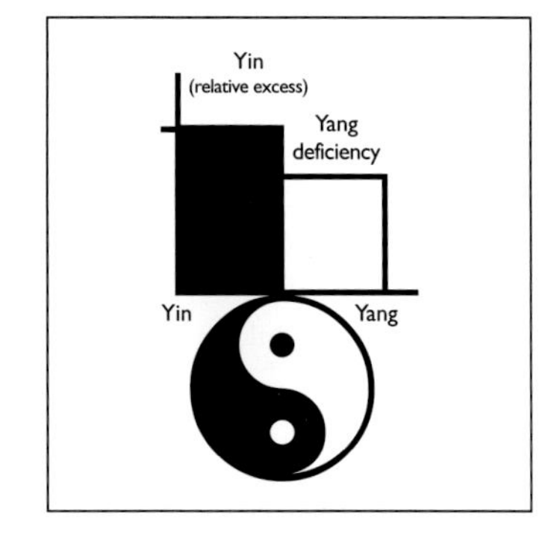

COCA

Museum

Lieutt. L. Gibbon. 'Coca plantation' © Wellcome Library, London. Lithograph on paper, published by P.S. Duval & Co., Philadelphia. This was a coca plantation in Peru, showing the armed guard with dogs. It is interesting to reflect on the reverse scenario also now occurring. Anti-explosive dogs are being trained by police to walk through Colombian coca plantations to detect land-mines; these being placed there by the farmers/drug barons to ward off the police.

FOLLOWING PAGE. 'Coca and fragmentation of the soul', by Crispin Chetwynd. The etheric body and metabolism of the user often become scattered and incoherent, thus blueprints are shown torn and misaligned in the illustration. The base chakra may become especially fragmented in the addict, symbolised by the shattered planetoid/asteroid within which the plant is rooted. The diverging pyramids symbolise the separation of the spiritual and physical bodies, normally these would be united into a tetrahedral geometry. The soul or higher self is left in a spaced-out state within the upper left-corner.

Various disorders of soul and body result from the situation, which can usefully be categorised miasmatically. The resulting state of consciousness may become one of fragmentation, delusional paranoia, schizoid tendencies and other psychotic states of mind (a syphilitic situation). The misty foggy background to the image suggests a similar state of mind (equivalent to the sycotic miasm). The spaced out consciousness may lead to a tubercular state of separation and flightiness. The lack of astral body connection to the physical-etheric can cause the psoric state of apathy and fatigue.

Original

Astrology

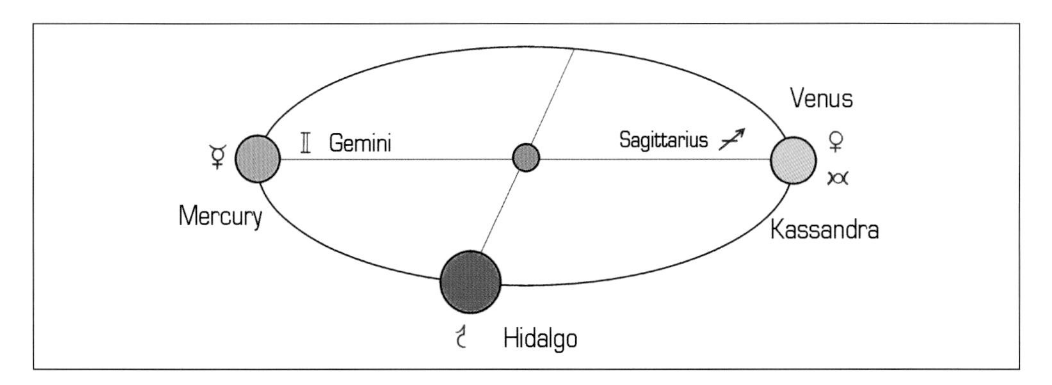

Mercury in Gemini opposite Venus conjunct Kassandra within Sagittarius, squared by Hidalgo.

Oriental

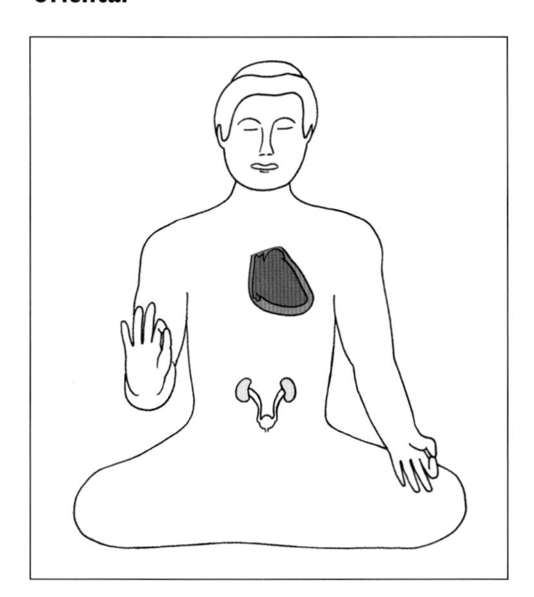

Kidney yin deficiency, with external heat invasion of pericardium and phlegm-fire within heart.

Related images

p.5 Foetal distress, umbilical cord around neck
p.443 Respiratory distress syndrome
p.619 Shingles
p.3 Trigeminal neuralgia
p.574 Peripheral neuropathy
p.528 Migraine visual aura
p.572 Optic nerve pathway
p.571 Retinal degeneration
p.573 Tunnel vision

COCCULUS INDICA

Museum

'Woman in pray for a sick child'. Unknown Italian painter (P.G.R.) in 1887 © Wellcome Library, London. Whilst the woman prays for the ill child, there are intercessors in a fire. Four angelic beings are shown in flames, supporting her pray. Three are child-like, the other an old man. As an interpretation, this is reminiscent of the doctrine of the Guardian Angel, that there are specific angelic beings assisting the healing and bodily regeneration of the physical body during a soul's particular incarnation. In some cultures these beings are also described as the inner phantom, Guardian at the Threshold or etheric double. The fiery state shown in the painting indicates the presence of salamander fire elementals, which provide the driving force for the other three elemental types (sylphs of air, undines of water and gnomes of earth). The four could therefore also represent the elemental beings. These provide the building blocks for the regeneration of the physical-etheric body. The seated being in the upper part of the fire may be a symbol for the Higher Self of the child, or a higher spiritual being acting as a guide. The kneeling woman's gaze is firmly fixed on this figure. The painting conveys the power of prayer in inviting such healing forces to the sickroom.

Original

'Cocculus indicus and the spiritual sojourn of deep sleep', by Tessa Gaynn. There are several interpretations possible to illustrate features of the remedy. For example, several incarnations of the soul are shown. Each pod-like chamber houses the physical and subtle body of that incarnation, whilst the central upper figure represents the higher self or soul providing the thread of consciousness linking all incarnations into the one individuality. With the ending of a physical incarnation (i.e. through death), the soul can carry over information from that life into the next. Generally, this transmission would encompass all that had remained unresolved or unlearnt during that particular incarnation, and is stored temporarily within an etheric seed atom to relay into the embryonic body of the next life. Another interpretation is that each pod contains the phases of sleep during one life, and receives healing from the soul during such periods of the diurnal rhythm. Any past, future or alternate life experiences may thereby be relayed into the super-consciousness of sleep, enabling the personality to receive dream messages from its soul. Dreams are therefore not always concerning the replaying of experiences from the waking phase of the day. Various aspects of the plant are also shown in the centre, including a leafy twig, flowering twig, the blossom in magnified view and fruit.

Astrology

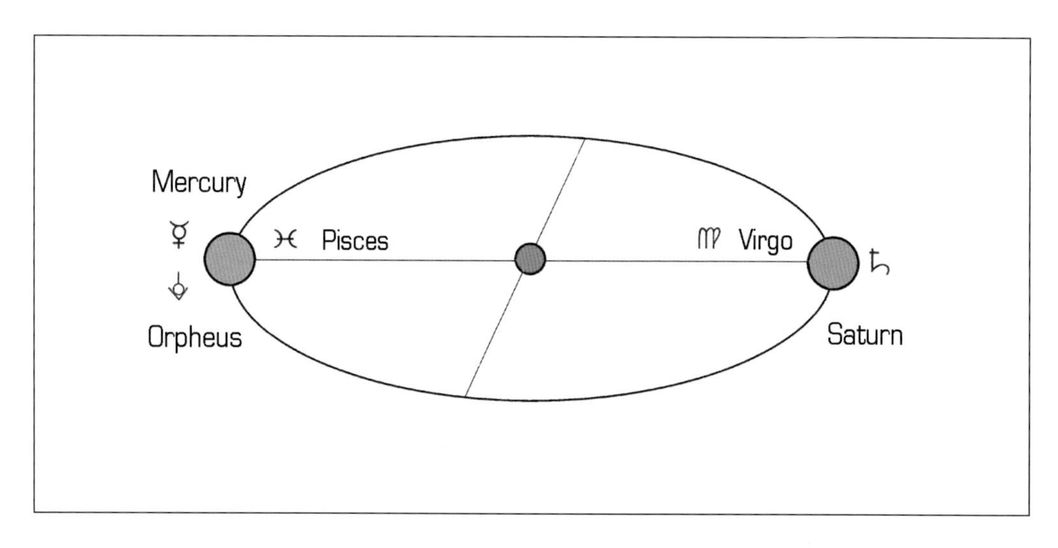

Mercury conjunct Orpheus within Pisces, opposite Saturn in Virgo.

Oriental

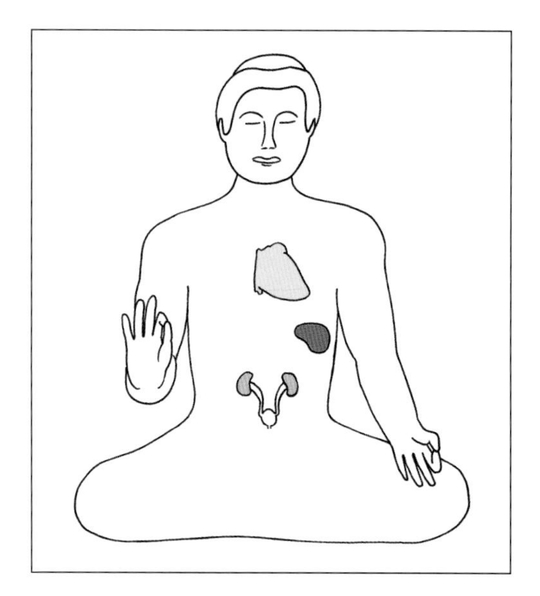

Kidney essence deficiency, with spleen chi deficiency and heart blood deficiency.

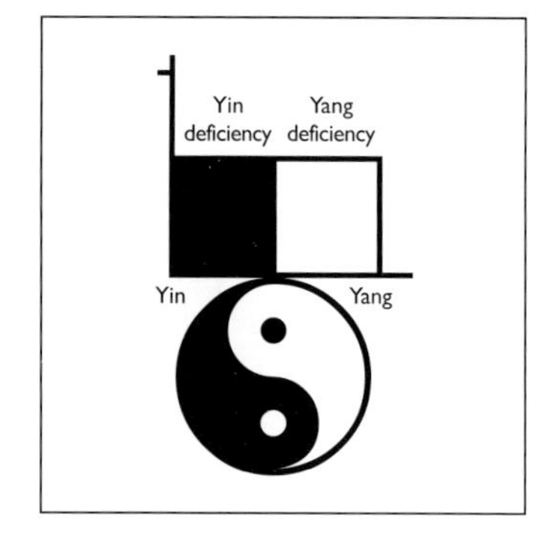

Particulars

Normal ear anatomy

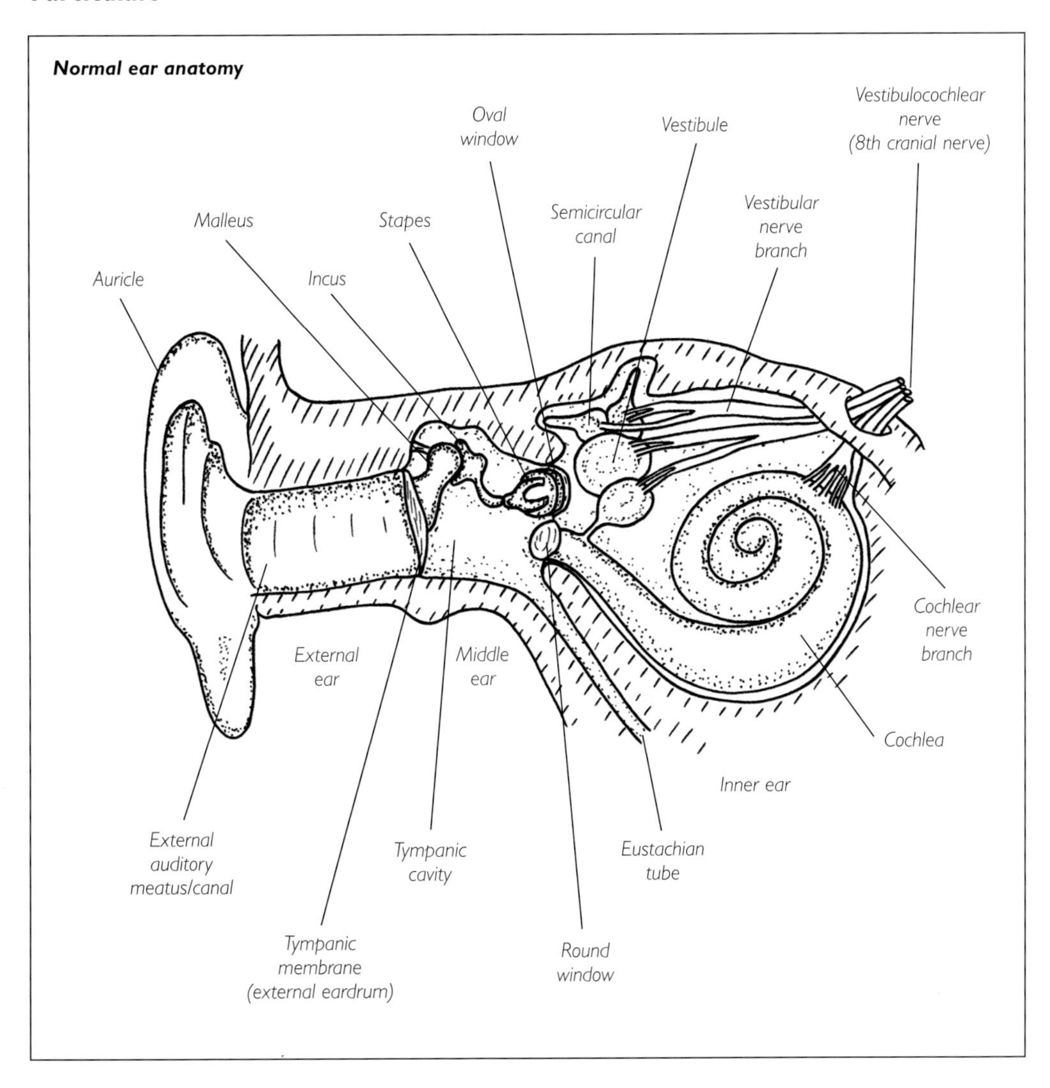

The ear is a sensory organ for both hearing (to the auditory part of the 8th cranial nerve) and equilibrium/balance sense (vestibular part of the nerve). The external ear consists of the auricle (collects the sound energy) and external auditory meatus (a narrow canal to conduct sound to the tympanic membrane). This eardrum vibrates to the sound waves, converting these into mechanical energy. The middle ear consists of three small bones called ossicles (malleus, incus, stapes) linked by synovial joints. These vibrate with the movement of the tympanic membrane, amplifying and conducting this vibration to the oval window – which is the interface to the inner ear. From the middle ear cavity, the Eustachian tube runs to the nasopharynx throat area, enabling outside air pressure to equilibrate to that of the middle ear. The inner ear is within a cavity of the temporal bone and consists of a series of bony walled interconnecting chambers and passages filled with a fluid (called perilymph). Within this is another series of similarly shaped chambers and passages filled with another fluid (called endolymph). The vestibules and semicircular canals deal with equilibrium/balance sense, whereas the cochlea deals with discernment of sound (tone, pitch, frequency). The impulses from both are finally passed into the brain through the vestibulocochlear (8th) cranial nerve.

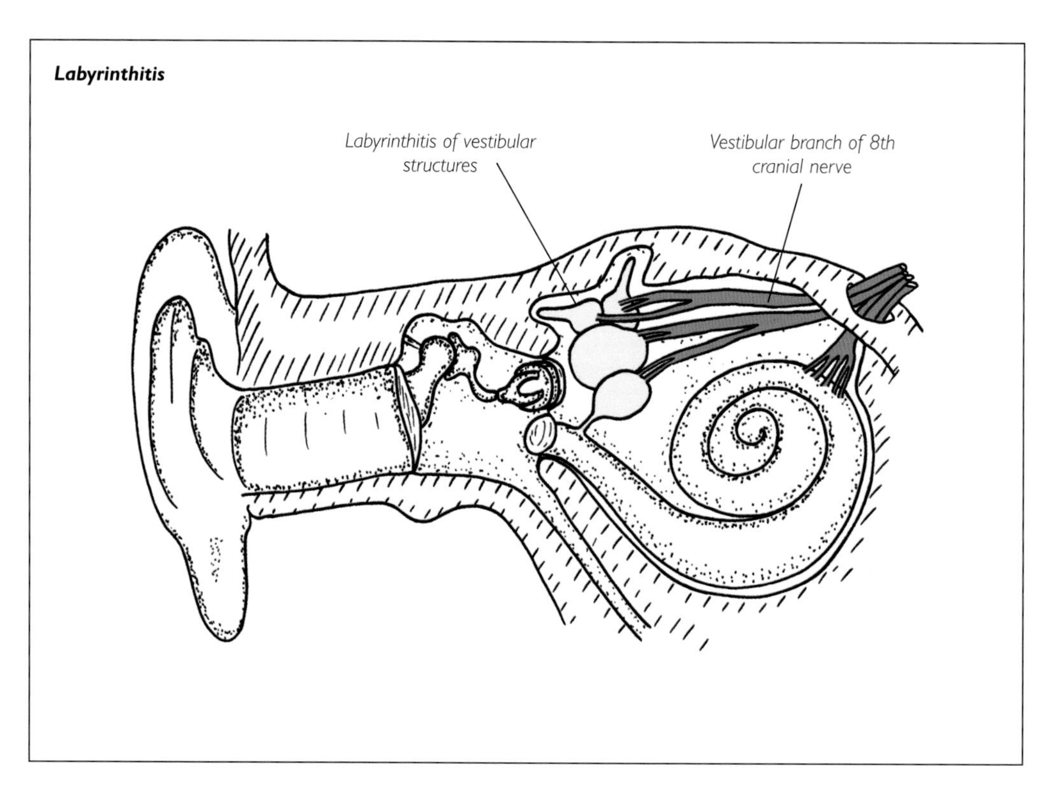

The vestibulocochlear (VIII) cranial nerve has two parts, the cochlear branch which receives auditory fibres from the cochlea, and the vestibular branch which receives transmission from the three semicircular canals, saccule and utricle. Collectively these latter chambers provide position sense. Labyrinthintis involves inflammation of these chambers, causing symptoms such as vertigo (illusion of movement in relation to the surroundings), vomiting and loss of balance.

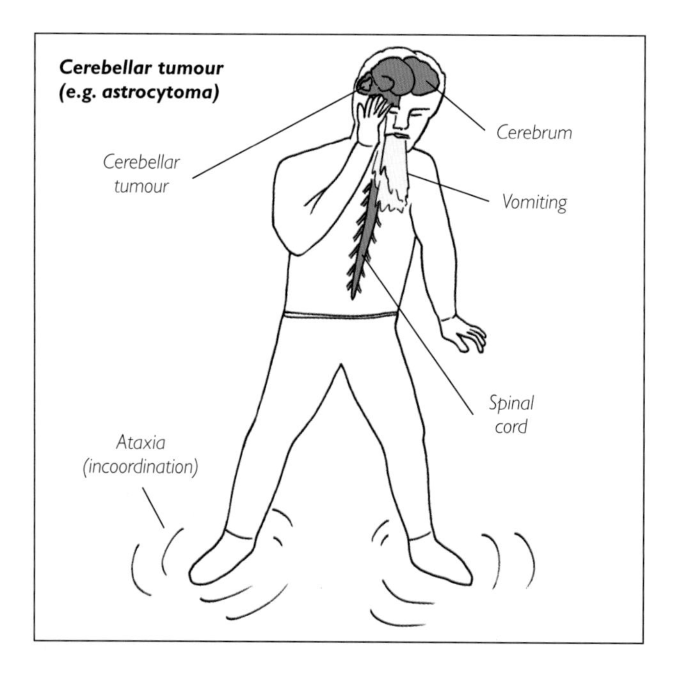

There are various ways of categorising brain tumours, e.g. benign or malignant, primary (begins within the brain) or secondary (metastases from elsewhere). An example is shown here of a brain tumour within the posterior brain compartment, within the cerebellum. Examples, especially in childhood, are medulloblastoma or astrocytoma. Brainstem gliomas are also an example within the brainstem. Symptoms are typically due to nerve tissue compression (i.e. paralysis) and raised intracranial pressure (i.e. headaches, vomiting and blurred vision). Ataxia and incoordination occur from disruption of the cerebellar-spinal nerve pathways.

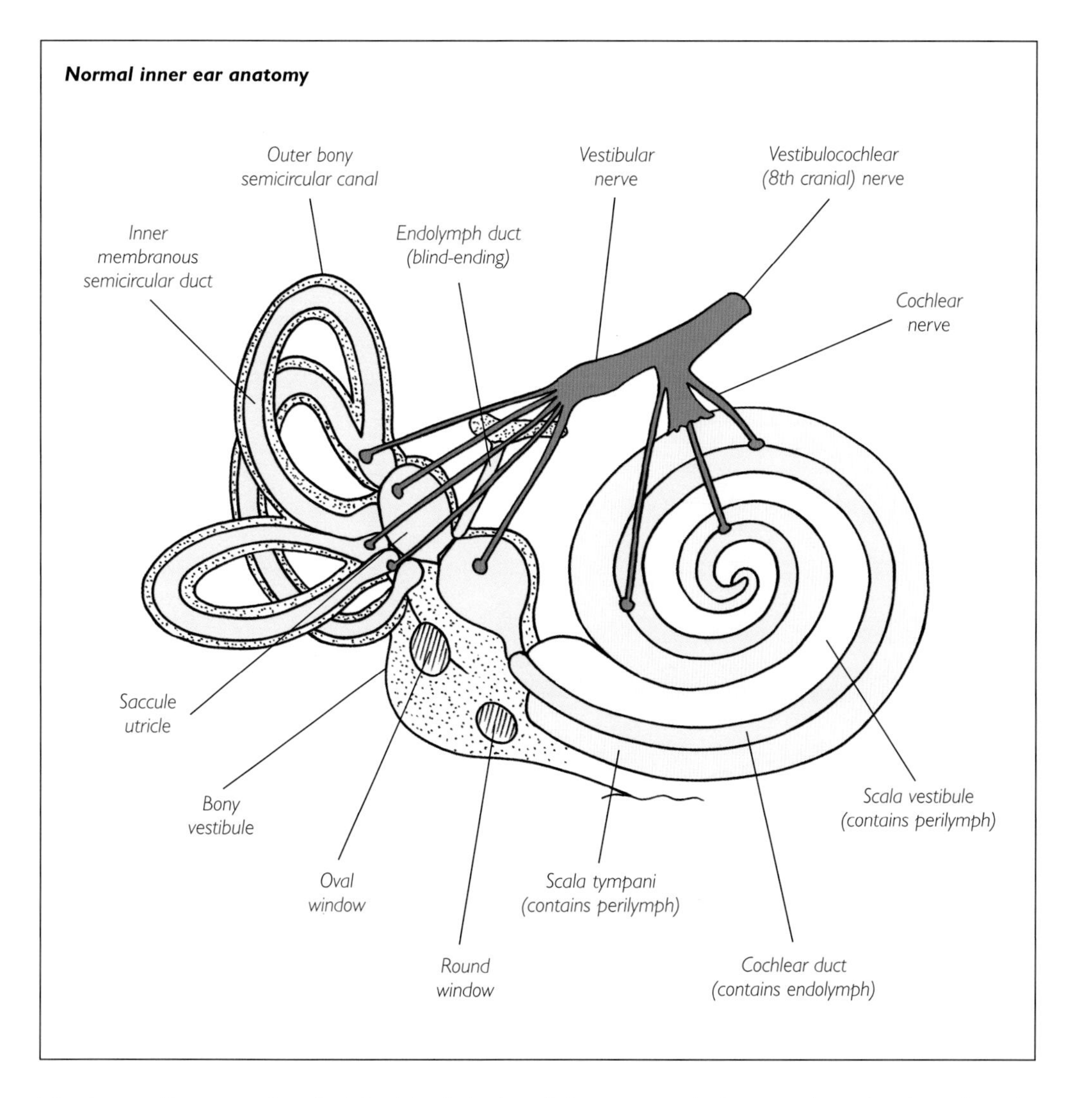

The internal/inner ear is called the labyrinth since it is composed of a complicated series of canals. There is an outer bony labyrinth that encloses an inner membranous labyrinth. The bony labyrinth is divided into the semicircular canals, the vestibule, and the cochlea. The first two deal with equilibrium and balance sense; the last structure deals with hearing. The bony labyrinth is filled with a fluid called perilymph, which is chemically similar to cerebrospinal fluid, and thereby surrounds the membranous labyrinth. The two membranous labyrinth is lined with epithelium and follows the same form as the bony labyrinth; it contains a fluid called endolymph – which is chemically similar to intracellular fluid. The three semicircular canals are arranged at right angles to each other. Along with the vestibule, they can sense resting and dynamic equilibrium or balance. The cochlea resembles a snail shell, making almost three turns around its central bony core. It is divided into three channels, separated from each other by a Y shaped partition wall. One of the channels, called the scala vestibule, ends at the oval window. The other channel, called the scala tympani, ends at the round window. The third channel is the cochlear duct or scala media. There are hair cells which function as receptors for hearing, lying on the basilar membrane, which separates the cochlear duct from the scala tympani. The vestibular nerve transmits the signals from the semicircular canals and vestibule. The cochlear nerve transmits signals from the cochlea. The two branches combine as the vestibulocochlear (8th) cranial nerve, which leaves the ear to the brain.

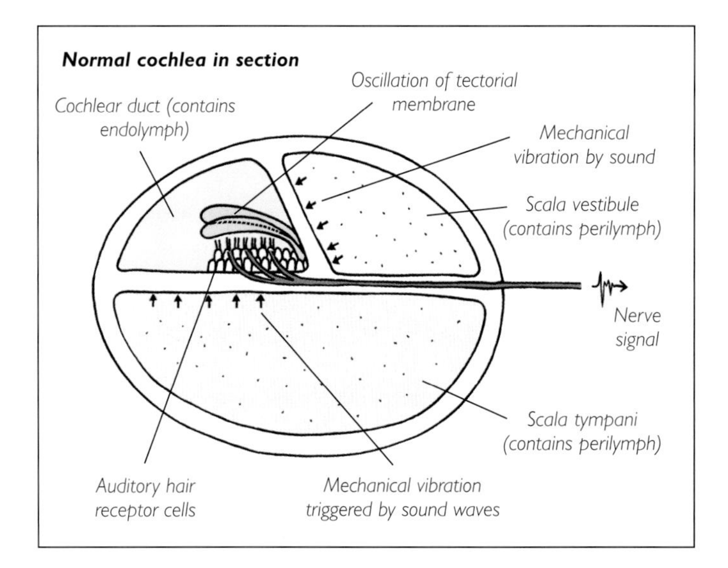

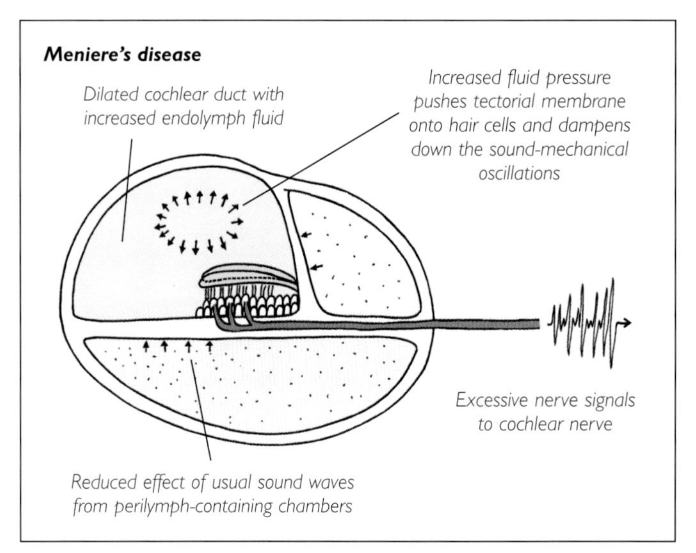

The hair cells within the cochlear duct are supported by bone and fibrous basilar membrane. It is covered by a flexible fibrous glycoprotein blanket called the tectorial membrane. This is known collectively as the organ of Corti. The tectorial membrane vibrates from the sound waves and scrapes against the receptor hair cells. This converts the mechanical energy into nervous signals, the electrical signals are conducted along the bipolar nerve cells to the cochlear part of the 8th cranial nerve.

Meniere's disease is characterised by recurrent attacks of vertigo, tinnitus and deafness. There is a dilation of the endolymph containing cochlear duct. This causes excessive stimulation of the hair receptor cells. Episodes are usually accompanied by vomiting, and can last minutes to hours. Eventually deafness can result from permanent damage to the receptor cells.

Related images

p.219 Pain assessment chart
p.574 Peripheral neuropathy
p.35 Spinal myelitis
p.18 Parkinson's disease
p.17 Alzheimer's disease
p.277 Motor neurone disease
p.586 Muscle wasting
p.232 & p.343 Multiple sclerosis
p.233-234 Epilepsy

COFFEA CRUDA

Museum

Jan Steen (1626-1679). 'The Tooth Drawer'. The Hague, Mauritshuis Netherlands © Photo Scala, Florence. The procedure is obviously painful, even to watch.

Original

'Coffea arabica and the sympathetic nervous system', by Loolie Habgood. The plant is depicted overlying the spinal cord, with the sympathetic nerve ganglia (collections of neurone cells) on each side of the cord and plant. A bunch of fruit is shown to the right. Around the brain (the cerebrospinal fluid ventricular system profiled within) are a hierarchy of angels to symbolise the higher faculties of thought and feeling.

Astrology

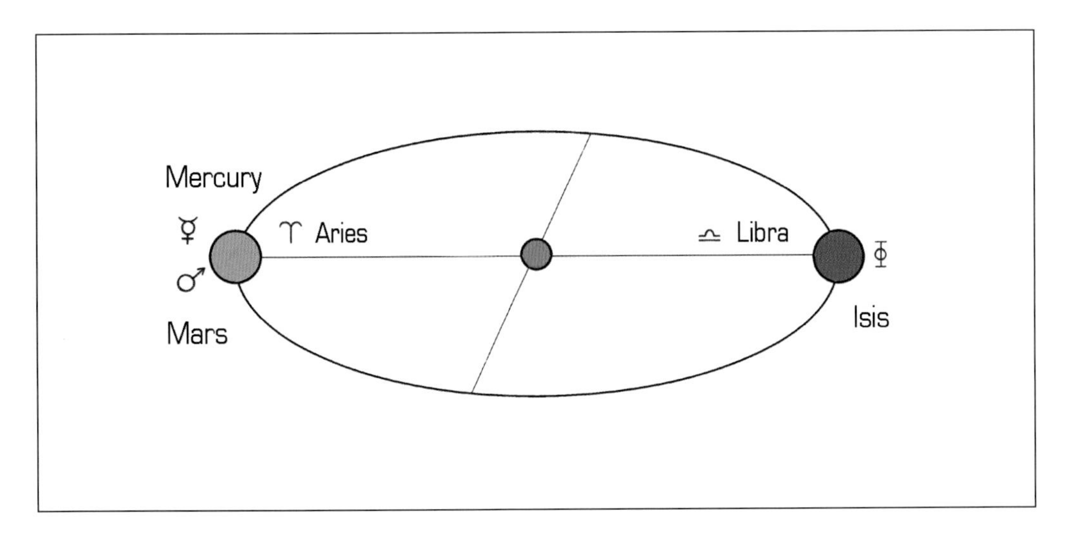

Mercury conjunct Mars within Aries, opposite Isis in Libra.

Oriental

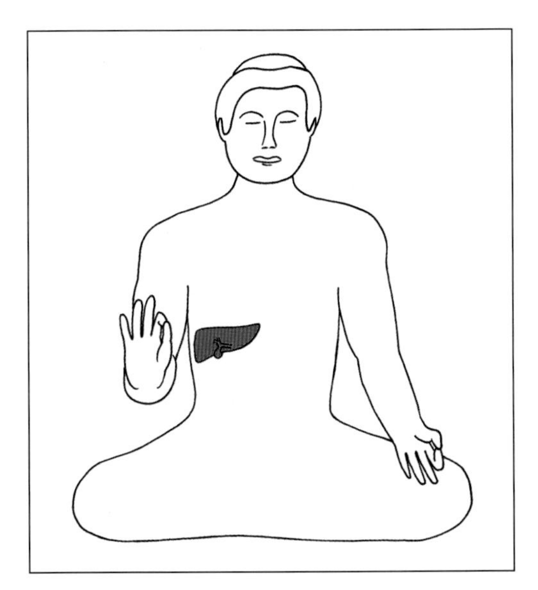

Liver heat and fire blazing.

Particulars

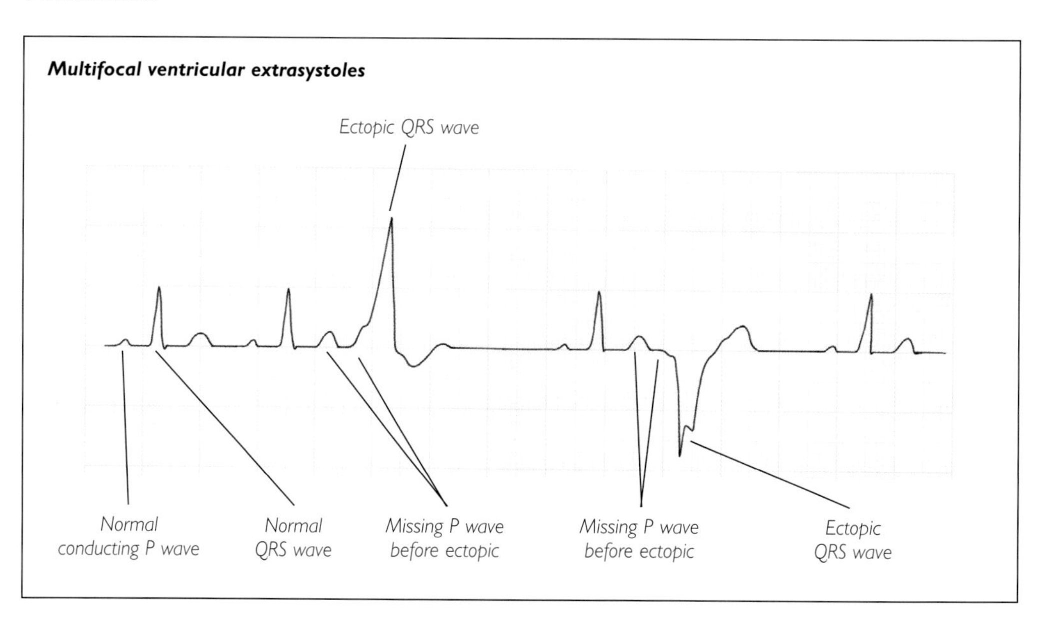

Ventricular extrasystoles or ectopic beats are extra beats within the cardiac ventricles that are out of normal rhythm. They are broad wave complexes, indicating their electrical origin is within the ventricular muscle wall, rather than the sino-atrial pacemaker or atrial muscle wall (when the ectopic would be a narrow-shaped complex wave). The two ectopic beats shown here are clearly different in shape, size and orientation, thus indicating their different origins within the ventricles. There may be no symptoms, or palpitations (sensation of extra beats, missed beats or heavy beats), or a deterioration into more serious rhythm disturbances.

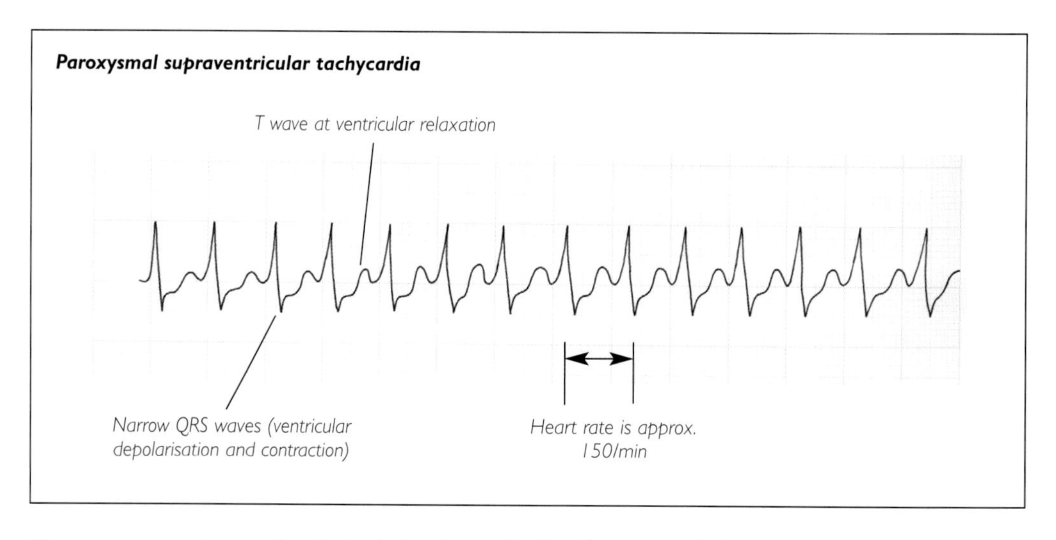

There are many types of pathological tachycardia (fast heart rates). A supraventricular type has its electrical signal originating above the heart ventricles, e.g. from the atrial walls or junctional nerve-conducting tissue. The narrow QRS waves indicate the arrhythmia is of a supraventricular nature (broad QRS waves being of a ventricular origin). The term paroxysmal indicates its intermittent nature. Symptoms may include dizziness, collapse or chest pains at the time of such episodes.

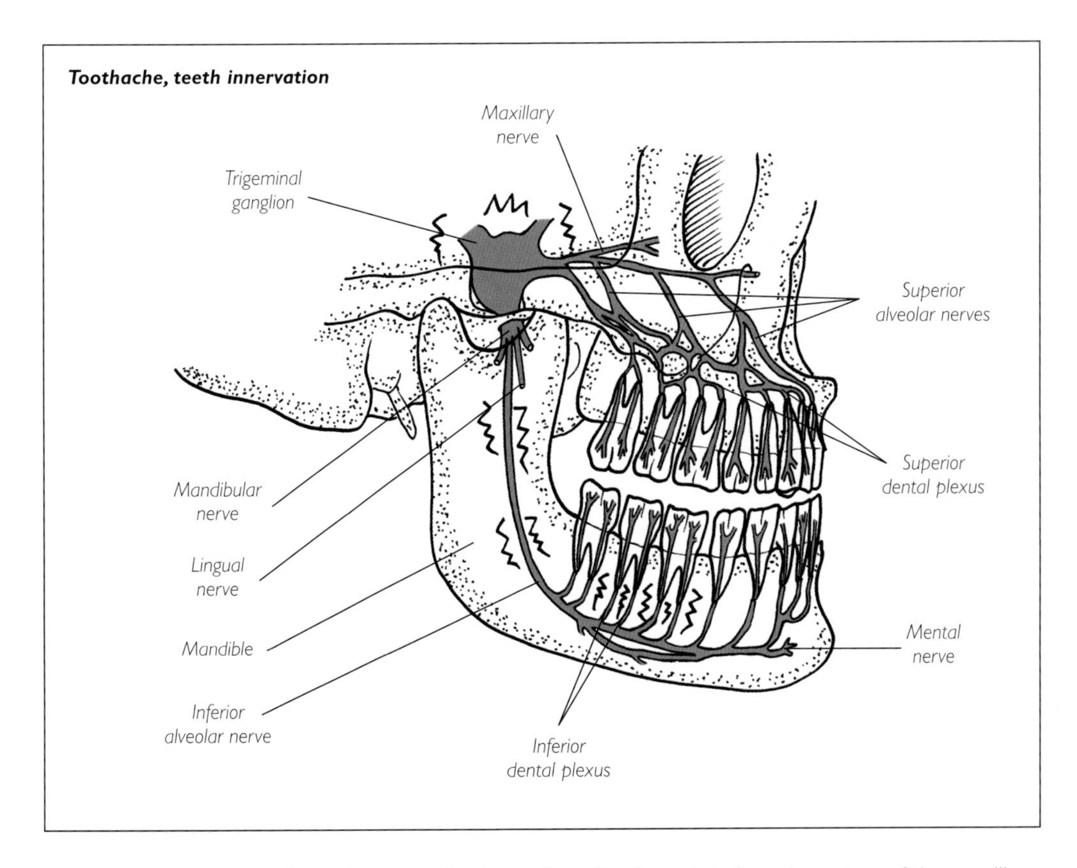

The sensory nerve supply to the upper jawbone (maxillary) teeth is from branches of the maxillary nerve, which divides into several alveolar nerve branches. The sensory supply to the lower teeth is from the inferior alveolar nerve, a branch of the mandibular nerve. All these nerves ultimately derive from the trigeminal nerve, branching from its ganglion junction point. Invasion of the pulp of a tooth by a cavity results in infection and irritation of the tissues within this pulp cavity. The swollen tissues at the pulp cause the pain of toothache. If this deteriorates then the root canal may necrose or die off under the pressure and the infection spread into the periodontal tissues around and below the teeth. Pus can track into the nasal cavity or the maxillary sinus, to cause sinusitis. Conversely, sinusitis can stimulate the nerves entering the teeth to simulate a toothache.

Related images

p.503 Teeth circulation and nervous system
p.503 Tooth abscess
p.3 Trigeminal neuralgia
p.4 Bell's palsy
p.527 Headache
p.72 Asthma

COLCHICUM AUTUMNALE

Museum

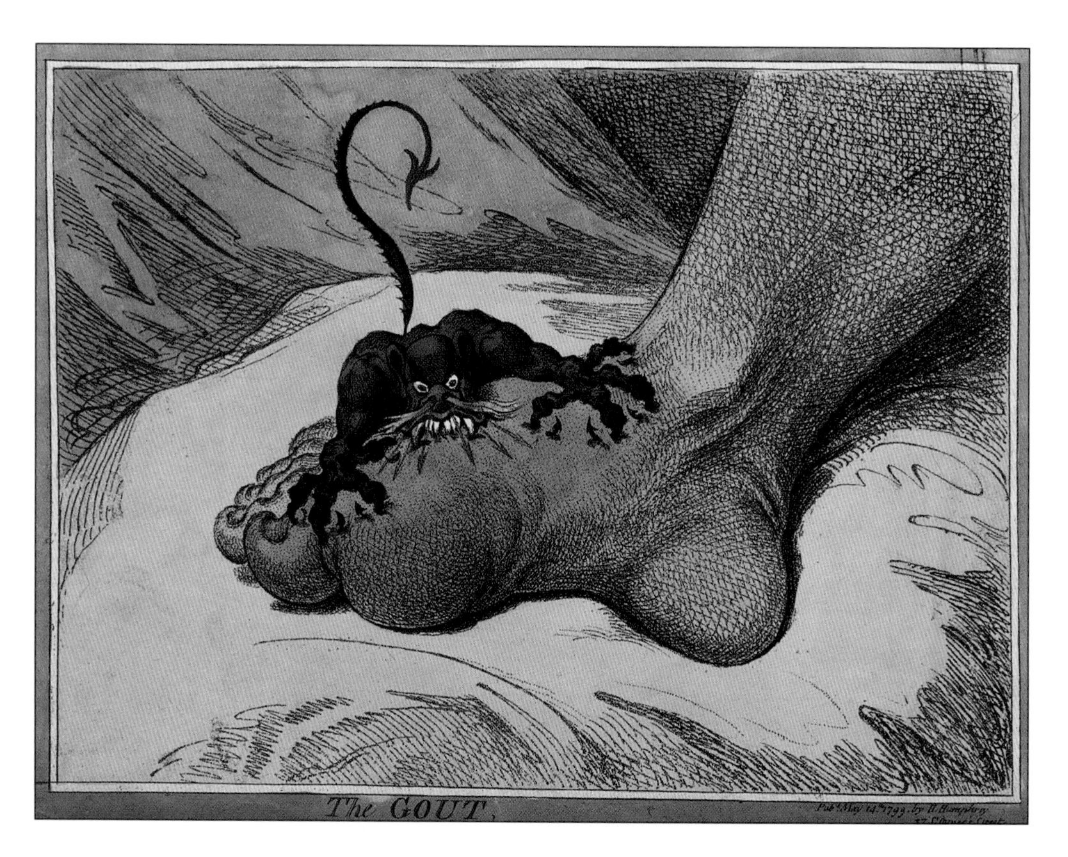

James Gillray (1757-1815), 'The Gout' © Wellcome Library, London. (1799) Soft ground etching and aquatint, with watercolour, publisher H. Humphrey. Gillray was one of the most important English caricaturists of the Romantic period. He was especially scathing of political figures. His eyesight began to seriously fail in 1806, he then developed alcoholism and depression, a physical and mental breakdown and finally lapsed into insanity 1810 (with subsequent suicidal attempts). This seems all the more ironic given the nature of many of his works, which portrayed the dangers of human weakness leading to madness. Gout mainly affects the big toe, and especially historically in drinkers of the upper social classes. Other caricaturists often depicted the sufferer surrounded by healthy young ladies, so Gillray chose to emphasise the inflamed toe in his painting. Gout is shown as a demon with a pointed tail ready to inflict more pain on the victim with its fangs.

James Gillray (1757-1815), 'Gouty King George IV', etching with watercolour (1824). © Wellcome Library, London. This is a unsympathetic portrayal of the King, renowned for his debauchery. His bloated state is evident, as he rests his gout inflamed foot on a cushion. His ruddy and besotted facial complexion suggests pain as well as a history of heavy drinking, further evidenced by the bottle on the table. His vanity is revealed by the mirror next to him, and the nine portraits behind him chronicle his past extravagant styles of dress. Meanwhile he studies the diversions of Purley for entertainment. The lettering states: "All the world's a stage – and one man in his time plays many parts, & c & c."

FOLLOWING PAGE. 'Colchicum autumnale and the fertile goddess', by Loolie Habgood. The blossom is shown appearing before the leafy foliage; note the lack of bracts (stalks) in the flower and the underground rhizome (swollen stem base). The sheathed fruit is shown to the right. The forces of motherhood are represented by the voluptuous fertility talismans underground, in keeping with the Greek myth of the descent of Persephone (daughter of Ceres-Demeter the goddess of crops and Earth fertility) into the underworld. Colchicum takes its name from Colchis, the area of the sorceress Medea, daughter of the king of Colchis. This kingdom on the shores of Pontus (Black Sea) was also the land where the Golden Fleece was kept in a consecrated grove and guarded by an ever-vigilant dragon. The plant was also called 'mysteria' by the Greeks and associated with the Eleusinian Mysteria (secret initiations) of the goddess, Demeter. The plant blooms in the autumn when Demeter's daughter, Persephone must leave the land of the living to spend four months with Pluto in the underworld. Medea fell in love with Jason of the Argonauts when he came to win the Golden Fleece. Having knowledge of all plants with the power of enchantment, she could communicate with nature spirits and plead favours from Pluto and Persephone. However, she also resorted to murder to gain for Jason and in the end even killed her own children when Jason told her he was going to marry someone else. Medea assisted Jason to obtain the Golden Fleece, betraying her family and possibly even killing her brother in the process. She then fled with Jason as his wife.

Original

Astrology

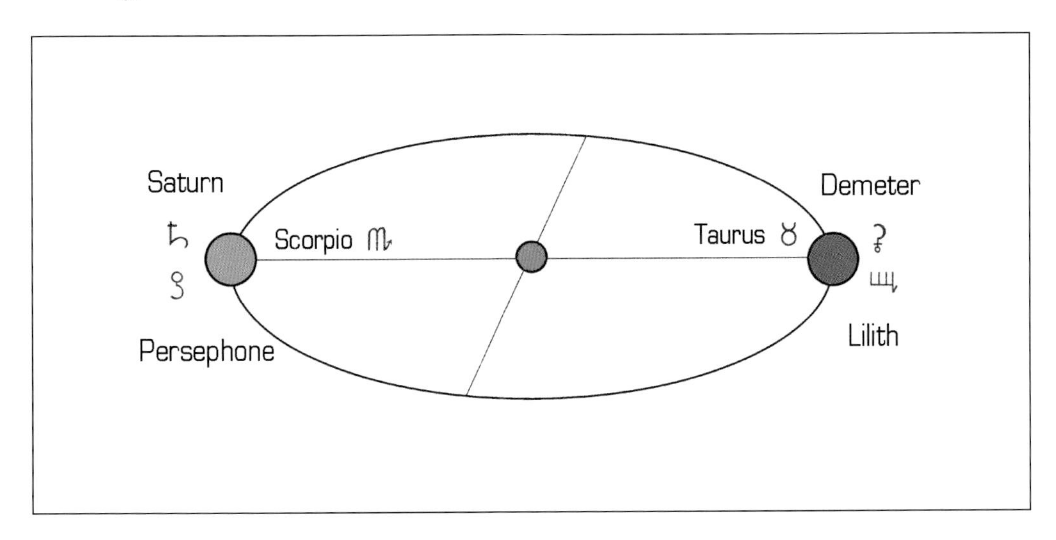

Saturn conjunct Persephone within Scorpio, opposite Demeter conjunct Lilith within Taurus.

Oriental

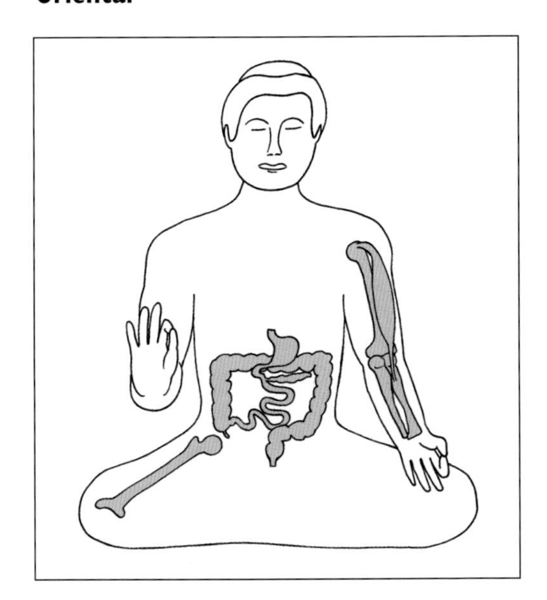

Cold invasion and cold lodged within stomach and intestines, with cold painful obstruction syndrome of bones, joints and muscles.

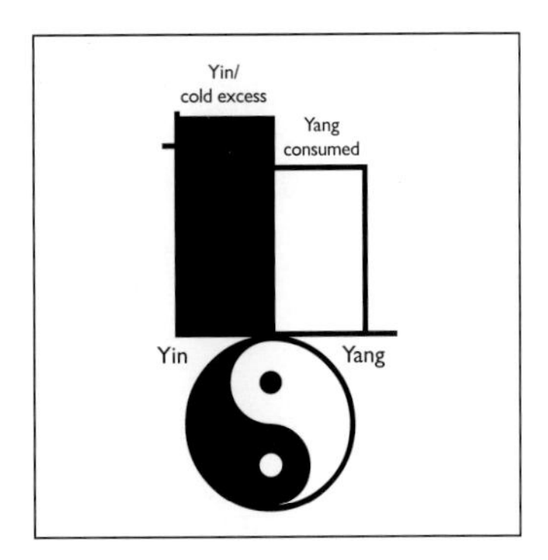

Particulars

Microscopy of synovial fluid

Synovial fluid can be aspirated by syringe and needle for various investigations, e.g. microbiological culture for any infections within the joint, and microscopy for various deposits or inclusions. Lymphocytes and other white cell types will indicate various inflammations. Cartilage fragments may be visible in osteoarthritis. In this image the crystals of gout and pseudogout are shown, both types of crystal-induced arthritis where crystal debris collects within the joint cavity. Polarised light microscopy is used in this investigation, whereby the crystals exhibit different colours depending on their orientation to the light.

Gout x-ray of foot

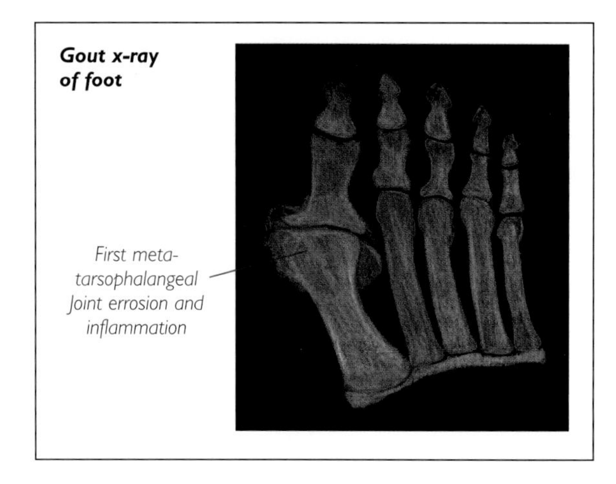

Gout is a disturbance of purine metabolism (which is produced from the recycling of DNA) where uric acid concentrates in the blood and body tissues. Arthritis occurs from the deposition of urate crystals in the joint. This triggers a severe inflammation in the joint and erosion of articular cartilage. The most frequent joint involved is the first metatarsophalangeal joint of the big toe, which becomes very swollen, red, hot, tender and painful. This x-ray shows marked destruction of the bone and cartilage with punched-out areas in the bones from urate deposits.

Related images

p.222-223 Gallstones
p.222 Fatty liver
p.223 Jaundice
p.133 Liver failure and ascites
p.347 Polymyalgia rheumatica and temporal arteritis
p.56 & p.340 Rheumatoid arthritis
p.248 & p.250 Renal failure and dialysis
p.471 Prostate hyperplasia and complications
p.730-732 Thyroid disease and goitre

COLOCYNTHIS

Original

'Colocynthis and Old Moon gestation', by Tessa Gaynn. The creeping plant is shown in its fruiting stage. It especially resonates with the Old Moon or Lemurian stage of Earth, with a large Moon close to the swampy watery ground. Lunar beings are represented by large amorphous microbe-like entities suspended within the milky soup-like atmosphere. The worm process relates to the anabolic building-up forces needed to create embryonic tissue. This embryo is at a primordial stage of humanity, showing a cyclopean single eye and a relatively undifferentiated body. Nutrition is provided direct from the planet, as shown by the orange-red coloured umbilical cord connected to it. An interesting analogy is the scarlet-worm ('Cermes vermilio', possibly referred to in the Bible as 'Tola'ath shani') which feeds on oak and is used to produce red dye. The female wingless insect stage adheres to the plant and sucks sap using a long beak. It remains motionless and when dead its body become shelter for the eggs deposited beneath it. These then metamorphose through the worm to insect stage. The dye is made from the dried bodies of the females. The Old Testament mentions the worm in the story of Jonah. After this prophet converted and saved the pagan Assyrians he left their city Ninevah in displeasure at the Lord for being lenient to non-Jewish people. Whilst sleeping, a gourd tree grew over him, its shadow protecting him from the Sun. But the next day, God allowed a worm to smote the gourd till it withered. The worm was also attributed with rock-splitting properties. King Solomon built his legendary Temple through this means, the worm known as 'schamir'. The Temple was to be constructed without any use of hammer, axe or tool of iron. The theme behind these accounts is that the Lemurian human still had a milky-white sap like blood, a plant-like vegetative consciousness and fish-like body. There was no iron in the blood. Subsequent to the Fall or descent into matter, the human body progressively hardened (i.e. stone or mineral needed internalisation) and blood became red. The worm process was required to assist these transformations.

Astrology

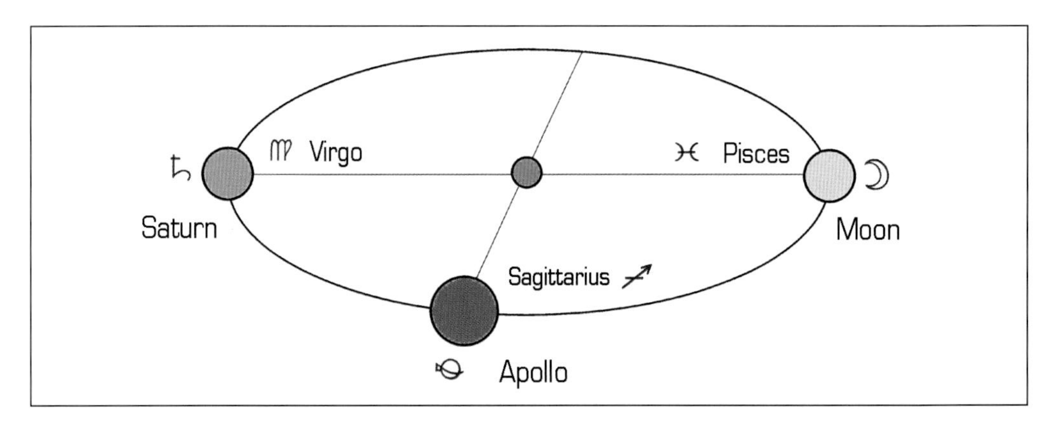

A particular pattern is the Moon in the sign Pisces, opposed by Saturn in the sign Virgo and a square to each by Apollo in Sagittarius.

Oriental

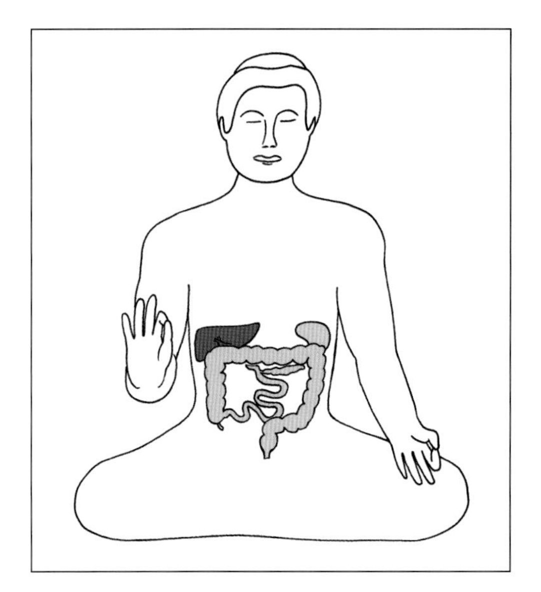

Liver chi stagnation/constraint with rebellious chi of intestines and spleen.

Related images

p.485 Irritable bowel syndrome and hyper-peristalsis
p.222-223 Gallstones and biliary colic
p.582 Infectious gastroenteritis
p.10 Sciatica
p.3 Trigeminal neuralgia

CONIUM MACULATUM

Museum

Charles Alphonse Dufresnoy (1611-1658). 'Death of Socrates' Galleria Palatina, Florence © 1990, Photo Scala, Florence – courtesy of the Ministero Beni e Att. Culturali. In 399 BCE, three citizens of Athens brought legal proceedings against Socrates, accusing him of denying the city's gods, introducing a new religious belief system and corrupting the young men of Athens. The prosecutors demanded the death penalty. Although Socrates could have saved his life by renouncing his own philosophy, he refused to do so, defiantly telling the jury: "So long as I draw breath and have my faculties, I shall never stop practicing philosophy and exhorting you and elucidating the truth for everyone that I meet… And so gentlemen… whether you acquit me or not, you know that I am not going to alter my conduct, not even if I have to die a hundred deaths". Hence he was condemned and made to die through drinking the poison hemlock. The painting shows Socrates sitting in his Athenian jail, surrounded by concerned and lamenting friends. He is about to swallow the poison, yet appears calm and defiant to the last. The story and the painting depict the power of holding true to your philosophy, a word that means philo (love), sophia (wisdom). It is not a hot-headed or bullish courage that Socrates demonstrates, but that borne from the nature of transcendence and mastery.

FOLLOWING PAGE. 'Conium maculatum and release of souls caught in purgatory', by Loolie Habgood. The astral air-related energy is shown flowing around and through the plant as indicated by the streams of air. This air flow reaches souls trapped in an underworld region below, suffering purgatory and punishment. A black crescent Moon is shown to the left of the plant, and a black Sun on its right – both coloured in this way to symbolise the karmic nature of these souls' journeys. Meanwhile Guardian Angels hover to each side, ready to assist those souls desirous of stepping off the wheel of karmic rebirth. Other souls are suspended within the clouds above, in their stages between incarnations as they transit the astral plane (4th dimension).

Original

Astrology

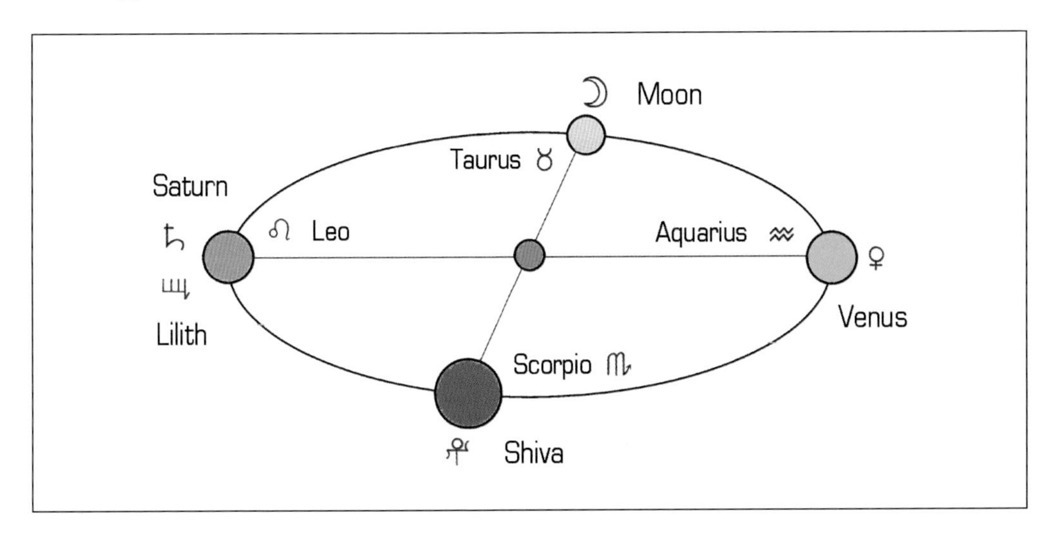

Grand cross, Saturn conjunct Lilith within Leo opposite Venus in Aquarius, and Moon in Taurus opposite Shiva in Scorpio.

Oriental

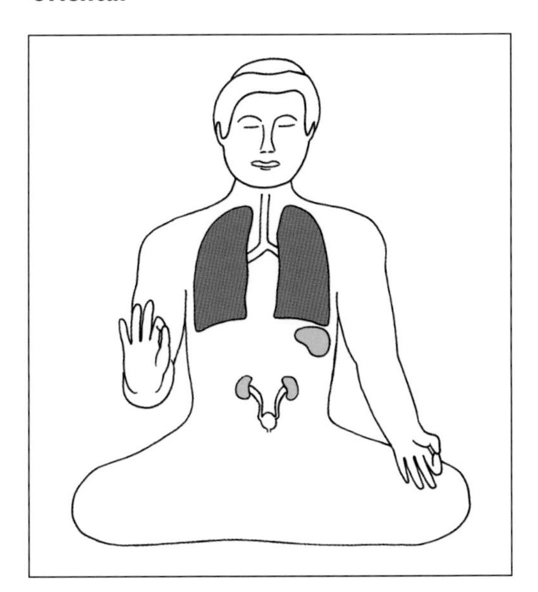

Kidney and spleen yang deficiency, with lung chi deficiency.

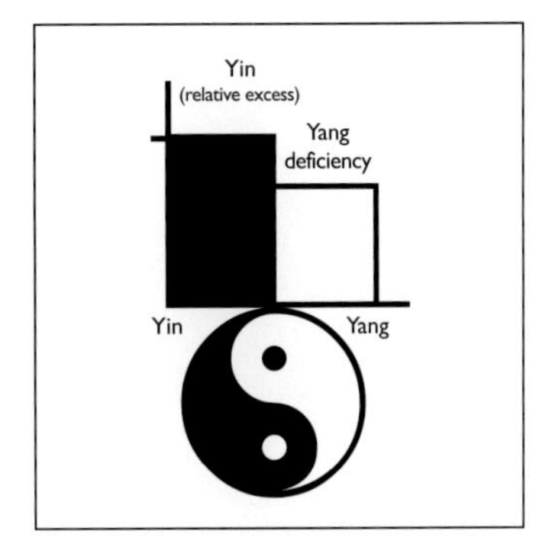

Particulars

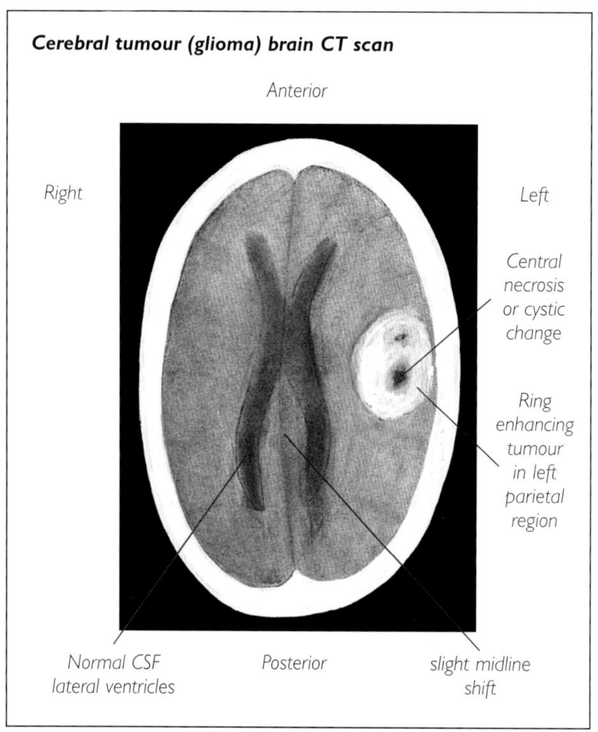

Cerebral tumour (glioma) brain CT scan

Gliomas are the most common type of primary tumour of the brain. They originate from the supporting cells of the brain rather than the neurones themselves. There are several subtypes of gliomas, depending on the actual cell type of origin, e.g. astrocytoma, oliodendroglioma, ependymoma and so on. The clinical features depend on the size, location and growth rate of the tumour, e.g. to cause focal stroke-like effects of paralysis or fits, or raised intracranial pressure with headaches. Typical CT scan appearances are a mass with a thick ring enhancement of contrast medium (i.e. the radioactivity labelled marker is selectively taken up by the rim of the tumour) with translucent (dark coloured)) central areas of cyst or necrosis. Despite being large it usually has only a small mass effect (i.e. not much midline shift within the brain).

Cerebral cancer, secondary metastases, brain CT scan

Anterior

Right

Left

Ring-enhancing mass in left temporal-parietal region

Ring-enhancing mass within inner capsule basal region

Ring enhancing mass at occipital region

Posterior

Odema surrounding the tumour

Metastatic cancer with spread to the brain is a severe stage of the disease. The symptoms depend on the location of the tumour, but usually include headaches, and frequently also fits, hemiparesis and mental changes. A CT scan is performed with the injection of intravenous contrast medium, and will reveal cancer deposits from 1cm in diameter in size. The lesions are variably sized and ring-enhancing with the contrast selectively taken up by the rim of the lesions, and central necrosis (dark centres). Mass effect also leads to extensive odema around the metastasis (as dark regions of the brain around the mass). It can also lead to hydrocephalus and obstruction to CSF flow – which leads to dilated CSF ventricles.

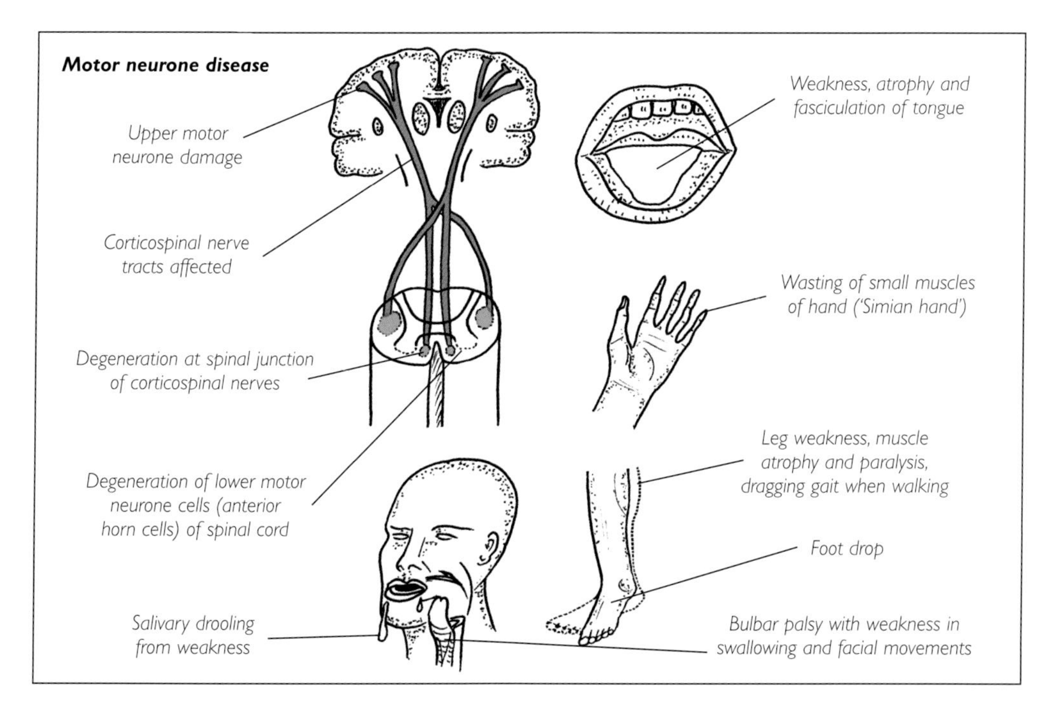

Motor neurone disease (primary) affects the motor neurone cells of the spinal cord, brainstem and cerebral cortex. There is progressive muscular atrophy with usually asymmetrical lower motor neurone disease. Bulbar palsy affecting the brainstem causes weakness of the tongue, soft palate and larynx. There is degeneration of the corticospinal and/or corticobulbar tract (the cerebral motor cortex to brainstem nerve fibres).

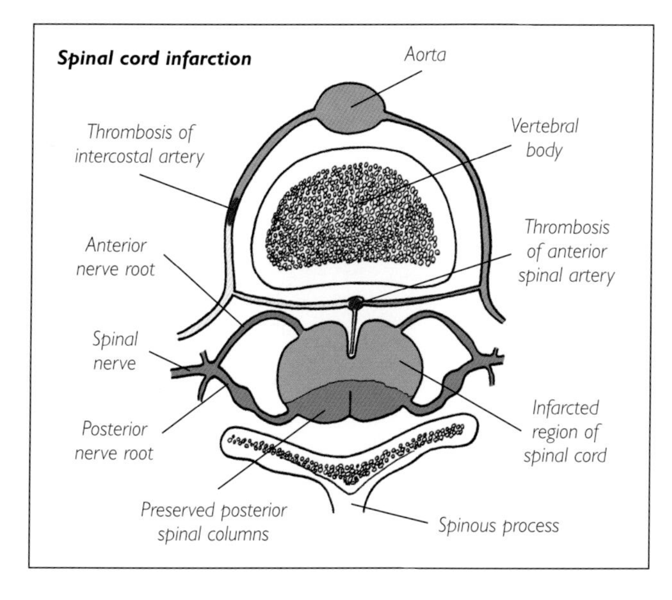

Infarction of the spinal cord is a cause of acute spinal cord syndrome. There is obstruction of the arterial flow to part or whole of the spinal cord at the level of the damage. Occlusion of the anterior part of the spinal artery damages the anterior (front) two-thirds of the spinal cord. This can be caused by obstruction at the aorta by e.g. dissecting aneurysm or aortic clamping during heart surgery. Thrombosis may have developed in the various arterial branches, e.g. one of the intercostal arteries and the anterior spinal artery branches – as shown in this example. There is loss of the anterolateral spinal cord (coloured brown for this image). This includes loss of motor function (lateral corticospinal tracts and anterior motor cells), loss of pain and temperature sense (spinothalamic tracts) – but preservation of the position and vibration sensation (i.e. posterior columns not affected). These occur at and below the level of damage, often along with back pain at that level.

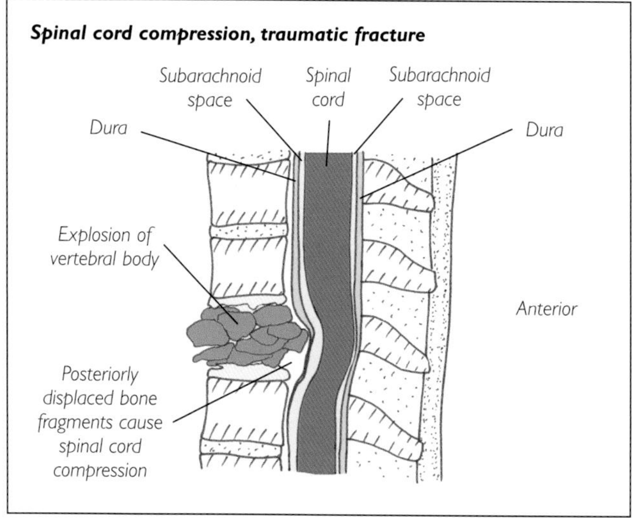

Spinal cord injuries are common, especially in motor vehicle accidents, also missile/knife wounds, athletic injuries, birth injuries, diving etc. Injuries can be based on sudden flexion, hyperextension, rotation or compression of the vertebral column. Severe trauma can cause explosion of a vertebral body. Here some displaced bone and disc material is shown causing spinal cord compression. Neurological deficit can include severe burning pains in the body regions supplied by the damaged nerve roots, and acute loss of sensation and/or motor function.

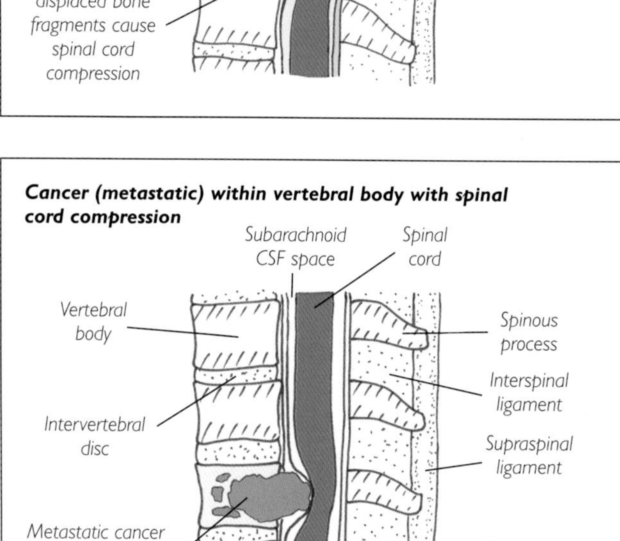

Metastatic cancer is the most common cause of an acute spinal cord syndrome of paresis or paralysis, especially in middle and elderly patients. Most will already have a known diagnosed primary tumour, but a spinal presentation may be the first indication of their malignancy. There may be acute onset back pain with numbness and weakness of the legs, followed rapidly by change of bladder control (e.g. urinary urgency or retention) and paralysis of the body below the lesion.

Related images

p.35 Spinal myelitis
p.364 Syringomyelia
p.658 Spina bifida
p.206-210 Cancer and malignancy
p.474 Sperm morphology
p.474 Vasectomy
p.470 Prostate benign hyperplasia
p.471 Prostate cancer
p.258 Labyrinthitis

CRATAEGUS OXYACANTHA

Original

'Crataegus oxyacantha and the Transfiguration of Christ', by Loolie Habgood. The tree is shown against a backdrop of the Divine or Cosmic Heart of God. Twigs at the flowering and the fruiting stage are to the right. In western culture, the plant is sacred to Jesus Christ. The entombment of Christ is shown below, during which He entered a limbo period within the underworld of humanity – so as to free those souls caught in purgatory. The Resurrection, Transfiguration and Ascension of Christ are then revealed above, with golden rays streaming from His heart centre.

Astrology

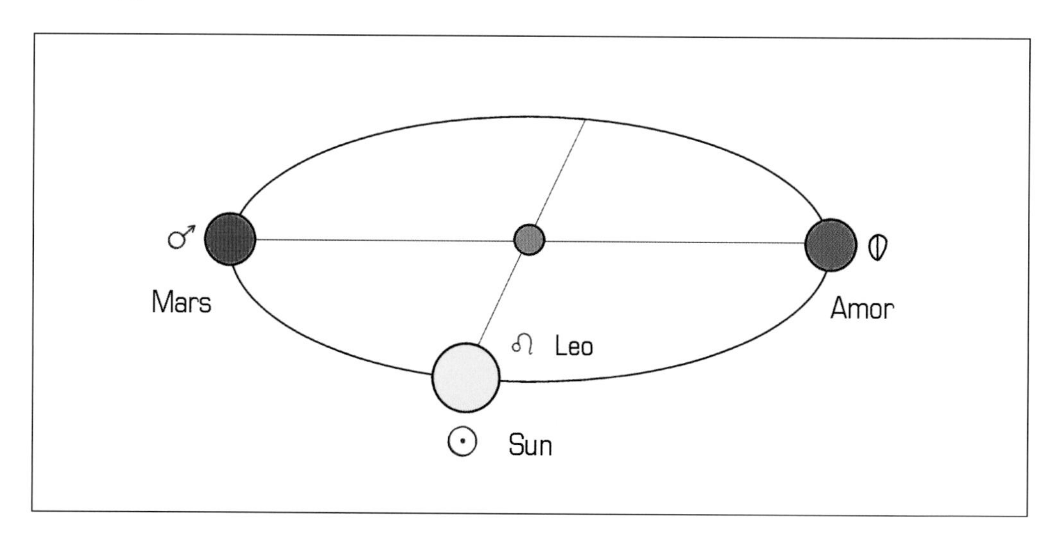

Mars opposite Amor, squared by Sun.

Oriental

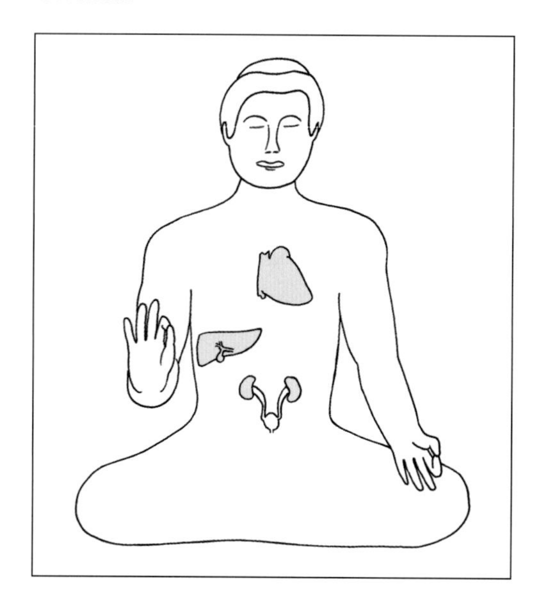

Heart yin/blood deficiency with liver & kidney yin deficiency.

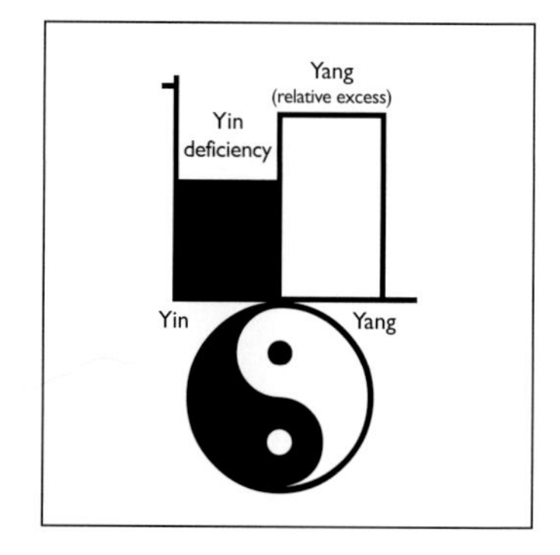

Particulars

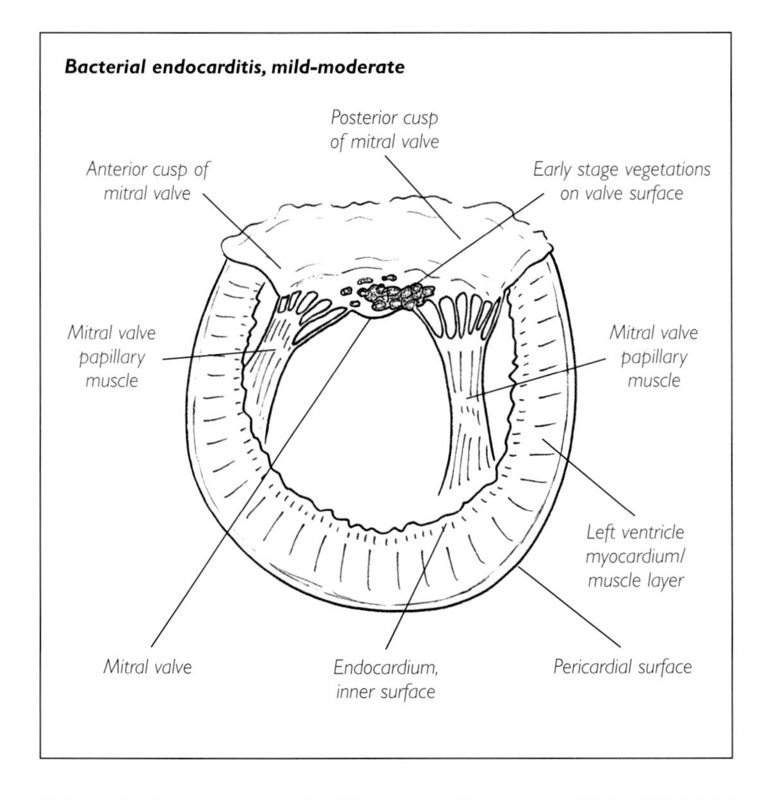

Bacterial endocarditis is a bacterial infection of the heart endocardium (the inner lining). It particularly affects the valves, the most common sites being the mitral and/or aortic valves. Any previous rheumatic fever increases the risk of this infection. There is fibrous thickening of the valve cusps along the line of its closure. Vegetations are also deposited on the valve cusps, composed of fibrin clot, platelets, culture growths of live bacteria and granulation tissue (repair tissue). These vegetations can range from early stage barely visible flat plaques to large verruca-like masses. An early stage is shown here.

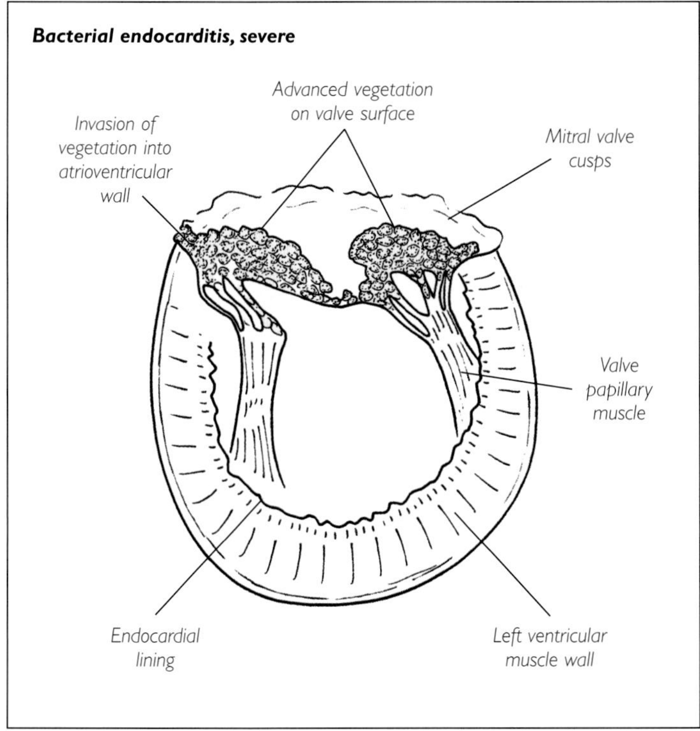

In advanced bacterial endocarditis there is greater spread of the vegetations on the valve affected, and then onto other valves and into the cardiac muscle wall. The valve/s become more damaged with perforation of the cusps, incompetence of closure and regurgitation of the bloodstream on attempted valve closure. Mitral valve regurgitation would then lead to progressive left ventricular heart strain. Fragments of the vegetations may detach to embolise or obstruct arteries downstream, e.g. to cause a stroke, kidney infarcts, spleen damage, retinal infarcts etc.

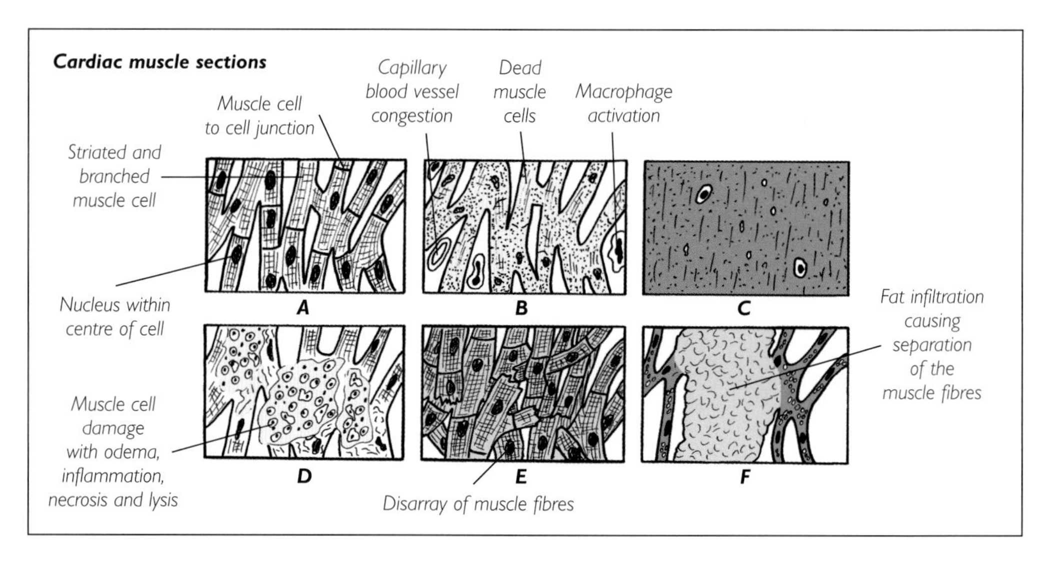

Various histological sections of cardiac muscle are shown.

A – Normal cardiac muscle cells. These are striated and interconnected, such that electrical depolarisation is easily transmitted throughout the muscle tissue.

B – Acute myocardial infarction after 24 hours, up to 3 days. Dead muscle cells are losing their striations and nuclei; there is breakdown of cell junctions. Neutrophils and macrophage white cell infiltration occurs to scavenge dead tissue with capillary congestion as a inflammatory reaction.

C – Post-myocardial infarction, weeks to months later. There is now scar tissue with only occasional muscle cells.

D – Myocarditis, inflammation of the myocardial muscle wall by, e.g. viruses, bacteria, chemical toxins or rheumatic fever. There is muscle fibre destruction and lysis (dissolving) with odema and inflammatory cells infiltrating the tissues. The symptoms are usually dull chest pain and fever, with the risk of progressive heart failure.

E – Hypertrophic cardiomyopathy usually affects young adults and has a genetic risk factor. There is hypertrophy or enlargement of muscle cells with marked irregularity of orientation and therefore chaotic contraction. There is risk of heart failure and it can be a cause of sudden cardiac arrest and death.

F – Fatty infiltration most often affects the right ventricle and separates the muscle fibres. In severe cases there is heart failure. Smaller lipid deposits inside the cells, however, are more likely to occur in metabolic disorders and chronic anaemia.

Related images

p.300 Heart failure, right-sided
p.520 Valvular disease, aortic regurgitation & p.519 Mitral stenosis
p.443 Arteriosclerosis & p.574 Hypertension
p.561 Diabetes mellitus
p.295 Renal artery stenosis
p.475 Urine microscopy
p.470-471 Prostate hyperplasia and complications

CROTALUS HORRIDUS

Original

'Crotalus and Lachesis entwined in the Fall', by Caroline Hamilton. The snake in the act of biting is a Crotalus, whilst the snake looking upward with an open mouth is Lachesis. Both snakes are represented spiralling down an erupting volcano to indicate the descent or Fall of the fiery human Soul-Spirit into the physical realm. The imagery of two snakes is prevalent throughout world cultures and religions. The serpent and dragon are sometimes interchangeable in esoteric symbols, and the fiery nature of the dragon is suggested by the lava. Furthermore, two serpents entwined in a vertical fashion upwards (along a central staff) is part of the caduceus, a symbol of the resurrection back into the spiritual state. The snakes connected together at the neck are a theme on the 'ouroboros', which is normally a serpent eating its own tail. This symbol represents the ending leading to the beginning, the totality of evolution in a cycle, and the slaying and begetting of oneself. It reflects the processes of disintegration and reintegration amidst the chaos of the waters before the coming of light. The two serpent theme is also related to the two Trees within the Garden of Eden story: the serpent of the Tree of Life is regarded as beneficent (and concerned with Resurrection), whilst the serpent of the Tree of Knowledge was malefic and involved in the Temptation. The downward moving serpent represents the Night or Sleep of Brahman, the creator God in Indian cosmology, whilst the upward serpent is the Day or Wakeful Brahman immersed in creative manifestation.

Astrology

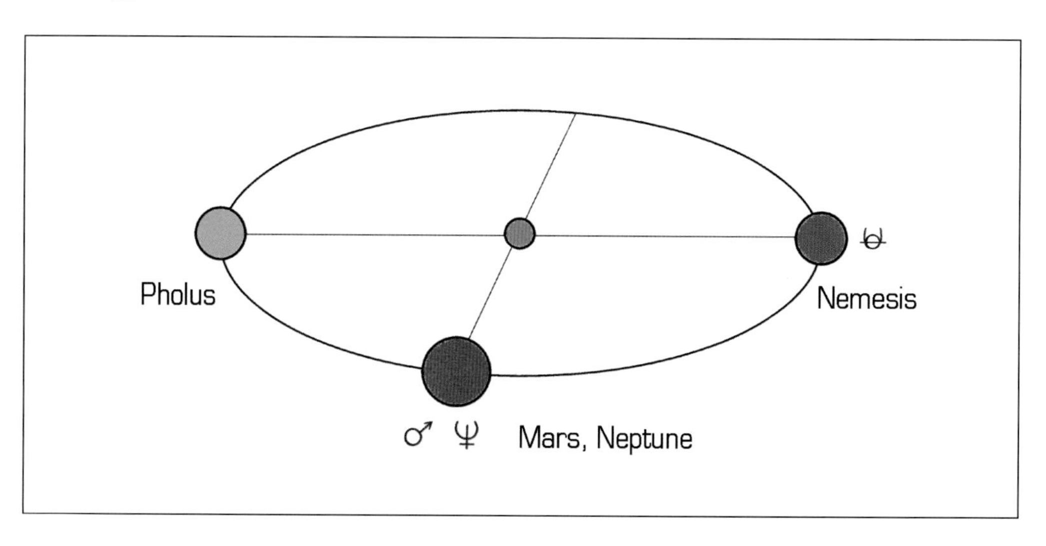

Mars conjunct Neptune, square to Nemesis opposite Pholus.

Oriental

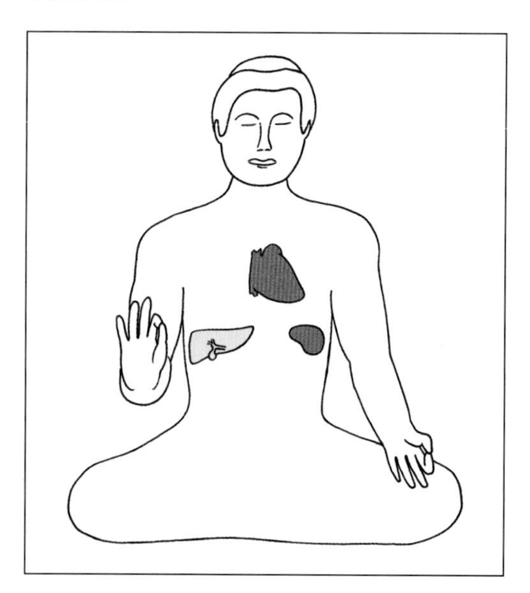

Liver blood deficiency, with spleen chi deficiency and empty-heat within the heart.

Particulars

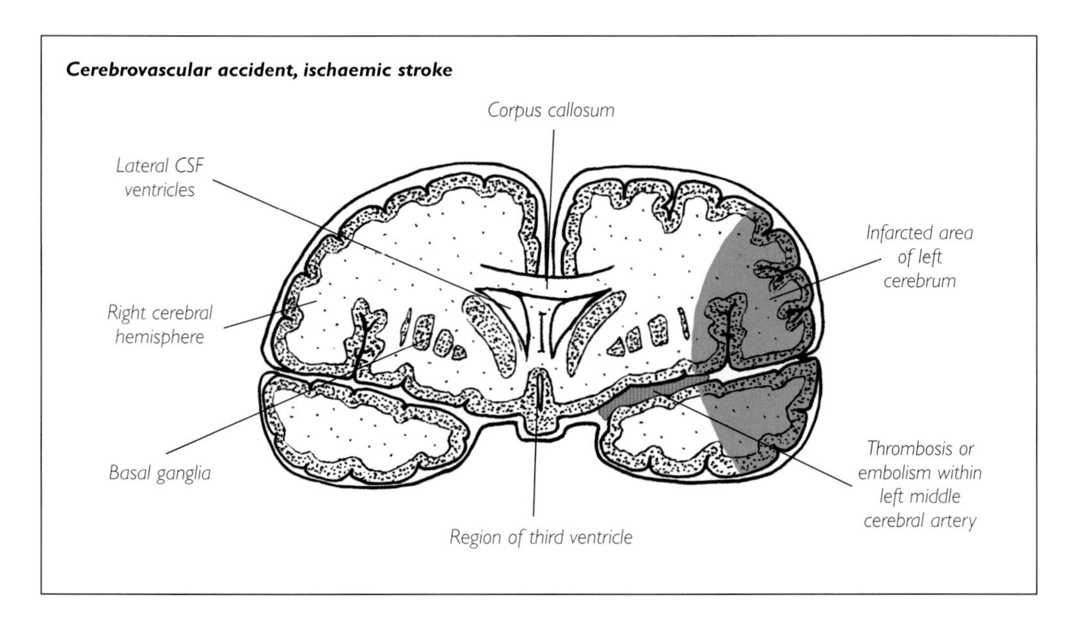

An ischaemic stroke is where inadequate blood flow leads to an area of cerebral infarction or cell death. On the other hand a haemorrhagic stroke causes damage through bleeding into the brain substance or subarachnoid space and pressure displacement of the brain. An ischaemic type can be either due to a thrombotic formation of a blood clot at the site of occlusion, or an embolic clot arising from the blood vessel proximally (e.g. from within the carotid neck arteries) or from the heart.

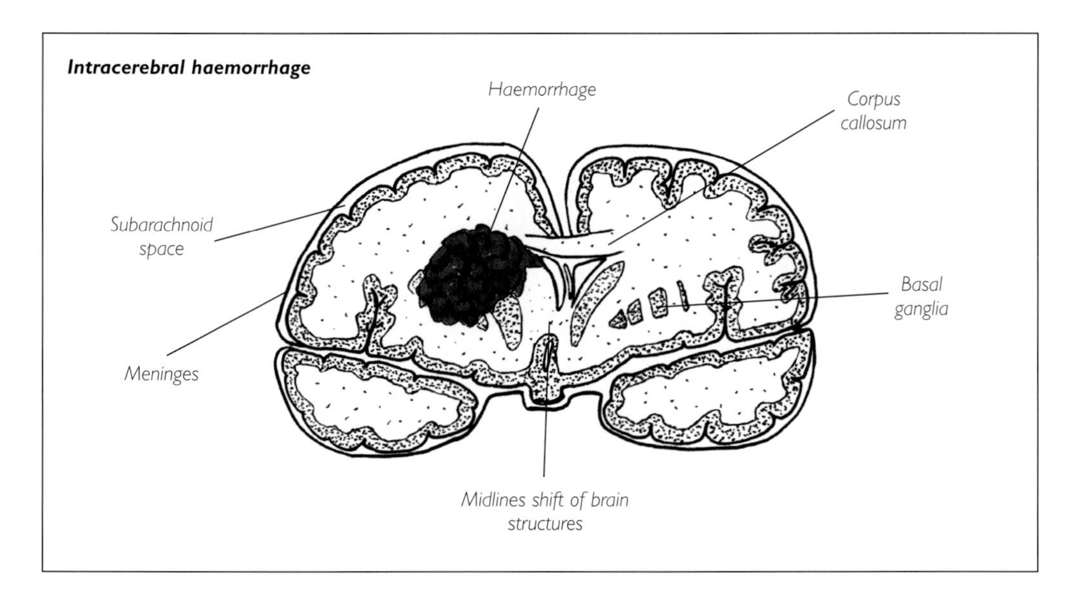

A stroke due to bleeding into the brain substance is usually caused by hypertension. If the haematoma is large then severe headache and then loss of consciousness may occur, as well as signs of acute paralysis or nerve deficit in the affected regions.

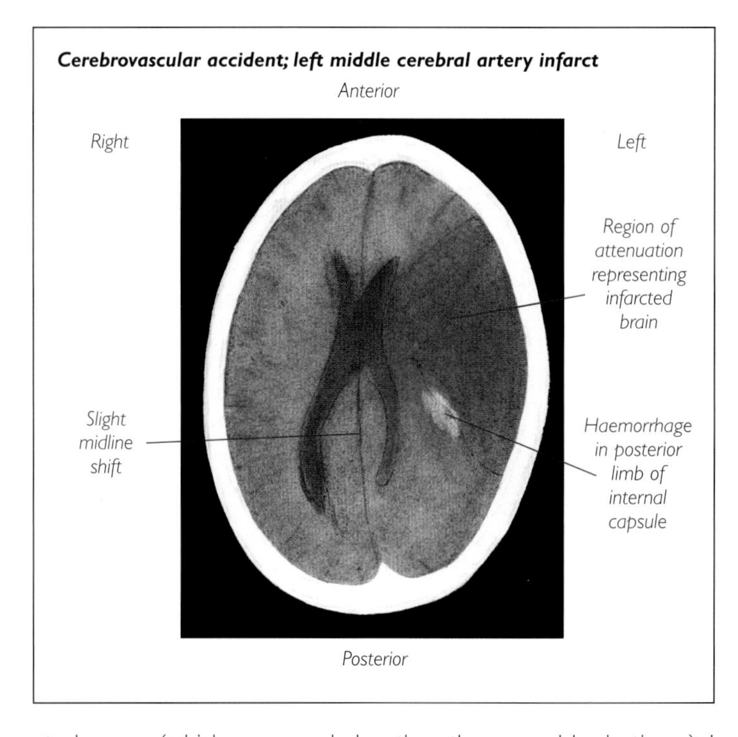

Cerebrovascular accident; left middle cerebral artery infarct

Haemorrhage can be recognised on a CT scan since blood within the subarachnoid or within the brain substance is sufficiently different in density to the normal brain tissue. Hence a stroke with haemorrhage is more readily demonstrated in the early stages by CT scan than for a non-haemorrhagic ischaemic stroke (thrombotic or embolic). A CT scan within 24 hours of this latter ischaemic stroke will show very slight loss of differentiation between the grey and white matter of the affected brain region. About 1 week after the onset there is a clear loss of attenuation in the stroke area (which appears darker than the normal brain tissue). In this example, the illustration features predominantly an infarction of the left middle cerebral artery brain territory (e.g. by thrombosis), 3 days after onset, with the loss of attenuation (darkening) in the damaged brain region. Also there is some haemorrhage in the posterior limb of the internal capsule, and slight mass effect (i.e. a midline shift towards the right from the increased tissue pressure on the left).

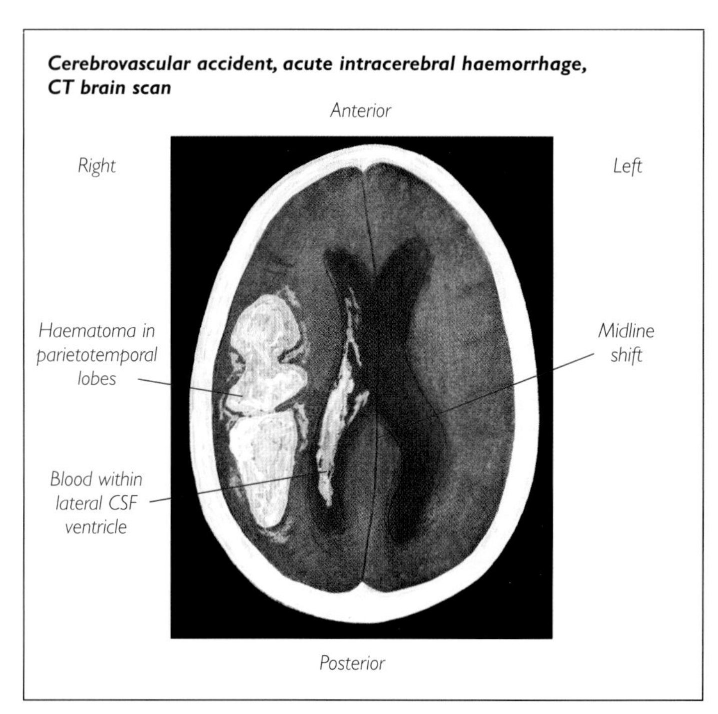

Cerebrovascular accident, acute intracerebral haemorrhage, CT brain scan

Here an example of a haemorrhage stroke is shown, where rupture or bleeding from a blood vessel has caused haematoma within the brain substance. This is the irregular large hyperdense mass in the right parieto-temporal region. Blood has also entered the ventricular system (lateral right of the ventricle). There is midline shift toward the left.

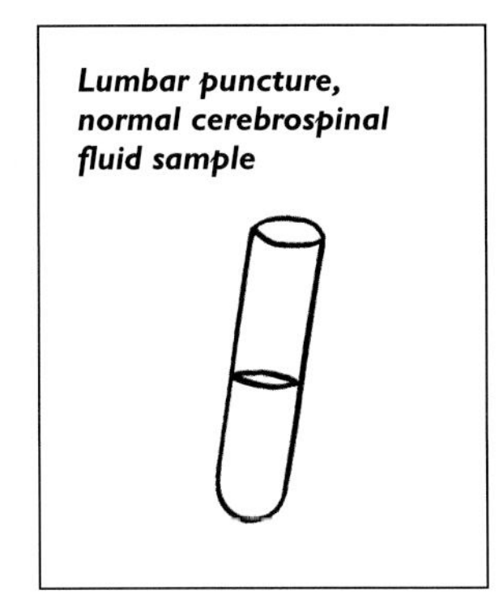

The cerebrospinal (CSF) fluid (see also Apis p. 54-55) can be tested by microscopic examination, chemical analysis, electrophoresis (to e.g. define the types of proteins and antibodies present) and culture and serology for any microbes. The normal CSF has a crystal clear, colourless appearance, a pressure reading of 60-150mm of water (when the patient is lying down), a cell count of 5 cells per mm^3 of fluid (which are mostly mononuclear cells and not polymorphonuclear white cells), a protein content of 0.2-0.4 grams per litre, a glucose concentration about one-half to two-thirds that of blood glucose and an antibody fraction (IgG class) which is less than 15% of the total CSF protein and not containing oligoclonal bands on electrophoresis (which would otherwise suggest multiple sclerosis). The CSF changes in meningitis depend on whether the cause is viral or bacterial. A bacterial infection causes a turbid or purulent (creamy coloured) appearance, with raised numbers of mononuclear white cells (e.g. 50 per mm^3) and polymorph white cells (200-300 per mm^3), raised proteins and less glucose than normal. For a bleed involving the subarachnoid CSF space (e.g. a ruptured intracranial aneurysm or a major intracerebral haemorrhagic stroke) then the CSF may initially be visibly blood-stained.

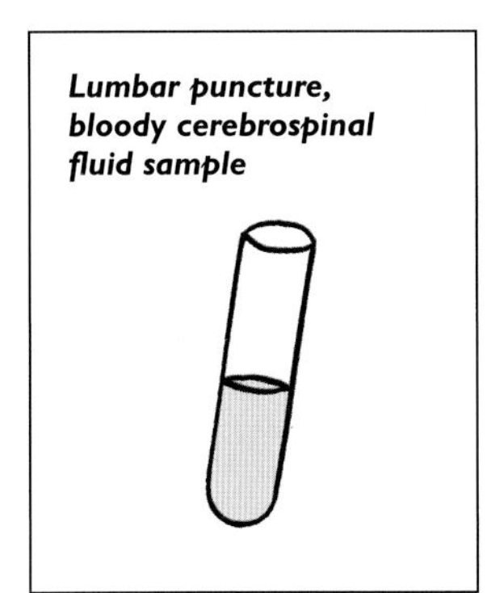

The normal CSF has a crystal clear, colourless appearance. For a bleed involving the subarachnoid CSF space (e.g. a ruptured intracranial aneurysm or a major intracerebral haemorrhagic stroke) then the CSF may initially be visibly blood-stained. Note that a traumatic tap (i.e. where the lumbar puncture needle has impinged a blood vessel en route) will also produce a bloody CSF sample, but the reddened colour progressively clears as successive samples of CSF are withdrawn, whereas a true CSF bleed will show the same redness throughout all test tube samples. The CSF becomes yellow (known as xanthochromia) several hours after the subarachnoid haemorrhage due to the destruction of the red blood cells, releasing bilirubin as the haemoglobin pigment breaks down.

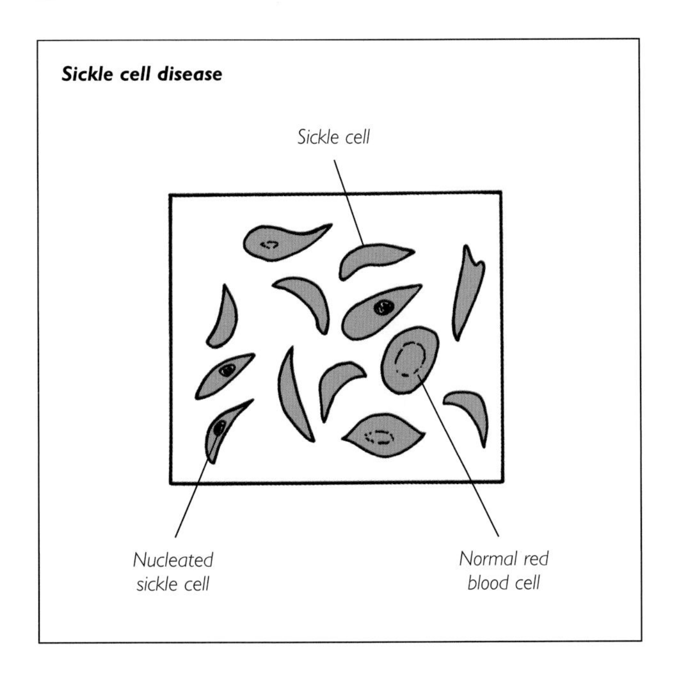

Sickle cell disease is very common in Central Africa, also occurring in the Mediterranean, Caribbean, Middle East and Indian populations, and within the black population throughout the world. It is a genetic mutation of the haemoglobin pigment within the red blood cells, causing this molecule to crystallise out when the oxygen levels falls. This leads to sickle shaped distortion of the red cells, which then easily haemolyse (rupture). The consequences are haemolytic anaemia, pigment gallstones (from the excessive haemoglobin bilirubin turnover), obstruction of the small blood vessels by the sickle cells. This last complication leads to strokes, bone damage and skin ulcers.

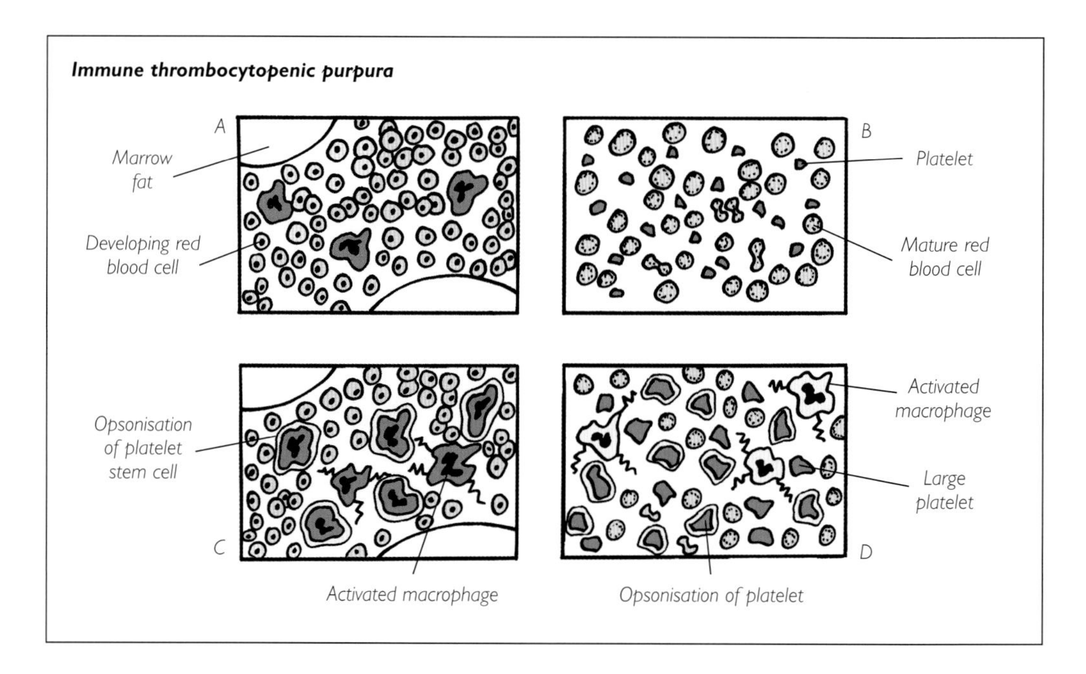

A – normal bone marrow film. B – normal peripheral blood film. C – abnormal bone marrow film. D – abnormal peripheral blood film.

Idiopathic immune thrombocytopenic purpura is a disease of platelets caused by antibodies directed against the platelets and platelet stem cells. It can occur in an acute form (often in children after a viral infection) or as a chronic disease (mostly in adults and then associated with an autoimmune collagen-vascular disease such as systemic lupus, or with a lymphoma/leukaemia). There is some degree of inhibition of the normal platelet production in the bone marrow, and the blood platelet count falls. Furthermore the platelets that are present within the blood are young, immature and large in size. Activated macrophages are also present, which attach to the platelet stem cells alongside the opsonisation or coating of immune complexes caused by antibody-antigen interactions. Symptoms can include bleeding episodes (e.g. nosebleeds, easy bruising, heavy periods) and these can be life threatening.

Related images

p.180 Gastrointestinal bleeding
p.376 Bone marrow failure
p.454 Lymphangitis
p.320-322 Retinal disease, various
p.317-318 Eye trauma
p.732 Exophthalmos, hyperthyroid eye disease
p.442 Retinal detachment
p.258 Labyrinthitis
p.260 Meniere's disease
p.193 Cancer of tongue
p.97 Tongue tie
p.444 Trachea-oesophageal fistula
p.444 Oesophageal cancer

CUPRUM METALLICUM

Museum

Sandro Filipepi, il Botticelli. 'The Birth of Venus' (1485 circa) tempera on canvas. Galleria degli Uffizi, Florence, Italy © Photo Scala, Florence – courtesy of the Ministero Beni e Att. Culturali. Most birth stories describe her mother to be a sea nymph, Dione, or otherwise Nereid, who flowed continuously throughout the world's oceans. Dione was also one of the Titans, monstrous daughter of Uranus the Sky and Gaia the Earth. Her parentage also made Venus a sibling of the Fates, who weave the contracts of karma and the Furies, who punish the guilty. The scene shows the central figure of Venus standing in a giant scallop shell surrounded by roses with golden hearts (these also came into being at the moment of her birth). She was born of the sea from the blood dripping from Uranus as he was castrated by his son Cronos. On the left are Zephir and Chloris (flying wind-spirits) with entwined limbs, moving her towards land (considered to be ancient Cyprus). The ruddy Zephir is the 'west wind' puffing vigorously, whilst fair Chloris sighs the warm breath that finally lands her ashore. On this right side is a flowering orange grove corresponding to the sacred garden of the Hesperides. Note how each white blossom is tipped with gold, the dark green leaves similarly have a golden spine and outline and the tree trunks have diagonal lines of gold. This precious metal symbolises the solar and heart forces. The nymph is one of the three 'Hours', ready to cover her with a beautiful cloak. They represented the seasons and were attendants of Venus. The lavishly embroidered garment of the Hour and the cloak are decorated with red and white daisies, yellow primroses and blue cornflowers – spring flowers in keeping with the theme of birth. Around her neck, Venus wears a garland of myrtle (which is sacred to her) and a sash of pink roses. She epitomises the ideal of beauty, even though Botticelli has painted her neck unusually long, with steep angles to the shoulders and a strange attachment of her left arm to the body. This could be some form of fascio-scapulo-humeral dystrophy, with muscle degeneration about the shoulders and the face may develop pouting lips and a transverse smile. Nonetheless, these slight deformities create a line of harmony, pose and delicacy upon the shell. They are also suggestive of the esoteric idea that the ancient Venusian civilisation was plagued by genetic deformities after mismatched and excessive genetic inbreeding. It also pre-empts the future marriage of Venus to Vulcan, the crippled god of blacksmiths. She eventually separates from this union and continues her relationship with Mars/Ares, the god of war.

Sandro Botticelli (1445-1510), 'Venus and Mars', (circa 1480) tempera on wood. © National Gallery, London. Venus was the goddess of love and beauty. She had many lovers and suitors, but was married to the lame and handicapped god Vulcan, the blacksmith god of fire. This marriage represents the capacity of Venusian genetic codes (which engage with the kidney ancestral chi) to heal genetic mutations within the race. Her true love was, however, Mars, the god of war. Their child was the beautiful goddess Harmonia. One day, whilst Venus and Mars were together they were caught in an invisible but powerful net by Vulcan, and then exposed to the ridicule and laughter of the other Olympian gods. In this painting, Venus has conquered Mars (who has fallen asleep), signifying that love conquers war, or that love conquers all. Note the comparison with the astronomical bodies: Venus has been transformed into a cloud-covered furnace by the greenhouse effect, whereas the lack of atmosphere has locked Mars into a deep icy freeze. The weapons of Mars are in the hands of the fauns and all thoughts of war have been banished from his mind. Venus is clothed in the rich garments of the upper class and rather than portraying eroticism is radiating an energy of peace. The two characters are nonetheless equally balanced and virtually mirror each other. An inverted triangle is created by their bodies, with the lance forming the base – providing a harmony despite the tight confines of the canvas. The artist's interpretation of the love scene between Mars and Venus is more reflective of the spiritual love as understood by the Platonic Academy. This thrived during his time and was influenced by the ancient ideals of Plato.

FOLLOWING PAGE. 'Cuprum and the descent of Venus-Aphrodite', by Sylvie Borel. The goddess Venus is standing in a scallop shell as she lands on Earth. She is surrounded by foam, indicating the mixing of air-related astral energy with the watery etheric. Copper beams radiate from her source planet, Venus, in the right upper corner; these contain spirals of DNA to represent the Venusian genetic blueprints seeded into humanity. Electricity is the dense material manifestation of astral energy, and is indicated by the cosmic lightning at the left upper corner and the electric current surging into the Earth grid toward the planetary core.

Original

Astrology

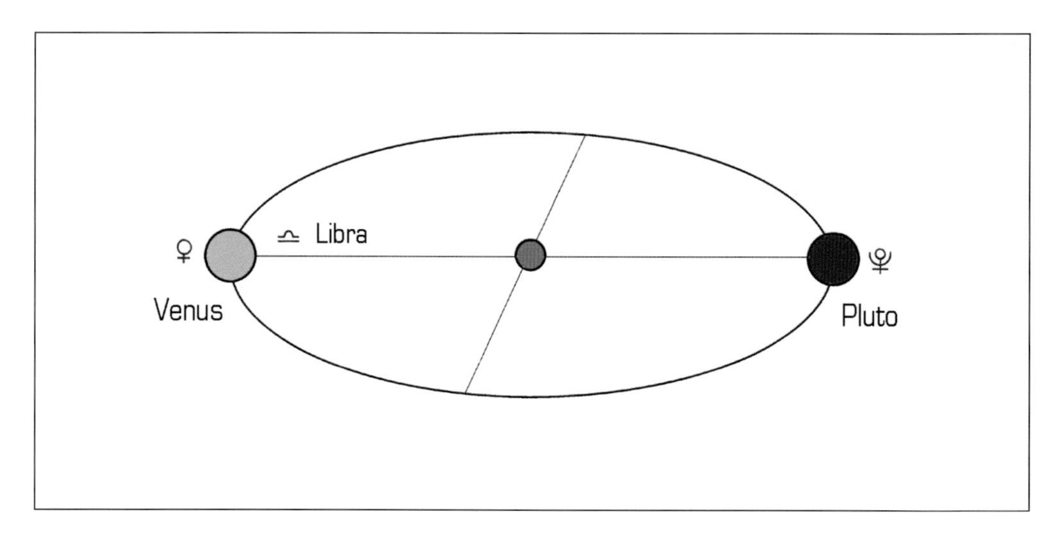

Venus in Libra opposite Pluto.

Oriental

Kidney and liver yin/blood deficiency, with interior wind invasion of brain and muscles.

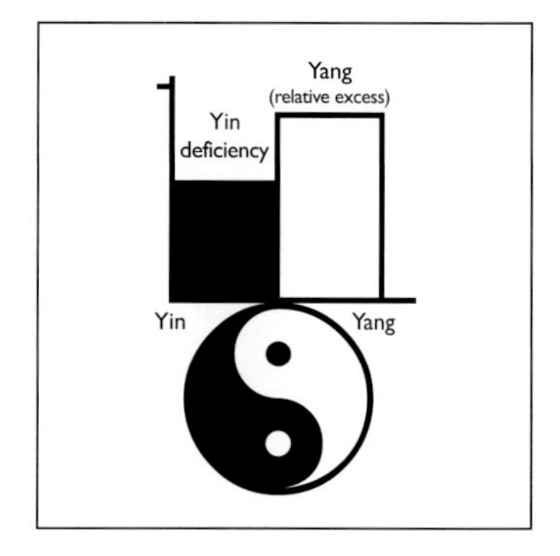

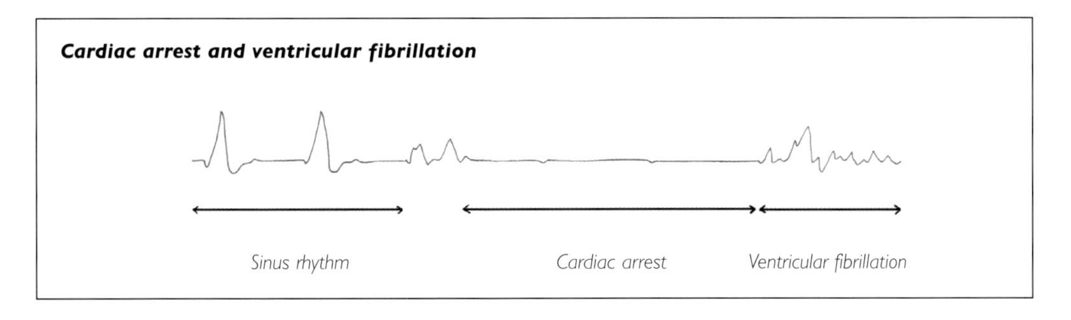

A cardiac arrest is represented here, with cessation of heart beats. This has been followed by ventricular fibrillation, which is a very rapid and irregular activation of the heart ventricles with no actual mechanical effective movement of the cardiac chambers. The patient is without a pulse and becomes unconscious. The ECG shows rapid and shapeless waves with no organisation.

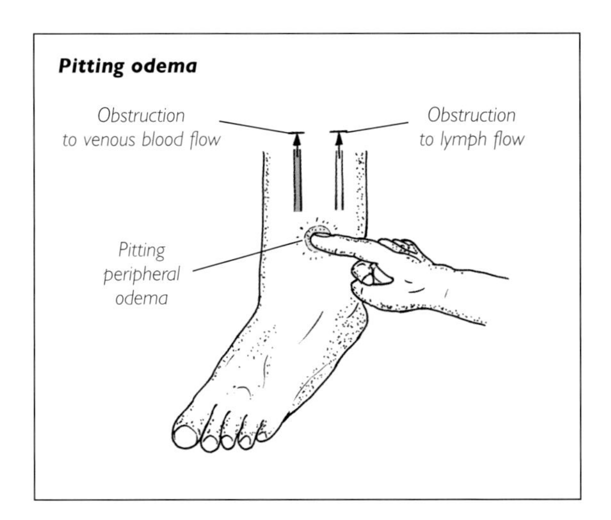

Odema is a sign of increased extra-cellular volume of fluids. It can be local or systemic. The factors influencing tissue fluid distribution include the return of blood in the veins, permeability of the capillaries, oncotic pressure (mostly due to the concentration of serum albumin protein, higher values cause more fluid retention in the blood vessel), and the degree of lymphatic drainage. Causes of odema include heart failure, reduced serum albumin levels, liver cirrhosis, sodium excess and retention in the blood (e.g. from drug side effects), lymphatic obstruction, and various kidney diseases (e.g. nephrotic syndrome).

Related images

p.82 Pacemaker ECG
p.264 Supraventricular tachycardia ECG
p.383 Ventricular tachycardia
p.383 Ventricular fibrillation
p.145 ECG myocardial ischaemia and infarct
p.451 Myocardial infarction
p.144 Coronary artery disease
p.144 & p.147 Coronary angiogram and angioplasty
p.81 Post-myocardial infarct ventricular aneurysm
p.133 Liver failure and ascites
p.321 Arteriosclerosis and hypertension in eye
p.321 Retinal artery occlusion
p.528 Migraine visual aura
p.470-471 Prostate hyperplasia and complications

DROSERA ROTUNDIFOLIA

Original

'Drosera roundifolia and the swamp of Old Moon', by Joanna Campion. The scene is an imagination of Old Moon, when the Moon was still merged with the planet. The round leaves growing from a basal collection are shown, with their sticky glandular hair projections. The ground is swampy and boggy, indicating the densest formation of the planet as a suspension of liquid and solid, rather than rocky hard ground. The atmosphere was milky, cloudy and thickly veiled. The development of the water element facilitated the creation of colour and sound ether (etheric energy carrying varying light and tone frequencies). Stars within a night sky were not visible at that period. Strange animal and plant forms are also visible, although creatures appear to blur into each other due to the lack of definite boundaries of identity or ego. Strange insect-like creatures hover above the plant. Both the animal and plant nature is thereby hybridised into its further evolution.

Astrology

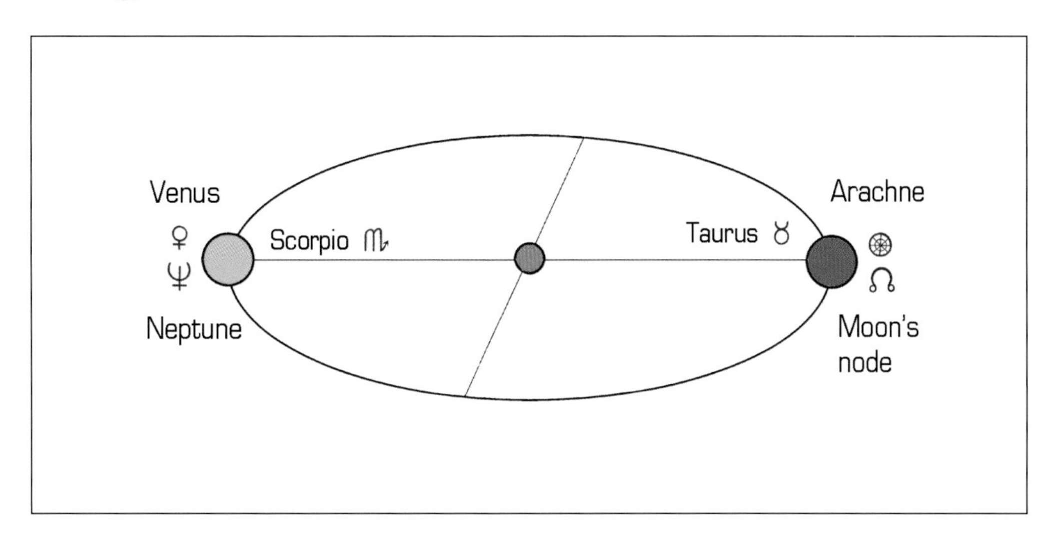

Venus conjunct Neptune within Scorpio, opposite Arachne conjunct Moon's node within Taurus.

Oriental

Spleen yang deficiency, with phlegm-damp of lungs.

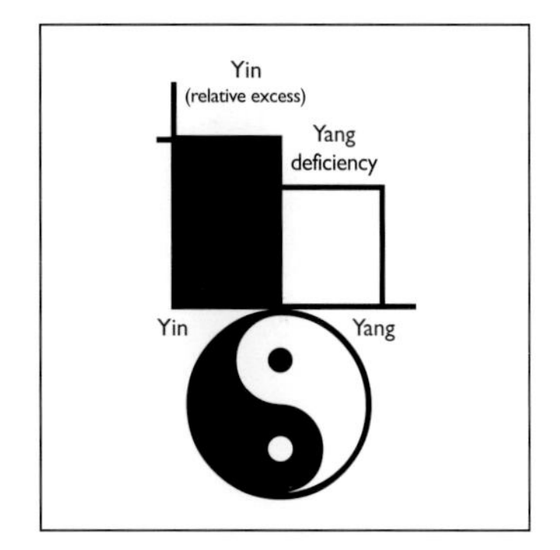

Particulars

Bronchiectasis

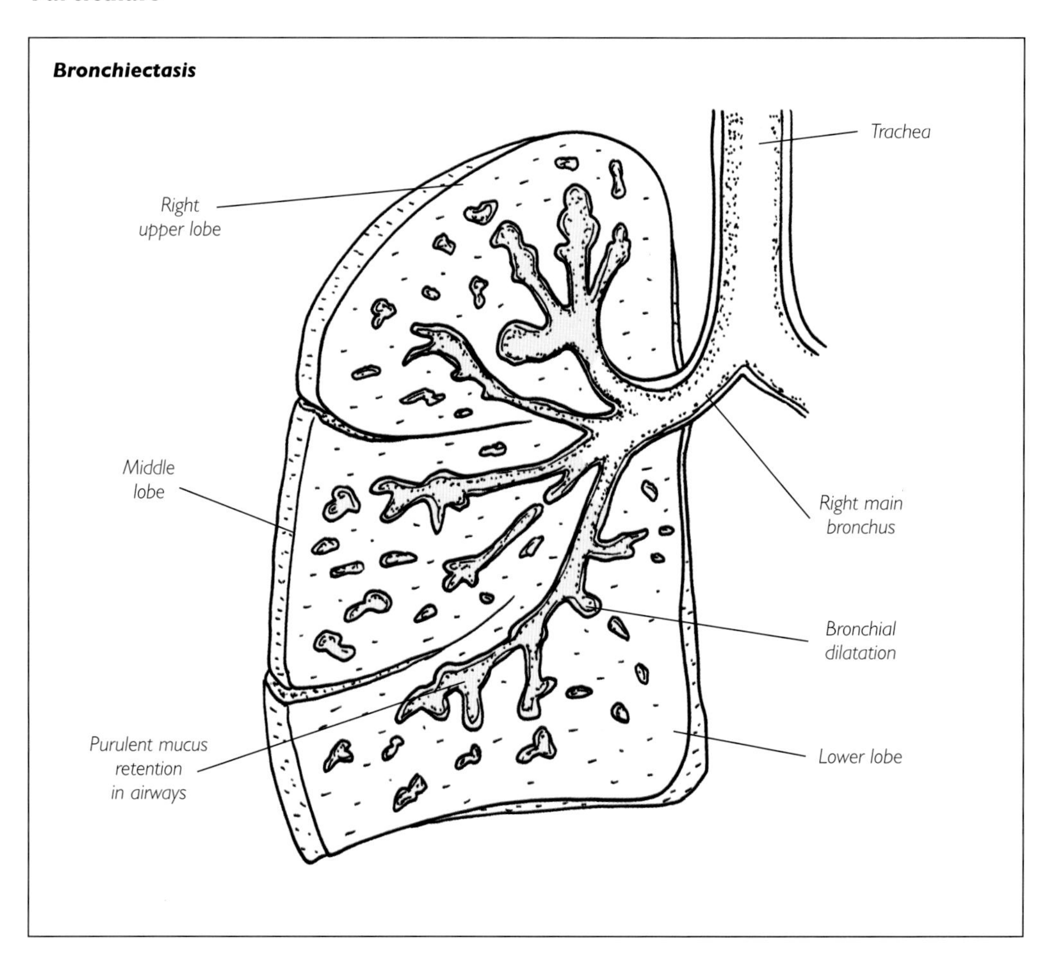

Bronchiectasis is characterised by dilatation of the bronchi, due to a weakness of the bronchial wall. This weakness may be congenital (e.g. associated with cystic fibrosis) or acquired (e.g. secondary to tuberculosis or bronchial obstructions from foreign bodies or tumour). The symptoms are usually a chronic cough with large amounts of purulent sputum, haemoptysis (coughing of blood) and recurrent chest infections.

Related images

p.737-743 Tuberculosis and tubercular miasm
p.504 Chronic bronchitis
p.198 Emphysema
p.95 Cystic fibrosis
p.314 Osteomyelitis
p.586 Muscle wasting
p.208 Malignant melanoma
p.720 Condylomata warts

DULCAMARA

Original

'Dulcamara and the forces of Light', by Loolie Habgood. A sample of fruit is also shown at the lower right corner. The plant family (Solanaceae) is characterised by the balance between the qualities of lightness and darkness. In this illustration, a relatively greater degree of light is shown around the plant (along with angelic hierarchies), which is in keeping with it's slightly less poisonous nature as compared with Belladonna.

Astrology

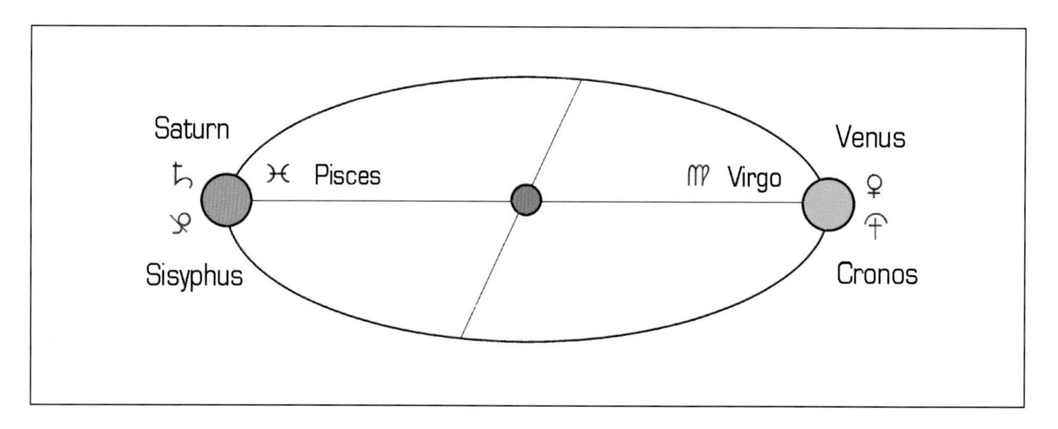

Moon conjunct Hebe within Capricorn, opposite Saturn conjunct Circe within Cancer.

Oriental

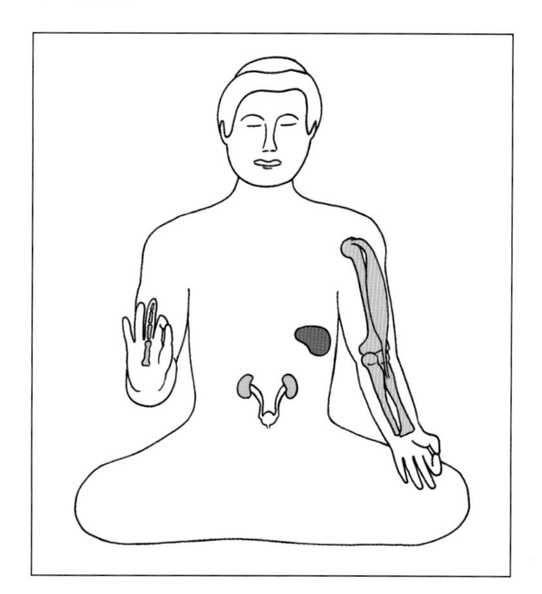

Kidney yang deficiency with spleen chi deficiency, and cold-damp painful obstruction syndrome of bones, joints and muscles.

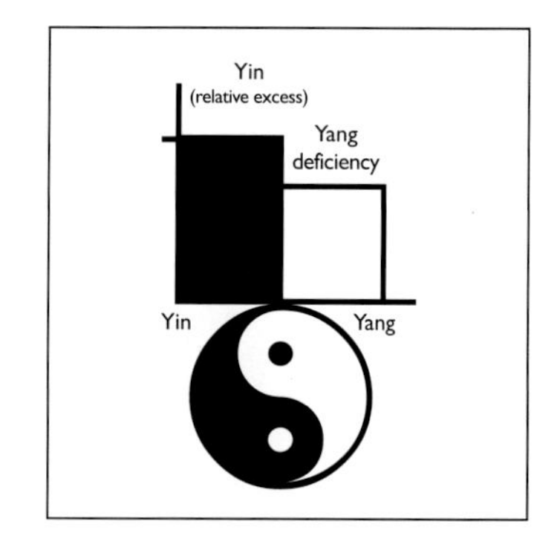

Related images

p.408 Sinusitis and nasal polyps & p.501 Otitis media and glue ear
p.504 Chronic bronchitis & p.306 Bronchiectasis
p.95 Cystic fibrosis
p.720 Condylomata warts
p.718 Pyelonephritis
p.339 Osteoarthritis & p.56 & p.340 Rheumatoid arthritis
p.562 Herpes virus

ELAPS CORALLINUS

Original

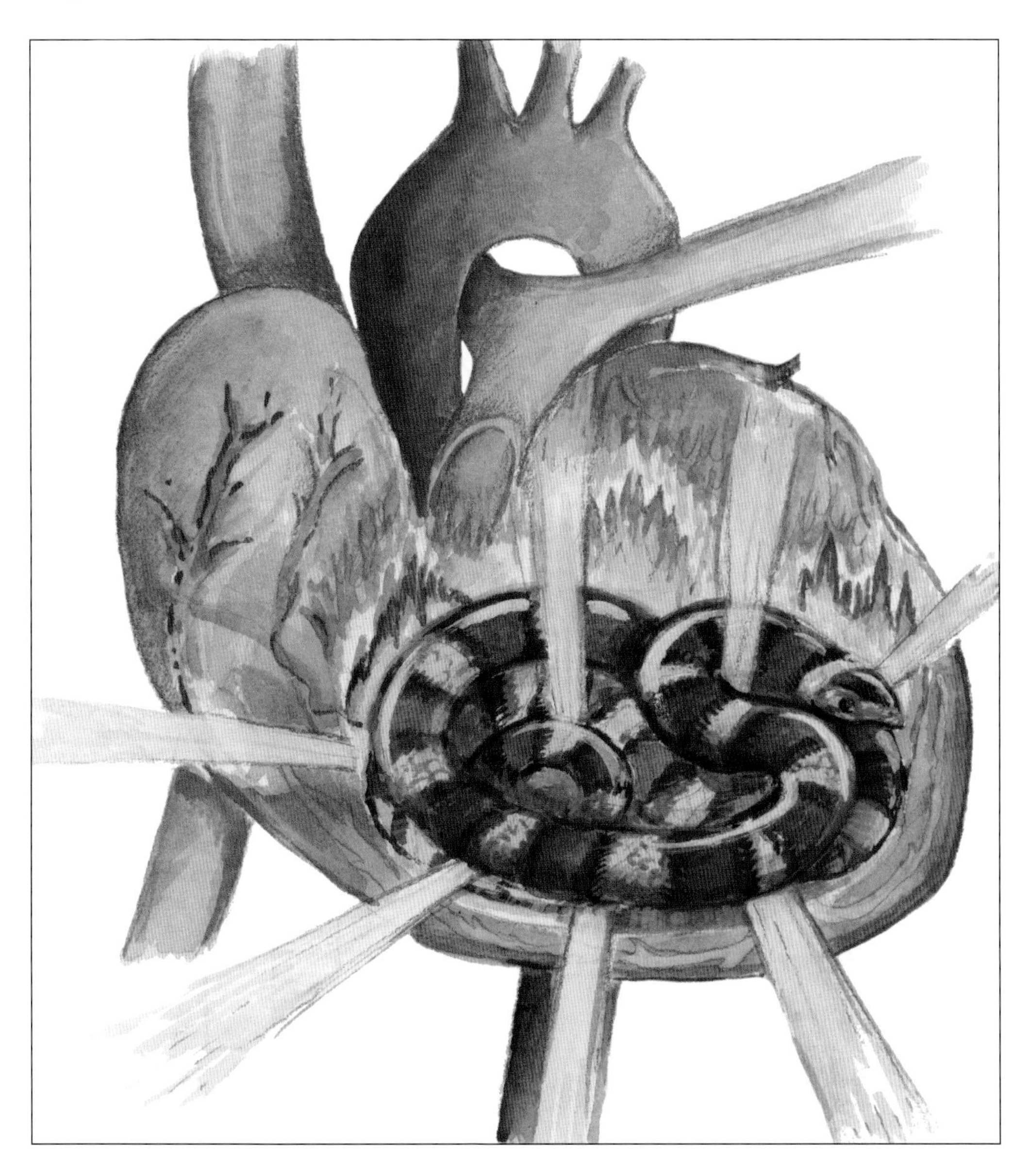

'Elaps corallinus and the Heart centre', by Loolie Habgood. A key site for the action of snake remedies is the heart and cardiovascular system, as illustrated here for the coral snake. The interior septal walls between the cardiac chambers have been left out for clarity. The remedy will foster the warmth activity of the Ego within this organ, as represented by the radiations of light. Note there are three colourations of flames around the snake: pink, yellow and blue (as viewed from the right ventricle toward to the left). These symbolise the spiritual principle of the Three-fold Flame of Divinity, representing the Trinity. The blue flame connects to the Father-Will aspect of Godhead, the pink flame connects to the Mother-Love, and yellow-golden to the Christ-Wisdom aspect.

EUPATORIUM PERFOLIATUM

Original

'Eupatorium perfoliatum and bone energy circulation', by Sophie Harrison. Note the stalkless leaves are perforated through by the stem. The plant is shown growing out of bone matrix, its roots continuous with the lamellae of the bone. The bluish venous and red arterial blood vessels penetrate the periosteal surface layer (the single epithelial layer of blue cells). The compact bone matrix is composed of layers of mineralised matrix (lamellae) around central (haversian) canals. Star and cosmic light is shown spiralling into the bone through the plant.

Astrology

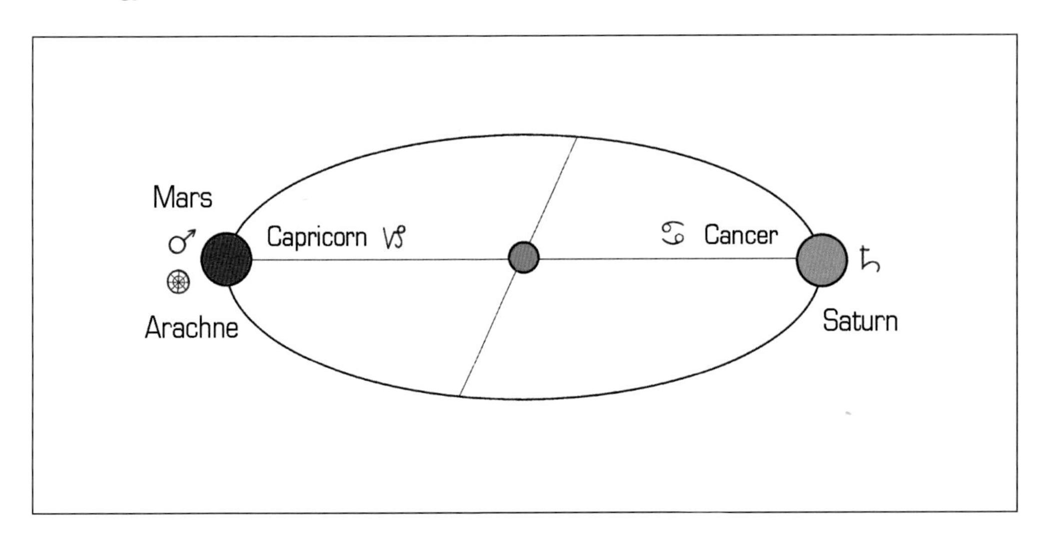

Mars conjunct Arachne within Capricorn, opposite Saturn in Cancer.

Oriental

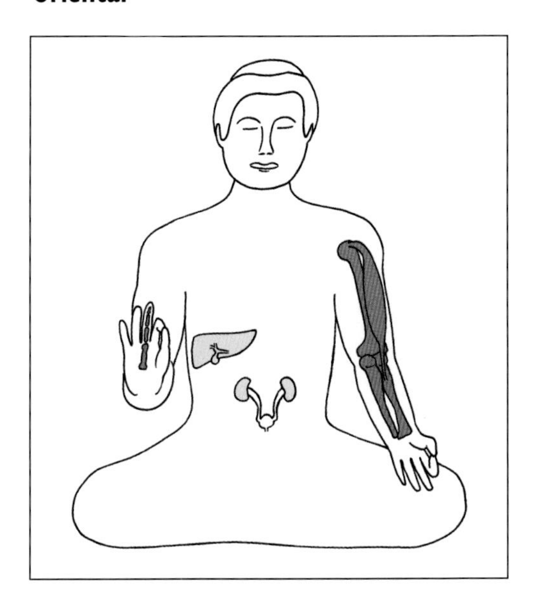

Kidney and liver yin/blood deficiency, with phlegm-heat lodged within bones and joints.

Particulars

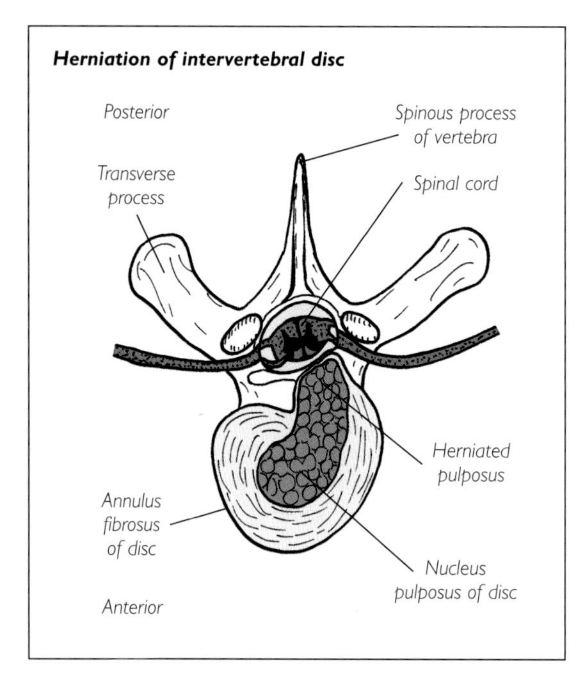

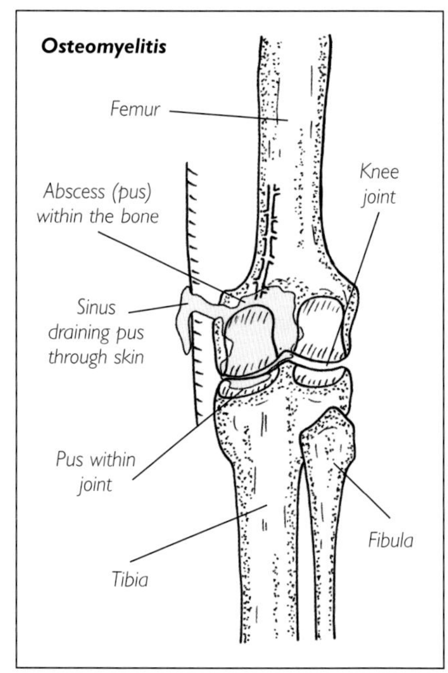

Intervertebral discs (between the vertebral bodies of the backbone) function as shock absorbers and are constantly undergoing compression. However degeneration and weakness of the anterior and/or posterior ligaments on each side of the discs can occur. If the compressive pressure is great enough then pressure within the softer central nucleus pulposus of the disc can cause this to rupture through the more fibrous outer annulus fibrosus of the disc. The protruding material can press posteriorly onto the spinal cord and spinal nerves, causing acute pain.

Osteomyelitis is usually caused by bacterial infection of bone, most commonly staphylococcus species. The microbes may reach the bone through the bloodstream from a focus of infection elsewhere, e.g. infected skin. The infected pus spreads through the bone cortex and can invade the joint. If it penetrates the periosteum (outer lining of bone) then a sinus channel can drain to the skin. There are symptoms of bone pain and fever.

Related images

p.278 Spinal cord compression from cancer
p.689 Fracture healing
p.278 Spinal cord compression from vertebral fracture
p.688 Basal skull fracture
p.173 Greenstick fracture
p.227 & p.229 Malaria
p.222 Fatty liver
p.133 Liver failure and ascites
p.527 Cluster headache
p.528 Migraine visual aura

EUPHRASIA OFFICINALIS

Original

'Euphrasia officinalis and the light-sensitive retina', by Nadine Kardesler. The plant is shown growing within the vitreous humor of the posterior chamber of the eye, above the retina. The lowest level of cells are the rods and cones, the actual light-sensitive cells. The middle cell layer is composed of bipolar cells, which transmit the electrically converted signal to the nerve ganglion cells forming the upper retinal layer. Rays of light are shown streaming toward the retina; these are streaming from the lens and anterior chamber above (not shown).

The eye can only be understood in relation to the whole body and the subtle bodies: etheric, astral and Ego. Weakness of the etheric body relates to liver yin/blood deficiency, causing poor nourishment to the eye. Symptoms include eye fatigue, dull vision, sensitivity to light and loss of visual acuity. Astral deformities indicate emotional states, such as joy, sadness, grief, and are revealed in the eye through its lustre, pupil expansion/contraction and tears, e.g. fear causes pupil dilatation. Weak soul incarnation (deficient Ego) also leads to pupil dilatation, i.e. the ego has weakly taken hold of the eyes. The eye is shaped by the entire cosmos, its spherical shape an image of the universe. Fibres of the lens and iris radiate from a central point, representing radiation from Source. The retinal arteries have branches often numbering four, symbolising the relation of the pulse and breath (4:1) and esoteric number of the Earth. The eyes absorb light and are connected to the light processes within the brain. This affects diurnal rhythms, carbohydrate metabolism, pineal function, melatonin secretion and the Ego. Hence in certain pathologies with disturbance of the vitreous humor, this appears like a collection of twinkling stars under the microscope. In retinitis pigmentosa there are black star-shaped pigment deposits on the retina that look like burned out stars. When the eye is under-supplied with astral and etheric forces, retinal detachment and/or retinal degeneration may occur.

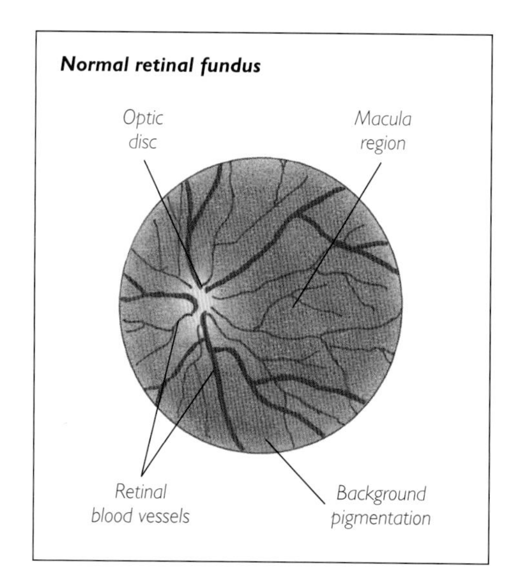

The optic disc is a round or slightly oval shaped pale structure, which indicates the exit of the optic nerve from the eye. It has a cup-like central depression, from which radiate the retinal blood vessels, these branching and spreading over the whole fundus. Normally the vessel walls are transparent; the blood column is therefore visible. The arteries appear a brighter red than the slightly purplish veins. The arteries are also slightly narrower than the veins. The macula is the most important photoreceptive area of the retina, being the site for central and colour vision. It is sited about two disc diameters to the temporal side of the optic disc. It is usually slightly deeper in tint than the surrounding fundus. The background general pigmentation varies in people and in races. It is usually orange or orange-red, but may be greenish in dark coloured races.

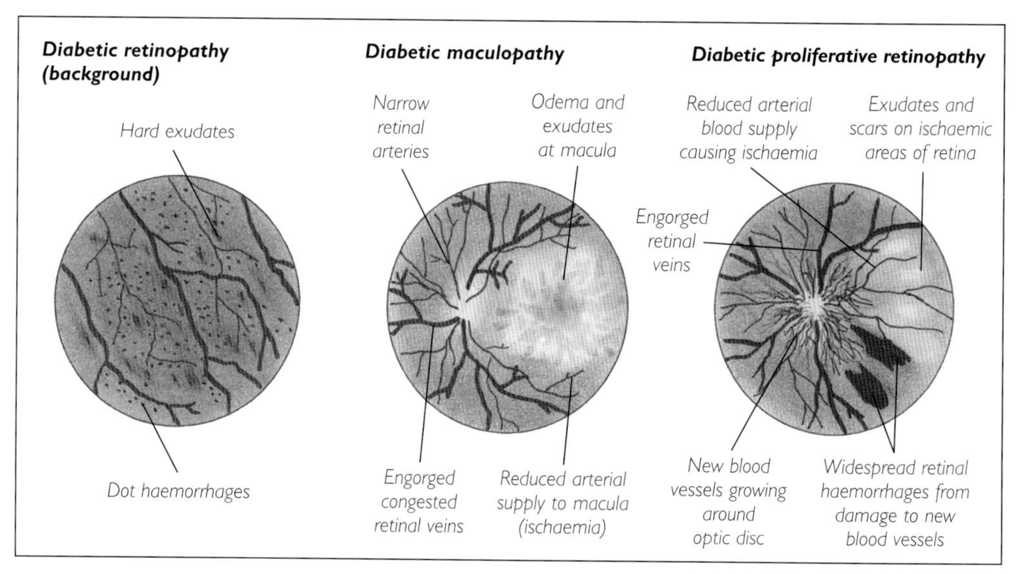

Diabetes, especially long-term, tends to cause retinal damage. The early signs are engorgement or congestion of the retinal veins, then degeneration of the vessel wall with the formation of micro-aneurysms (small dilated parts). This leads to small dot-shaped haemorrhages and hard exudates (fluid leaks) scattered around the retina. If the disease progressively worsens then maculopathy or proliferative retinopathy can occur. Further exudates and dot haemorrhages cause damage to the macula, with loss of central vision. There is odema or fluid leakage into the macula. Furthermore, ischaemia or loss of blood supply to the macula worsens the central vision. In proliferative retinopathy, new blood vessels are formed in the fundus, at any location but especially around the optic disc. This is a reaction to the chronic retinal ischaemia (i.e. from the arteriosclerosis and reduced arterial supply). These new blood vessels are not as well supported by connective tissue bridges to the retinal wall, and are liable to rupture and bleed. Such bleeding may be very heavy and cause widespread vitreous haemorrhage. The scarring around the damaged and repairing vessels also pulls on the retinal layer, with the risk of retinal tears and retinal detachment. All these problems can cause serious loss of vision.

FEL TAURI

Original

'Fel tauri reaching toward the planet Mars and constellation Taurus', by Esther Lane. The relationship of the bull to the zodiacal constellation of Taurus is portrayed, the central bright star in the upper right corner being Aldebaran, and the Pleiadian star cluster shown faintly at the uppermost corner of this constellation. The red planet Mars is shown as an intermediary, as well as influencing the iron-process within the gallbladder.

Astrology

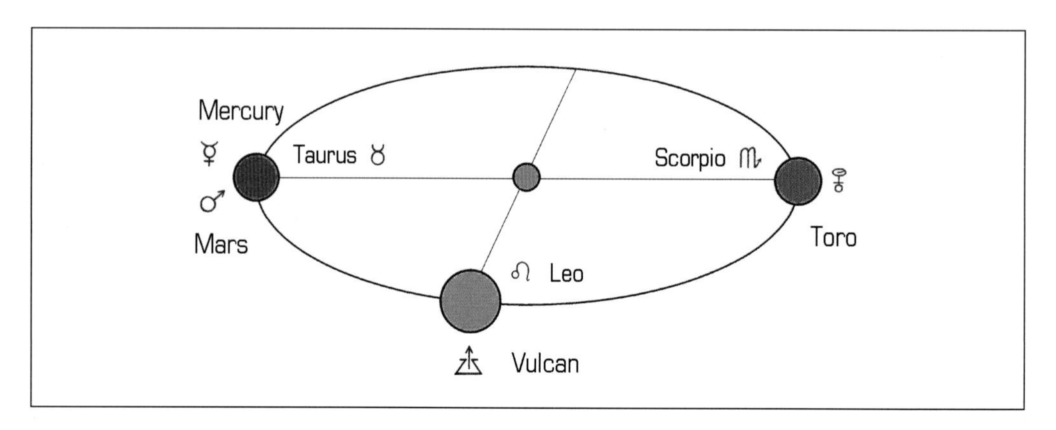

Mercury conjunct Mars within Taurus, opposite Toro in Scorpio, squared by Vulcan in Leo.

Oriental

Liver yin/blood deficiency with gallbladder yang deficiency.

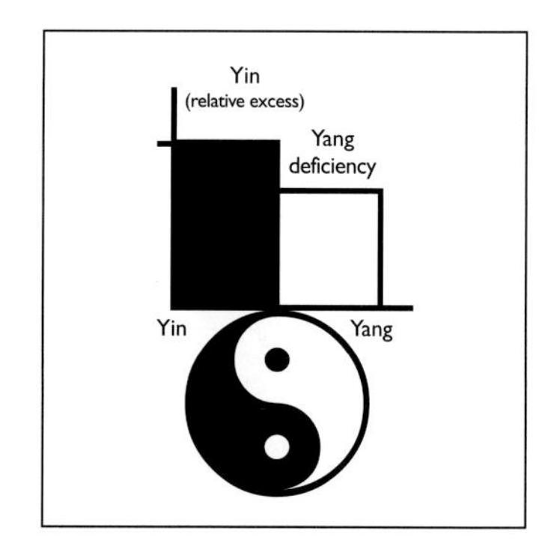

Related images

p.222-223 Gallstones & p.224 Hyperlipidaemia
p.223 Jaundice & p.561-562 Hepatitis
p.222 Fatty liver & p.133 Liver failure and ascites
p.470 Pancreatic failure
p.541 Peptic ulcer
p.36 Hiatus hernia
p.451 Myocardial infarction, acute

FERRUM METALLICUM

Original

'Ferrum metallicum and Mars the god of war', by Jemma Hone. The red planet Mars is shown at the upper left and radiations of iron descend to Earth – representing the thrust of incarnation. The god Mars represents the forces of will and determination to overcome the Earthly realm, eventually to aspire towards higher initiations. A particularly useful meditation is to combine the state of Buddha-hood with the dynamic of Mars, so as to transform aggressive energy into that of cooperation and universal goodwill.

Astrology

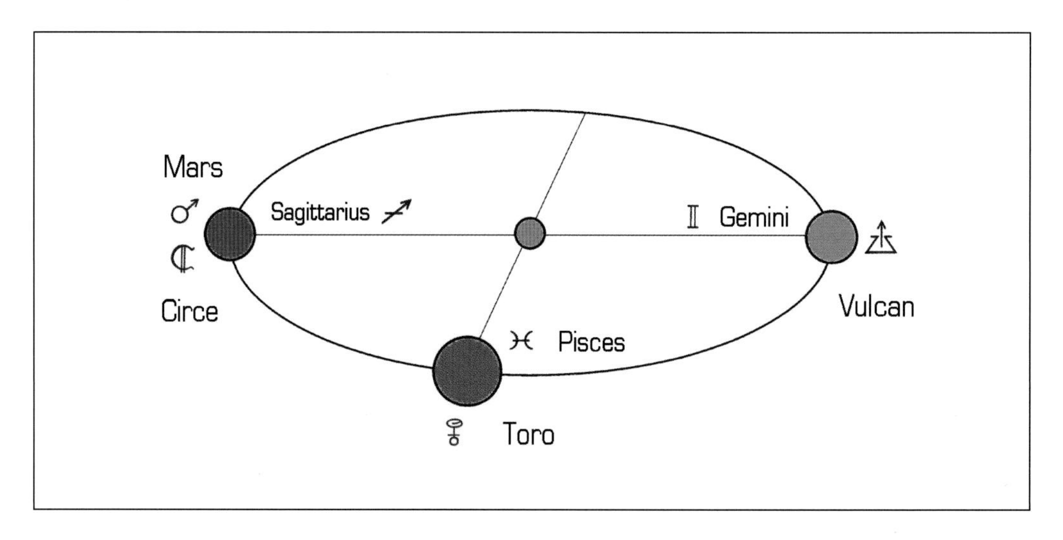

Mars conjunct Circe within Sagittarius, opposite Vulcan in Gemini, squared by Toro in Pisces.

Oriental

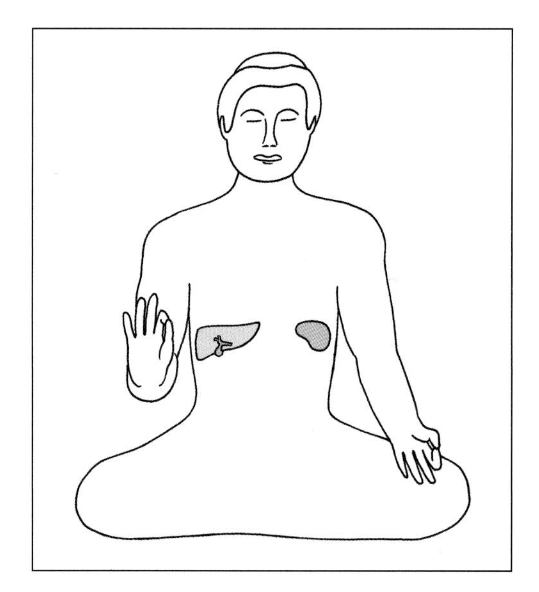

Spleen and liver blood deficiency, with gallbladder yang deficiency.

Particulars

Normal red blood cells, blood film

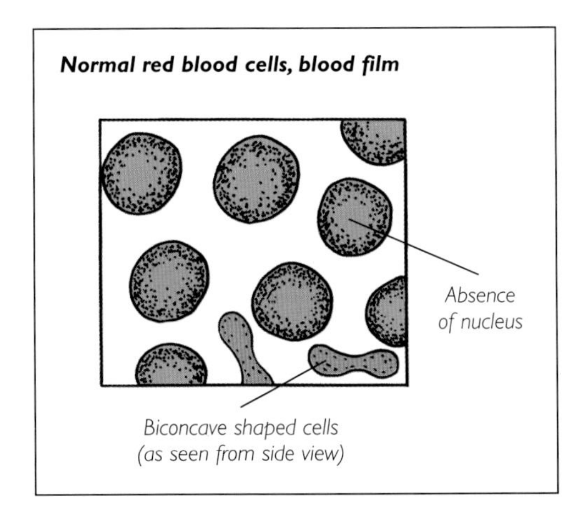

Anaemia, blood film

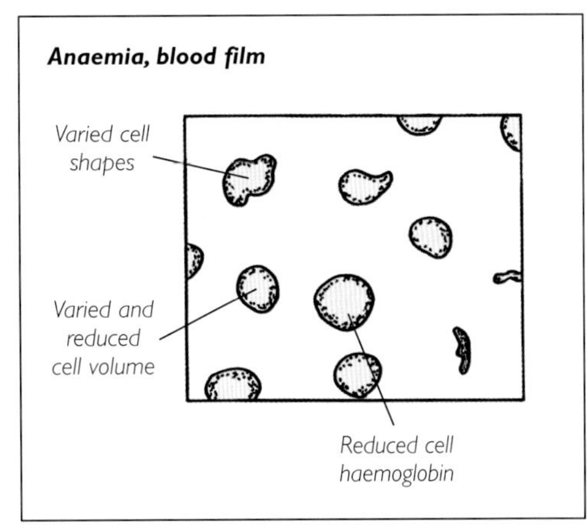

Red blood cells within the peripheral blood are normally fairly uniform in size and shape, with a biconcave disc shape. All peripheral blood cells are created from pluripotential stem cells within the bone marrow. Red cells pass through several stages in the bone marrow before being released. During this process they initially possess a nucleus (with genetic material), but this progressively shrinks and then is removed. More and more haemoglobin (the red iron containing, oxygen carrying, red pigment) is laid into the cell. Therefore, any nucleated red cells in the peripheral blood are a sign of undue haemopoiesis (red cell production) outside of the bone marrow, and in certain bone marrow diseases. Normally the red cells survive about 120 days in the peripheral blood, and are then scavenged and recycled, predominantly by the spleen.

Koilonychia, iron deficiency anaemia

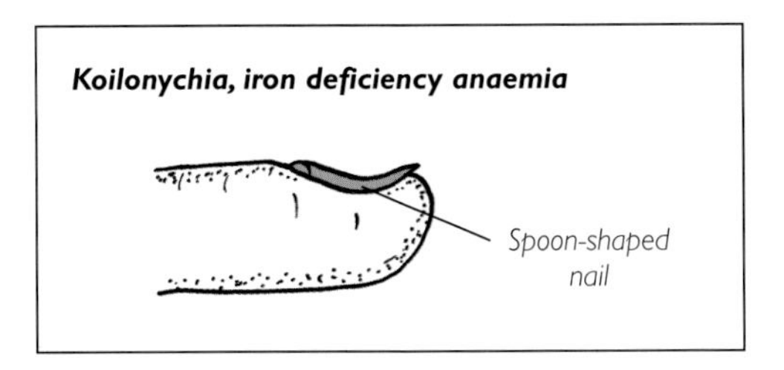

There are three main types of anaemia as based on the initial blood investigations: (1) hypochromic macrocytic anaemia with a reduced mean cell volume and reduced haemoglobin concentration in the red blood cells; (2) normochromic normocytic anaemia with normal levels of haemoglobin and cell volumes, and (3) macrocytic anaemia, where the mean cell volume is increased. An example of the first category is shown here in the blood film. The cells have reduced red haemoglobin pigment colouration, are smaller in size, and with poikilocytosis (variation in shape) and anisocytosis (variation or deformities in size). This is a typical appearance of iron deficiency anaemia. Causes of this include blood loss from haemorrhage, or from reduced iron absorption in the gut.

Koilonychia is a term given to spoon-shaped nails (indented concavely) and is typically a feature of iron deficiency anaemia. Causes of this type of anaemia include chronic bleeding.

Related images

p.650 Acne rosacea
p.180 Gastrointestinal bleeding
p.288 Immune thrombocytopenic purpura
p.485 Irritable bowel syndrome, hyper-peristalsis

FERRUM PHOSPHORICUM

Original

'Ferrum phosphoricum and the Mars-Venus process within red cell formation', by Nathalie Nahai. Stages of red blood cell formation are shown, those cells at the upper pole being as yet within the bone marrow, the final mature biconcave cells shown at the lower pole ready for release into the peripheral blood. The initial cell at the top is more or less spherical, contains a nucleus of genetic material and has a blue cytoplasm. This stage is influenced by the Venus-Copper process (Venus depicted as the bluish planet on the right side), and relates also to the phosphoric element of the remedy. The cell receives a progressively greater influence from Mars (the red planet to the left), which radiates the iron process. The incorporation of iron into the haemoglobin replaces the initial copper carriage of oxygen. Note the loss of nucleus shown by the middle layer cell on the right. The central individual symbolises the strengthening of the human ego and will-power through this evolution of the blood.

Astrology

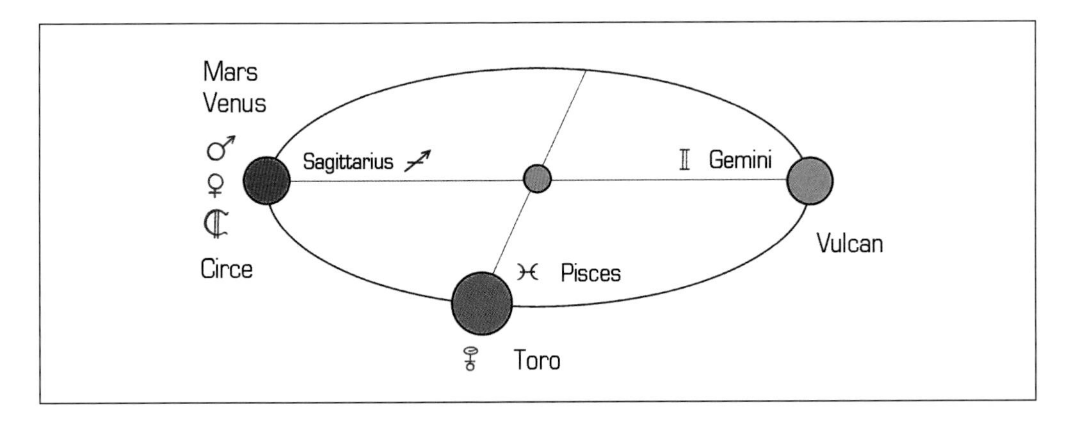

Mars conjunct Venus and Circe within Sagittarius, opposite Vulcan in Gemini, squared by Toro in Pisces.

Oriental

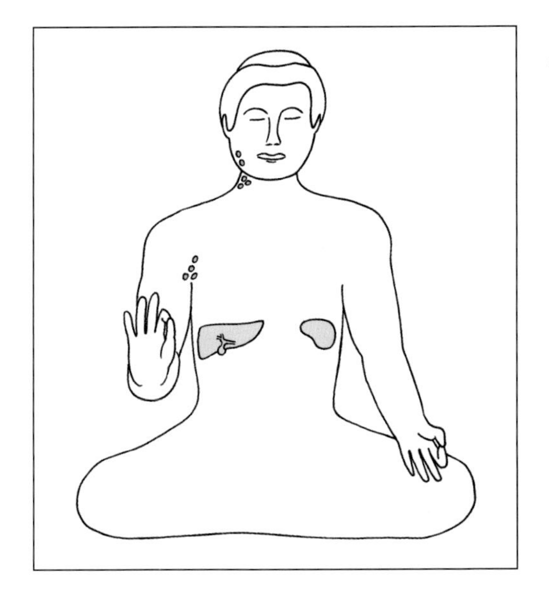

Spleen and liver blood deficiency, with external wind-cold invasion of defence chi/lymph nodes.

Related images

p.103 Fever, temperature measurement
p.103 Tonsillitis
p.4 Croup
p.265 & p.503 Toothache
p.3 Trigeminal neuralgia
p.527 Cluster headache

FLUORIC ACID

Original

'Fluoric acid and the Transpluto region of space', by Tessa Gaynn. The cosmic and cathartic nature of the remedy is portrayed by the explosion of a planetoid in the outer reaches of our solar system. Such events tend to occur far beyond Pluto, within the Kuiper belt and Oort cloud – zones containing an enormous number of planetoids and icy rock. Fragments of debris are shown hurtling as newly formed comets, towards the Earth and Moon near the middle of the illustration. Particular angelic beings are involved in such space activities. Cherubim and seraphim especially regulate the activity of comets, which represent harbingers of transformational signals into the rest of the solar system.

Astrology

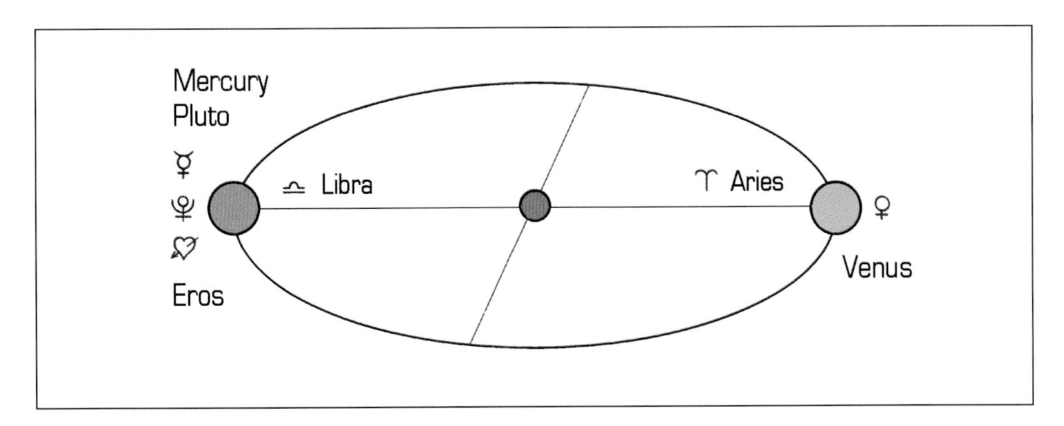

Mercury conjunct Pluto and Eros within Libra, opposite Venus in Aries.

Oriental

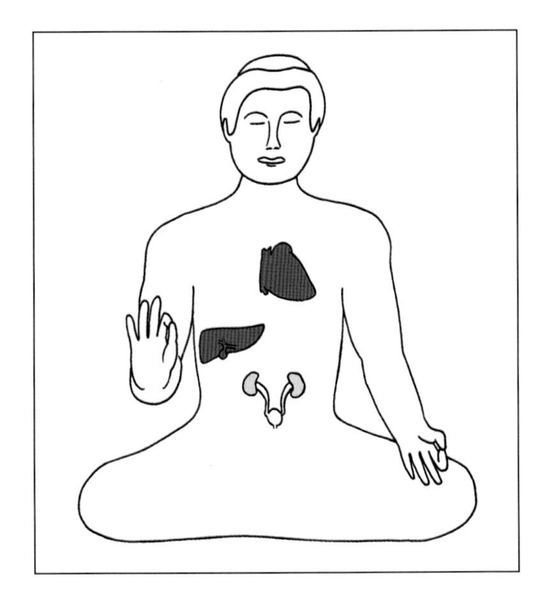

Kidney yin deficiency, with liver fire and empty-fire blazing within heart.

Related images

p.13 Allergic rhinitis
p.3 Trigeminal neuralgia & p.10 Sciatica
p.265 & p.503 Toothache
p.758 Varicose veins
p.656 Alopecia
p.461 & p.463 Uterine prolapse
p.172 Osteogenesis imperfecta, brittle bone disease & p.171 Osteoporosis
p.470 Prostate hyperplasia

FOLLICULINUM SARCODE

Original

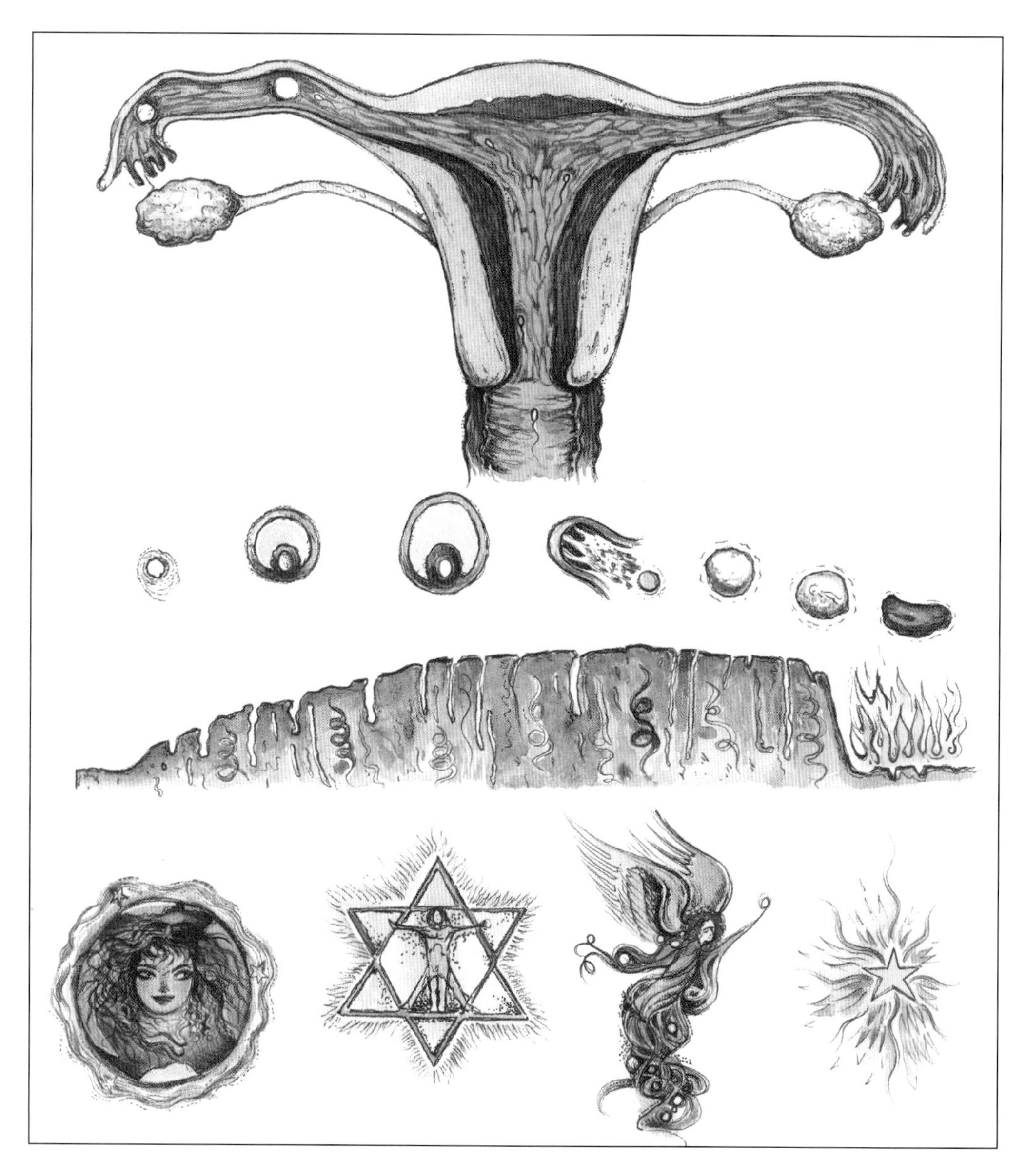

'Folliculinum and esoteric physiology of the menstrual cycle', by Katherine Mynott. The upper image shows the overall layout of the female reproductive system, with two ovaries on each side (supported by suspensory ligaments to the central uterus). Two stages of an ovulated ovum (egg cell) are shown on the left-hand side, and stages of sperm transit shown from the high vaginal cavity toward the ovum at mid-fallopian tube level. The next row of images depict stages of follicle development within the ovary and ovulation (release of egg cell), followed by the corpus luteum changes within the residual follicle at the ovary. The image below this shows the buildup of endometrial lining within the uterus, followed by a stabilisation or plateau stage and then menstrual shedding as the period in the 4th week. The lowest level of images show spiritual aspects of the cycle. Earth Mother forces on the left coincide with endometrial buildup and follicle development. The Star of David image of the perfected human (Adam Kadmon) activates at the middle point of the cycle during ovulation. The maturation plateau stage of the cycle coincides with the angelic figure, representing the movement of the astral body. Finally, the star with its heat radiations represents the Ego forces active during the period.

BELOW. 'Girl walking through fire', by Joanna Campion. The ovary, egg cell and etheric energy held by the female carry the entire blueprint history of the human race, from the perspective of anthropogenesis. A sense of biography at multiple reality levels is suggested by this illustration as a girl walks through fire and several crystalline structures. These include the stages of her personal biography, her ancestral lineage, multiple past incarnations and the generations of the collective human root race.

Astrology

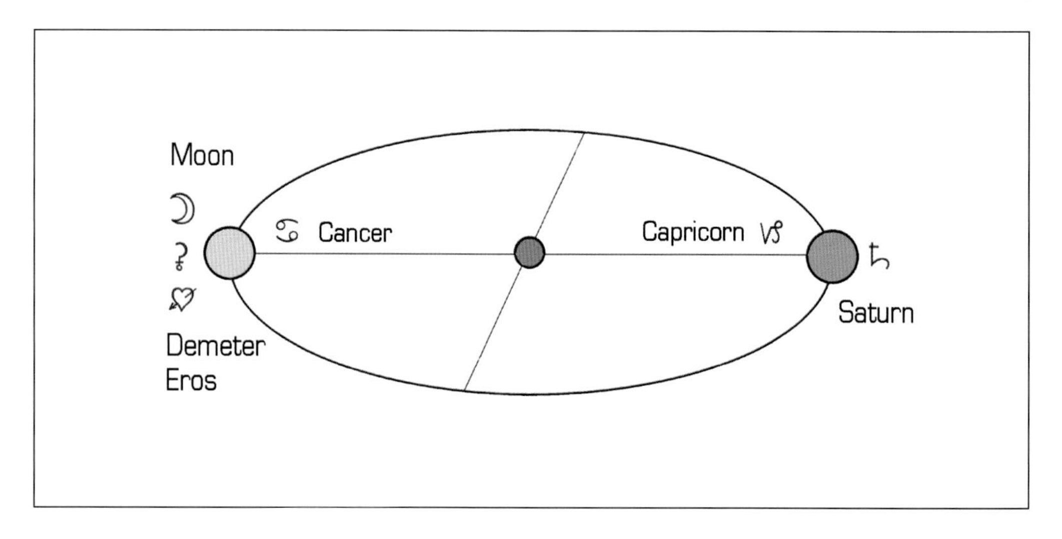

Moon conjunct Demeter and Eros within Cancer, opposite Saturn in Capricorn.

Oriental

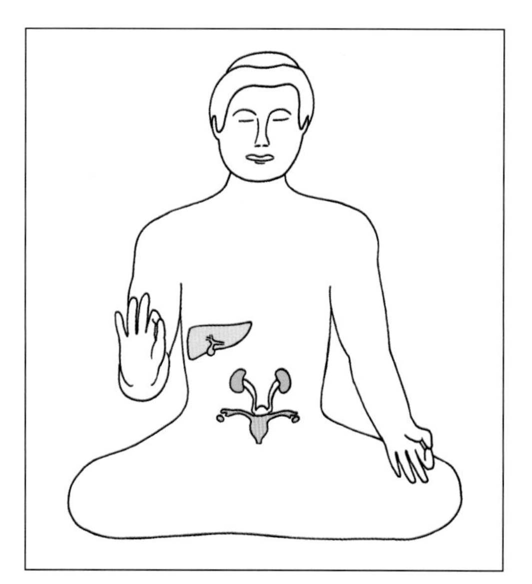

Kidney yang deficiency, with liver blood deficiency, and damp accumulation/invasion of lower burner/uterus/ovaries.

Particulars

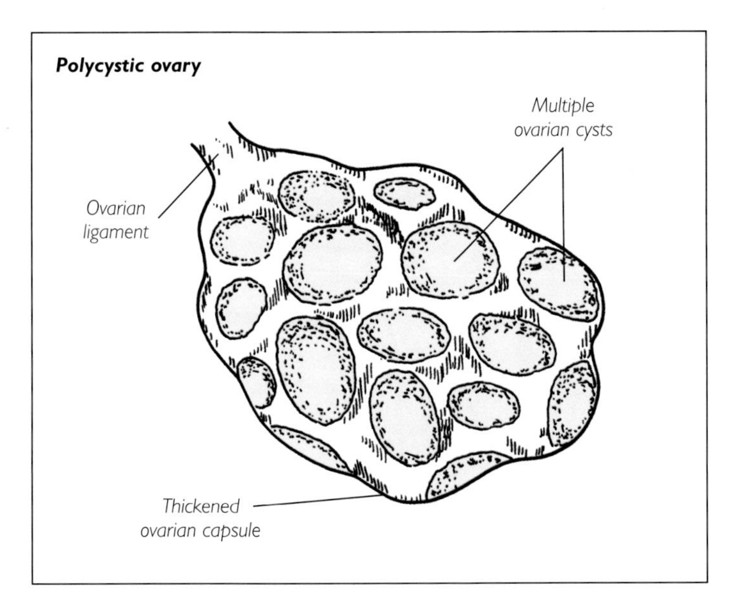

Polycystic ovarian syndrome is characterised by the formation of multiple small cysts in the ovaries. There is also lack of egg cell ovulation or release, infertility and excessive androgen hormones (often manifesting as excess hair growth or hirsutism), menstrual disorders and mild obesity. The ovarian capsule is thickened. Within the ovary the many cysts are 2-6mm in diameter, with the follicles in arrested stages of maturation, and clumps of androgen hormone producing cells.

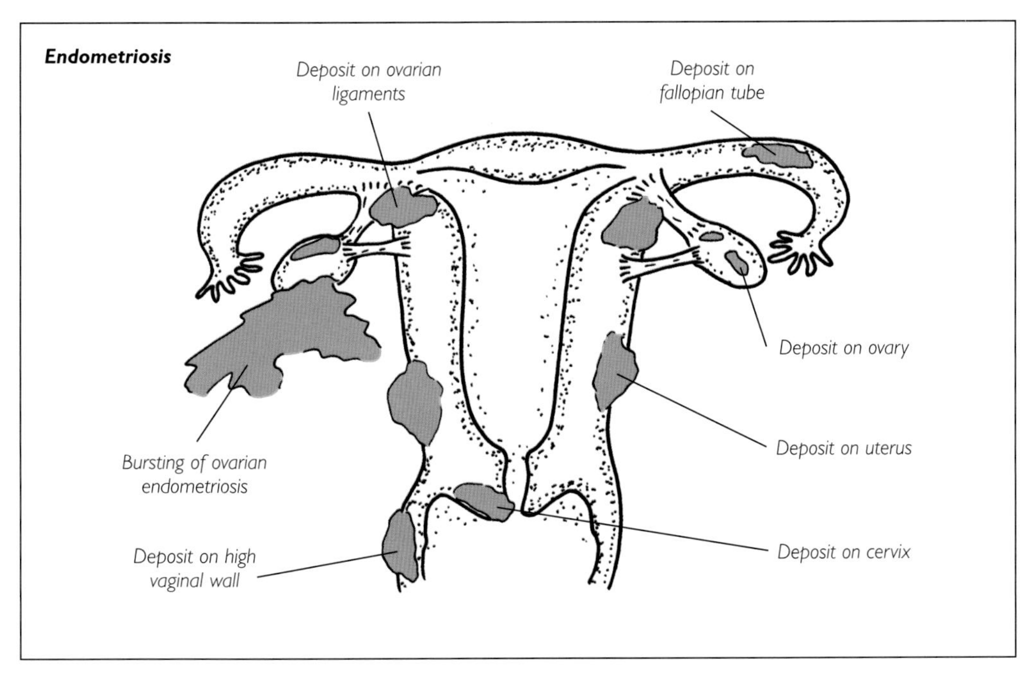

Endometriosis is characterised by deposits of endometrium outside of the uterine cavity, instead of residing only as the inner uterine wall. Such deposits may be anywhere, but usually on the other parts of the genital tract and pelvis. Less commonly these deposits are on the bowel caecum, appendix, bladder, rectum, and umbilicus. The ovarian hormones have an effect on the deposits as well as the normal uterine lining; therefore they are liable to haemorrhage during the time of menstruation (as shown for the right ovarian endometriosis here). Adhesions or scar tissue then develops, leading to infertility. There is a relationship to the cancer miasm and sometimes an endometrial deposit will undergo malignant change.

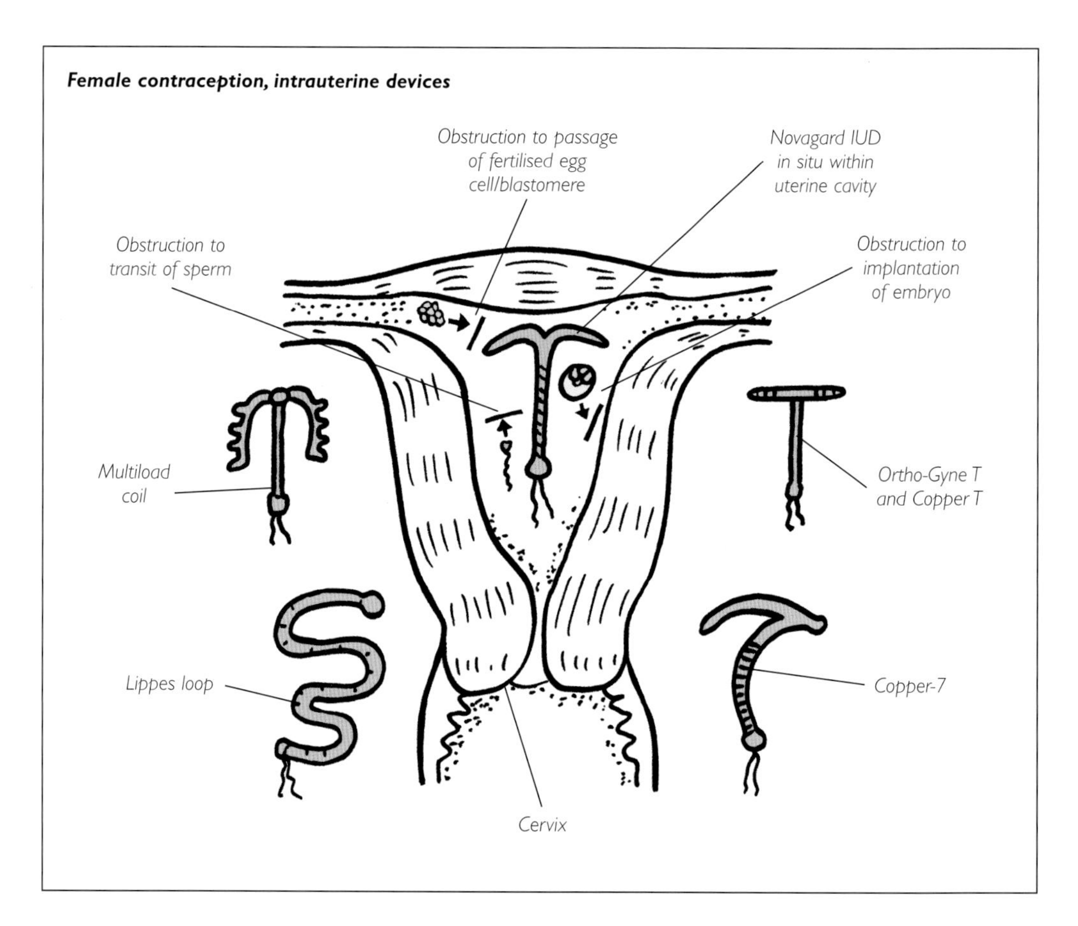

An intra-uterine contraceptive device (IUCD) is a small plastic carrier with a vertical stem (having copper wiring or banding around it) and a head of 'T' or similar shape. It is inserted using an introducer and through the cervix, the head opening up once within the uterine cavity. The gradual absorption of copper requires the device to be renewed every 3-5 years. Instead of copper the device may contain progesterone drug, which reduces the menstrual loss of blood as well as being contraceptive. IUCDs' act by interfering with implantation of the fertilised egg (blastocyst stage). They also inhibit the passage of sperm through the uterine cavity. Complications of IUCDs' include heavier menstrual bleeding (except for the progesterone releasing types), infection (pelvic inflammatory disease) which can cause long-term infertility, perforation through the uterus wall into the peritoneal cavity and failure of the device with the risk of pregnancy.

Related images

p.98 Genital underdevelopment (although relates more to female problems)
p.139-140 External virilisation
p.57 Ovarian inflammation
p.210 Ovarian cancer
p.427 Ultrasound polycystic ovary
p.490 Pelvic inflammatory disease
p.650 Acne rosacea

GELSEMIUM SEMPERVIRENS

Original

'Gelsemium and the inflammatory reaction', by Jemma Hone. The plant is shown surrounded by etheric and physical mucus, the orange-red colouration highlighting the congestion of blood that occurs during inflammation. Viruses and bacteria float within the scene. Above are white cells performing various roles during the immune reaction.

Astrology

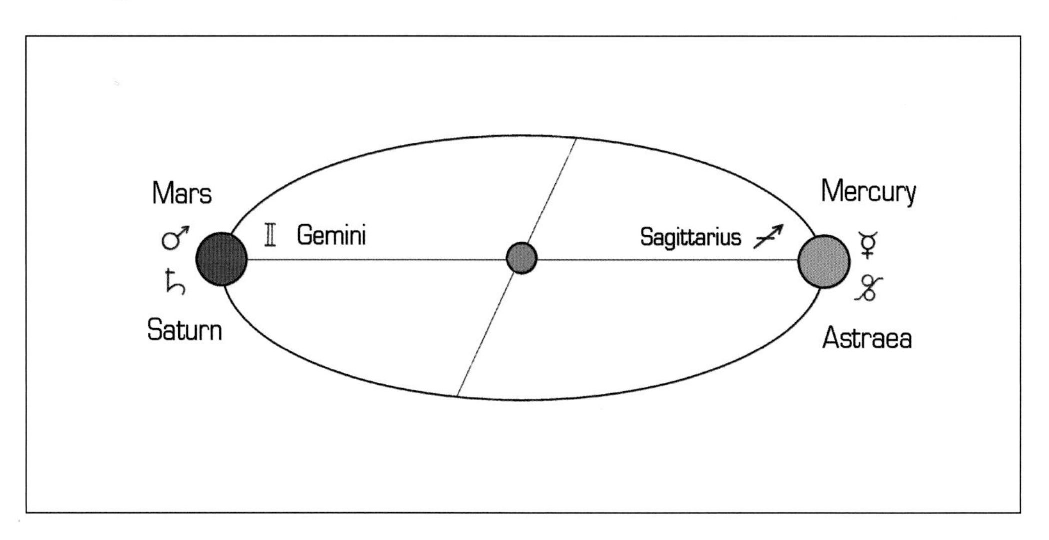

A particular pattern is Mars and Saturn in conjunction within the sign of Gemini, opposed by Mercury conjunct Astraea within the sign of Sagittarius.

Oriental

Spleen yang deficiency with damp-heat and phlegm-damp congestion of brain, lymph and muscles.

Particulars

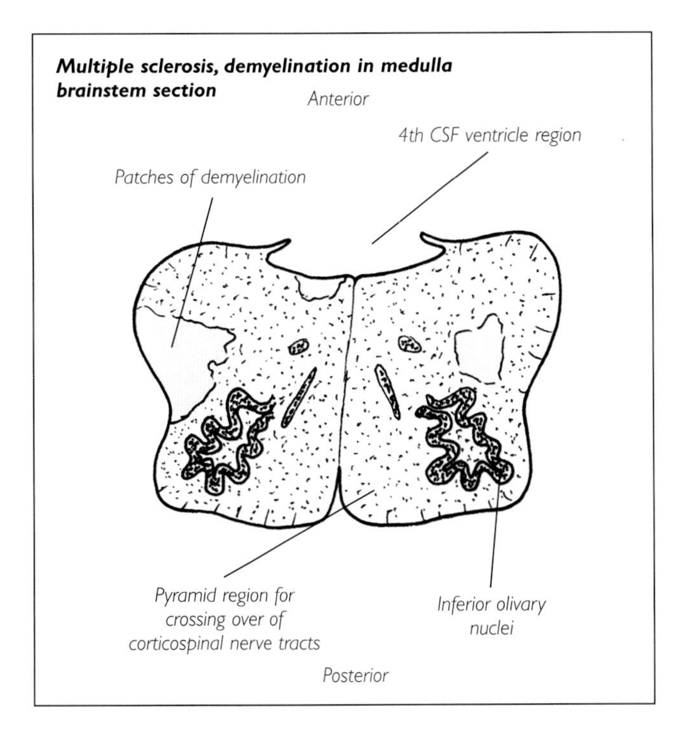

Multiple sclerosis is characterised by demyelination, i.e. focal loss of the myelin sheath around the nerves in the nervous system. Initially there is an inflammatory reaction with infiltration of lymphocytes and macrophages past the blood-brain barrier to destroy patches of the myelin sheath. The underlying axon nerve cell is spared. Microglia and astrocytes (the supporting cells around the nerve cells) proliferate as a reaction to form a scar. The area of demyelination and glial scar is known as a plaque, and appears as a pale-grey rubbery material. The extent and location of the plaques determines the symptoms and signs. In this example, three plaques are shown in the medulla oblongata of the brainstem.

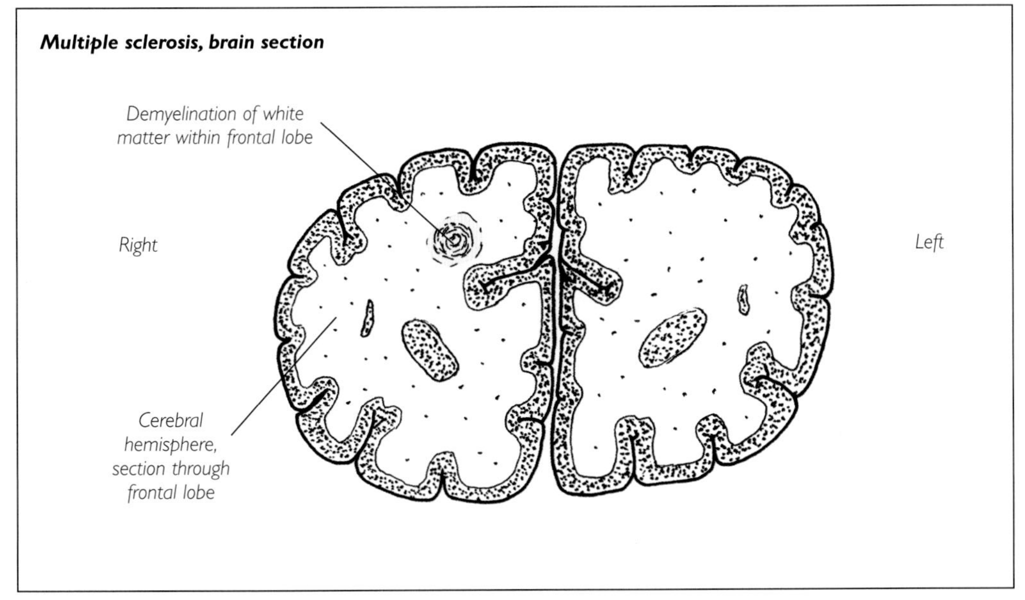

Multiple sclerosis is characterised by episodic loss of the myelin sheath around nerve fibres and can occur anywhere in the nervous system. It typically has a relapsing-remitting course (coming and going). There is a localised inflammation with scar formation, known as a plaque. This has a grey rubbery appearance, or as a white shadow on CT scanning. Symptoms therefore depend on the actual nerve fibres affected and can be very variable.

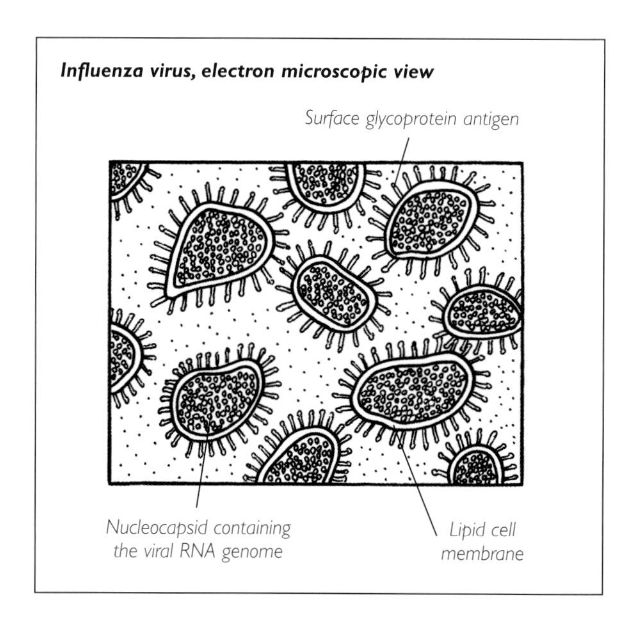

Influenza virus is the cause of influenza, an acute contagious infection of the upper respiratory tract. The virus is spherical (or sometimes filamentous) and covered by protruding antigens of glycoproteins. There are many hybrid virus types due to genetic variability of the RNA and the different membrane antigens. Infectious episodes can vary from minor epidemics to major pandemics. The onset has acute and high fever, headache, muscle pain and debility, and often dry cough, sore throat and nasal discharge. Usually it lasts 3-5 days, but may be complicated by secondary bacterial pneumonia (especially in the elderly) with the risk of fatality.

Related images

p.232 Multiple sclerosis
p.18 Parkinson's disease
p.277 Motor neurone disease
p.417 Myasthenia gravis
p.527 Headaches
p.528 Migraine visual aura
p.347 Temporal arteritis
p.56 Glomerulonephritis
p.582 Infectious gastroenteritis

GLONOINUM

Original

'Glonoine and fire of the salamander', by Loolie Habgood. 'Nature' is a term used to describe various world processes. However, no actual random or un-intentional processes ever occur. All activities within nature are out of the intention & activity of etheric beings called elementals. There are 4 types of elementals, the fire elementals called salamanders. (The others are sylphs/air, undines/water & gnomes/earth elementals). Glonoine facilitates the fire elementals, shown here by 2 salamanders igniting the human on the surface. The creatures are sited in a subterranean realm, known also as the 2nd dimension. During Atlantis, humanity was blocked in its warmth nature, due to weak development of the Self/individuality. Fire elementals worked in a distorted way upon humans, leading to various diseases (e.g. cancer or organ failure, from a deficiency of the warmth organism).

Astrology

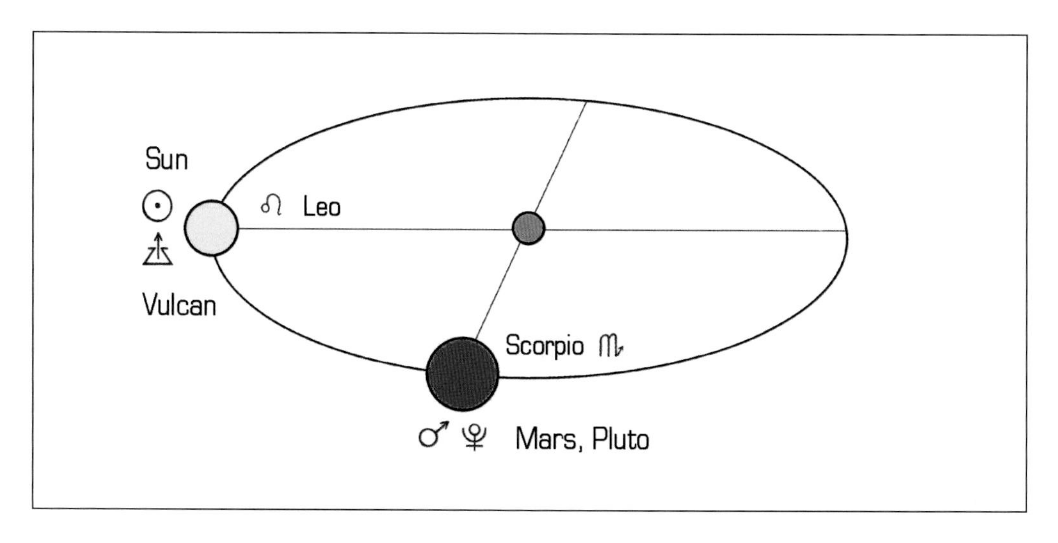

Sun conjunct Vulcan within Leo, squared by Mars conjunct Pluto within Scorpio.

Oriental

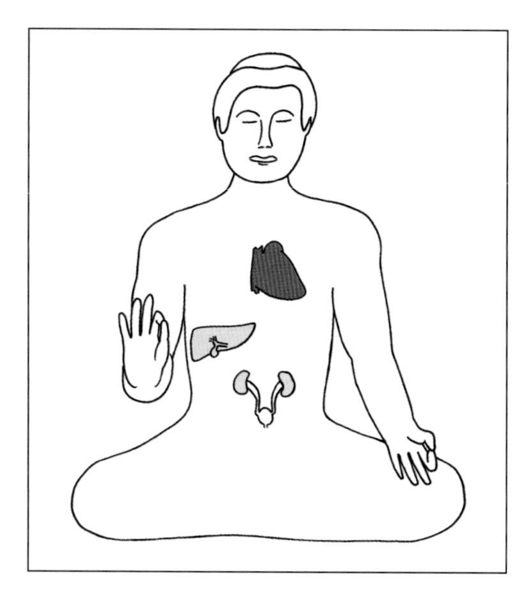

Kidney and liver yin deficiency, with empty-fire blazing within heart.

Particulars

Temporal arteritis (Giant cell arteritis)

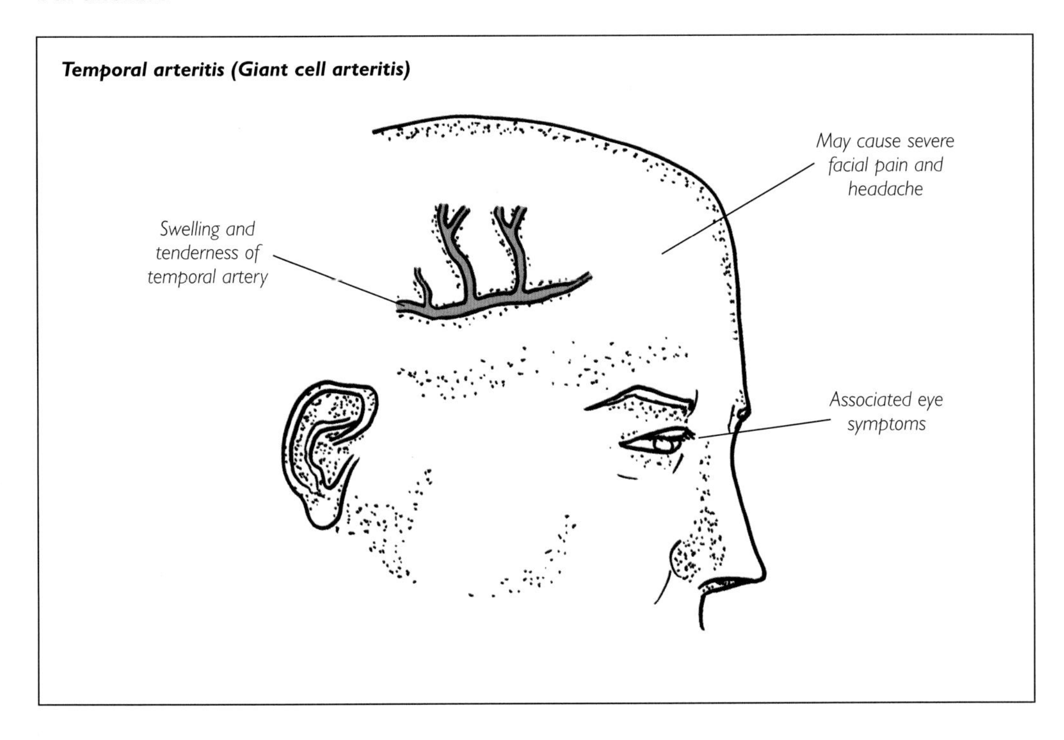

Temporal arteritis (also called giant cell arteritis) is characterised by inflammation of large arteries and occurs in association with polymyalgia rheumatica (with severe inflammatory pain and stiffness of the shoulder, neck, hips and lumbar spine). The arteritis typically affects the occipital or temporal (this latter is shown here) arteries. There are severe headaches, scalp tenderness, jaw pain on eating, fever, malaise, fatigue and palpably swollen tender temporal arteries. If the ophthalmic arteries are also affected then sudden visual loss can occur, which can be temporary or permanent.

Related images

p.527 Cluster headache
p.528 Migraine visual aura
p.258 Labyrinthitis
p.260 Meniere's disease
p.451 Myocardial infarction, acute
p.574 Hypertension
p.264 Supraventricular tachycardia
p.642 Pre-eclampsia

GRAPHITES

Museum

Constantin Meunier, 'On the way home from the mine', © Ny Carlsberg Glyptotek, Copenhagen. Coal is of course a species of carbon. The sheer physicality of the coalminers, but also their abject weariness is evident in this wall sculpture.

FOLLOWING PAGE. 'Graphite and Earthly representation of the Divine image', by Lorraine Spiro. The divine image and similitude of Adam Kadmon (the perfected human made originally in the likeness of God) is represented suspended in space above. This collective-based blueprint is projecting onto an individual soul's incarnation onto the Earth below. Similarly, graphite-based carbon can become the earthly/material mirror of a crystalline diamond-based carbon structure within the spiritual realm. Other building structures on the planet symbolise sacred megaliths (e.g. Stonehenge or Avebury within England, widely used by ancient cultures) as a way of anchoring cosmic forces. The image demonstrates the principle of the macrocosm and microcosm as one, i.e. 'As above, so below'. There is a spiritual counterpart to everything on Earth. Humanity is at a stage where focus on the physical body has become paramount. Those of the materialistic bent would overly focus on the Earthly body, whereas the spiritually oriented may overly seek to escape from the Earth into the realm above. Sometimes a soul is stuck, hovering in a 'No man's land' or limbo state within the lower astral, as it did not complete necessary lessons on the material plane. A balance should be struck, uniting spiritual and earthly for true realisation of the soul's purpose.

Original

Astrology

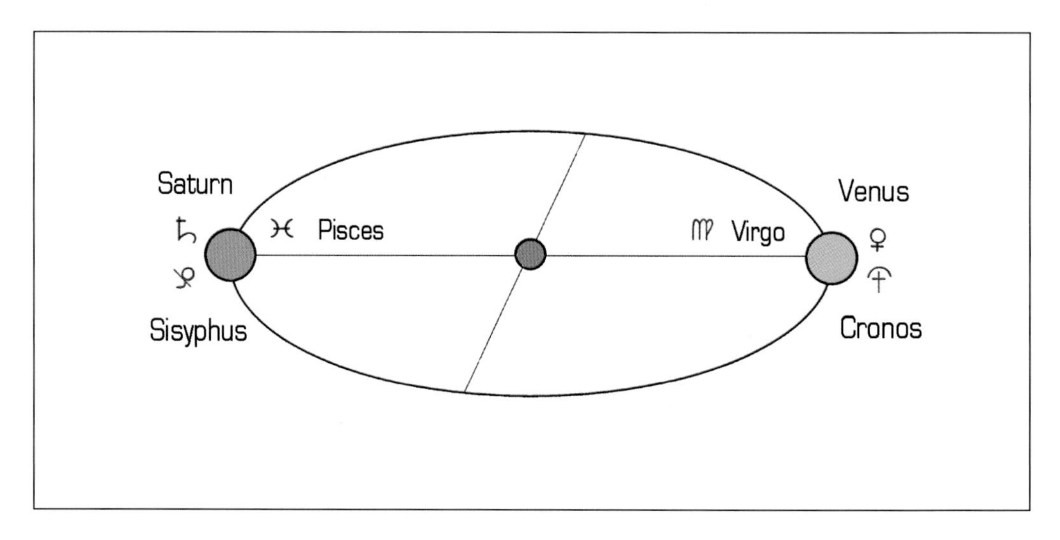

Venus conjunct Cronos within Virgo, opposite Saturn conjunct Sisyphus within Pisces.

Oriental

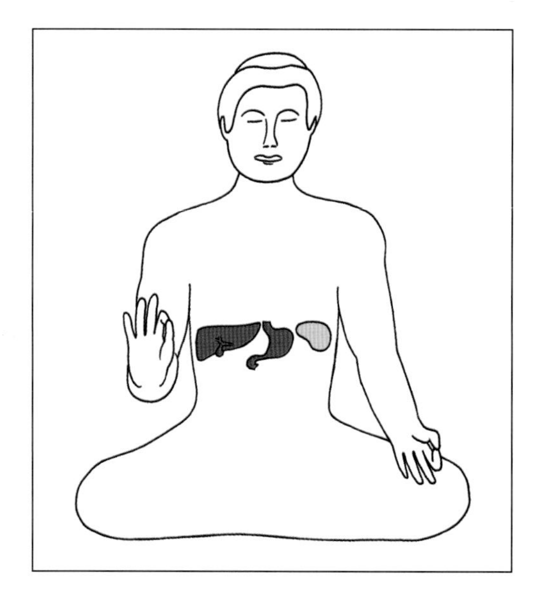

Liver chi stagnation and stomach food retention/stagnation, with spleen damp congestion.

Particulars

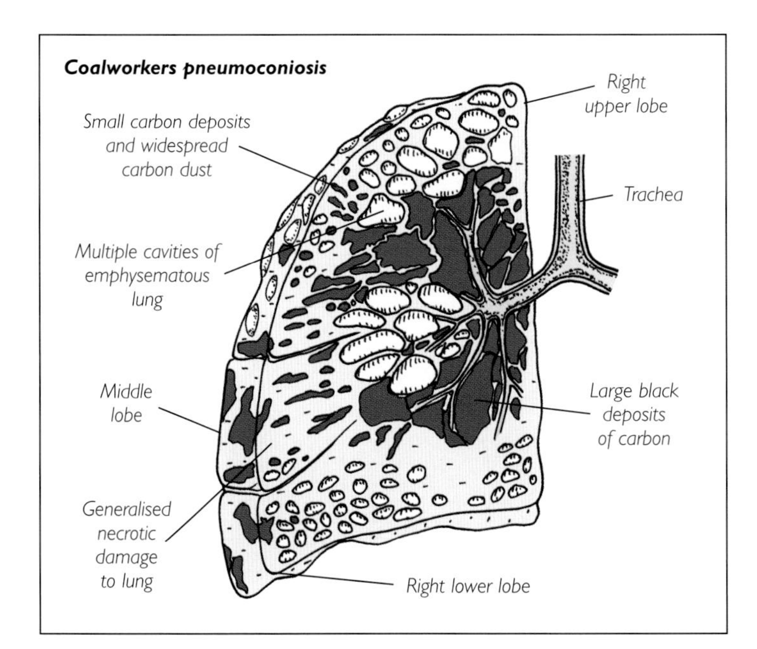

Coalworkers pneumoconiosis is an occupational disease where inhaled carbon dust settles in the alveoli and respiratory bronchioles. This leads to scarring and localised emphysema (collapse of the alveolar structural walls with bullous cavities). Nodular deposits of carbon build up into large visible masses, with widespread fibrosis and scarring throughout the lungs in severe disease. Eventually lung failure and right-sided heart failure can occur.

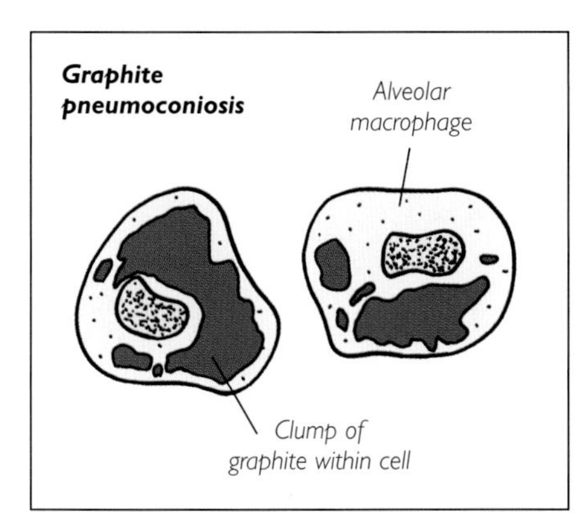

Many types of inhaled respirable particulates can lead to pneumoconiosis and the risk of lung failure in the long-term (e.g. silica, asbestos, coal). Graphite (as carbon particles usually with traces of quartz impurities) powder is commonly generated in certain industries, such as mining, steel manufacture, lubricant manufacture etc. It leads to a similar pathology and clinical pattern as coal workers pneumoconiosis, with nodular deposits, a fibrotic reaction and emphysema. As part of the inflammatory reaction in most types of pneumoconiosis, the macrophages reside at the alveolar phagocytose and retain the contaminates – as shown for graphite in this image.

Related images

p.571 Peptic ulcer & p.36 Hiatus hernia
p.501 Otitis media, glue ear
p.339 Keloid scar
p.71 Eczema with lichenification & p.75 Psoriasis
p.738 Tuberculosis with silicosis
p.95 Cystic fibrosis
p.504 Chronic bronchitis
p.198 Emphysema
p.28 Supplementary oxygen therapy
p.562 Herpes virus

GUNPOWDER

Museum

ABOVE. William Clowes (author). 'A proved practise for all young chirugians, concerning burning with gunpowder, and wounds made with gunshot, sword, halbard, pyke…' © Wellcome Library, London. Heerto is adjoined a treatise of the French or Spanish pockes, written by John Almenar. Illustrated plate, folio B2r of book. Two men are surrounding and attempting to surgically treat a seated man, injured by gunpowder.

PRECEDING PAGE p.352. Jacopo Coppi (1523-1592). 'Invention of Gunpowder', Palazzo Vecchio (Studiolo), Florence © 1990 Photo Scala, Florence. The central figure supervising the production depicts Friar Roger Bacon. In the lower left corner the carbon constituent is being prepared. The pestle just above may contain the sulphur powder being ground. The saltpetre solution is poured in the lower right side container. The purity and consistency of the mixtures is being checked on the table to the middle right. The use of gunpowder is graphically display in wartime with explosive cannon-shot at the upper left corner.

Original

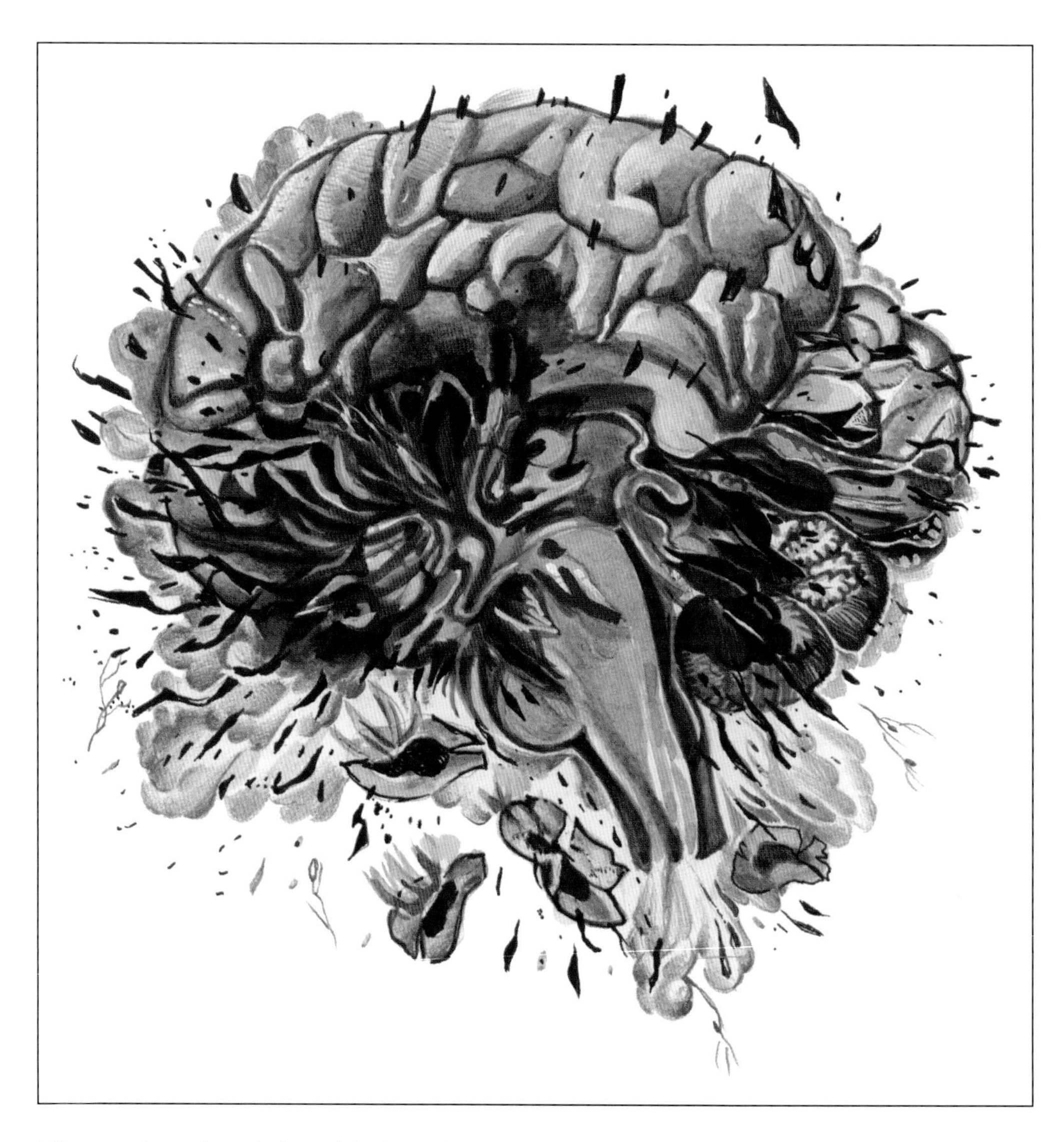

'Gunpowder and explosion of the hypothalamus', by Katherine Mynott. The catharsis and complete loss of function is obvious when such a destructive material as gunpowder explodes within the hypothalamic region, at the base of the brain. This is used as a symbolic representation of destruction by blood toxins and severe heat/fire within the blood. Rifts within the blood-brain barrier can lead to blood-borne infection (sepsis) to enter the brain. The intense heat disseminates throughout the immune and regulatory systems to cause tissue necrosis and gangrene. White cells are shown burning up just below the brain. Shards of black nerve tissue scatter within the ensuing smoke.

An inflammatory reaction on the surface of the brain may occur as a sign of encephalitis and meningitis, shown as red congestion on the surface of the brain and surrounding cloud-like mucus. There is loss of the normal homoeostatic regulation within the hypothalamus, leading to fevers, deranged temperature control and weak immune responses.

Astrology

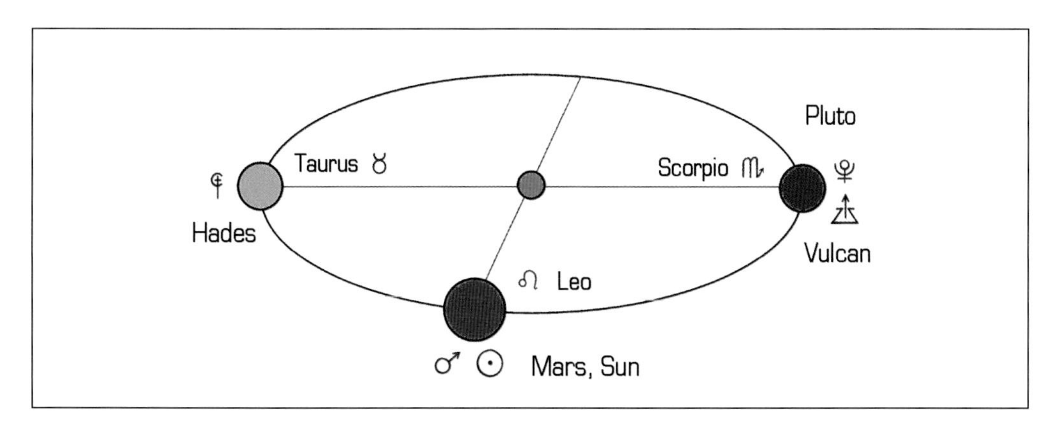

Sun conjunct Mars in Leo, square to Hades in Taurus opposite Pluto conjunct Vulcan in Scorpio.

Oriental

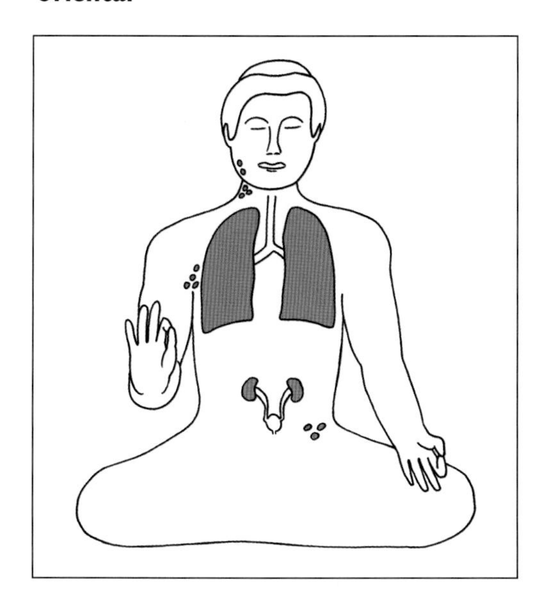

Phlegm-heat within kidneys, lungs and defence chi/lymph nodes.

Related images

p.593 Adrenal atrophy & p.376 Bone marrow suppression
p.374 Immune system and pathogens & p.177 Open wound
p.390 Phantom amputation pain & p.640 Peripheral vascular disease and gangrene
p.277 Motor neurone disease & p.586 Muscle wasting
p.707 Neuropathic joint
p.641 Bowel infarction & p.44 Abscess with necrosis
p.90 Pyrexia of unknown origin and subdiaphragmatic abscess
p.606-612 Radiation and radiotherapy effects

HECLA LAVA

Museum

'Mount Hecla seen from the sea'. Etching with engraving, by unknown artist. © Wellcome Library, London. Note the clouds of steam present over the volcano crater after a recent eruption.

FOLLOWING PAGE. 'Hecla lava and fiery forces within the skeleton', by Martin Jezierski. The pool of sulphur and therefore heat lodged within the planet is seen around the pelvis, to symbolise the grounding of Ego forces (through warmth activity) into the axial skeleton. Mount Hecla is depicted in eruption mode, releasing this heat, spewing lava and superheating surrounding water into steam. Superimposed is a large image of the human mandible, with electrical heat and light forces penetrating through the bones into the subterranean world below. At the top of the vertical portion is the joint process articulating with the temporal bone (TMJ joint). The upper margin of the body of the mandible contain the sockets for the lower teeth. A polarity can be seen within the skeleton. Thus, there is a polarity between the mandible and the femur of the leg, with a similarity between the rising part of the mandible and the upper femur. Since the mandible is related to the leg, therefore the bones connecting to each of these should also be related. Hence the temporal bone (connecting to the mandible) can be compared to the pelvic hipbone (connecting to the femur). In the hipbone there is the joint socket (acetabulum) for the femur and behind this is the opening formed by the pubic bone and ischium. Similarly, within the temporal bone, behind the joint socket for the mandible (temporo-mandibular joint), there is the acoustic opening. Furthermore, the ten toes would reflect the 10 milk teeth initially present in the lower jaw of the baby infant. The reason for juxtaposing the mandible and pelvis in this painting can thereby be appreciated.

HELLEBORUS NIGER

Museum

Max Ernst (1891-1976), 'Celebes' (1921) oil on canvas. © Tate, London 2006 and © ADAGP, Paris and DACS, London 2006. The central mechanical rounded monster is a transformation of a Sudanese corn-bin, thereby creating a disturbing dream-like and surreal image out of something very ordinary. It is a two-legged, drum-like monster standing firmly on the ground, with a geometric design on its top. A headless female figure raises her arm, and fish are swimming in the sky. Celebes is in fact one of the Greater Sunda Islands of Indonesia. The title derives from a German children's rhyme, the first sentence of which is: 'The elephant from Celebes has sticky, yellow bottom grease...'

In terms of symbology, the bull archetype in mythology relates to the physical body and a bull's head is visible on the creature. The painting illustrates the therapeutic principle in Helleborus. When the etheric body is held back or undifferentiated, i.e. not permeated sufficiently strongly by Ego ad astral forces, then the physical body appears misshapen, pre-pubescent or immature. The seven year stages of soul development or unfoldment are relevant, a particular disorder within the 2nd period (age 7-14 years) of importance. During the 1st seven year period (to age 7), the child is learning to grasp its physical body with the forces of warmth and soul (literally coagulating into and hardening its body). During the 2nd period the etheric vitality used for this physical incarnation is freed up to engage with the life of thinking, permeating the head pole and providing imagination as well as preparing the body for the coming puberty. It is from puberty and age 14 (3rd seven year period) that the astral body can mould the etheric-physical into greater definition, with a heightened state of feeling, desire or emotion. The sense of self or Ego may then take hold of the bodily apparatus prepared for it at age 21, the coming of age. Due to the weak penetration of the physical-etheric body by Ego and astral forces, fluid retention and obesity is also common, hence the rise in child obesity over recent years. The sensual torso in the lower right has clearly completed the stage of secondary sexual development and represents the astral body abnormally separate from its physical-etheric counterpart, whilst the central object remains pre-pubescent, in keeping with the above interpretation.

Original

'Helleborus and formation of the embryo', by Jasmine Mercer. An early stage human embryo (approximately the 6 week stage) is attached to the root of the plant, indicating the therapeutic relationship between the two. The landscape is a primordial world of elemental forces. Various primitive creatures are included, such as starfish, jellyfish and filamentous forms. Sun and Moon forces play out in dynamic creativity in the background.

Original

'Hyoscyamus niger and magical powers of the soul', by Caroline Hamilton. Note the twisted stem and the black-purple markings at the centre of the flowers, sometimes regarded in folklore as eyes of the devil or other malevolent beings. Various uses of the plant are shown, such as below the casting of spells by witches, the movement of souls in transit between lives along the middle (the bodies shown in burial wrappings) and above are figures in meditation or trance.

'Hyoscyamus and the subconscious realm', by Katherine Mynott. The realm of the shadow and subconscious is shown in this illustration, as an underground cavern. This realm ultimately lies within each individual human soul. Within it lurks the repressed experiences of the soul, with reference to unfinished tasks and painful memories often from past lives. The Earth realm storing this is the second dimension and lower levels of the fourth dimension (astral plane). Such memories can be accessed across the subconscious collective pool of humanity and thus affect multiple souls. Hence portals are shown within the underground cavern, which interconnect with the subconsciousness of other humans. This particular human has entered his own subconsciousness in this picture, seeking to transform the debris. Angels assist the incarnated souls in countless ways – such as repairing and healing the physical-etheric bodies during nightly sleep of the soul. A Guardian angel is shown at the stairway to the cavern; it is a particular angel that assists the human soul in the management of the many alternate and parallel realities, which the soul experiences through the material plane. Each human soul has their unique guardian, helping to stabilise the personality during periods of crisis. As part of the enlightenment process the individual faces their Guardian at the Threshold, and in doing so are able to take mastery again over their vehicles and bodies.

Astrology

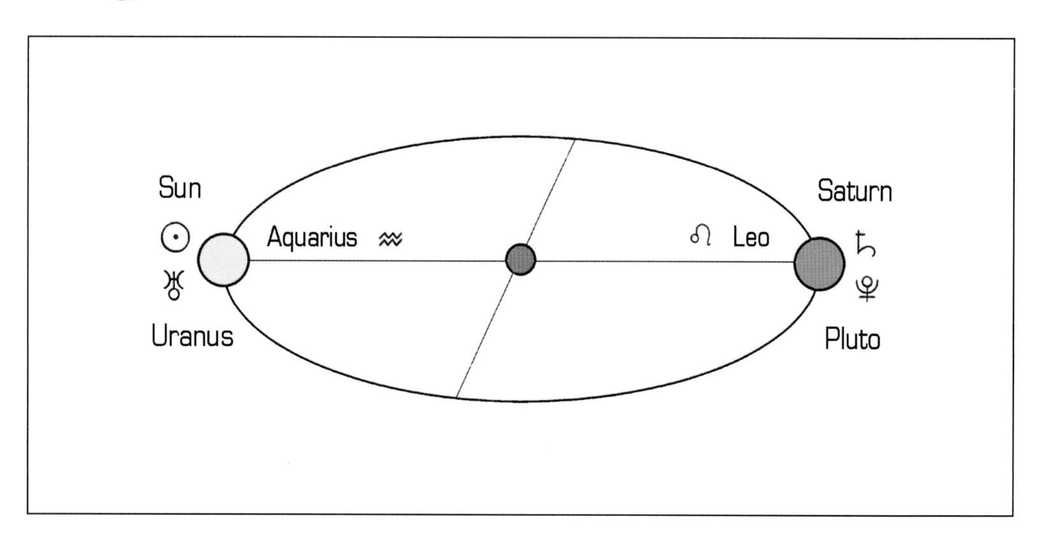

Sun conjunct Uranus within Aquarius, opposite Saturn conjunct Pluto within Leo.

Oriental

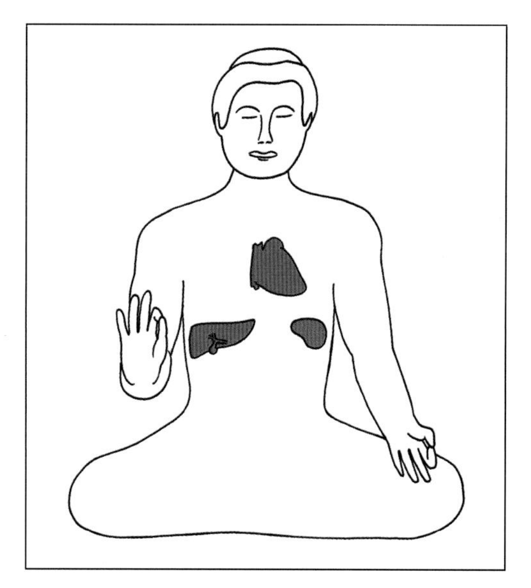

Spleen chi deficiency, with liver fire and phlegm-fire blazing within heart.

Particulars

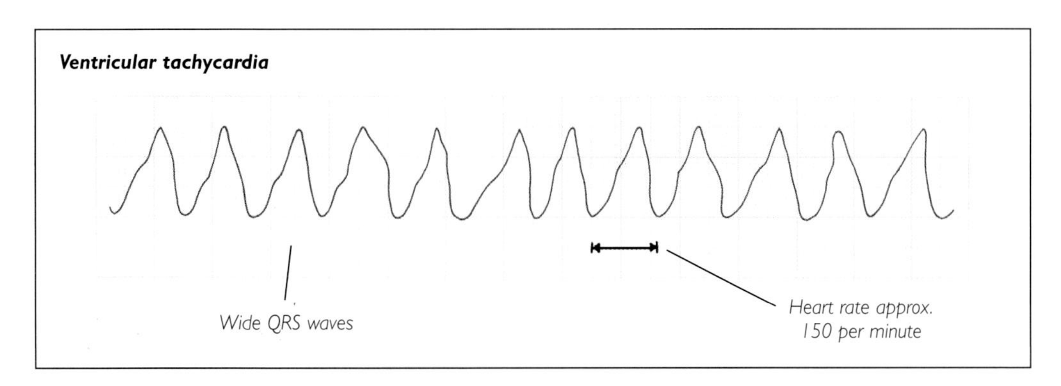

Ventricular tachycardia is defined by the presence of three or more ventricular (i.e. wide-spaced QRS waves) occurring at a rate of 120/min or more. There are usually symptoms of low blood pressure, dizziness and perhaps collapse. It can be an emergency situation and deteriorate into ventricular fibrillation and cardiac arrest.

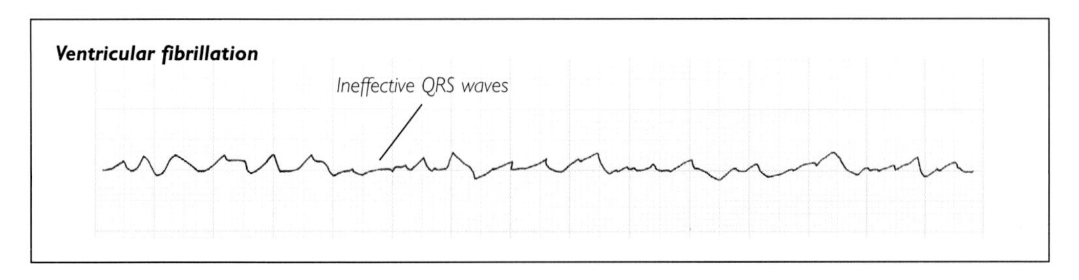

Ventricular fibrillation is characterised by very fast and irregular electrical activation of the heart ventricles but without any true mechanical action. There is therefore no cardiac output or pulse, the patient is collapsed, unconscious and stops breathing. The ECG shows shapeless rapid fluctuations but no actual proper waves. This fatal rhythm is often triggered by a ventricular ectopic beat (especially when in the context of an ongoing myocardial infarction) or as a deterioration of ventricular tachycardia. The only allopathic treatment is emergency electrical defibrillation and resuscitation.

Related images

p.233-234 Epilepsy
p.10 Torticollis
p.485 Irritable bowel syndrome and hyper-peristalsis
p.18 Parkinson's disease
p.202 Glasgow coma scale
p.479-480 Rabies infection
p.55 Encephalitis
p.54 Meningitis
p.282 Cardiac muscle sections and cardiomyopathy
p.264 Supraventricular tachycardia
p.451 Myocardial infarction

HYPERICUM PERFORATUM

Museum

PRECEDING PAGE. Gustave Moreau (1826-1898), 'The Apparition' (1874-76 and 1897) oil on canvas. Musée Gustave Moreau, Paris © Photo RMN / © René-Gabriel Ojéda. The subject is the story of Salome and the beheading of Saint John the Baptist. Parts of the painting appear unfinished, with large vertical sections left rendered in shades of ochre and brown. Typical of Moreau's work, the female figure exhibits beguiling charms, enchantment and corrupted decadence. The background appears to be a mixture of palace, temple and cathedral. Only the apparition has a definite presence, being the bloody decapitated head of St. John the Baptist. He stares at Salome and radiates light beams all round. Meanwhile Salome, in semi-veiled nudity, extends her arm and gazes imperiously towards him. This painting had shocked the conservative audience at the time of showing in the Parisian Salon, branding Moreau as decadent, in response to which he refused to exhibit his works for many years. According to the Gospel of Matthew, John the Baptist had been arrested for criticising the marriage between King Herod Antipas and his half-brother's ex-wife Herodias. In Roman pagan and Tuscan folklore, Herodias (also known as Aradia) was the daughter of the Roman goddess Diana and Lucifer. She became the evil mother of Salome through her first marriage. Although Herodias wanted to have John killed, her new husband dared not, knowing his holy nature. Later, on his birthday, Herod asked his stepdaughter to perform a dance. Note that the daughter's actual name is left out of the Gospel, it was only later Christian history that gave her the name Salome. Salome so enchanted Herod with her performance of the 'Dance of the Seven Veils' that he promised her anything she desired. Herodias seized this opportunity to demand the head of John. The episode has also become the source for the common phrase 'bring me his head on a platter' as a metaphor for anger or retribution.

Mystical wisdom also describes the seven veils as dreams, reason, passion, bliss, courage, compassion and knowledge. These veils are based on the seven sacred planets as symbolic aspects of the soul. Another interpretation of the Dance of the Seven Veils is the sacred journey of the priestess. This begins with the annual symbolic death of the king, his descent into the underworld and his retrieval by the goddess/priestess. To do this, she had to remove a garment at each of the seven gates en route. The priestess was known as 'Salome' or 'Shalom' (meaning 'Peace'). The veils thereby represented earthly illusions being stripped away. In this manner the beheading of John could be seen as a sacrificial death of the king and pre-empting of the descent of Christ into the underworld subsequent to His own crucifixion. A similar theme is found in the mythology of the goddess Ishtar, the Babylonian goddess of love and fertility. She descended into the underworld for six months of each year in order to meet Death and attempt to end all suffering on earth, during which time the surface was barren and inhospitable. For the other six months it was her husband Tammuz who went below, and the earth was fertile again. For her descent, Ishtar had to part with one of her seven earthly attributes at each of seven gates (a guardian residing at each one), thereby arriving naked and defenceless. This reflected the ideal death journey of every mortal soul. Nonetheless, history tended to portray Salome and her dancing as decadent and evil. Another connection was made with the so called 'Whore of Babylon', with whom all the kings of the world had fornicated. This being was described as sitting on a scarlet beast with ten horns and seven heads, and she held a gold vessel full of the horrid products of her conception. She also became intoxicated with the blood of the witnesses to the crucifixion at Golgotha. The whore represents the aspect of the human that has lost itself to matter, i.e. 'fornication' with matter should create spiritually pure and harmonious art, not something base or corrupt. She was also the anti-Grail, the true Grail being the inner Chalice or receptacle for the pure Soul-Spirit to descend into and reside within the body.

Original

'Hypericum and death of John the Baptist', by Katherine Mynott. St. John's decapitated head resides above the plant, its blood spilling onto the leaves (which thereby retain a blood-red spotty pattern) and his headless body. Note the leaves of the plant are close to the stem. Angels hover in support on each side. On the ground are several of the saints to illustrate the collective unity of the ascended masters. They express a mix of veneration, devotion and dismay. At the foreground is St. Francis Xavier, whilst at the back, from the far left to the right, are Mary Magdalene, St. Philip the Apostle, St. Charles Borromeo, St. Veronica (with the face of Christ on her wipe-cloth), St. Rock and St. Peter the Apostle. John the Baptist also received a certain initiation known as the Angel-Aquarian (Waterman) initiation. This is where he becomes an angelic being and reveals traits of a future stage of the human known as consciousness-soul. Indeed, this is indicated by Russian iconography in religious art, where John is often shown with the wings of an angel. Therefore, at the point of Golgotha, John in the spiritual realm is channelling down and preparing the human race to enter the future Aquarian age, when humans will become more at one with their Spirit-Self as consciousness-soul beings. In the Gospels this stage is also referred to as the 'Son of Man'. (See also p.108-112.)

Astrology

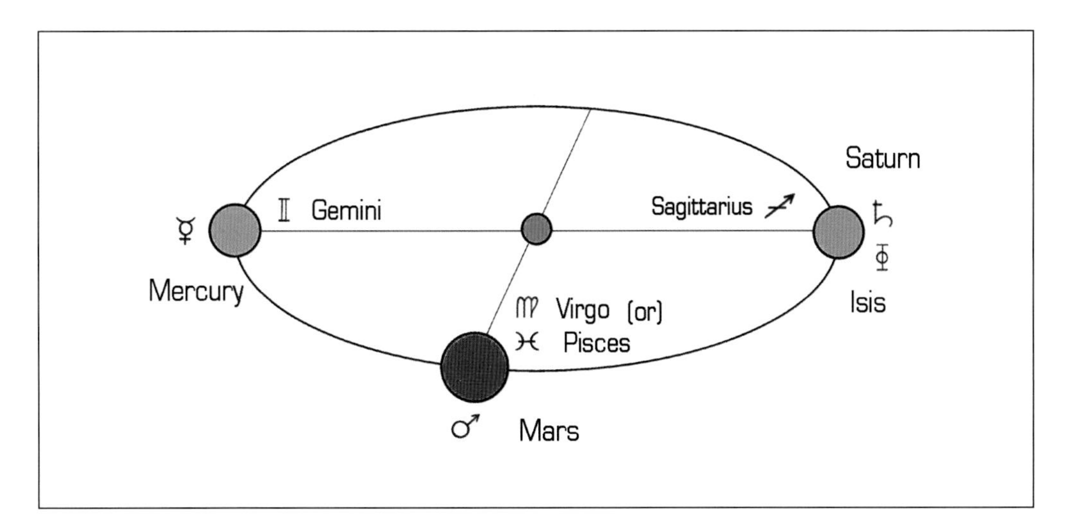

Mercury in Gemini opposite Saturn conjunct Isis within Sagittarius, squared by Mars (in Virgo or Pisces).

Oriental

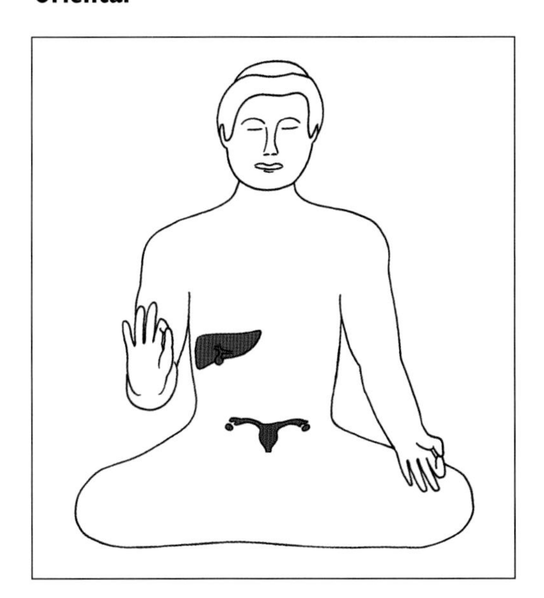

Liver chi stagnation with uterus/lower burner blood stasis.

Particulars

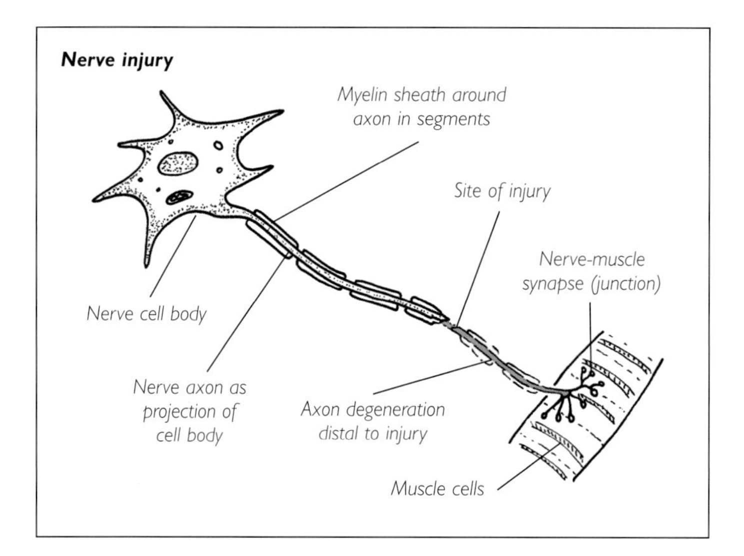

Nerve injury may occur at different sites of the nerve, to the cell body, axon fibre, myelin sheath, to the surrounding connective tissue or nutrient blood supply. If the cell body is damaged this will cause progressive loss of the whole axon. With damage only to the axon and/or myelin sheath then nerve regeneration is possible by growing new axon, typically at a rate of 1mm per day.

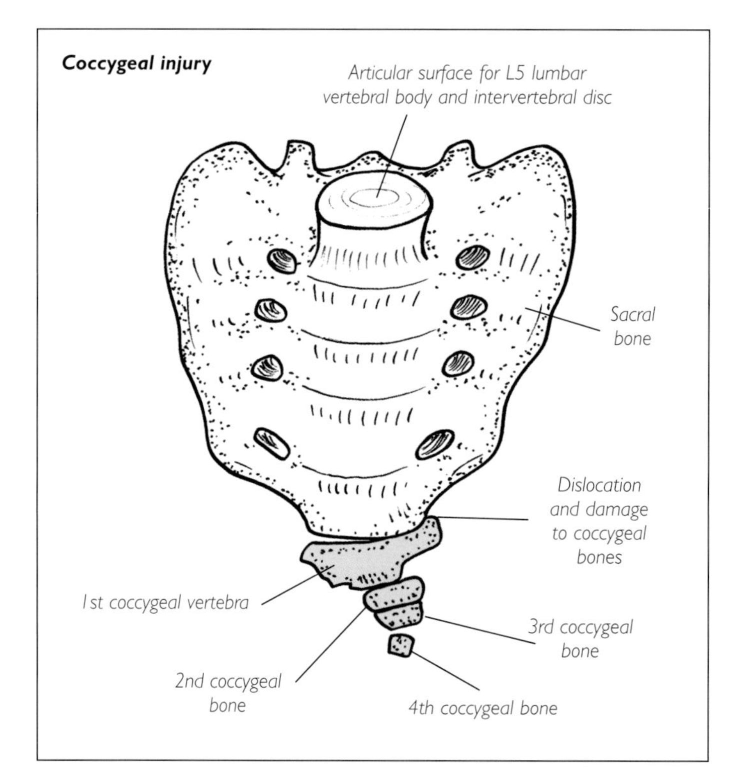

The coccyx (tailbone) is the remnant of the embryonic tail – which is present until the 8th week of gestation life. It is composed of four small vertebrae, but occasionally there is one more or one less than this number, the Co1 (1st coccygeal) vertebra is the largest and articulates with the sacral bones above. The lower 3 coccyxes often fuse with each other during middle life to form a beak-like shaped bone (hence its name coccyx means cuckoo). Later, in old age, the 1st coccyx often also fuses with the sacrum above. In females the curve of the coccyx is less anterior (less pushed forward) to enable the pelvic outlet to be larger and function as part of the birth canal. During labour the 1st coccyx vertebra flexes and extends with the sacrum. The coccyx do not contribute to supporting the body weight alongside the rest of the vertebral column, but do provide attachments for part of the gluteus maximum (buttock) and coccygeus muscles, and for the anococcygeal ligament. In severe or unusual injuries the coccyx may separate from the sacrum, such as from a fall directly onto the buttocks. There is coccydynia (pain in the coccygeal region), often aggravated by sitting.

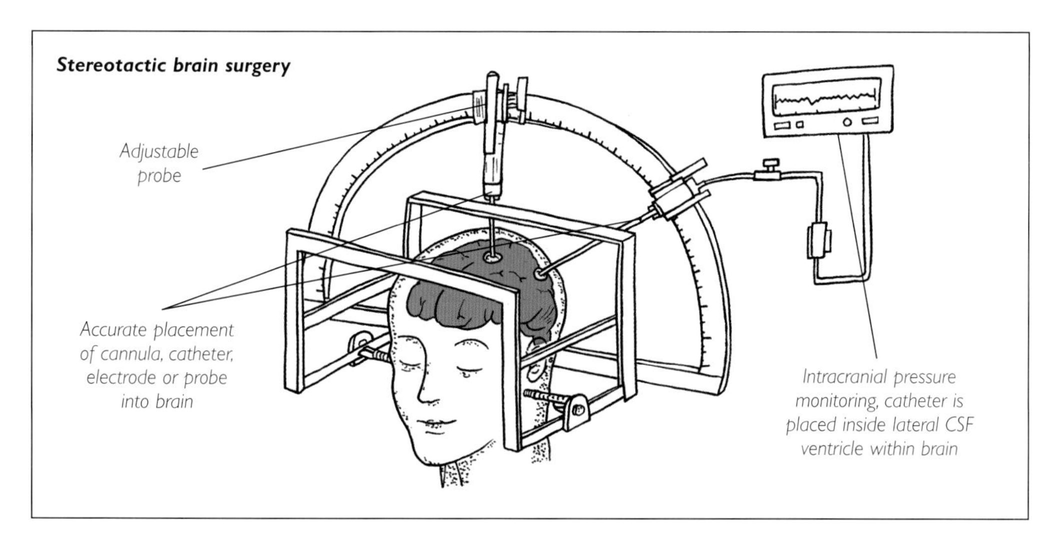

Stereotactic techniques have developed to allow accurate placement of probes and surgical instruments to predetermined target sites within the brain. Many different types of stereotactic frames are available, one example shown here. Combined with radiology, such as CT scanning, and an accurate brain atlas, there can be anatomical localisation to within 1mm. Various energies can be transmitted by the probe to destroy or manipulate a brain pathology, e.g. heat via a radiofrequency current by electrode, cold via a cryogenic probe, or implantation of a radioactive seed such as yttrium for localised radiotherapy. Pain fibres can be destroyed (usually in the thalamus) for treating severe pain refractory to other treatment methods. Focal psychosurgery can be attempted, e.g. subacute tractomy has been used for severe depression. Intracranial cerebrospinal fluid pressure can also be monitored, by inserting a catheter into a lateral ventricle. This is used, e.g., when investigating normal pressure hydrocephalus, or in post-operative monitoring. Note, however, a stereotactic frame is not necessarily needed for CSF pressure monitoring, as localisation is usually easily effected manually.

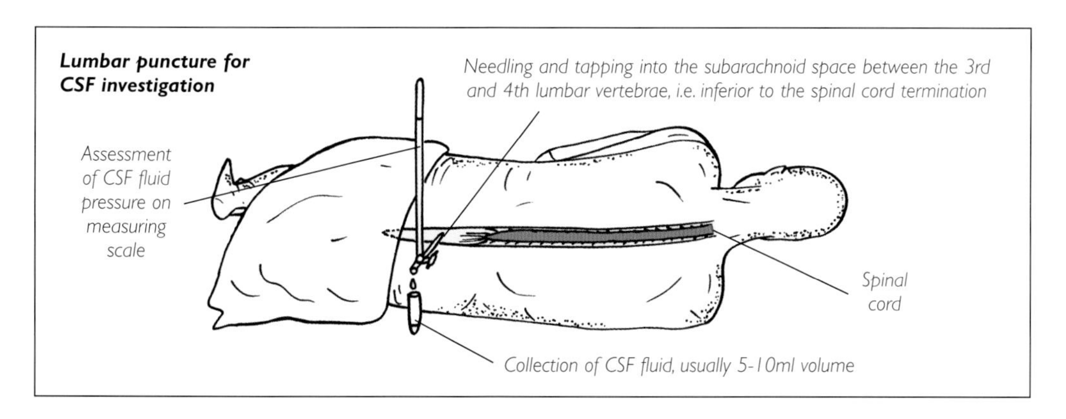

A spinal tap (see also p.54-55 and p.389) is performed below the level of the spinal cord as shown (a line drawn from the highest points of the iliac crests of the pelvic base passes through the 4th lumbar vertebra to help surface localisation). After the CSF sample has been withdrawn, leakage of the fluid from the site of tapping can cause severe headache, so the patient should remain lying down for 8-24 hours post-procedure to minimise this leakage. A raised CSF pressure occurs in raised intracranial pressure or cerebral odema of any cause. The CSF is bloodstained in subarachnoid haemorrhage. Meningitis can be investigated by culture and microscopy of the sample to determine the microbial pathogen involved and antibiotic sensitivity.

IGNATIA AMARA

Museum

'Prince Siddhartha sees the three signs', volume 3 of a palm leaf Burmese manuscript. © Wellcome Library, London. The image is used to demonstrate the extremes an individual may experience, of material and spiritual life. As a young man, Prince Siddhartha is shown travelling to a park in a palanquin with his courtiers and soldiers. He sees three of the signs, an old man, a sick man and a corpse, which profoundly affect his conscience. These three signs lead to his renunciation of the secular life. Buddhism has its roots in India around 2500 years ago, being founded by a Hindu prince, Siddhartha Gautama, who became known as the 'Buddha' meaning 'The Enlightened One'. His incarnation began in a rich county of northern India around 560 B.C., ruled by King Suddhodana. The Queen, Maha Maya, had a strange dream of a white elephant carrying a lotus flower, which walked around her three times and then pierced her with its tusks in her right side. This is remarkably in keeping with the concept of the trinity, and the entry into her liver (right side) of the world karma with its redemption (symbolised by the elephant and lotus). The wise councillors of the couple predicted that a great and noble son would soon be born. At his birth Siddhartha immediately made seven steps (symbolising the seven root races of humanity) and his skin was golden in colour (i.e. a Christed being). Fortune-tellers then predicted he would either become a great king, or, if he were to leave the court would become an enlightened being. His path would then become revealed upon seeing four special signs – an old man, a sick man, a dead man and a forest monk. As a boy, Siddhartha excelled in his studies and was very popular, strong and handsome. His father, however, in an effort to prevent him receiving the special signs that would divert him from his kingly future, ordered that no sick or old people or any signs of death should ever be allowed near the prince, and no monk was allowed within a mile of him. Siddhartha went on to marry and have children. Yet all the while he felt there was something more to life and to his destiny. One day, at age 29 (note that this equates to his Saturn return from an astrological standpoint), he instructed his coachman Channa, to take him for a drive into the city. The King's precautions at last began to fail, for the prince saw a hunched-up weary looking old man. Upon asking Channa the meaning of this he realised that all people eventually grow old and cannot escape the clutches of time. The deeper meaning behind this sign was the realisation that linear time is ultimately false and to be transcended into spiritual immortal time. Siddhartha was much worried, and the next day again went out with Channa for a drive. This time he saw a sick man who was writhing in pain on the ground. He realised then that any person has the capacity to get ill. The deeper esoteric significance is that he realised that true health must come from within, from the union of one's spirit and body. Until then, humanity had resorted to imploring the gods and higher spiritual beings for healing, but Buddha was to bring about a path of true healing from one's own ego. The next day, Siddhartha saw a funeral procession with a dead person and mourners all around. He discovered therefore that all people have a lifespan and ultimately die. The fourth time he went out, Siddhartha came across a wandering monk, who, despite his ascetic appearance and begging bowel, appeared serene and peaceful. He realised the path of a pure heart and his need to leave the palace to adopt the same lifestyle. For the next six years he wandered, learnt yoga and meditation from two great religious teachers, fasted for long periods and practiced extreme austerities. He could reach the formless realms, but could not yet achieve enlightenment. His flesh became so wasted that he was skeletal. Instead of finding superhuman powers and strength he only became progressively weaker. He realised there must be a better middle way to enlightenment, and so began to eat again and regain his strength. He then sat at the foot of a Bodhi (Bo) tree and began to transform the desire nature rather than escape from it. He discovered great joy and pleasure through the control of desire and with one-pointedness. He dissolved his past life karma and purified all aspects of his being. He transformed and then transcended the nature of pain. He was intensely tested by Mara, the great tempter, but could not be swayed from his purpose. Finally darkness and ignorance was dispelled and he became the Buddha. In his next phase of teaching others, the Buddha knew it would be difficult for humans to understand the nature of material attachment, desire and lust. But he also knew that ultimately self-realisation involves finding the still point in the centre, rather than being polarised into the excesses or the suppression of the material nature. It is interesting that Buddhism is unusual in not originally deriving from a belief in an ultimate God, although it recognises heaven, hell, gods and goddesses. Its emphasis is instead on ethical behaviour and development of right character, and provides for a non-violent path to liberation from karma and reincarnation.

Esoteric teaching, based on anthroposophy, furthermore describes the purpose of the Buddha. The Buddha is connected to the Initiations available through the planet Mars, through which He provides the correct morality to prevent unnecessary war-like tendencies or aggression. He provided humans with the capacity to develop the 16-petalled lotus blossom, a higher organ of perception residing within the astral body and especially connected to the throat chakra and larynx. Half of its 16 petals have already been prepared for humanity; the other 8 must currently be developed by each individual. This depends on the 'rightness' in the quality being mastered. The first quality to develop is described as 'right opinion', i.e. being without sympathy or antipathy. This leads to the second, 'right judgement', followed by voicing the 'right word', then the 'right way of acting', then 'right point of view', 'right habits' and 'right memory' (i.e. not forgetting one's lessons) and finally 'right attitude of contemplation' (a state of consciousness which interlinks all of one's incarnations). In a future stage of humanity, these qualities will be present inherently in all, rather than currently sought after by the few.

Andrea Pozzo (1642-1709), 'Entry of Saint Ignatius into Heaven: central part'. Church of Sant' Ignazio, Rome © 1990 Photo Scala, Florence. Pozzo was a Jesuit brother having great faith, and commissioned to produce various important and lavish works of art for the Jesuit churches. The church of St. Ignatius was built as a Roman college/church and founded in 1551 as a school of grammar, humanities and Christian doctrine, teaching free of charge. It was placed on the location of the Temple of Isis in Imperial Rome, being the heart of the Egyptian district. This school was the model for many other contemporary and later schools and universities. After the canonisation of St. Ignatius in 1622, it was decided to also build a temple to him at the college itself. This church extension was eventually opened in 1650. However, the dome painting by Pozzo was no longer visible by the mid-1700's due to the accumulated lampblack from candles. Furthermore, an explosion from a powder magazine in 1891 opened up tears in the canvas. A recent restoration was effected in 1963. To describe the painting using the words of Pozzo himself: "Jesus [carrying the Cross] illuminates the heart of St. Ignatius with a ray of light, which is then transmitted by the Saint to the furthermost corners of the four quarters of the earth, which I have represented with their symbols in the four sections of the vault." In reference to the missionaries he writes: "The first of these indefatigable workers is St. Francis Xavier, the Apostle of the Indies, who is seen leading a vast crowd of Eastern converts towards Heaven. The same kind of scene is depicted with other members of the Society of Jesus in Europe, Africa and America." The painting displays an endless sense of perspective, and events have been portrayed in grand theatrical style. Mary, and the Holy Ghost is shown as a illuminate dove next to Christ. The heavens seem to stretch into infinity. St. Ignatius is not actually at the ideal centrifugal point where the rays of Christ would meet, but nonetheless becomes the focal point around which all the other figures are arranged. Pozzo also painted foreshortened columns as an extension of the church architecture to enhance the sense of infinity. He was a master in creating optical illusions within restricted architectural spaces whereby the designs appeared larger than their true size.

Original

'Ignatia amara and the supremacy of the Empyrean', by Iona Mackenzie (empyrean) & Nadine Kardesler (plant parts). Various parts of the plant are portrayed below, i.e. a flowering twig, fruit in whole and cut section, a seed and a flower in side and front view. Above is the empyrean, an archaic term for the abode of the gods and angels, the plane of Heaven especially containing the pure elements of divine fire. Through the remedy comes apotheosis, the elevation of an individual to the rank of such divine beings.

Astrology

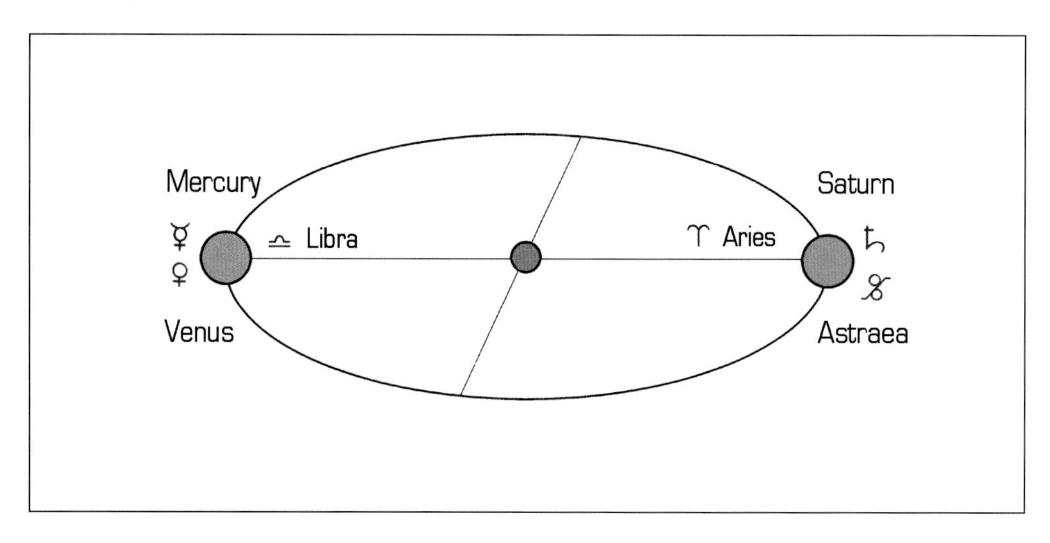

Mercury conjunct Venus within Libra, opposite Saturn conjunct Astraea within Aries.

Oriental

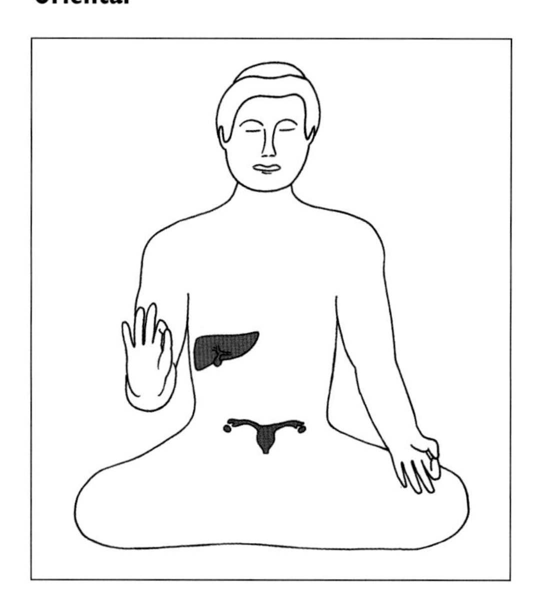

Kidney essence deficiency with liver blood/yin deficiency. Interior wind invasion of heart and phlegm obstruction of throat/thyroid.

Particulars

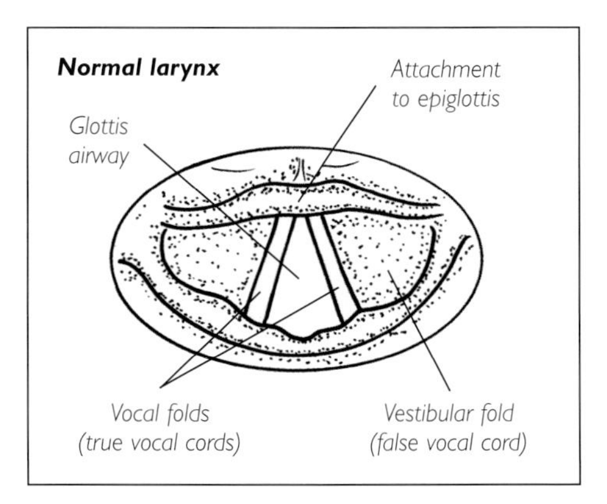

The larynx provides the means for the production of sound by manipulating the movement of air. It also protects the lungs from aspiration or inhalation of solid matter. The vocal folds are mucosa lined ligaments stretching across the cartilage linings on each side of the larynx. These are moved side to side depending on need, e.g. are momentarily closed (adduction) when building up the air pressure to cough and brought closer together to produce sound of varying pitch and volume. In normal breathing they are kept open (abduction). The vestibular folds are fibrous tissues that passively move in accordance with the vocal folds.

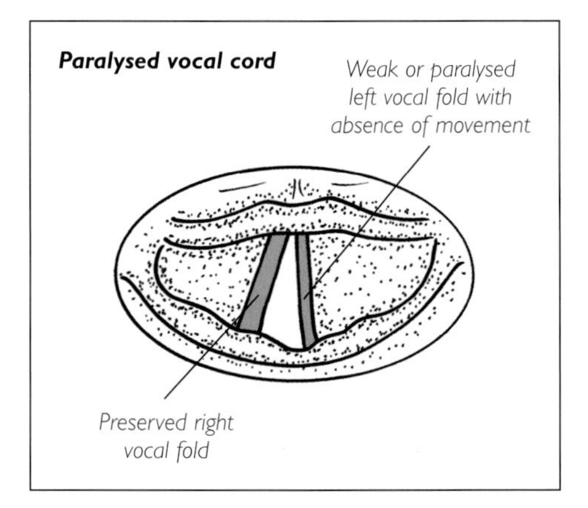

Laryngeal nerve palsy or damage can cause the vocal folds on that side to become weak or paralysed. Bilateral nerve damage will affect both vocal cords; here the left side is shown affected. Causes of nerve damage include pressure from a thyroid goitre, damage done during throat operations or the infiltration of cancer. There will be a change of voice. Laryngeal paralysis can also occur in Botulism infection. The causative microbe, Clostridium botulinum release neurotoxins that block the nerve-muscle junction. Other features initially are vomiting and diarrhoea. After laryngeal and pharyngeal paralysis there is generalised paralysis and lung failure.

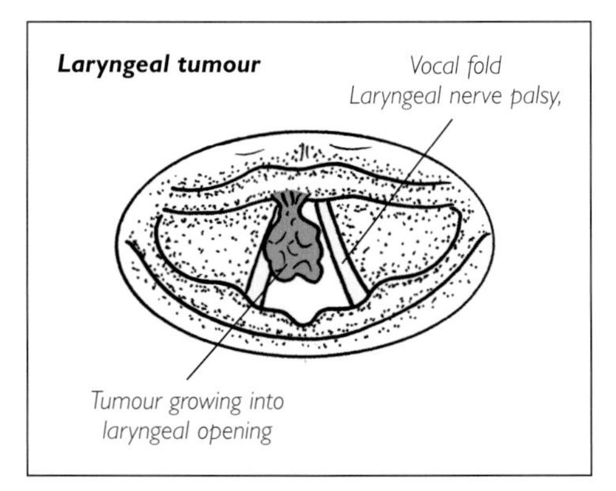

A tumour growing within the larynx needs investigation to exclude cancer. Smoking and asbestos exposure are risk factors for cancer. It may otherwise be a benign nodule or cyst. The symptoms include a hoarse voice, or loss of voice (from disordered movement of the vocal cords) and a stridor or wheezing sound on inspiration from the partial airways obstruction. Smaller vocal cord nodules can also be found in singers and frequent speakers.

Related images

p.232 & p.343 Multiple sclerosis
p.10 Torticollis
p.139-140 External virilisation
p.390 Phantom amputation pain

IODUM

Original

'Iodum and Atlantean battle between forces of light and dark', by Loolie Habgood. The landscape has a brown iodide colouration. Although duality is ultimately an illusionary program within humanity, this conflict was especially heightened during the latter days of Atlantis. The forces of light and good are represented by the humanoid on the right foreground and angelic being hovering above. Extraterrestrial activity is represented by the UFOs' high above (especially from the constellations and star systems of Orion, Sirius, Pleiades and Lyra). Although most alien influences were positive, some negative or dark aliens were also present. They are projecting yellowish light from their throat chakras, carrying the iodine process of communication at this centre. Dark beings are shown by the greyish entities on the left and the dragon above, emitting reddish rays out of the throat chakras and spewing fire respectively. Pink-red rays spiral out of the solar plexus of the beings, symbolising the increased activity (particularly with the Mars forces) of this chakra during this epoch. The subtle body undergoing development during this root race was the emotional/astral, but negative states of entrapment, paranoia and vulnerability also occurred. The ultimate karmic problem during Atlantis was theft of soul parts or the energies of others for personal gain. Beings attempted to entrap and steal from each other. The image shows a foggy atmosphere; this had become thick with the human emotional smog of lower astral clutter, and the stars became hidden from view. This caused further alienation, such that during the midpoint of the Atlantean root race the world and humanity were at their densest state of separation from the spiritual realm.

Astrology

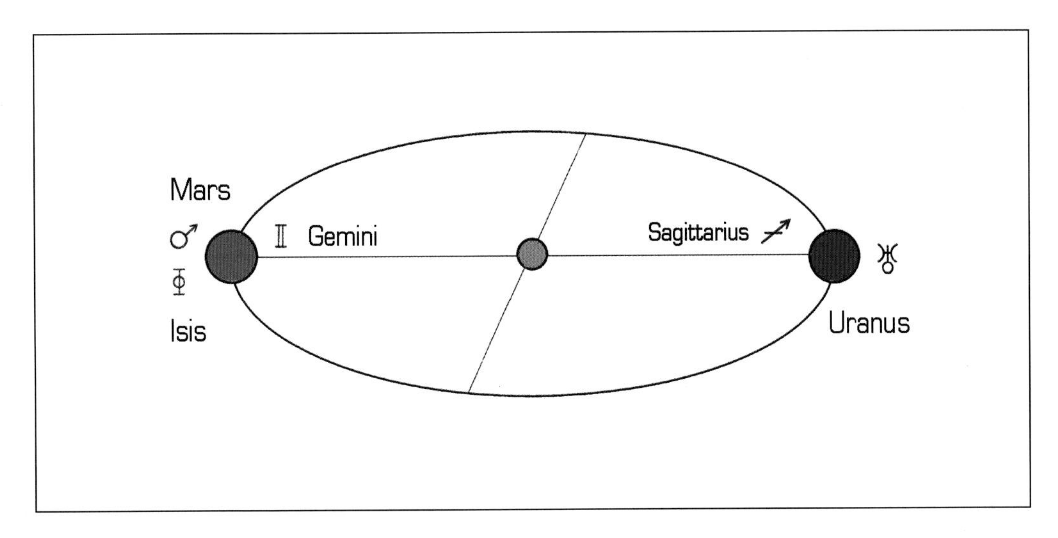

Mars conjunct Isis within Gemini, opposite Uranus in Sagittarius.

Oriental

Spleen chi deficiency with phlegm-fire within stomach.

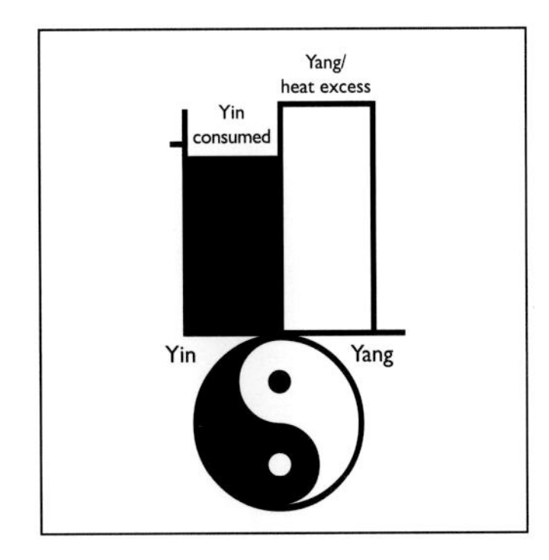

Particulars

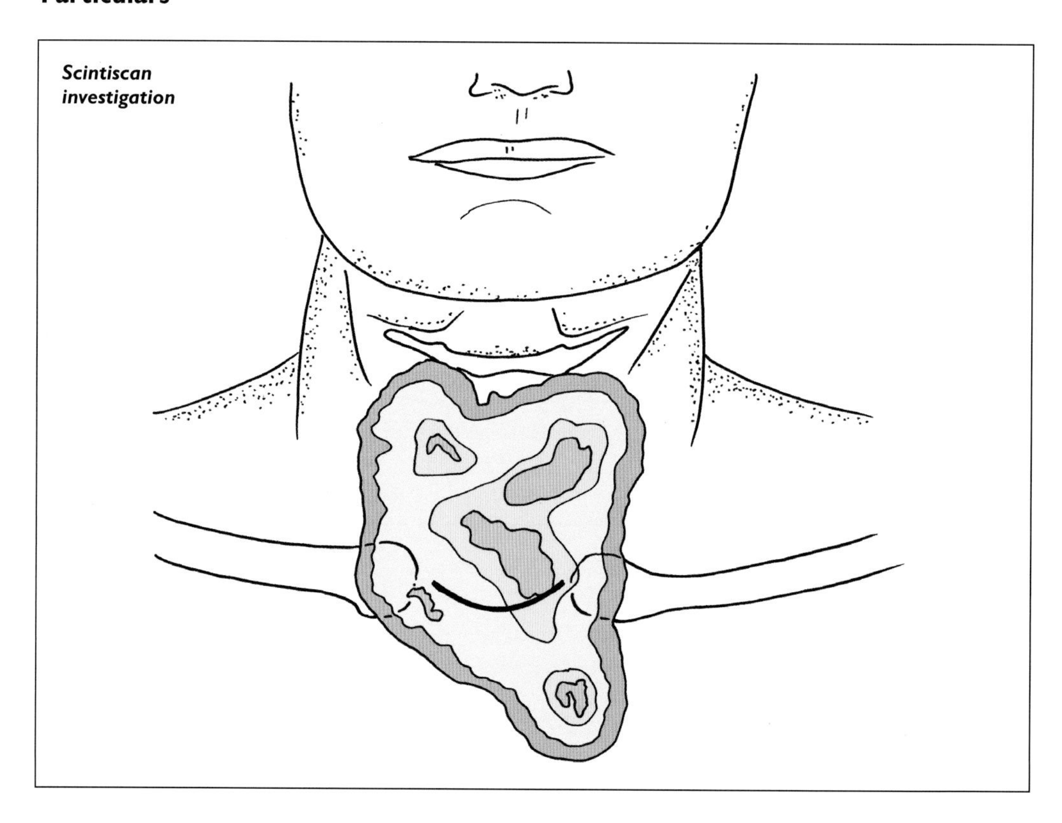

This image shows a scintiscan investigation. There is enlargement of the thyroid gland with extension down behind the sternum (retrosternal space). The procedure uses a radioactive isotope (radionuclide), which emits gamma rays. There are different types of radionuclides. Different radionuclides collect or concentrate in different tissues, hence enabling specific radionuclides for scanning of parts of the body. Radioactive iodine injected intravenously is rapidly taken up into the thyroid gland. Thyroid cells which are most 'active' will take up more of the radionuclide and thereby emit more gamma rays than less active or inactive parts. Gamma rays, being similar to x-rays, may be detected by a gamma camera and a computerised image built by converting the differing intensities of radioactivity emitted into different colours or shades of grey. Areas of tissue emitting the most gamma rays are usually shown as red spots ('hot spots'). Low levels of gamma rays may be shown as blue ('cold spots'), with various other colours for the spectrum in between. In this example of the assessment of hyperthyroidism some hot spots or nodules are a focus of overactive metabolism. These may require biopsy to exclude a malignant transformation.

Related images

p.729-732 Thyroid disease
160 Cushing's syndrome
p.98 Genital underdevelopment
p.103 Tonsillitis
p.420 Candidiasis
p.13 Allergic rhinitis

Astrology

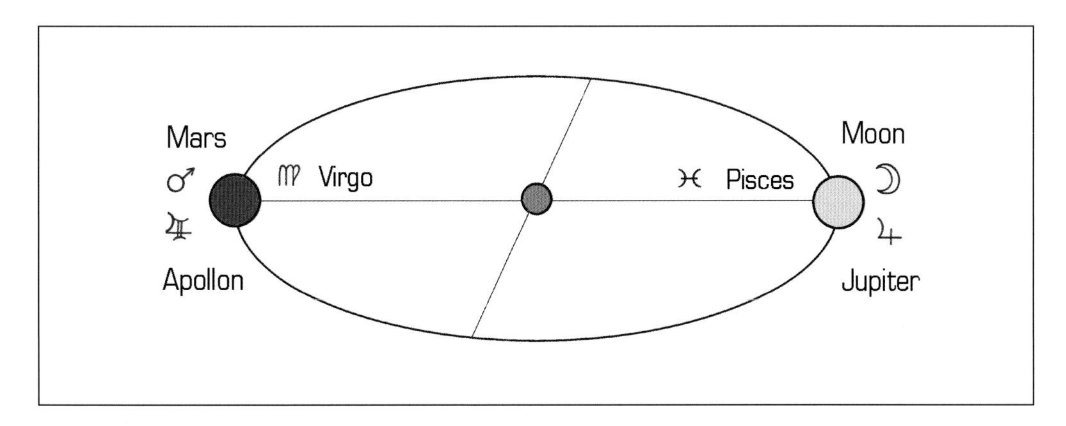

Moon conjunct Jupiter within Pisces, opposite Mars conjunct Apollon within Virgo.

Oriental

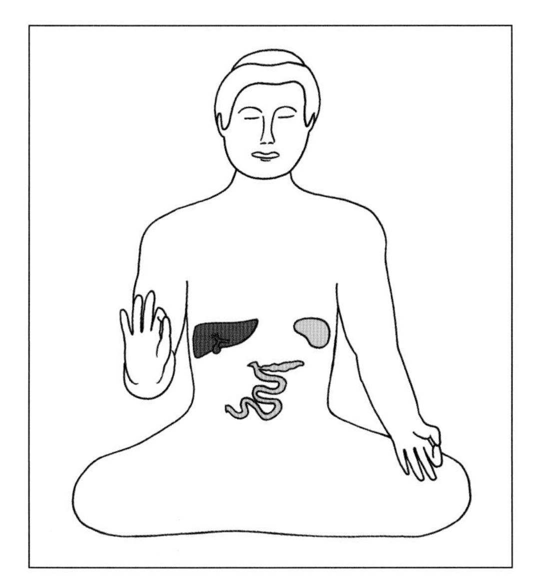

Liver chi constraint/stagnation, with damp obstruction/congestion of spleen and intestines/pancreas.

Related images

p.561-562 Hepatitis & p.222 Fatty liver
p.222-223 Gallstones & p.223 Jaundice
p.133 Liver failure and ascites & p.470 Pancreatic failure
p.527 Cluster headache & p.528 Migraine visual aura
p.603 Splenomegaly
p.408 Sinusitis & p.95 Cystic fibrosis
p.621 Capsulitis, frozen shoulder & p.620 Supraspinatus tendonitis

KALI BICHROMICUM

Original

'Kali bichromicum and ancient plant evolution', by Caroline Hamilton. Potassium processes relate to those of the plant, and to the intracellular metabolism. These dynamics are related to an earlier stage of evolution, typically Old Moon when the world had three primordial kingdoms of plant-mineral, plant-animal and animal-human. Here the layer of cells depicts both plant and animal cellular features. They are shown as an epithelium or surface, which is best suited to receive the plant-oriented etheric forces streaming into the planet. The etheric realm is composed of wide flowing sheets of energy, and is particularly captured by plants through their leaf surfaces. The cells are shown with green vessels containing the plant-related chloroplasts, harnessing light beams into glucose through photosynthesis. The red inclusions within the cells represent mitochondria, the actual energy-producing site. The surface area of the cells is greatly increased by their microvilli hair-like projections on the upper surface. The central darker nuclei contain the genetic material for producing proteins and guidance of the cellular metabolism. The light beams, however, are shown radiating with difficulty through a milky-soup like atmosphere. This limits the degree of photosynthesis possible. Whitish mucus is also shown below the cells. This indicates the mucus prevalent in this remedy, and is also representative of the ancient atmosphere of Old Moon.

Particulars

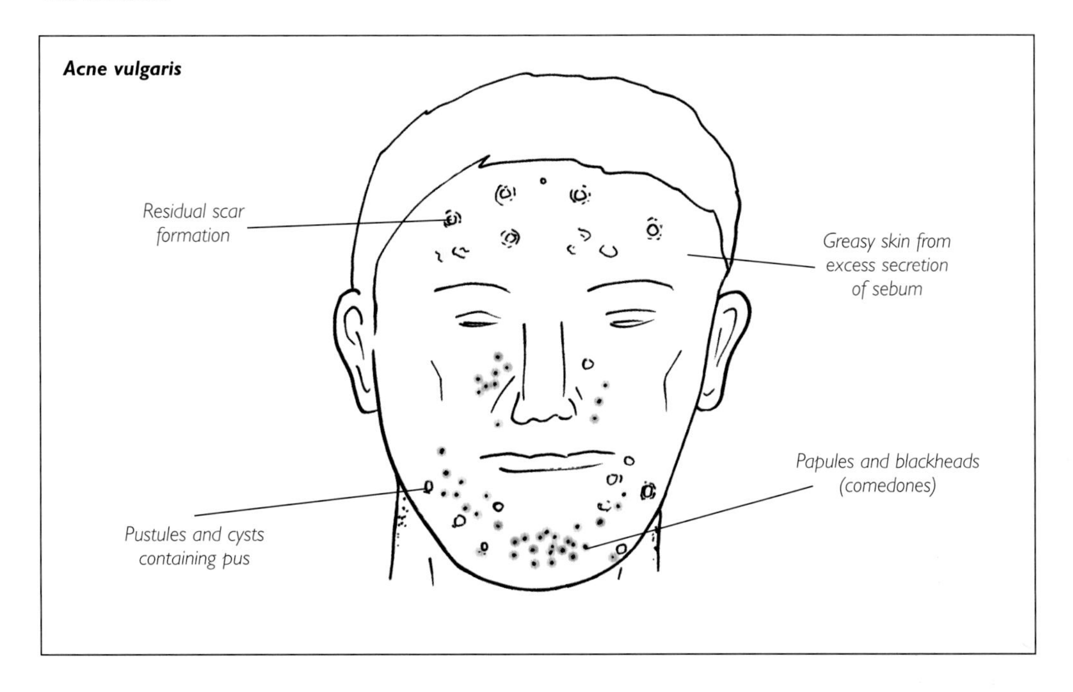

Acne vulgaris is an inflammatory disorder of the skin follicles, especially during adolescence. There is abnormal excessive sebum production, androgen hormone stimulation and colonisation of the follicles by a microbe (prorioni bacterium acnes). Obstruction of the sebaceous ducts occurs. This develops into a comedone (blackhead), a dark plugged up follicle, or to a small papule or lump. Severe scarring can occur, especially when cysts of pus are produced.

Related images

p.233-234 Epilepsy
p.96 Growth chart
p.258 Labyrinthitis
p.260 Meniere's disease
p.650 Acne rosacea

KALI CARBONICUM

Original

'Kali carbonicum and movement of the soul into the etheric body', by Jasmine Mercer. The central figure symbolises the developing personality as it anchors greater levels of its soul-spiritual nature, shown as a beam of descending white light. The Self must permeate the physical-etheric body and its solid-water elements, as indicated by the controlled mobilisation of the watery etheric forces around the individual.

Astrology

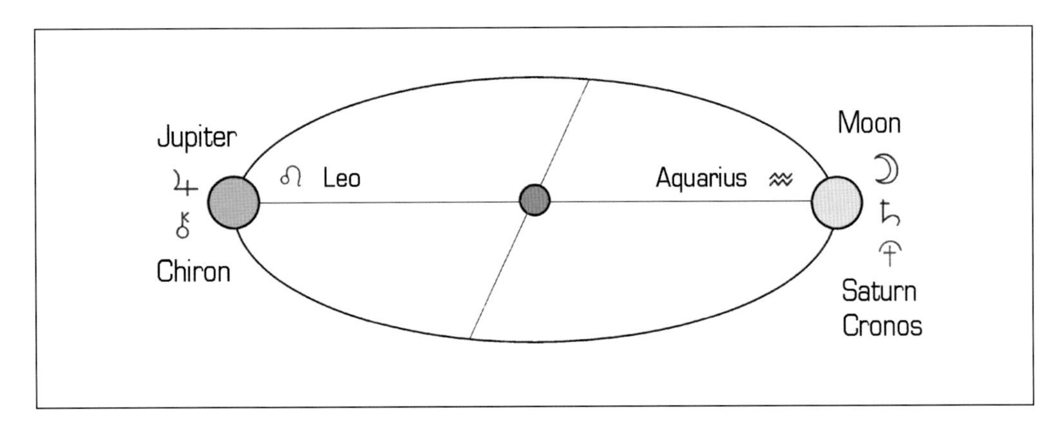

Moon conjunct Saturn and Cronos within Aquarius, opposite Jupiter conjunct Chiron within Leo.

Oriental

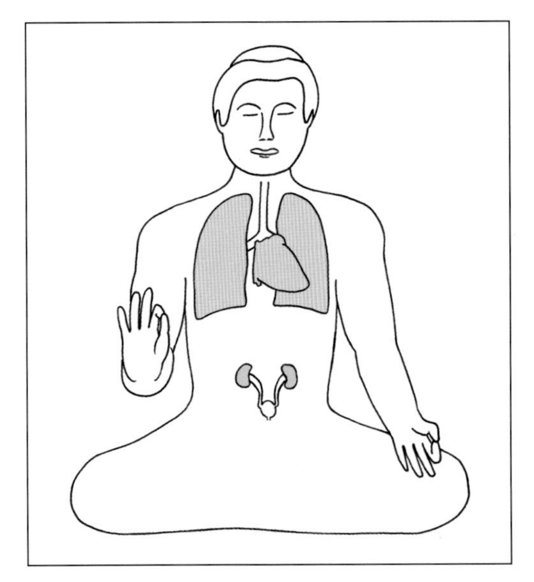

Kidney yang deficiency, with water overflowing within heart and lungs.

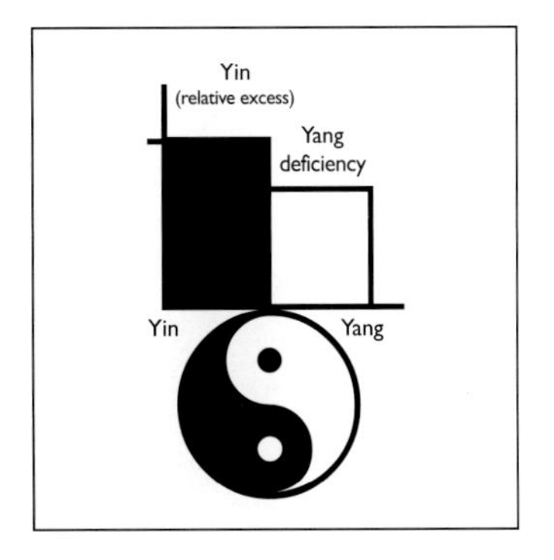

Related images

p.300 Heart failure, right-sided
p.582 Infectious gastroenteritis
p.10 Sciatica
p.504 Chronic bronchitis & p.198 Emphysema
p.50 Sleep apnoea & p.737-743 Tuberculosis
p.543 Haemorrhoids

KALI PHOSPHORICUM

Museum

Auguste Rodin 'Le Penseur', 'The Thinker' Inventory no. S.1295, bronze 180 x 98 x 145 cm, Photography: Jerome Manoukian © Musée Rodin, Paris. Rodin has been described as the Wagner of sculpture – with his vision of man in his misery and yet heroic greatness he revived the deadened art of sculpture in the late 19th century. He had a passion for Dante's 'Inferno' and for the works of William Blake; their description of the journey into hell became an inspiration for characters in his art. The Thinker is the exploratory central figure for his project 'The Gates of Hell', which is related to the portal doors also known as the 'Gates of Paradise' from the Old Testament, but with twisted and anguished figures inspired from Michelangelo's 'Last Judgement'. Rodin never finished this huge work, working on it intermittently until 1900. The Thinker was meant to be Dante in front of the Gates of Hell, pondering on his great poem. In answer to why Dante is shown naked, Rodin himself said: "Thin ascetic Dante in

his straight robe separated from all the rest would have been without meaning. Guided by my first inspiration I conceived another thinker, a naked man, seated on a rock, his fist against his teeth, he dreams. The fertile thought slowly elaborates itself within his brain. He is no longer a dreamer, he is a creator". He has powerfully captured the essence of the thinker, poet and creator as one being, whose thoughts can penetrate into the realities of the underworld and the collective.

Original

'Kali phosphoricum and the vitalised nervous system', by Yubraj Sharma & Esther Lane. The figure is modelled on The Thinker, with the central nervous system traced within. The nature of the thought-forms travelling through the nervous tissue markedly affect the vitality of this system. Spiritualised thinking based on the reception of the channelled thought-forms of one's Soul-Spirit is more conducive to health than mundane or confused thinking. The state of depression especially relates to repeated memories and mental attachments creating a state of feeling earthbound.

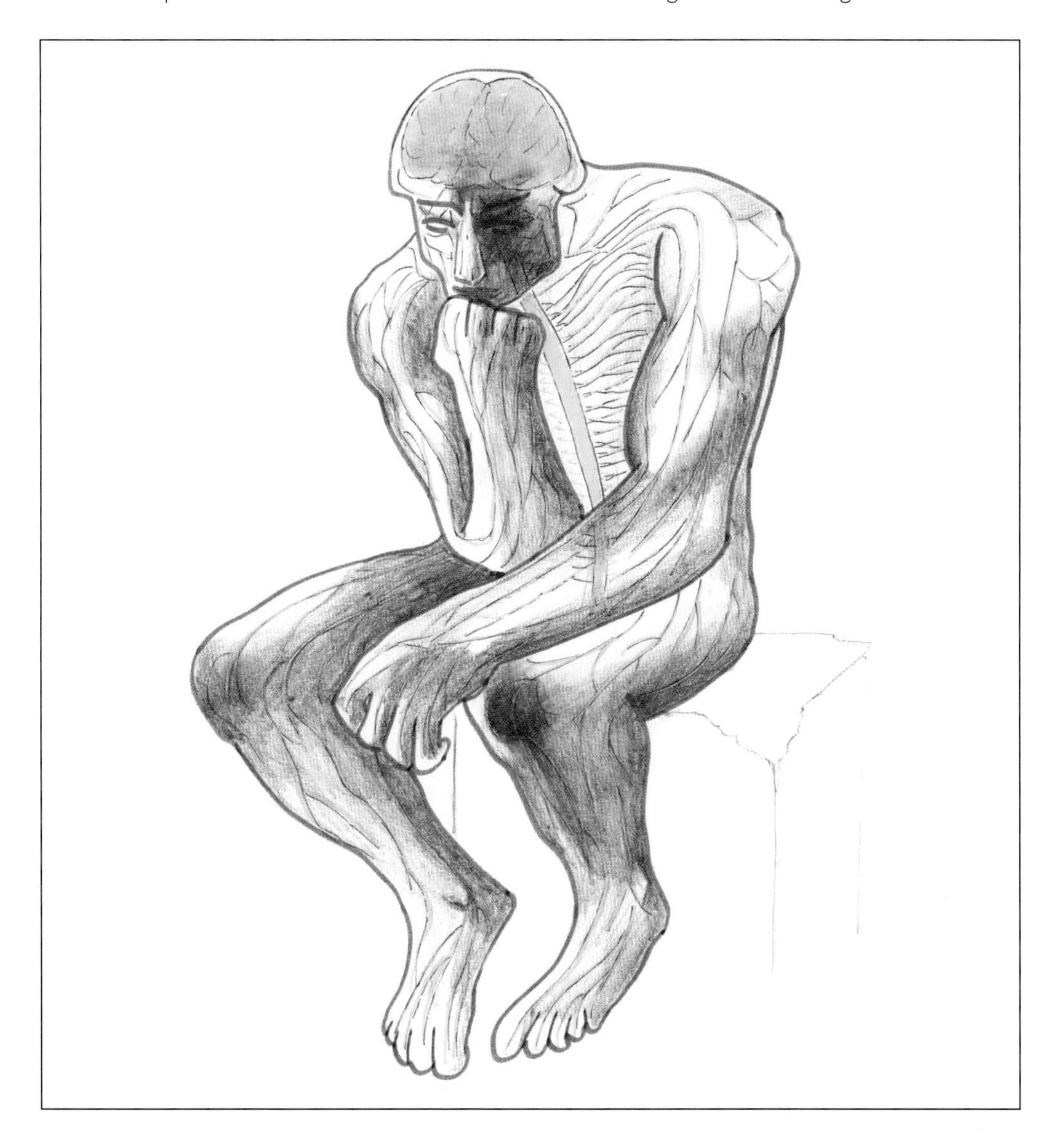

Astrology

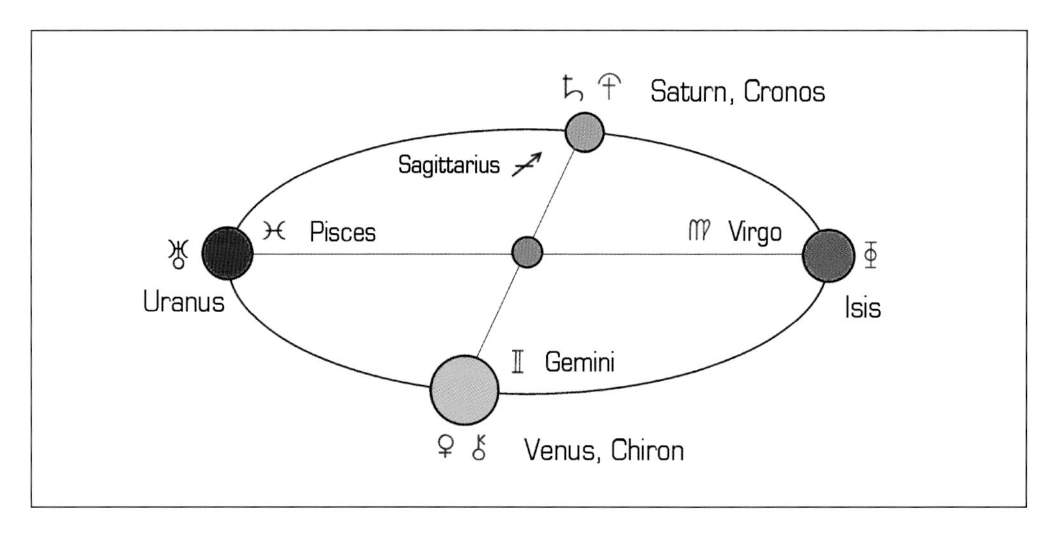

Grand cross, Uranus in Pisces opposite Isis in Virgo, and Venus conjunct Chiron within Gemini opposite Saturn conjunct Cronos within Sagittarius.

Oriental

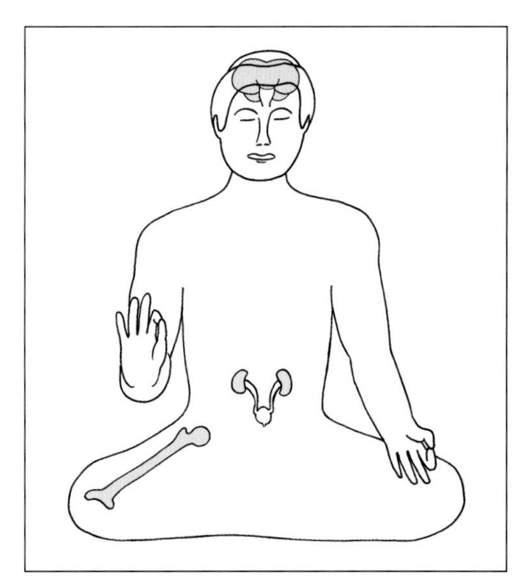

Kidney yin deficiency with yin deficiency of brain, nerves and bone.

Particulars

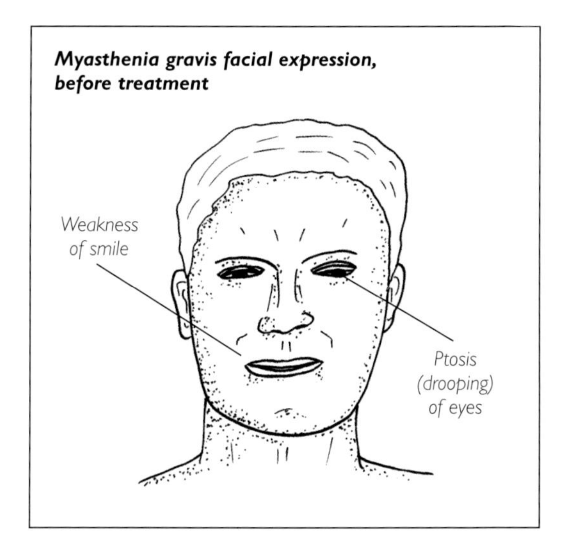

Myasthenia gravis facial expression, before treatment

Myasthenia gravis is an autoimmune disease, where antibodies bind to the postsynaptic part of the nerve-muscle junction, to block the action of the chemical neurotransmitter acetylcholine. Thus nerve signals are blocked from muscle expression. There is a bulbar nerve palsy/weakness, with initially fluctuating and intermittent double vision, ptosis (drooping eyelids), slurred speech and difficulty chewing. Progressive disease leads to difficulty in using larger muscle groups, especially arms and neck – with the need to support the head to stop drooping.

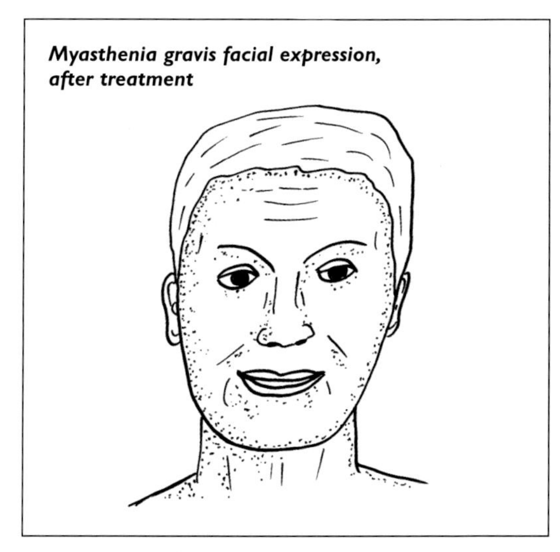

Myasthenia gravis facial expression, after treatment

The specific defect in myasthenia gravis is a block at the nerve-muscle receptor, which normally utilises the chemical neuro-transmitter acetylcholine at the synaptic gap. Allopathic drug treatment therefore attempts to improve the action of acetylcholine and stimulate the receptor for longer. Such drugs, e.g. pyridostigmine, typically block the recycling breakdown of acetylcholine, hence prolonging its availability at the synapse. The diagram shows the effect after such drug treatment, with return of strength to the facial muscles. The duration of a action of a typical drug dose is 3-4 hours, hence repeated dosing is needed.

Related images

p.232 & p.343 Multiple sclerosis
p.586-587 Poliomyelitis
p.277 Motor neurone disease
p.586 Muscle wasting
p.35 Spinal myelitis
p.752 Pineal tumour
p.40-41 Pituitary tumour
p.376 Bone marrow suppression

KREOSOTUM

Original

'Kreosotum and the primordial soup', by Yubraj Sharma. An ancient stage of Earth evolution is depicted, equivalent to early Lemuria (Old Moon). The central grey-black area represents a river of crude oil or petroleum, a liquid flow of partially decomposed organic life. On either side is a primordial sea with solar/yang forces on the left, and lunar/yin forces on the right. In the left-hand sea lie stages of the primitive human embryonic external male genitalia and testes development, and early stages of spermatogenesis (sperm production). In the right-hand sea lie a collection of egg cells within a polycystic looking primordial ovary. Further on, there is a human embryo within the early few weeks of gestation (with its umbilical cord attached to the Moon), and primitive embryonic external female genitalia with the ovarian sequence of follicle development/ovulation. Within the upper part of the central crude oil is an orange-red depiction of the androgynous stage of external genitalia, equivalent to the early weeks of embryogenesis, before it has been segregated into male or female forms. This is symbolic of the stage just prior to the segregation of primordial Adam/human into the Adam-male and Eve-female. Just below this, within the central river is an (light-brown) image of a egg cell fertilised by sperm, where the pronuclei of 23 chromosomes each are about to merge. Throughout the illustration are various primordial sea-creatures, primitive and modern fishes – to highlight the organic nature of the remedy. Furthermore, fish-like forms indicate the early Lemurian root race stage of humanity, during which sexual differentiation occurred (see also p.92-93). The picture also demonstrates the action of the remedy is to demarcate and waterproof (cf. use of petroleum products such as asphalt to waterproof and cover road surfaces and roofs). This defines and differentiates the male and female structures from each other within the developing embryo.

LAC CANINUM

Museum

PRECEDING PAGE. Masaccio (1401-1428), 'Expulsion from Paradise' (1427), fresco panel Santa Maria del Carmine, Florence © 1991, Photo Scala, Florence / Fondo Edifici di Culto – Min. dell'Interno. Adam and Eve are shown in a state of extreme desperation and despair, with tears that are heart-rending. They have been cast out for eating the fruit of the Tree of Knowledge, thereby having attained awareness of themselves (i.e. become incorporated by an Ego and 'come to their senses'). Note how Eve covers herself with her hands, an indication that she is now aware of her gender and sexuality. Their state of abandonment is heightened by depicting the heavenly place they have been expelled from by no more than a tall narrow archway behind them. It can only be imagined what paradise had looked like. Paradise will always be there, yet is now a place beyond one's reach – no longer a place belonging to humans. The angel with her sword brandished appears to be both punishing the couple and ensuring they cannot return whence they came. The landscape of Earth they are entering appears barren and infertile, in keeping with their having to from now on work the land to ensure their sustenance. The Fall coincided with the separation of the Moon from the Earth. If the Moon were to remain bound to the Earth, then the land would have indeed become desolate and lunar. Human bodies would have prematurely mummified or hardened. By separating, the Moon carried away the density of world memory and enabled the Earth to become fructified into a fertile body. The Moon beings especially involved in this process are equivalent to Jehovah-Elohim of the Old Testament. However, the couple are not actually looking forward towards their new earthly home, thus the true meaning of their Fall or descent from Grace is lost to them. They do not realise that the Earth has been prepared for their existence and evolution.

'Dog geoglyph', Nasca lines, aerial photograph (see p.22-23 for description of the Nasca plain).

Original

'Lac caninum and Sirian assistance of Earth transformation', by Iona Mackenzie. Centred high above is the Sirius star system, from which Sirian spaceships stream into Earth orbit. The dog (with pups) is depicted as a power animal spirit working in cooperation with these particular extraterrestrials. Below are scenes of catastrophic Earth changes, such as glaciations, volcanic eruption, flooding and tornadoes, in connection with end-times when human root races, civilisations and cultural epochs have gone through periodic upheaval and renewal. Hence, the dog has played various stabilising roles with humanity, such as guide-dog, rescue-dog etc.

Astrology

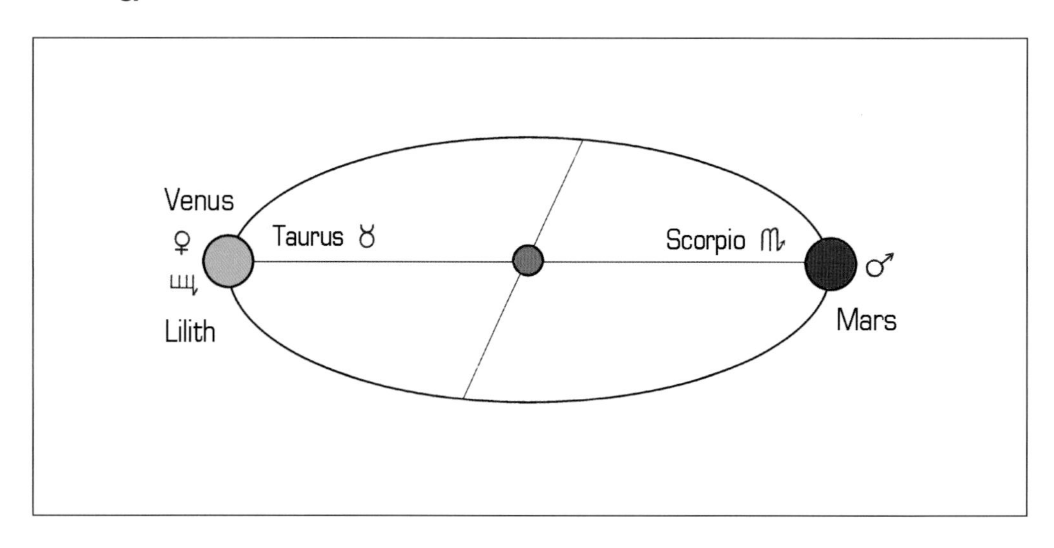

Venus conjunct Lilith within Taurus, opposite Mars in Scorpio.

Oriental

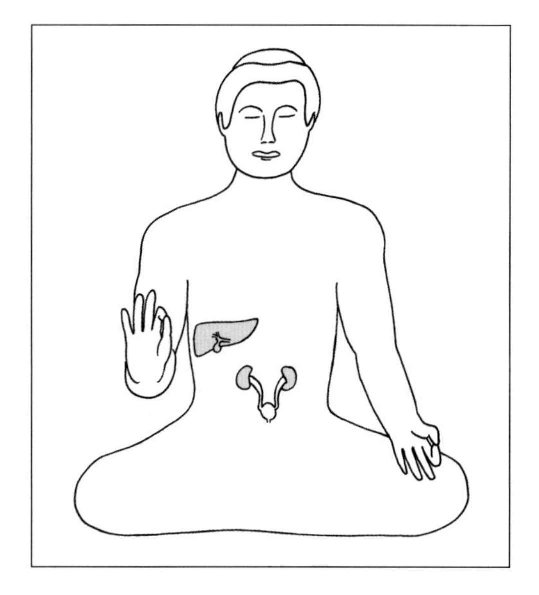

Kidney yin deficiency, with liver yin/blood deficiency.

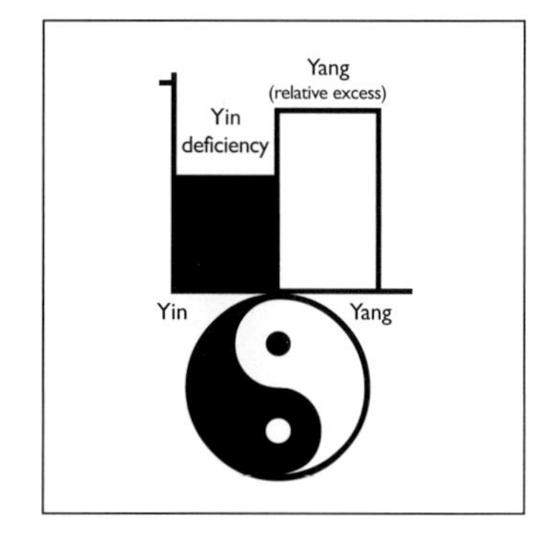

Particulars

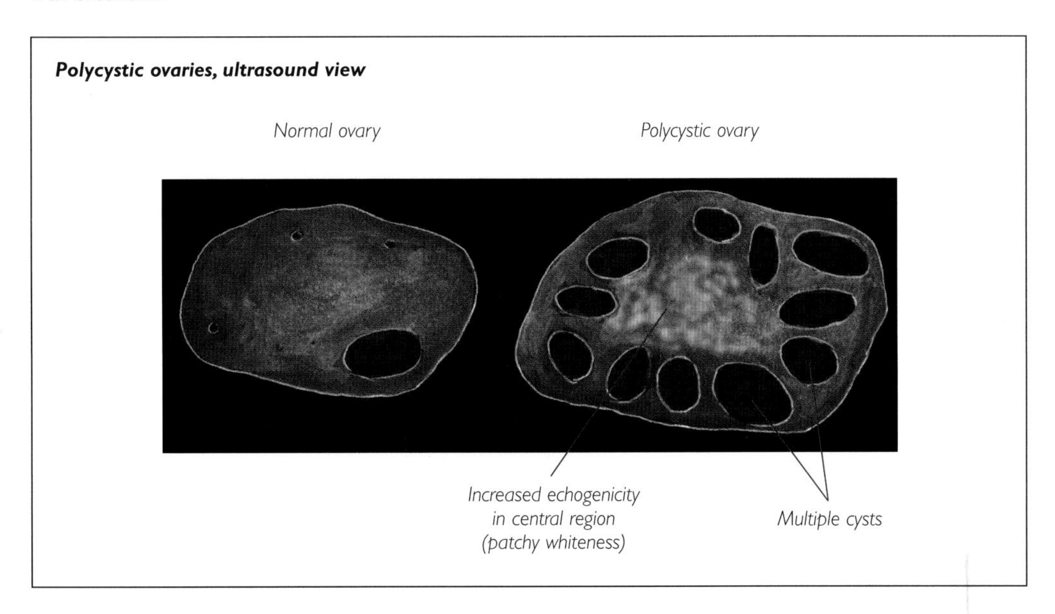

Polycystic ovaries, ultrasound view

Ultrasound of the ovaries will identify a polycystic pathology if present. Typical findings are of a thickened ovarian capsule, with multiple cysts (of 3-5mm diameter) and often increased echotexture of the central portion of the ovary (this latter finding is due to the increased hormonal metabolic activity).

Related images

p.335 Polycystic ovary
p.103 Tonsillitis
p.4 Croup
p.57 Ovarian inflammation
p.210 Ovarian cancer
p.335 Endometriosis
p.675 Female sterilisation
p.434 Mastitis
p.371 Breast abscess
p.528 Breast fibroadenoma
p.209 Breast cancer

LAC HUMANUM

Museum

Leonardo da Vinci (1452-1519), 'Madonna Litta' Hermitage Museum, St. Petersburg © 1990 Photo Scala, Florence. This has been regarded as one of the artist's great works. The theme is also known as 'Virgo lactans' – the breastfeeding Virgin Mary. 'Caritas' is also another term with mystical

MATERNAL LOVE
J. G. des. et fec.
Pub. Feb. 15 1796. by H. Humphrey. New Bond Street.
The Fashionable Mamma, — or — The Convenience of Modern Dress

overtones, referring to [continuation from p.428] a mother breastfeeding one or more children. Art historians often trace the imagery as a continuation of the ancient Egyptian art imagery of the goddess Isis suckling Horus, and that of the Greek goddess Hera breastfeeding Hercules. In Christian theology the theme of Jesus taking milk from Mary symbolised His humanising process, i.e. the Son of God taking on human body through the nature of Mary. In this particular painting, the Jesus Child's awkward posture and plain landscape has caused some to suggest it was probably completed by his pupil Boltraffio. There are nonetheless compositional difficulties with the lactans theme, in attempting to show a child's face alongside a frontally viewed mother, when it should be pressed to the breast. A typical solution to this during the Renaissance was to have the child temporarily disengage its mouth from the nipple in order to look toward the viewer, and furthermore this added an intelligent human quality to the Child. See further details on breastfeeding in Thymus gland, p.723. The breastfeeding theme in art was also often portrayed alongside the scene of Christ's crucifixion in art of the medieval period. There is an association between the lactation of Jesus by Mary, and the pouring of the blood of Christ into the world as an act of the saviour. Sometimes the Blood of Christ would be shown being collected in a chalice to represent the Grail Initiation. Therefore, the esoteric meaning behind the breastfeeding of the Holy Child can be appreciated – as a preparation for His role to come on behalf of the whole of humanity.

PRECEDING PAGE p.429. James Gillray. 'The fashionable mamma', or 'The convenience of the modern dress'. Etching with watercolour, 1796. © Wellcome Library, London. A fashionable upper class mother is wearing a dress with slits across the breasts so as to feed her baby just before dashing off to the waiting carriage outside – presumably to more important social engagements. She is clearly not connecting to her baby with any warmth or love, and it has to rush its feed before it is pulled away. Only the woman-servant appears to exude any tenderness towards the child. The painting on the wall shows a devoted wet-nurse or mother, holding her left breast using the pseudo-zygodactylous hand gesture (see 'Cimon and Pero' in Thymus gland p.723). The lady has therefore completely lost sight of the sanctity of breastfeeding.

FOLLOWING PAGE. 'Lac humanum, the pregnant mother and the evolution of the world', by Sophie Harrison. The image suggests how a conscious or spiritualised gestation or pregnancy will lead to harmonious balance in the postnatal period, promoting lactation and mother-child bonding. The mother receives the etheric blueprint of the planet within her womb during the gestation. She appears like a receptacle or bowl, in keeping with her yin nature – receiving the cosmic yang forces of an incarnating soul into her pelvis. The developing embryo therefore progressively descends to an Earth reality prepared for it. Indeed, where this becomes deranged, the child may grow up feeling alienated from the world. Warmth forces are shown stimulated within the heart and brow chakras, indicated by the glowing spirals and the redness in the aura around the chest region. This is an expression of the maternal love alongside the hormonal surges. Past life information from the incarnating soul is also streaming through the mother's brow chakra, thus she can build into the embryo's body those attributes needed to balance any residual karma or express latent abilities. She is receiving a light from the spiritual realm through her brow chakra. She also holds a Moon-like world in each hand, symbolising her divine goddess power of creation and indicating that lunar forces regulate the pregnancy. The breaking of the waters from the amniotic cavity reflect the flow of oceans and rivers of Earth, hence the benefit of a water birth to enable a graceful birth. This is also symbolic of an early stage of the human race (Lemurian) when the world was predominantly fluid-like, and human bodies were soft or gel-like. This principle is referred to in alchemy as the Universal Waters. Since the pregnant woman's aura is so much more open and permeable with world forces, then the problem of post-natal depression can sometimes develop were the woman to not return into full control of her physical-etheric body after labour and birth.

Original

'Lac humanum and streams of incarnating energy within the newborn soul', by Loolie Habgood. The mother is holding her newborn child at her breasts in passionate love, her warm breastmilk assisting the coagulation and mixing of several streams of incarnating energy. From the star above descends the soul-spiritual purpose of the child, with the perspective of its higher self. The winding red current from below represents those experiences from past life incarnations that are entering into the present incarnation. The straight brown stream from below represents the ancestral codes entering the baby's body, which would be largely equivalent to the modern concept of genetic inheritance and miasmatic influences. The mixing of all these within the baby is facilitated by the warmth between mother and child, this interaction symbolised by the two spirals connecting between the mother's heart chakra and that of her baby.

Astrology

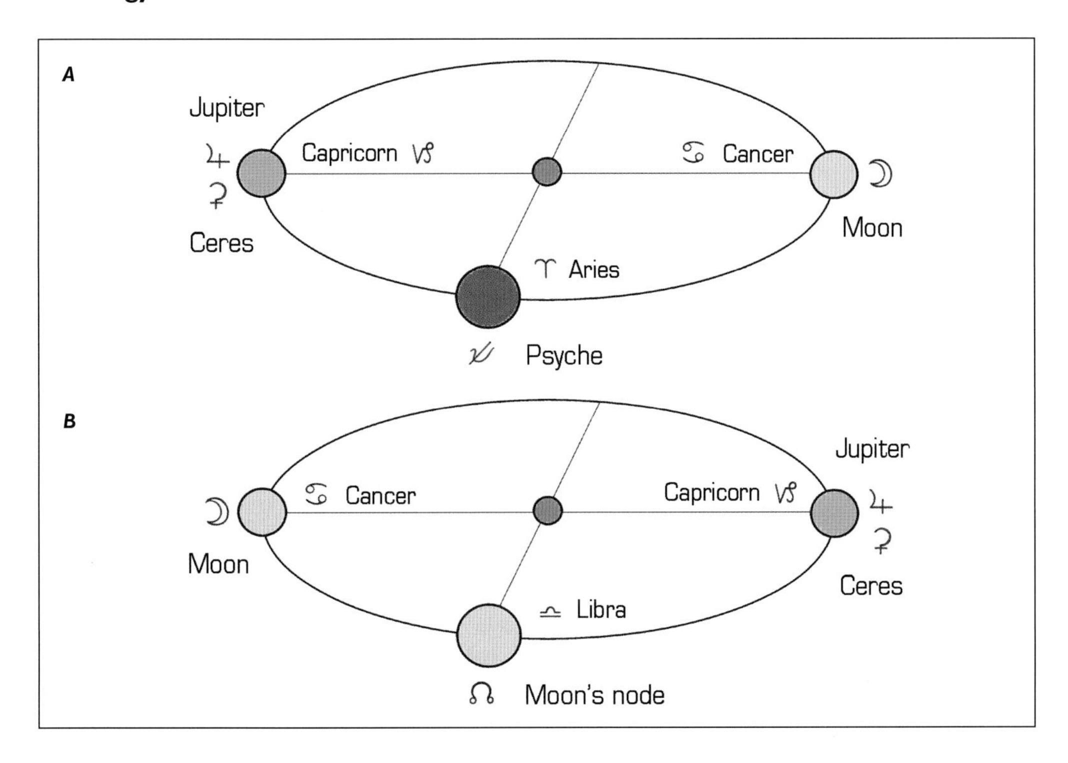

A – Jupiter conjunct Ceres within Capricorn, opposite Moon in Cancer, squared by Psyche in Aries.

B – Jupiter conjunct Ceres within Capricorn, opposite Moon in Cancer, squared by Moon's node in Libra.

Oriental

Spleen chi deficiency with deficiency (gathering) chi of lungs and heart. Chi deficiency of thymus gland.

Particulars

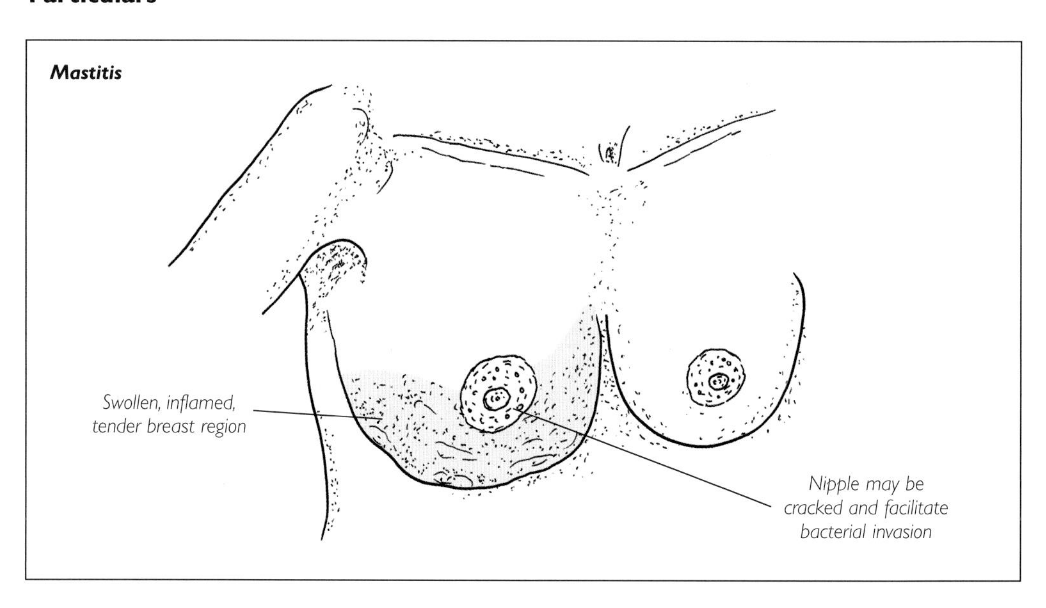

Breast milk engorgement (during lactation or breastfeeding) usually affects the whole of one or both breasts, whereas mastitis typically affects part of one breast. There are two main causes of mastitis – non-infective due to blocked milk ducts, and infective due to bacterial infection (usually invading through a cracked nipple). There is a rare risk of breast abscess.

Related images

p.376 Bone marrow suppression
p.369 Pneumonia stages
p.50 Sleep apnoea
p.96 Growth chart
p.327 Anaemia
p.207 Cancer growth chart
p.208 Leukaemia
p.507 Coeliac disease
p.171 Rickets
p.172 Osteomalacia
p.172 Osteogenesis imperfecta
p.505-506 Gum recession

LACHESIS MUTA

Museum

Albrecht Durer, 'Adam and Eve' (1504), engraving on ivory laid paper. Corte di Mamiano, Fondazione Magnani Rocca © 1999 Photo Scala, Florence. God created Adam in his own image (out of the dust of the Earth) and then breathed life into him. The first act of Adam is his giving names to the beasts of the field and the fowl of the air. Thereafter God caused a deep sleep to fall upon him, and whilst unconscious took one of his ribs with which to make woman, whom Adam named Eve. Although God has placed Adam and Eve in the Garden of Eden, to cultivate it and enjoy its fruits, the one prohibition was: "Of the Tree of Knowledge of good and evil thou shalt not eat it; for on the day that thou eatest thereof thou shalt surely die." Eve was induced by the serpent (later made into Satan) to eat the forbidden fruit, and she also persuaded Adam to partake of this. Until then they were nude, but their eyes' were opened, and they had to make aprons of fig leaves to cover their sexual features. Durer depicts Adam in keeping with Apollo Belvedere and Eve to Venus. They seem quite unconscious of their nakedness, yet already wear the fig leaves. The animals shown represent the various characters of the human. All features of the print are in balance. Thus, before biting the apple, Adam had harmony of the four temperaments, sanguine, phlegmatic, choleric and melancholic. The wise benevolent parrot is shown in contrast with the diabolical snake. The branch of mountain ash which Adam holds represents the Tree of Life, in contrast with the forbidden fig tree, which here represents the Tree of Knowledge.

David Humbert de Superville (1770-1849), 'The Flood'. © Prentenkabinet Rijksuniversiteit te Leiden, Netherlands. See description of Atlantis in Berlin wall, p.120. The Atlanteans eventually destabilised the planet too much for their civilisation to continue. There arose a great deluge, described throughout mythology. This cataclysm led to the submergence of Atlantis under what is now the Atlantic Ocean. The torrent of rain originated from collapse of a previously stable layer of water vapour (a firmament) in the upper stratosphere, which had provided a greenhouse effect to balance the weather. This layer was held in place by crystal-based devices beaming from ground. When the Atlanteans experimented with nuclear blasting, sonic bombs and deep excavations then these stabilising beams collapsed. Countries that hold the karma of this event tend to have unstable weather patterns. The survivors from Atlantis, including the spiritual initiates who knew that the destruction of their land mass was imminent, repopulated the globe at various sites, including Great Britain, Ireland, Egypt, North & South America, Sumeria, India, China and Tibet. These early cultures have started with very advanced spiritual belief systems and technology, yet without evidence of a previous long development. This is because they were start-up cultures deriving from exported knowledge out of Atlantis. In this image the artist depicts a desperate survivor of the flood surmounted by a serpent – symbolizing the force of sin and redemption. In the background a Guardian angel appears to show the path to freedom. By this point there was much heavy energy within the subconscious and lower astral realm that weighed the human race with karma, as symbolized by the huge Moon.

Original

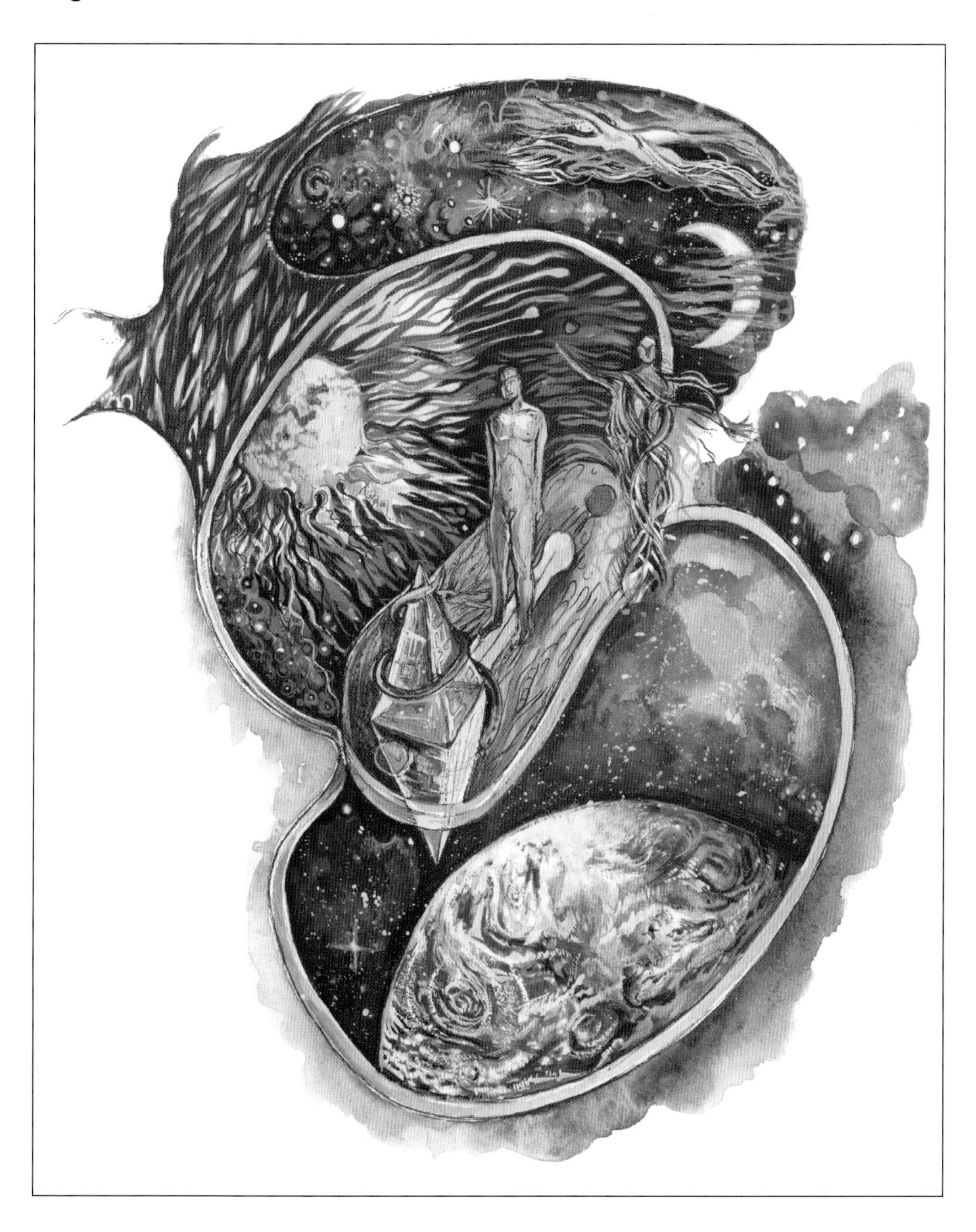

'Lachesis and genesis of the ego', by Katherine Mynott. The 17th day stage of the human embryo (after egg cell fertilisation on the 1st day) is depicted with symbolic themes. Embryology can only be properly understood in conjunction with knowledge of astronomy, the history of the planet, evolution, sacred geometry and numerology, amongst other fields. Embryogenesis, or the development of the embryo, is a re-capitulation of the development of the human race and the world. Historical ways of looking at embryology included pre-formation and neo-genesis. In pre-formation it was argued that what is coming into being into the Earth plane had already pre-existed and merely unfolds as it develops in the womb; in itself it already existed from the beginning. It further means the ovaries of Eve already contained all human beings to come and they simply unfolded from her, that God had put them all there. Neo-genesis would argue the embryo comes out of the void, out of chaos. Nothing was present at the beginning, everything is created afresh. Both approaches are correct and occur at the same time. The sequence of events from fertilisation is also depicted in Moldavite, p.512. Eventually, as shown here, at the 17th day, the centre is composed of a two-layered disc – representing the embryo proper. Indeed, most of the cells from the blastomere and blastocyst stages do not lead to the embryo at all, but to the surrounding supporting sheaths and tissues. This is a reflection of the formation of the world, its geology, plant and animal kingdoms – before the descent of humans into incarnation. Above the two-layered embryo disc is a cavity through which streams the forces of the Sun, this is the amniotic cavity. Below the disc is a cavity containing the blueprints of the planet Earth, this is the yolk sac or cavity. At one end of the disc (the pole of the future hind region) stands an angelic being and the crescent of the Moon, this is part of the future connecting stalk (allantois) and representing the astral realm. All around these structures is a cavity containing the starry night sky, this is the chorionic cavity. Before implantation into the uterus the embryo had been sleeping within the fluid or lunar sphere of the uterine cavity. Upon implantation its trophoblast breaks down the maternal tissue, invading deeper to eventually form the placenta. The embryo has small developing cavities above and below a two-layered disc of tissue: the yolk sac above and the amniotic cavity below. The whole is surrounded by the chorionic cavity. The days of genesis can be mapped into the whole arrangement. At six days of genesis there is still no trace of an actual human, this reflects the stage of 14-17 days of the embryo. Nonetheless, the human form is preparing itself. The chorionic cavity, the connecting stalk, amnion and the yolk sac are four enveloping structures of the embryo all fully developed by the 17th day. On this day the individuality of the human being may unite with its primordial body. Into the chorionic cavity enters the spiritual germ or its spiritual consciousness, the astral body comes to dwell in the connecting stalk (which will eventually lead to parts of the umbilical cord), the etheric body lives in the amnion and the yolk sac forms the foundation of its connection to the Earth and its physical development. Similarly, in chapter 7 of the first book of Moses there is a reference to the 17th day, 'in the 600th year of Moses life, in the second month, in the 17th day of the month, the same day were the fountains of the great deep broken up, and the windows of heaven were opened'. Then in chapter 8 after the flood is written 'and the Ark rested in the seventh month, on the 17th day of the month, upon the mountains of Ararat.' The 17th day is of great importance, mentioned twice in this book. It is on the 17th day that the ego, astral and etheric bodies descend, following the spiritual germ, which descended before them. The tissues these subtle bodies permeate now become something quite different from before. The original human here presents himself. Then comes the 6th day of genesis, beginning with the creation of the animals, and then 'One' comes among the animals, as the shepherd among sheep, and God says: 'Let us make Man'. At this stage the human is still an archetypal form and is described as a double figure, the lemniscate, where Heaven and Earth meet. This is represented physically on the embryonic disc as the primitive pit, from which derives the primitive streak. Into this primitive pit the human ego enters from outside on the 17th day. From the primitive streak there is a descent of cells into the depths of the disc, creating a middle third layer of tissue. The two-layered embryonic disc has now become a three-layered disc. This central core of tissue develops into the notochord, the future spinal cord and brain – thus providing the capacity for future thinking life. A snake is shown entwined around a double pyramid at this point, next to which stands the archetypal form of the human ego. Similarly the Fall of the human soul into matter is symbolised by the serpent/snake within the Garden of Eden story. In various dualistic philosophies, such as Manichaeism and Catharism, this serpent is said to have actually entered into the body of the descending human, and thus incorporated itself into this material world. Luciferic influences through the serpent especially permeated the blood, whereas Ahrimanic forces entered through the nervous system. However, the serpent provided the capacity for resurrection and redemption out of matter, as well as the drive to Fall into this state.

'Venom apparatus of the snake', by Yubraj Sharma. The two venom glands are shown internally behind the scales just below the eyes, with ejection ducts toward the mouth fangs.

BELOW. 'The serpents of world-spirit and matter', by Rishav Shah. Two winged serpents are devouring each other, a theme found in many alchemical treatises. They represent the repeated alchemical processes of distillation and condensation. The upper serpent is the world-spirit, holding universal or cosmic consciousness, working into the divine dew of alchemy (and the salt process). The lower serpent signifies matter, the virgin earth and lunar forces for the purposes of manifestation, working into the sulphur process. The upper serpent therefore consumes everything and transforms all aspects of nature below.

Astrology

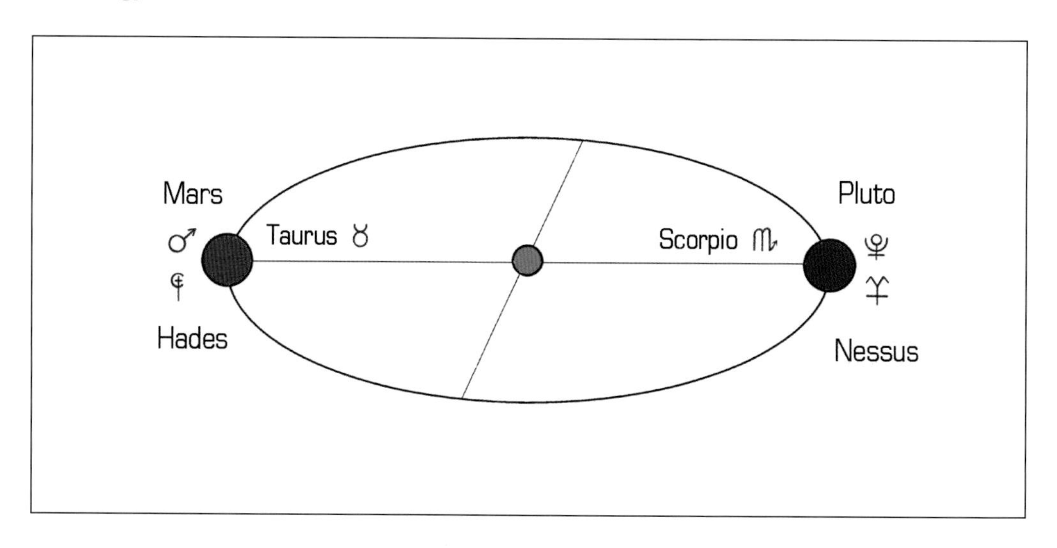

Mars conjunct Hades within Taurus, opposite Pluto conjunct Nessus within Scorpio.

Oriental

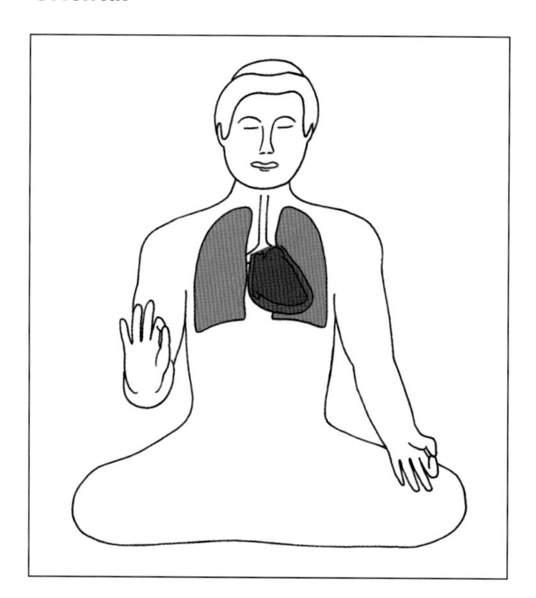

Phlegm-heat invasion of lungs and pericardium, with phlegm-fire harassing the heart.

Particulars

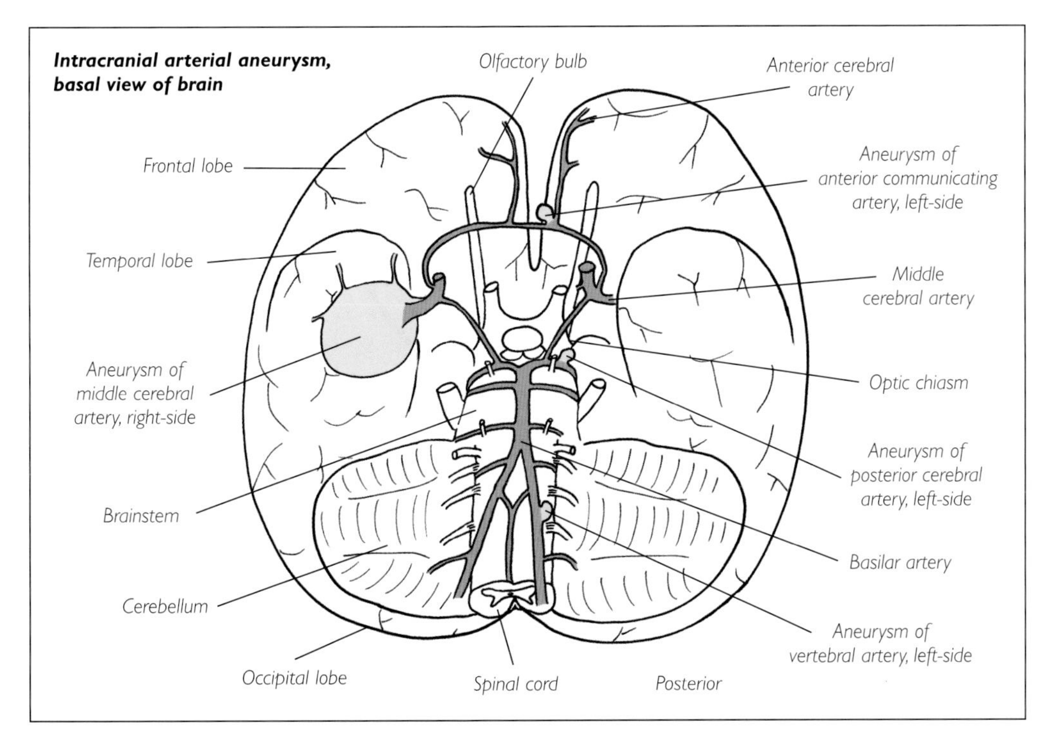

Aneurysms are localised dilatations of the blood vessels and can have congenital, traumatic, septic or atherosclerotic causes. Over 90% of aneurysms within the brain circulation are congenital. They have a saccular or berry-like shape. Many of them are at the circle of Willis (which consists of a loop of blood supply constituted by the vertebral-basilar artery supply from the back and the internal carotid arteries from the front). Aneurysms usually arise at a branching site or a curve of the artery involved. There are risks of rupture with haemorrhagic stroke (especially if hypertension is also present). Unruptured aneurysms may cause paralysis problems by compressing local nerve tissue, especially if gigantic (as shown by the example at the middle cerebral artery here).

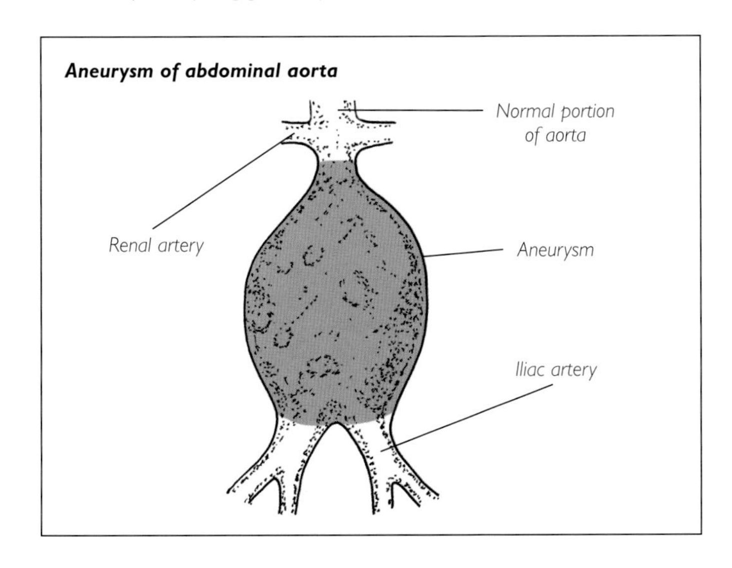

An aneurysm is a localised enlargement of an artery, but often indicative of wide-spread arterial disease such as arteriosclerosis. High blood pressure and weakness of the elastic and muscle components of the arterial wall contribute to the dilatation. Complications of abdominal aortic aneurysm include thrombosis and embolism to the leg arteries, and fatal perforation with haemorrhage.

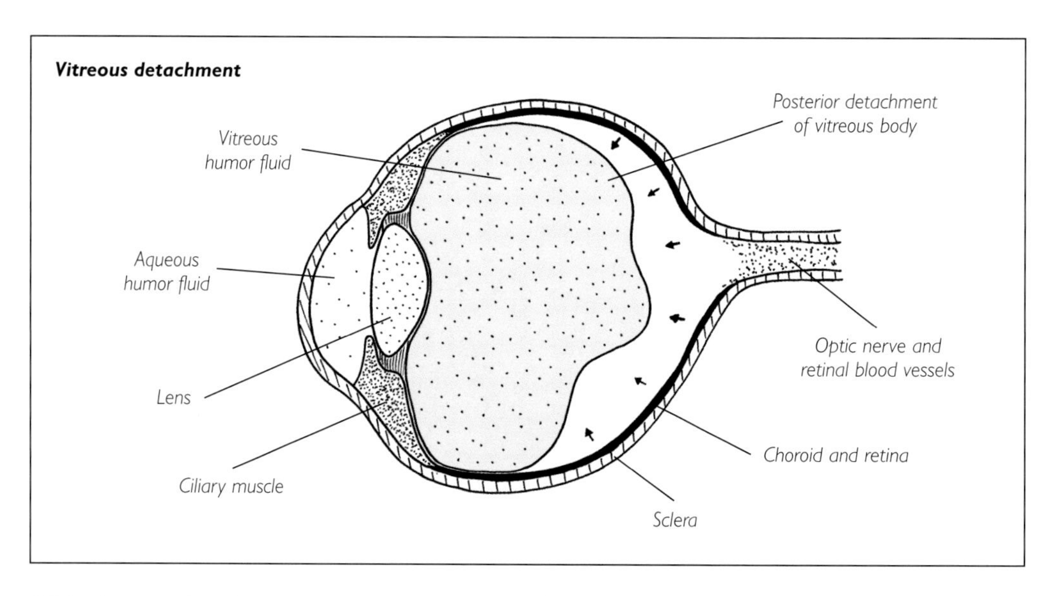

Mild vitreous detachment can occur as part of the ageing process. There is separation of the vitreous body (membrane lined gel-like fluid) from the retinal surface. This can appear like a shadow in the patient's vision, often perceived as a ring, which may be broken or irregular. However, significant vitreous detachment may also be complicated by haemorrhage, or more significant shadow distortion. Also the retinal layer can undergo traction and tearing as a further complication.

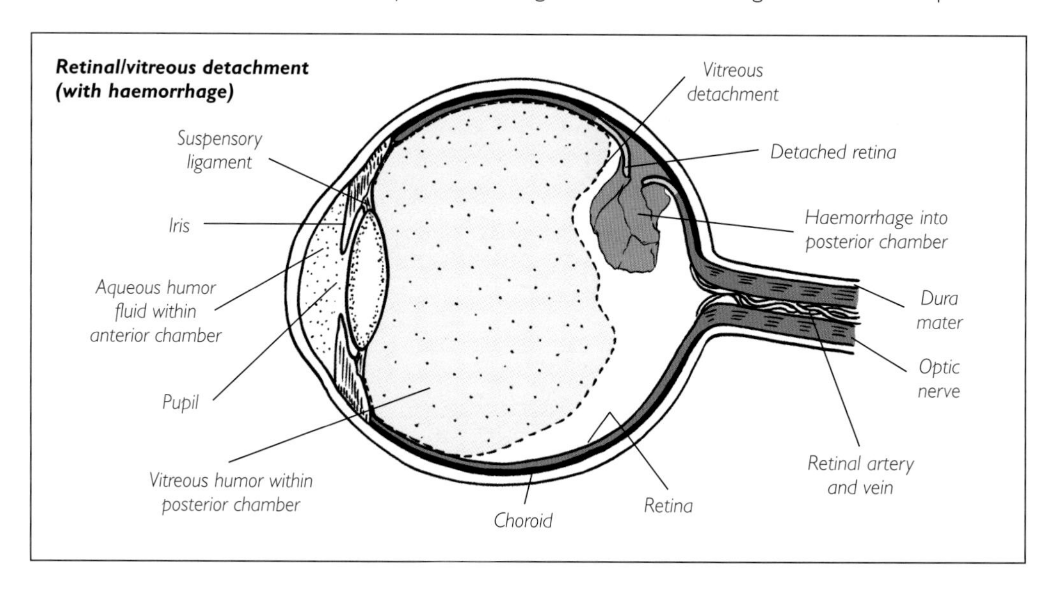

Retinal detachment is the separation of the two embryonic layers of the retina (i.e. the separation of the neurological retina containing rods and cones from the pigment epithelial layer of the retina). It is not the separation of the retina from the choroid. There is usually initially a tear in the neuro-retina which allows vitreal humor fluid to lift it away from the underlying pigment epithelium. Those at risk include patients with diabetic retinopathy, myopia (short-sight) and after cataract extraction surgery. There are shadows in the visual field, vitreous floaters and flashing lights. The vitreous humor (which is gel-like) itself can detach from the retinal surface during ageing. Bleeding into the vitreous humor or the space after a retinal tear will also worsen the traction separation of the retina and deteriorate the sight with the sensation of floating spots.

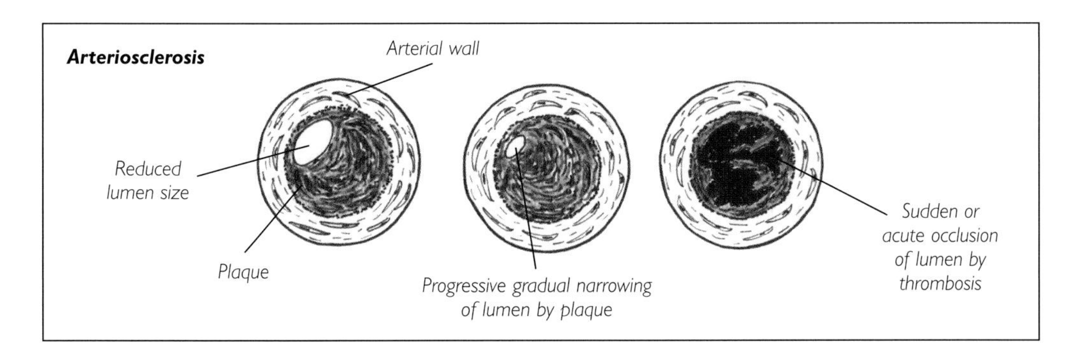

Atherosclerosis affects large and medium sized elastic and muscular arteries. There is progressive deposition within the intimal wall of the inflammatory cells, smooth muscle cells, lipids and connective tissue – all collectively known as a plaque of atheroma (A). This reduces the size of the lumen. Progressive accumulation of the plaque with further lumen narrowing (B) leads to ischaemia of the supplied organ/tissues, e.g. cardiac ischaemia (with symptoms of angina). Also an acute closure of the lumen can occur from a thrombosis on top of the atheroma. This is usually precipitated by fissuring (cracking) or ulceration of the plaque, which leads to internal wall haemorrhage of the plaque, which leads to internal wall haemorrhage and clot formation (C).

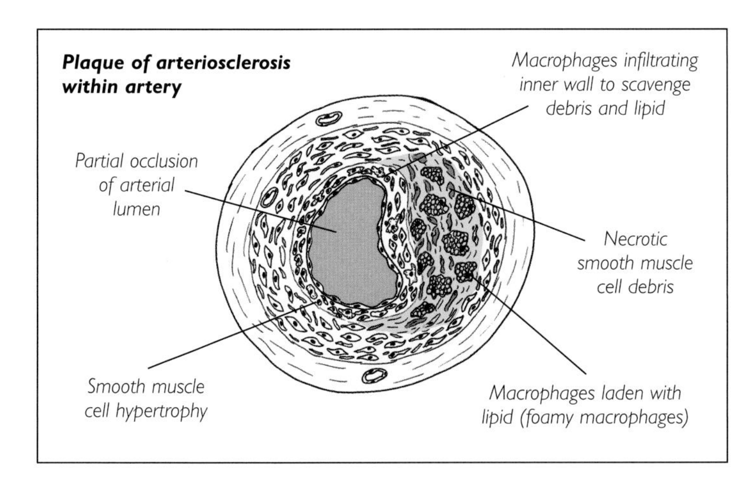

Arteriosclerosis is a disease of medium and large sized arteries, with progressive accumulation within the wall of inflamed cells, smooth muscle cells, lipid and connective tissue. The macrophages are laden with lipid deposits. The resultant plaque narrows of the lumen.

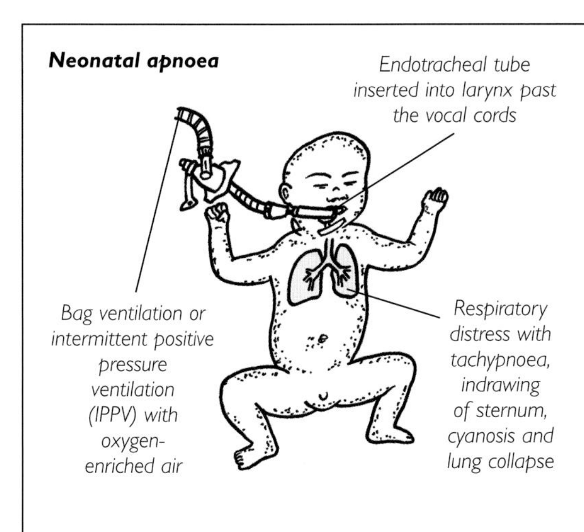

Respiratory distress may occur at birth from lung surfactant deficiency, a lipid which normally enables the alveoli and lungs to expand with air at birth. The lungs are immature, collapsed and filled with fibrinous exudates. Increased and rapid respiratory effort (tachypnoea) causes recession or indrawing of the sternum during inspiration. There is also grunting during expiration as air is formed through a partly closed glottis (throat) in an attempt to keep the alveoli open. Resuscitation is shown here, and often steroids are given to the mother at risk of premature labour in order to prevent the condition (through accelerating the production of surfactant within the foetus).

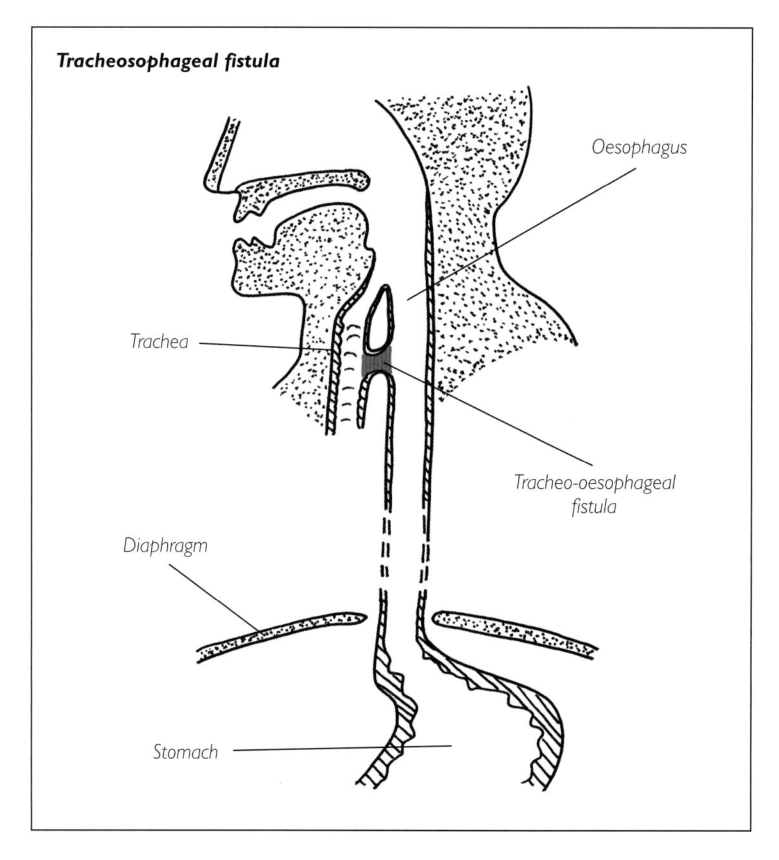

A tracheosophageal fistula is an abnormal channel between the trachea and the oesophagus. This could be congenital (present at birth), or acquired as a consequence of, e.g. perforation of the trachea or oesophagus, cancerous invasion, oesophagitis with erosions or external irradiation. As well as symptoms of the underlying disease there is the risk of abscess formation and aspiration of food into the airways with pneumonia.

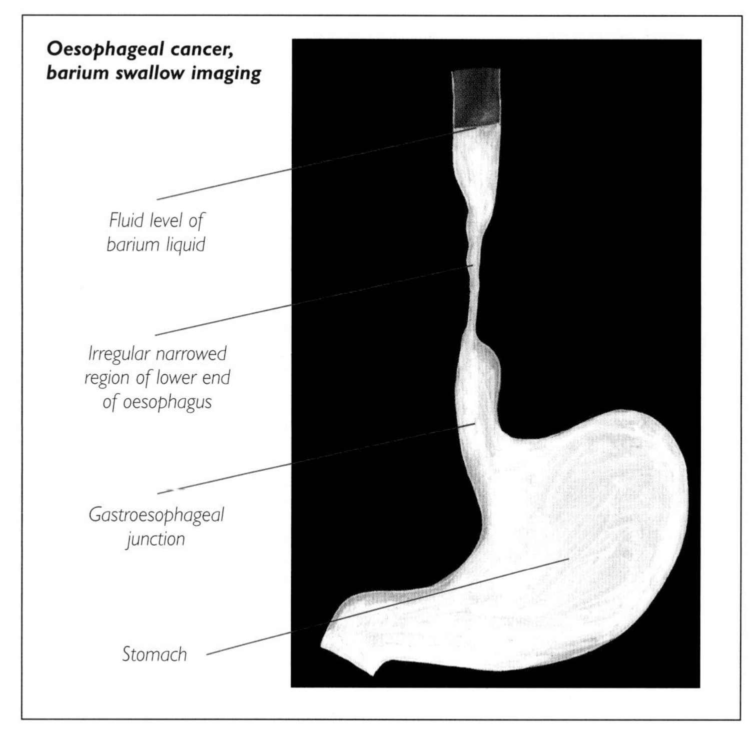

Barium swallow is an initial investigation of suspected oesophageal cancer. Further diagnosis requires visual confirmation and biopsy through an endoscope. Typical appearances of the barium image is an irregularly constricted region of the oesophagus.

Related images

p.50 Sleep apnoea
p.451 Myocardial infarction
p.81 Post-myocardial infarction aneurysm
p.299 Atrial fibrillation
p.91 Bradycardia with conduction block
p.383 Ventricular arrhythmia
p.282 Cardiac muscle sections
p.520 Congenital heart disease
p.519-520 Valvular heart disease
p.574 Hypertension
p.4 Croup
p.198 Emphysema
p.504 Chronic bronchitis
p.369 Pneumonia, stages
p.72 Asthma
p.571 Retinal degeneration
p.656 Cataract
p.317 & p.318 Eye trauma
p.321-322 Retinal circulation disease
p.527-528 Headache
p.103 Tonsillitis
p.368 & p.501 Ear infection
p.258 Labyrinthitis
p.180 Gastrointestinal bleeding
p.541 Peptic ulcer
p.44 Skin necrotic infection
p.44 Necrotic abscess
p.543 Haemorrhoids
p.133 Liver failure and ascites
p.542 Portal hypertension
p.187 Cystitis
p.718 Pyelonephritis
p.296 Kidney transplantation
p.474 Vasectomy
p.210 Ovarian cancer
p.490 Pelvic inflammatory disease
p.434 Mastitis

LATRODECTANS MACTANS

Original

PRECEDING PAGE. 'Latrodectans mactans and the cosmic web', by Nadine Kardesler. The Black Widow spider is suspended in the starry realm above (note the spider web shown is not typical of the web for this particular species), symbolising its particularly pronounced connection to the cosmos. A web strand projects to its earthly image, superimposed on the human heart, to indicate the marked effect it has on the cardiovascular system. Humanity is furthermore caught within a programme of duality-based thinking, which has its cosmic origin within the constellation of the Twins (Gemini).

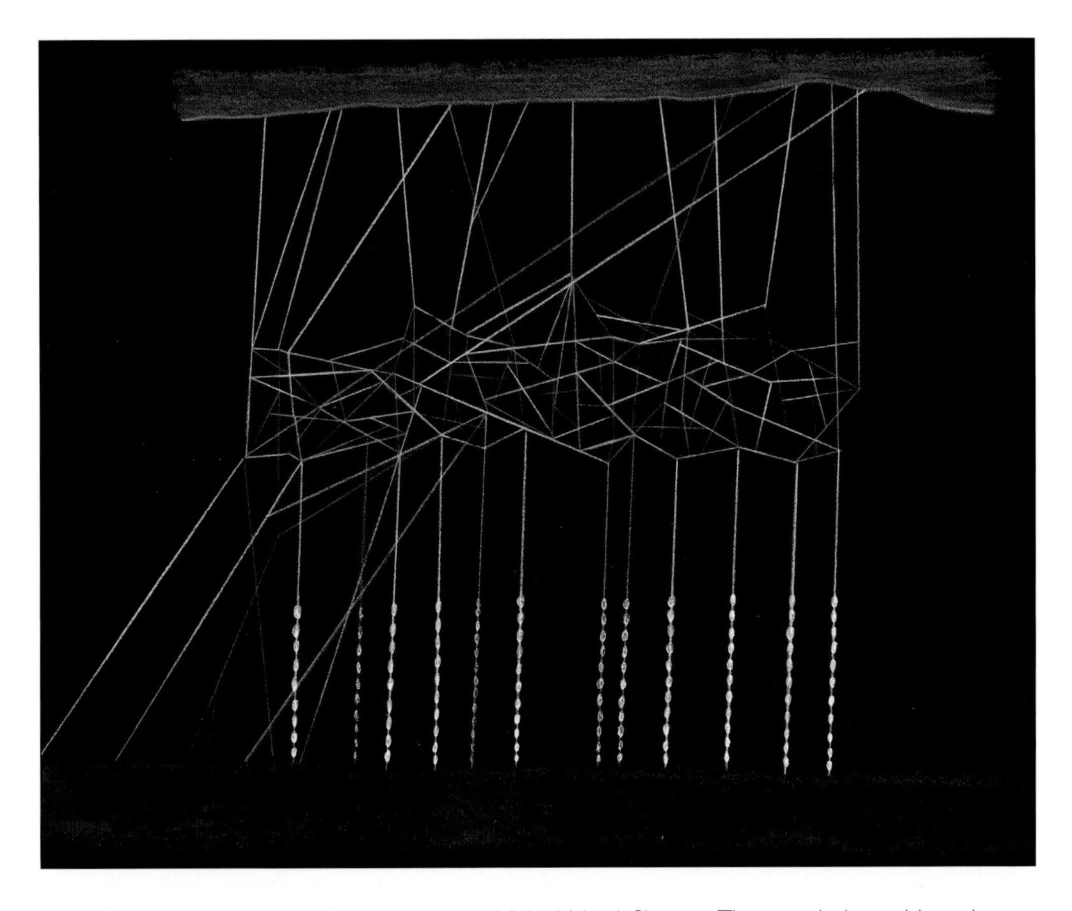

'Latrodectans mactans and its mesh-like web', by Yubraj Sharma. The wandering spiders do not make webs (e.g. Tarentula), but of the web spiders there are several forms. The orb-shape is the well known form, built by various spider families, consisting of radial threads converging on a central spot with a hub of frame threads. Other web types also exist, however, for example, the Agelenidae family build funnel shapes, the Linyphiidae build horizontal sheets, whereas the Theridiidae (the family of Latrodectans) build irregular meshes. In this illustration, the web is built between the upper green and lower brown surfaces. The upper fibres are supporting threads, leading to the middle section of an irregular tangle web. The vertical fibres attaching this to the ground are trap threads. These are studded with glue droplets. The oblique threads leading to the left-hand ground are mooring threads. The trap threads are very strongly bound to the tangle web, but break off from the ground substrate when an insect touches them, causing it to become helplessly suspended in the air. Whilst trying to free itself, the insect contacts the neighbouring trap threads to become even more entangled. In some species further threads are then thrown by the alerted spider onto the victim as it struggles, before biting it.

'Spider web and portal of cosmic light', © Ruth Carthew. A mixture of spider web types are shown, such as a radial orb at the lower left corner, and a tangle horizontal web along the upper corridor. The light flooding from the opening to the left symbolises the channelling of cosmic current through the matrix of the web, into a form available for life on Earth.

FOLLOWING PAGE. 'Nasca lines, spider geoglyph with Orion constellation' (see also p.22-23). The spider geoglyph is 150 feet long. Like all the Nasca images, it is composed of one continuous line, there is a thin waist with the eight legs splayed out. It was the second Nasca image to be discovered, by Dr. Kosok during his studies of the plain in the mid-1930s'. There are a number of straight lines running through the spider, these have been found to point to the heliacal rising of Orion over the past centuries of the Nascan culture. This is the moment when Orion rises above the eastern horizon just before the sunrise. By predictive advancement, the lines may also point to the heliacal rising moments of the Orion stars at a future stage of the human race. The stars of Orion have been shown superimposed on the spider. Across the waist lie the three belt stars, Alnitak (zeta Orionis ζ), Alnilam (epsilom Orionis ε) and Mintaka (delta Orionis δ). At the top left is Betelgeuse (alpha Orionis α), the visually largest and brightest star of this constellation, being a red supergiant with a diameter 800 times that of our Sun and 20 times the mass. At the top right is Bellatrix (gamma Orionis γ). Bottom right is Rigel (beta Orionis β), the second visually brightest star. Bottom left is Saiph (kappa Orionis κ). A method of locating Sirius, the alpha (α) star of Canis major (the Great Dog) is by tracing a line from Orion's belt. This projected star line matches the geological lines extending from the extreme of the bottom left leg of the Nasca image, indicating the ancients had depicted this constellation relationship between Orion and Canis major.

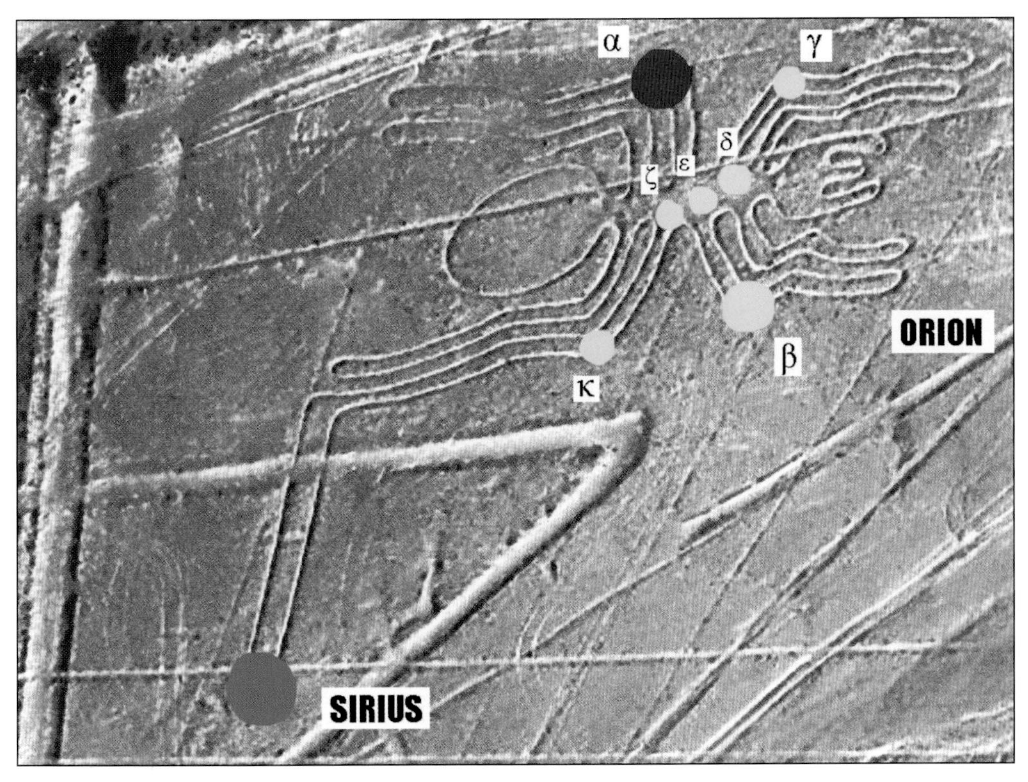
α
γ
δ
ε
ζ
ORION
β
κ
SIRIUS

Astrology

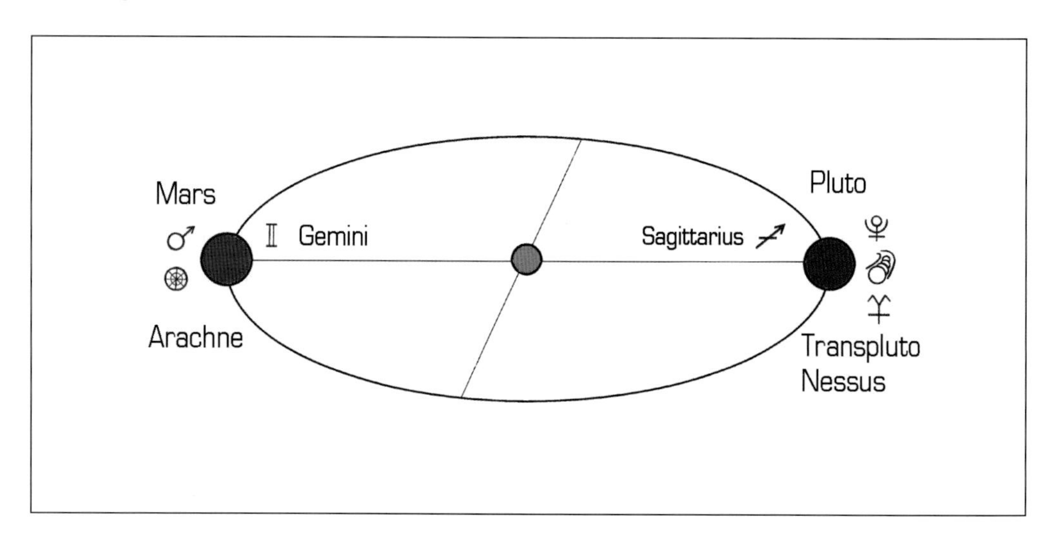

Mars conjunct Arachne within Gemini, opposite Pluto conjunct Transpluto and Nessus within Sagittarius.

Oriental

Liver fire with heart fire blazing and fire congealing within heart. Wind-stroke of brain.

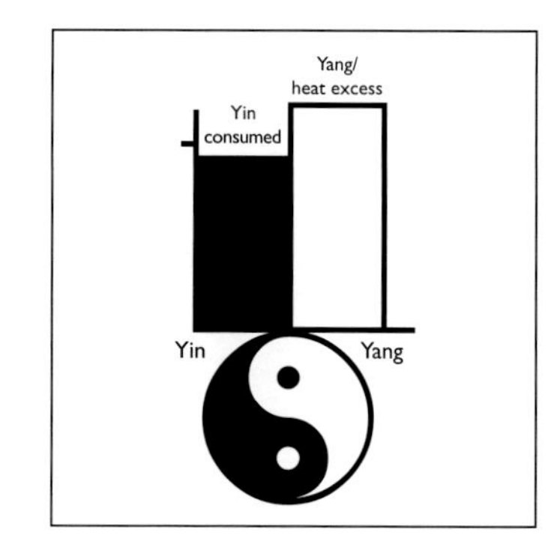

Particulars

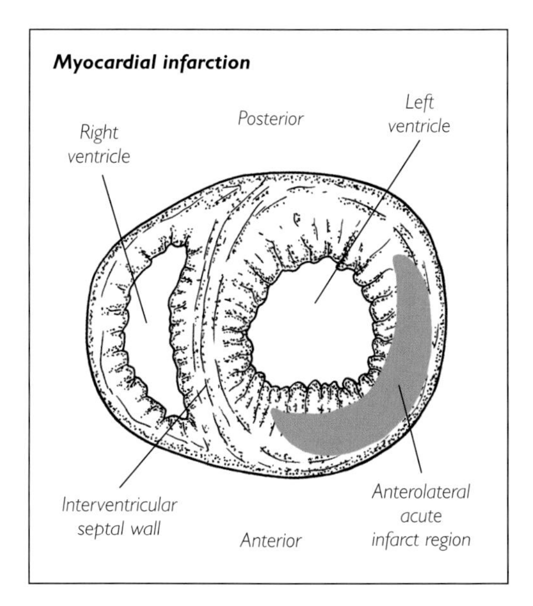

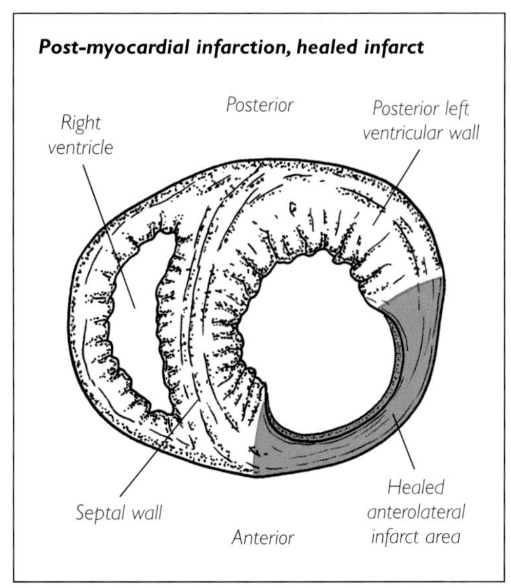

Myocardial infarction is death of cardiac muscle, typically seen with a background history of coronary artery disease, angina and progressive cardiac ischaemia. The symptoms are severe chest pain or oppression (classically radiating down the left arm but also to the jaw or right side), a sense of impending death, sweating (and without ease through rest or acute anti-anginal drugs). The infarcted tissue is partially scavenged by macrophages over time, but may also be partitioned off by fibrosed scar tissue. The region of the infarct shown in this diagram is the anterolateral part of the left ventricle.

After the initial acute stage of myocardial infarction the dead muscle needs to be scavenged. It is replaced by fibrosed tissue, although remnants of necrotic muscle cells may remain even for several years. If the infarct was through the full thickness of the ventricular wall (as in this example) then the healed area is also thinner than the surrounding viable muscle wall.

Related images

p.232 & p.343 Multiple sclerosis
p.586-587 Poliomyelitis
p.277 Motor neurone disease
p.311 Brainstem stroke
p.586 Muscle wasting
p.417 Myasthenia gravis
p.35 Spinal myelitis
p.278 Spinal cord compression
p.258 Cerebellar tumour and ataxia
p.145 ECG cardiac ischaemia and infarction
p.300 Heart failure, right-sided
p.282 Cardiac muscle sections

LEDUM PALUSTRE

Original

'Ledum palustre and pathogenic cold invasion', by Caroline Hamilton. The plants are shown growing within a snow-draped peaty soil, against a icy mountainous range backdrop. The invasion of elemental cold through a rift of the human defence chi leads to cold factor lodged within the joints, muscles and bone – attributing to much of the features within this remedy. In Oriental medicine the predominant external pathogenic factors that may invade joints are cold, damp, wind or heat. Generally, a mixture of factors will enter. The predisposing weaknesses leading to this problem include anaemia and blood deficient supply to the peripheral tissues, a lowering of defence chi from lung or adrenal-kidney exhaustion. For cold to invade there is usually a significant degree of kidney chi deficiency. Cold tends to then paralyse or restrict the movement of chi, literally freezing the energy flow within the meridians and channels. The symptoms are then a deep severe stuck pain. If the defence chi is able to mount a sufficient response there is fever and expulsion of the cold. Cold also often enters alongside damp factors, causing an additional swelling and fluid congestion within the joints and tissues.

Astrology

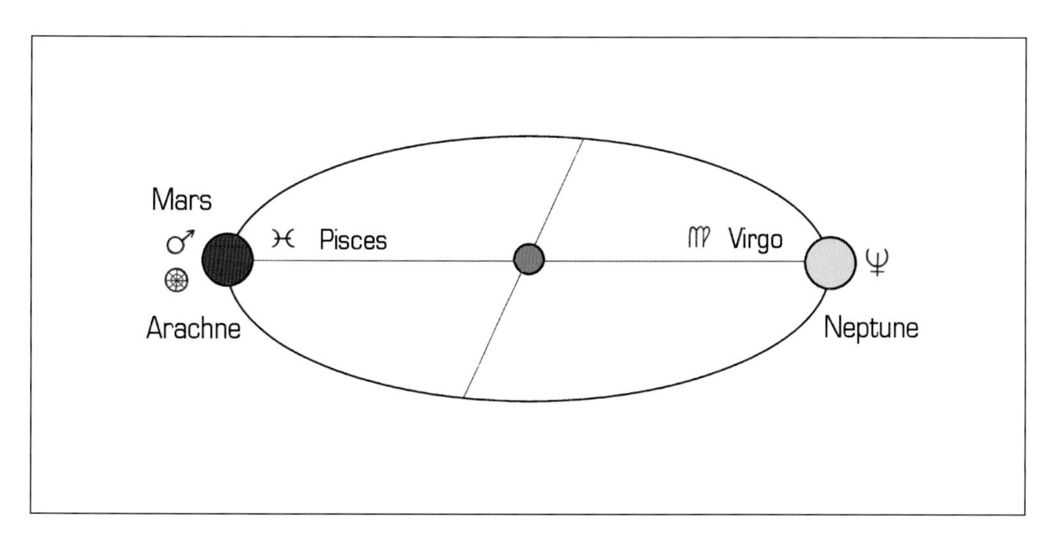

Mars conjunct Arachne within Pisces, opposite Neptune in Virgo.

Oriental

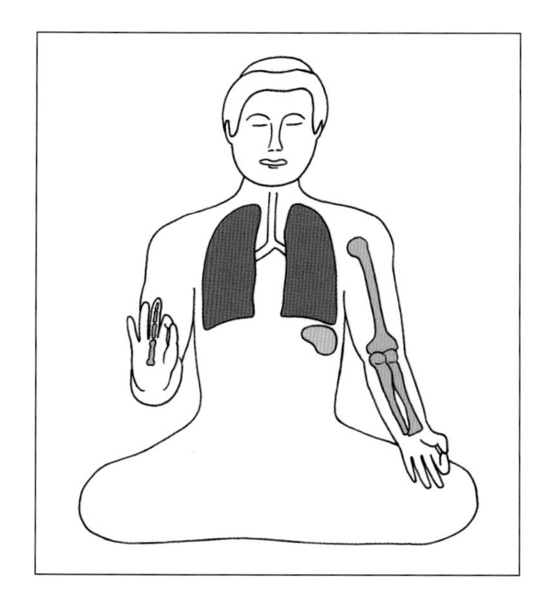

Cold-damp invasion of spleen, with lung chi deficiency. Cold-damp invasion with painful obstruction syndrome of bones and joints.

Particulars

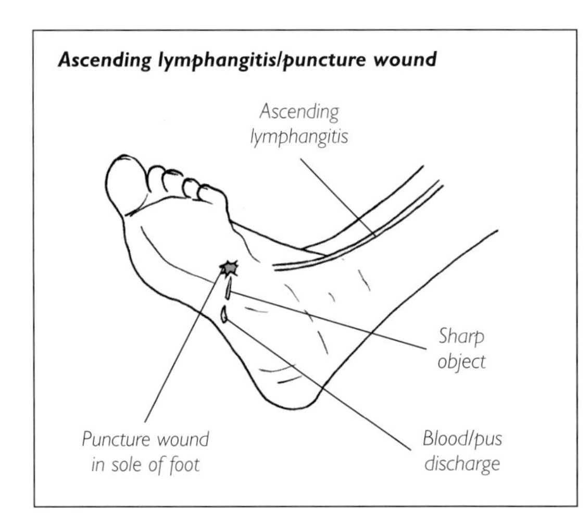

Clostridium tetani is the organism responsible for tetanus, and appear as gram-positive staining spore-bearing rods under the microscope. The organisms enter through a skin wound, and toxins produced therein travel through the bloodstream or within the nerves to reach the central nervous system. The neurotoxin then causes spasm of the jaw, facial and neck muscles (lockjaw and risus sardonicus) and dysphagia (difficulty swallowing).

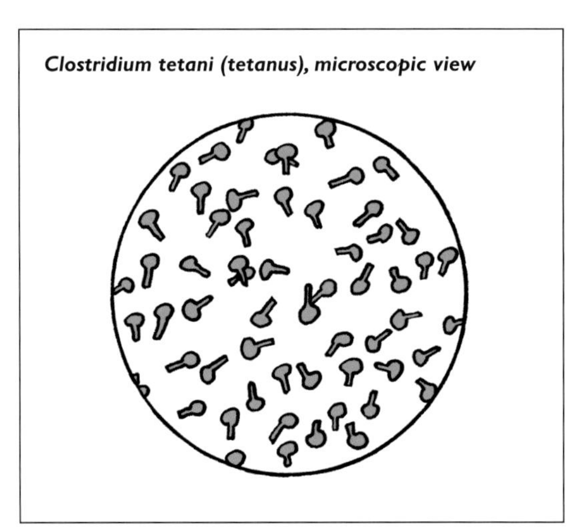

This demonstrates a typical puncture wound, with the risk of Clostridium tetani bacteria entering the wound. Deep wounds are most susceptible, as the microbes thrive best in an anaerobic environment (poor in oxygen). The tetanus toxin is produced locally and passes via the bloodstream or along nerves to reach the central nervous system. Furthermore, in any bacterial infection a local lymphocyte and inflammatory reaction can cause infection to ascend up the local lymph channels, with the lymphangitis reaching the draining lymph nodes (e.g. at the popliteal fossa behind the knees or at the groin). These glands become tender, slightly swollen and warm.

Related images

p.707 Syphilitic joint disease
p.707 Syphilitic saddle nose
p.708 Thoracic aortic aneurysm
p.270 Gout and pseudogout
p.619-620 Tendonitis
p.166 Ligament sprain
p.339 & p.660 Osteoarthritis
p.227 Mosquito bite
p.44 Necrotic abscess
p.317-318 Eye trauma
p.318 Iritis
p.319 Glaucoma

LILIUM TIGRINUM

Museum

PRECEDING PAGE. Doménikos Theotokopoulos, El Greco (1540-1614), 'Annunciation' (1596-1600). Galleria Estense, Modena, Italy © 2000, Photo Scala, Florence – courtesy of the Ministero Beni e Att. Culturali. The lily plant is traditionally associated with the Annunciation, one of the most popular themes throughout art. From the gospel of Saint Luke: 'In the sixth month, the angel Gabriel was sent from God to a town of Galilee called Nazareth, to a virgin betrothed to a man called Joseph, of the house of David, and the virgin's name was Mary. And coming to her, he said, "Hail, favored one! The Lord is with you." But she was greatly troubled at what was said and pondered what sort of greeting this might be. Then the angel said to her, "Do not be afraid, Mary, for you have found favour with God. Behold, you will conceive in your womb and bear a son, and you shall name him Jesus. He will be great and will be called Son of the Most High, and the Lord God will give him the throne of David his father, and he will rule over the house of Jacob forever, and of his kingdom there will be no end." But Mary said to the angel, "How can this be, since I have no relations with a man?" And the angel said to her in reply, "The Holy Spirit will come upon you, and the power of the Most High will overshadow you. Therefore the child to be born will be called holy, the Son of God. Mary then said: "Behold, I am the handmaid of the Lord. May it be done to me according to your word." Then the angel departed from her.'

El Greco shows the Virgin with a book in her right hand, indicating she is praying. She is dressed in red, a colour of divine conception. The archangel is surrounded by clouds and carries the lily flower as symbol of the Immaculate Conception to come. Note that the angel's outstretched hand points toward Mary's ear, signifying the entry point of the creative word or seed of God. The dove above them is the Holy Spirit, lighting up the Virgin. High above, to signify the great significance of the event, are angels rejoicing in the glad tidings. The words as described in the Gospel can almost be heard in the interweaving looks between the Virgin and the archangel.

The nature of the Immaculate or Virginal Conception is a great mystery, and is further explained in the next image text. It essentially required the walk-in or transmission into Mary of the state of Eve prior to the Her Fall from Grace within the Garden of Eden. Thus the Original Sin of sexual union underwent rescission, or return to an original state of divine union.

FOLLOWING PAGE. Bernardo Cavallino (1622-1654), 'Mary Immaculate'. Pinacoteca di Brera, Milan. © 1990, Photo Scala, Florence – courtesy of the Ministero Beni e Att. Culturali. The Nativity is a magnificent and complex event. The perfection of Jesus Christ required that He have a Virgin Conception and Virgin Birth. Thereby, His mother Mary, must also have had a Virginal perfect Conception and Birth, i.e. to be conceived without sin. Mary is said to be like Christ in all things except his Divinity. There are actually two differing accounts of this in the Gospels, in apparent conflict with each other. Thus, the birth of two Jesus children is actually described (see also p.110), one as a descendant from David's son Solomon (Matthew 1,6), the other from David's son Nathan (Luke 3,31). A unified view can be found in the teachings of Rudolf Steiner (anthroposophy). The Christ energy had to descend from the inner Sun into the flesh through the spilling of blood at Golgotha (see p.108-112). To bring this incarnation about, the body of Jesus had to be specially created to receive the Christ Spirit. Thus a pure ancestral blood lineage (specifically that of David) within the people of Israel was chosen. Furthermore, there were two Jesus children, born of two sets of parents. From the David-Solomon line came a masculine Kingly child (as indicated in the Matthew Gospels), whereas through the Nathan line came the more feminine child described in Luke. The names of the characters involved were changed to fit their new roles. Hence, no matter what their earlier names had been, the mother of Jesus became Mary, and his father Joseph. Mary and Jesus was the name of mother and child in both families. For the Matthew Jesus, 42 generations of ancestors can be traced from Abraham, through David, finally to Jesus. This could be divided into three groups of 14 ancestors. In each group was a particular future body of Jesus perfected, i.e. physical, then etheric and finally the astral body.

Zarathustra, the great spiritual initiate of the second post-Atlantean epoch (ancient Persia) was intimately involved in this preparation, even to temporarily incarnate into this Jesus child. By this means this Jesus child could receive the Sun wisdom of ancient Persia. The reason that 14 generations of ancestry are required for the development of each subtle body is that the genetic blueprints are most effectively transmitted from grandparent to grandchild, thus 2 generations are required for one genetic step. 14 generations are required for the 7 genetic steps necessary for each subtle body. It is pertinent that Egyptian mystery wisdom was utilised for creating the genetic steps within the people of Israel and therefore the Jesus bodies. Thus Osirus, the Lord of the Afterlife and Resurrection in Egyptian lore, was dismembered into 14 parts and resurrected in order to conceive the Horus child (a prototype of the later Jesus hero). Furthermore, there are 42 Assessor deities responsible for the initial judgement of the soul within the Halls of Amenti or 'Weighing of the Heart' ritual in the afterlife journey of the soul. These 42 Assessors are supervising the transmission of subtle information into the bodies of the following incarnations of the soul, depending on what is useful for the individual and collective.

On the other hand, into the other Jesus child, was incorporated the stream of the Buddha. Through this, that Jesus had the capacity to radiate compassion and conscience. The role of Mary as mother can now be understood. The human being was initially androgynous, and did not know its gender within the Garden of Eden. Through the Fall and the segregation of the human race into two sexes, heterosexual copulation could bring about the birth of another human. However, sexual behaviour became tainted by the sin of the Fall, which involved the infusion of Luciferic elements into the human astral/emotional body. However, there is one means by which the young Mary could become an Immaculate Virgin, which is to not be tainted at all by the 'sin' of sexual history. This was to receive the etheric body of the original Eve from the Garden of Eden, a part of this Eve that had never tasted the fruit and never left Paradise. This part of Eve had been deliberately held back by divine powers for just such a future event of the birth of the redeeming Saviour. This Eve had therefore never experienced generations of incarnations and maternity, thus remaining virginal. Indeed, Mary could remain virginal thereafter, even when entering into marriage and sexual union, for such a deep and lasting Eve influence continued into her physical and etheric body. This Eve entered into the Mary of the Nathan Jesus child, whereas the Mary of the Solomon Jesus was to give birth also to six siblings of Jesus (four brothers and two sisters, Matthew 6,3). By this means, the Nathan Jesus child received the absolute purity of spiritual codes directly from the Garden of Eden. The 'Nathan' family derived from Nazareth, whilst the 'Solomon' family originated from Bethlehem and travelled to Egypt (then to reside in Nazareth on their return). The two families were very close. Eventually the two children were to merge at age 12, through the death of the Solomon child and blending of his Ego into the Nathan child. This coincides with the sudden transformation of the Jesus child (described in Luke 2,41-51) at age 12 when he amazed all around him with his wisdom teachings. This phase of childhood is analogous to the 2nd seven year period of the soul's development (age 7 to 14 years), when the child is learning to separate from its parents, to imaginatively think for itself and receive greater wisdom teachings.

At the Fall of humanity, Luciferic forces had entered into the blood of the human, causing this to turn red with the iron nature of Mars and provide for personal or individualised will-power. Without such intervention, humanity would not have been able to undergo their karmic journey of reincarnation, and therefore Luciferic beings usefully provide the resistance against which the soul reclaims its spiritual heritage. In some portrayals of the Immaculate Conception, Mary-Eve is depicted crushing the serpent of the Temptation (out of the Garden of Eden) underfoot. This illustrates she had also caused the reversal of the descent of the Luciferic forces into the human body form, enabling the Christ resurrection codes to replace the Luciferic-shadow elements within human blood. Note how Mary is shown looking downwards (rather than upwards towards the descending soul of the Jesus child as yet within the spiritual world). This reveals her nature as Gaia, representing Mother Earth. Thus the triplicity of Cosmic Eve-Mary-Earth Mother becomes complete in her being.

Original

ABOVE. 'Lilium tigrinum and the Immaculate Conception', by Claire Stokoe. The plant is shown growing out of the external ear canal of the Virgin Mary, the stem travelling through the middle and inner ear cavities and the root reaching down to her larynx. Note the stamens reaching out far beyond the margins of the petals, as if yearning and reaching towards the realm above the flower. Superimposed on the middle and inner ear is the fallopian tube, with the ovary suspended just below the fimbriae collecting region of the tube. Thus the larynx coincides with the uterus in the diagram. From the left a portal has opened from the spiritual realm, out of which streams a divine impulse (indicated by the sperm cell) to penetrate and fertilise the Virgin with the Christ seed. An angel (as archangel Gabriel) hovers nearby as the announcer and witness.

LEFT. 'Lilium tigrinum and the Virgin and Child', by Mita Shah. Residing within the flower are the Virgin Mary seated with the Christ child on her lap, indicating the sanctity of their relationship. An angel stands beside the pair in adoration.

Astrology

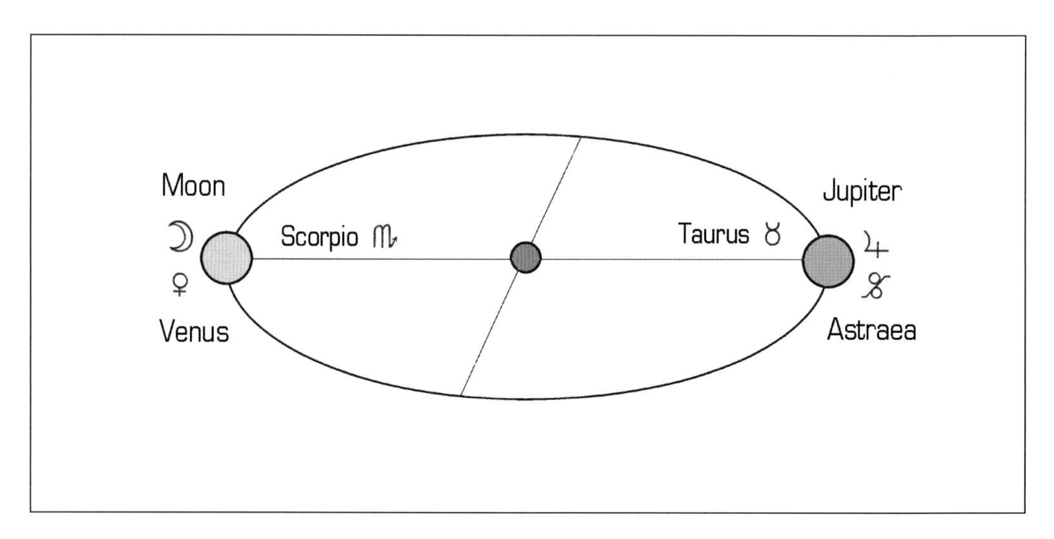

Moon conjunct Venus within Scorpio, opposite Jupiter conjunct Astraea within Taurus.

Oriental

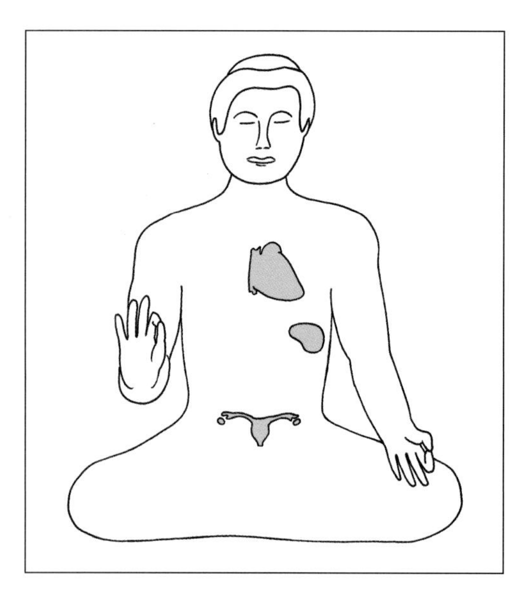

Yang deficiency and chi sinking within spleen, heart and lower burner/uterus.

Particulars

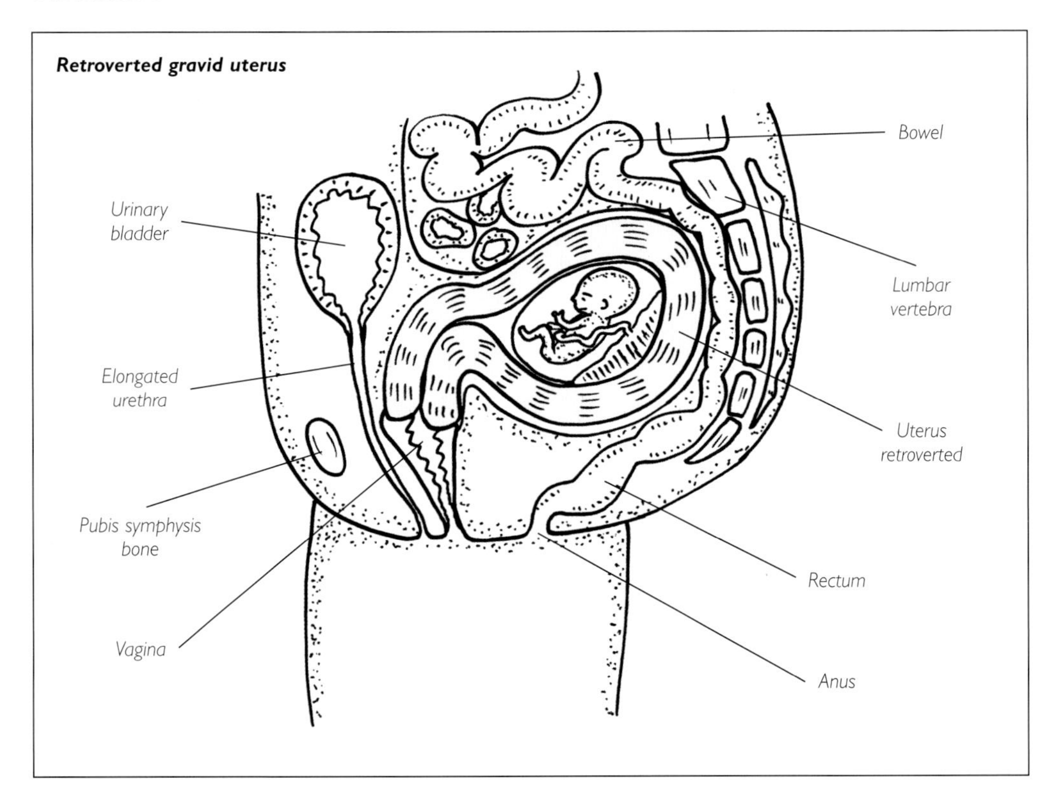

A retroverted uterus during pregnancy probably develops where a conception occurs in an already retroverted uterus. Usually this should spontaneously correct itself between the 9th and 12th weeks, but if not the uterus becomes incarcerated within the pelvis as it grows. The risk of this is increased if there are obstructions to its correction, e.g. pelvic adhesions. There is pelvic and back pain, defecation is painful and urinary symptoms occur from the compression and elongation of the urethra (i.e. frequent urination, infections and acute retention of urine may occur).

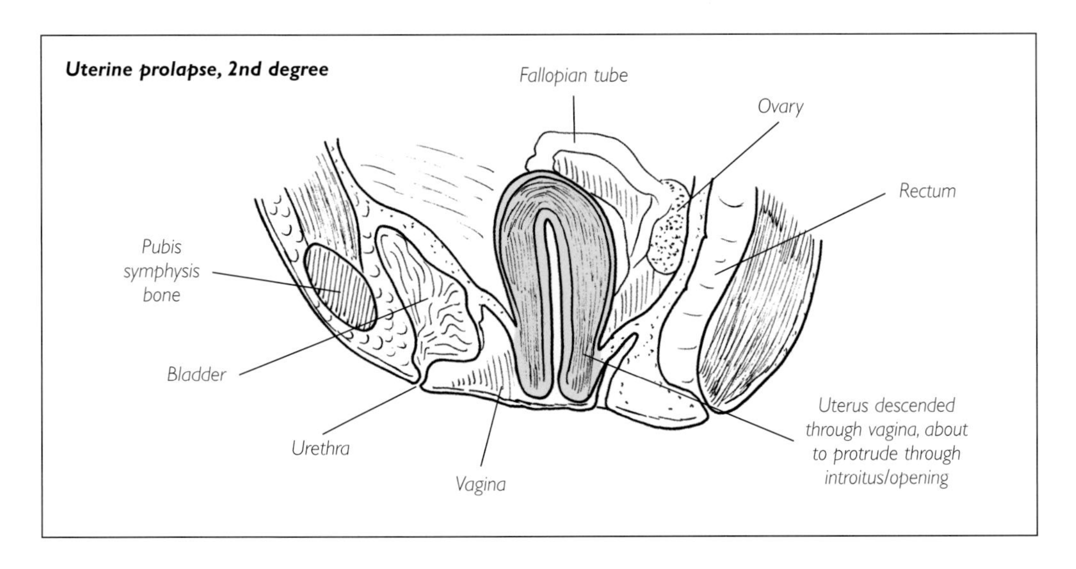

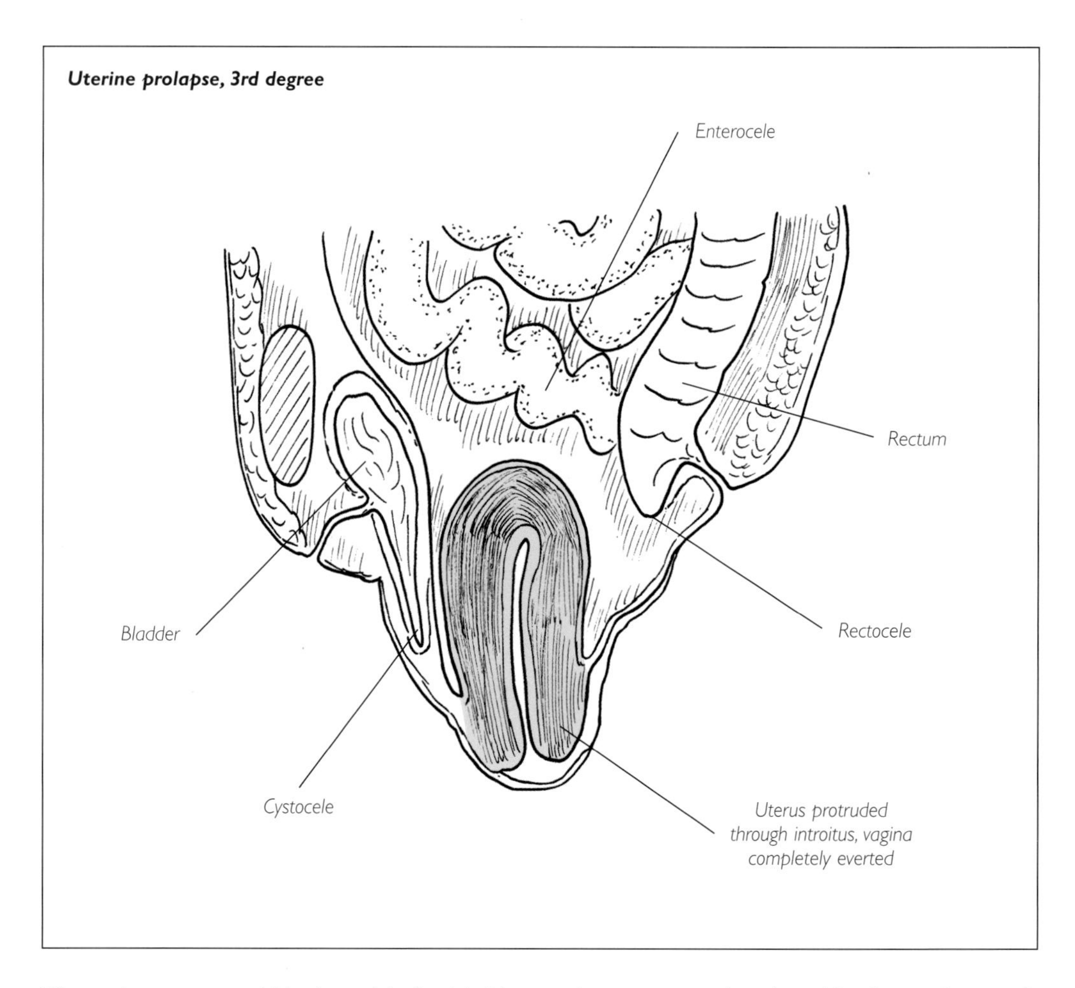

The various organs within the pelvis (i.e. bladder, urethra, uterus, vagina, sigmoid colon and rectum) pass through the central hiatus (gap) of the pelvic diaphragm but are also attached to the margins of the levator ani muscles on each side by fascia. With any rise in intra-abdominal pressure (e.g. when sneezing or coughing) these levator muscles tense up and cause narrowing of the pelvic diaphragm gap – thus preventing any undue prolapse downward of the organs. Damage to the levators can occur during childbirth (from tearing or overstretching). The vaginal walls are distended by similar events, which allows protrusion into the vagina of the bladder and urethra at the front (called a cystocele for bladder, urethrocele for urethral protrusion), and/or the rectum at the back (known as a rectocele). The uterus is also supported by several special ligaments, which can distend and tear during childbirth. Other factors causing prolapse states are congenital weakness of the connective tissues in general in some patients, ageing weakness, and loss of oestrogen after menopause. Uterine prolapse causes symptoms of a lump protruding from the vagina, slowly increasing in size, aggravated by standing or straining and eased by lying down or by pressure. There is also dragging pelvic discomfort, low backache, sometimes difficulty in defecation, painful intercourse, loss of libido, chronic urinary frequency and pain (from residual urine within the bladder). First degree uterine prolapse is where the uterus is within the vagina but not yet through the vaginal opening (introitus). In second degree prolapse the uterus has descended beyond the introitus. In third degree prolapse there is complete eversion of the vagina and the uterus fundus (normally the upper pole of the uterus) often then lies below the introitus and may become ulcerated in the process. The bladder, rectum and bowel can also become pulled into the vaginal space, causing a cystocele, rectocele and enterocele respectively.

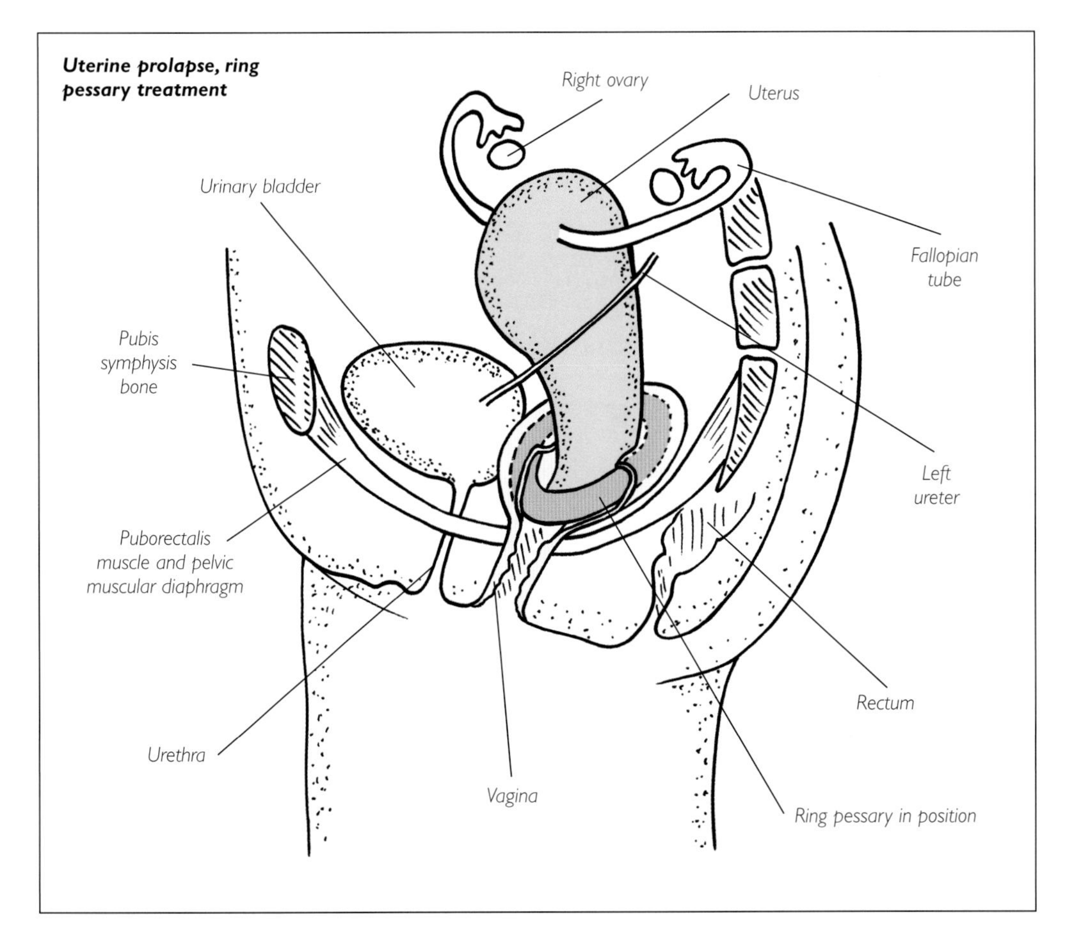

Non-surgical or conservative treatment is usually favoured for genital prolapse for patients who are frail, medically unfit or during pregnancy. One such method is the insertion of a non-irritating polythene plastic pessary to support the vaginal walls. The pessary is placed into the vagina above the level of the levator muscle insertion. It keeps the uterus elevated and is held in place by a sling of the levatores ani muscle. Complications can include infection and vaginal ulceration.

Related images

p.57 Ovarian inflammation
p.210 Ovarian cancer
p.335 & p.427 Ovarian cysts
p.335 Endometriosis
p.282 Cardiac muscle sections
p.264 Supraventricular tachycardia
p.264 Multiple extrasystoles/ectopic beats
p.281 Endocarditis
p.527 Headache
p.528 Migraine visual aura

LYCOPODIUM CLAVATUM

Museum

PRECEDING PAGE. Utagawa Kuniyoshi (1797-1861), 'Sugenoya Sannojo Masatoshi entangled in the streamers of a kusudama', from 'The Faithful Samurai' (ISBN 90-74822-17-7) © Hotei Publishing 2000 and David Weiberg. This image (print 1.33 of the book) is one of the famous series of images called the 'Seishū gishi den' (of 1847-48) and its follow-up 'Seishū gishin den' (1848). These are stories of 46 masterless samurai warriors (rōnin) and one foot-soldier (making 47 in all) of Akō in Japan. These men sought the revenge of the death of their lord, Lord Asano in Edo (present-day Tokyo region). Their leader had been ordered to commit suicide after a serious insult inflicted on Kira Kozuke-no-Suke during an official ceremony in Edo. Lord Asano was the feudal lord under homage to his shogun lord – Kira being the shogun's chief chamberlain. However, the act of revenge had been outlawed by that time, so the rōnin had sworn a secret oath. Interestingly, in keeping with some of the profile of Lycopodium, the rōnin had to pretend to have lost interest in their samurai code, and lead a life of drunken indulgence and womanising, to place their enemy off guard – for they were being spied upon. Finally, after a year of secret planning, they attacked the residence of Kira Kozuke-no-Suke. Apparently, Kira attempted to flee and hide, but was found by his charcoal shed. He was given the opportunity to commit suicide, but declined out of cowardice – whereupon he was ritually beheaded. Afterwards, as prescribed by custom, the rōnin willingly and proudly committed ritual suicide by disembowelment, as ordered by the judiciary. Despite losing much of their social and economic position within Japanese society, the samurai had not lost their code of honour. The original designer of the prints, Utagawa Kuniyoshi, devoted much of his life to celebrating the heroic past of his culture. In this particular print, Sugenoya Sannojō Masatoshi, one of the rōnin, is shown tripping up in the streamers of a kusudama, which is a scented ornamental betasseled ball used to deodorize clothes and rooms. Sugenoya Sannojō Masatoshi was the adopted son of Hanbei Masatatsu. Habei re-married after the death of his wife, but to a young girl. This new foster mother lusted after Sannojō, which caused great consternation to the young man, for his love and duty towards his father and Lord was paramount. Hanbei nevertheless suspected an affair and became resentful. Sannojō was sent on a lengthy business trip to defuse the situation, and on his return joined the rōnin conspiracy. It was said his will was stronger than iron and he considered his own life to be of no import.

FOLLOWING PAGE. 'Sugenoya Sannojo Masatoshi tripping in the growth of Lycopodium', by Antonia Chetwyn. The iron will of the rōnin is in keeping with the Mars-oriented drive of the gallbladder. However, this same drive and zeal may become self-destructive, inappropriate or engender hostility when excessive. Deficient gallbladder chi/yang may instead lead to confusion, apathy or timidity. In this illustration adapted from the preceding print, the warrior is caught by both the kusudama and the Club-moss. This is to symbolise the entanglement of obsolete emotional patterns based on bravado, duality-based hostility, revenge or anger on the personality.

Original

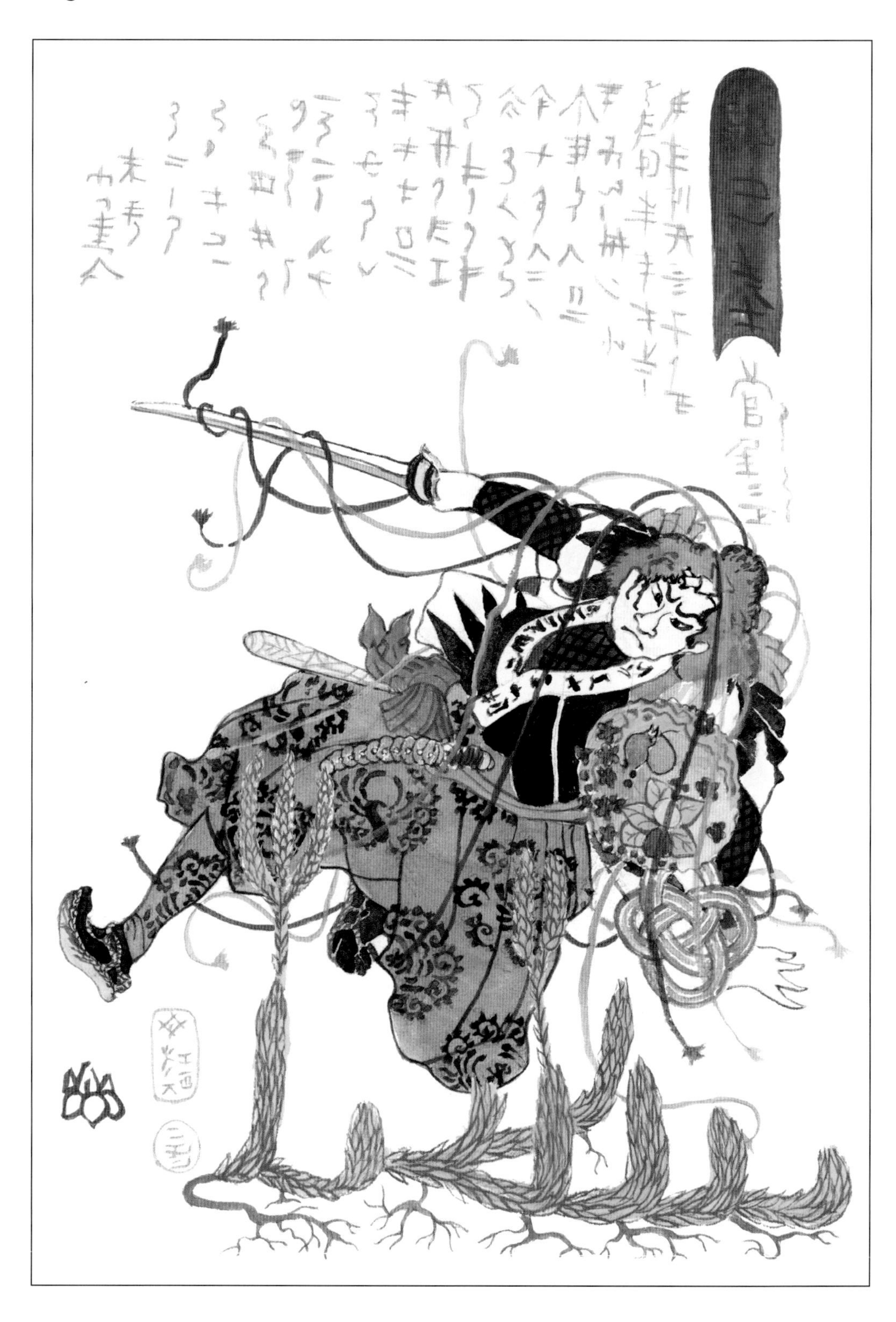

'Lycopodium clavatum and the age of dinosaurs', by Yubraj Sharma & Kathyrn Eastman. The plant was once a mighty component of prehistoric forests, as shown by the vegetation at the background – but depicted in huge stature. From left to right these are: Lycopodium clavatum (Running Clubmoss), Lycopodium annotinum (Bristly Clubmoss), Lycopodium clavatum again, Equisetum palustre (Marsh Equisetum), Lycopodium clavatum again, Equisetum palustre, Catharinea moorei (Japanese Bonsai Moss) and Selaginella martensii (Rowan's Selaginella). The illustration is set during the third age of the earth, the Mesozoic age, equivalent to the Lemurian. There is a new evolutionary impulse with more advanced creatures, humans having passed through the stage of the fish. It is the first emerging of the Self but as weird animal forms. The giant reptiles, known as the Saurians appear. These seemed furiously torn into many directions. The spiritual world is projecting onto them and yet they are also heavily bound to the Earth. There is a savage battle of direction and energy between the above and below. It continues from the Permian through the Triassic and the Jurassic periods. Thus the large dinosaurs appear clumsy and awkward. Some could raise themselves on their hind legs, but as if struggling for an upright position which they could not fully attain, being overwhelmed by body weight and gravity. It was during this Lemurian age that there was separation of the Moon from the Earth. This was a time of great struggle. Humans acquired the upright position during this cosmic event. The dinosaurs represent the astral body run wild. This explains their strange contradictory features in which old features intermingle with elements of the future. The birth of the human was still in the phase of its labour. Later, the mammals hold the imprint of the ego, although only humans reach the true rank of ego bearer. Dinosaurs thus rant and rage to symbolise the wild and chaotic impulses that coursed through evolution during this time. They represented the uncontrollable urges of the astral body, attempting to eventually come to a balance when the emotional body would be mastered by the human spirit and ego at future stages of evolution. The current, almost pitiful, state of Club Moss is shown by its present-time smallness in the immediate foreground.

Astrology

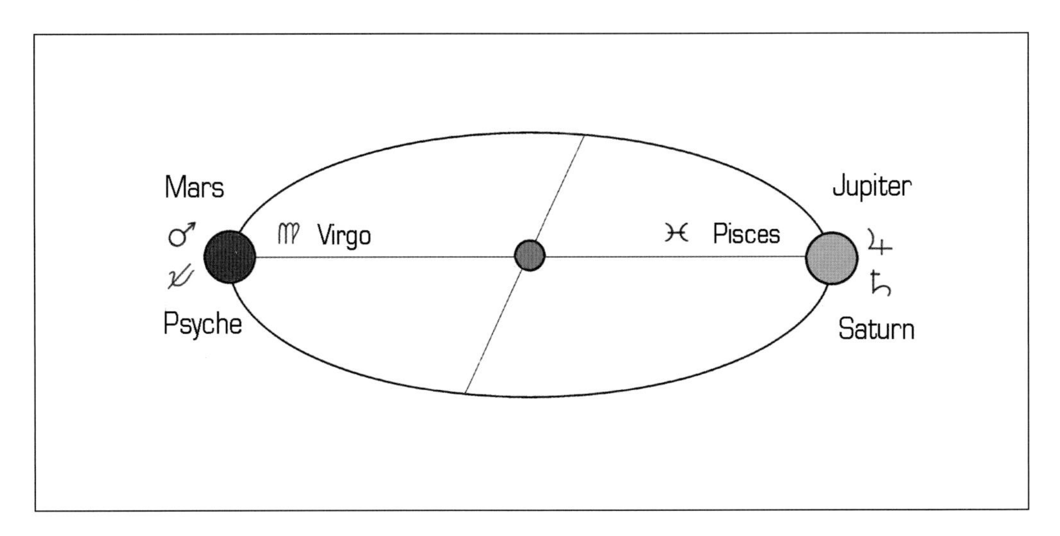

Mars conjunct Psyche within Virgo, opposite Jupiter conjunct Saturn within Pisces.

Oriental

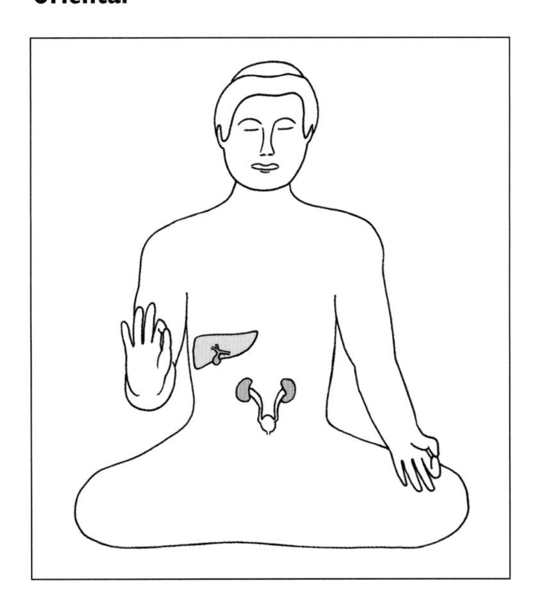

Kidney essence deficiency, with liver yin/blood deficiency and gallbladder yang deficiency.

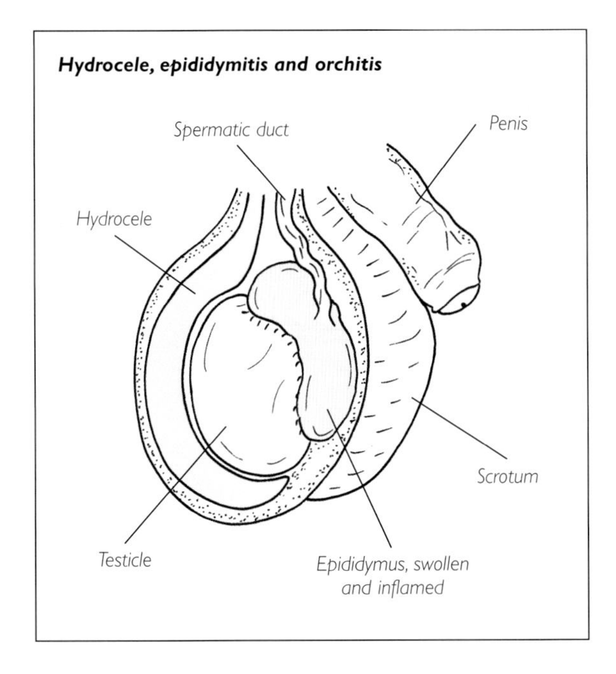

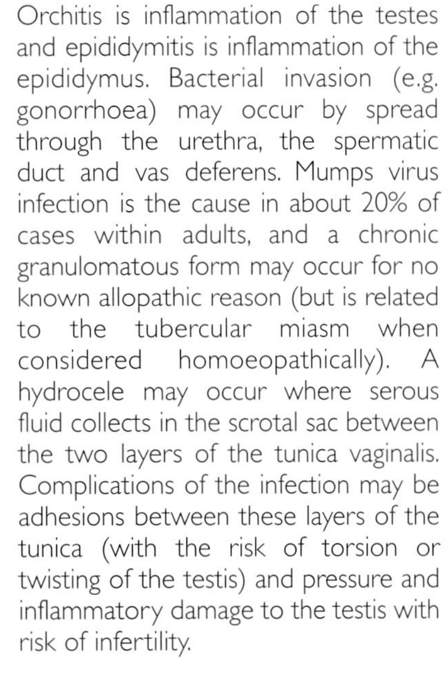

Orchitis is inflammation of the testes and epididymitis is inflammation of the epididymus. Bacterial invasion (e.g. gonorrhoea) may occur by spread through the urethra, the spermatic duct and vas deferens. Mumps virus infection is the cause in about 20% of cases within adults, and a chronic granulomatous form may occur for no known allopathic reason (but is related to the tubercular miasm when considered homoeopathically). A hydrocele may occur where serous fluid collects in the scrotal sac between the two layers of the tunica vaginalis. Complications of the infection may be adhesions between these layers of the tunica (with the risk of torsion or twisting of the testis) and pressure and inflammatory damage to the testis with risk of infertility.

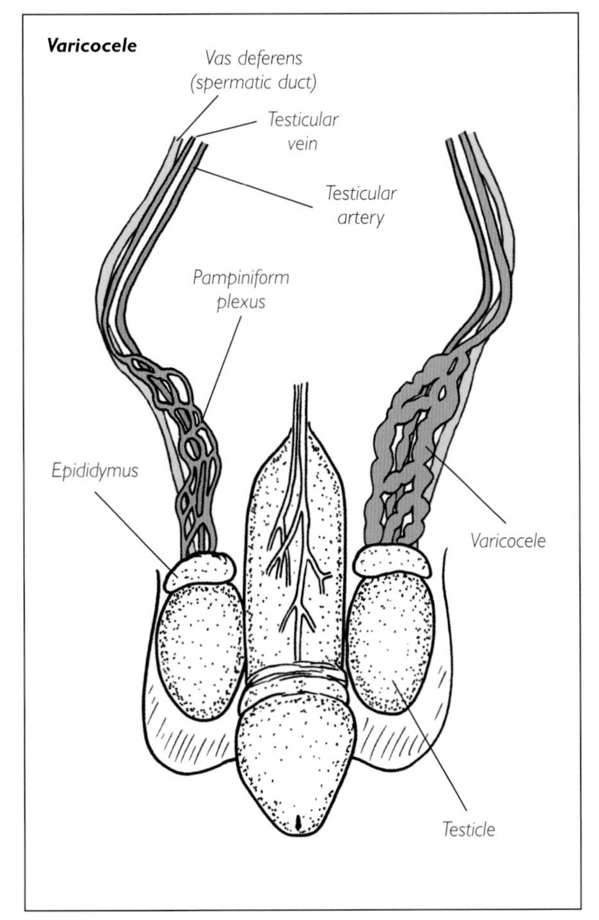

Some of the contents of the spermatic duct leaving the testes are shown in this diagram. A varicocele is a varicose vein of the pampiniform plexus. Up to 12 veins leave the testes and anastomise (unite) to form this pampiniform plexus, which normally has a vine-like or tendril-like appearance of a climbing plant. It surrounds the ducts deferens (spermatic duct) and arteries within the spermatic duct (the main artery being the testicular artery). The plexus eventually enters into the testicular vein. The causes of a varicocele include defective valves in the testicular vein, which would otherwise be preventing delay or congestion of venous blood flow. On palpation the varicocele feels like a 'bag of worms', and may cause a dull aching pain. The swelling disappears on lying down and appears again when sitting or standing. The scrotal temperature is raised from the increased blood volume; this is implicated as a cause of male infertility since sperm production requires a cooler temperature environment. Note that there are also nerves (sympathetic and parasympathetic and the genitofemoral nerve) and lymph vessels within the spermatic duct, but these have not been shown for clarity.

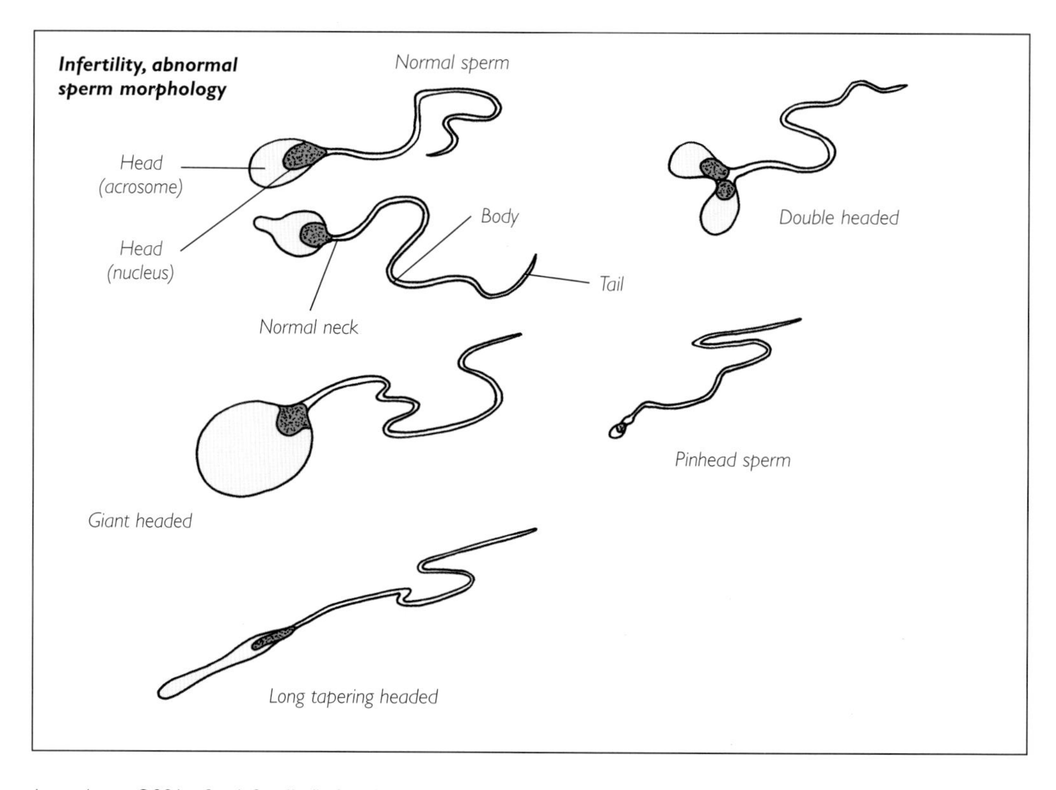

In at least 30% of subfertile/infertile couples there is a male factor. Sperm investigation includes an assessment of semen liquefaction, volume of ejaculate, sperm cell count, motility and morphology (microscopic appearance). Abnormal forms should not exceed 15-20% in normal semen, such distortions include heads with double structures, giant, pinhead or tapering head.

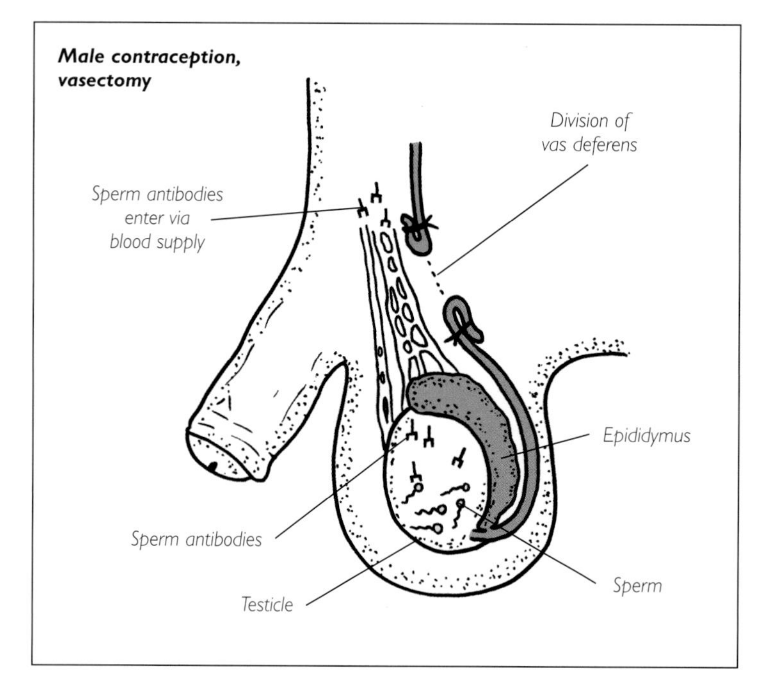

Vasectomy involves the division and ligation of the vas deferens and can be done under local anaesthesia. However, it can take a year before the ejaculate is completely sperm-free, due to several months of sperm storage capacity in the ducts. There is a possible long-term risk of sperm auto-antibodies developing, due to the systemic immune system reacting to the reabsorbed sperm. This will make it difficult or impossible to reverse the operation if the man wishes later to conceive.

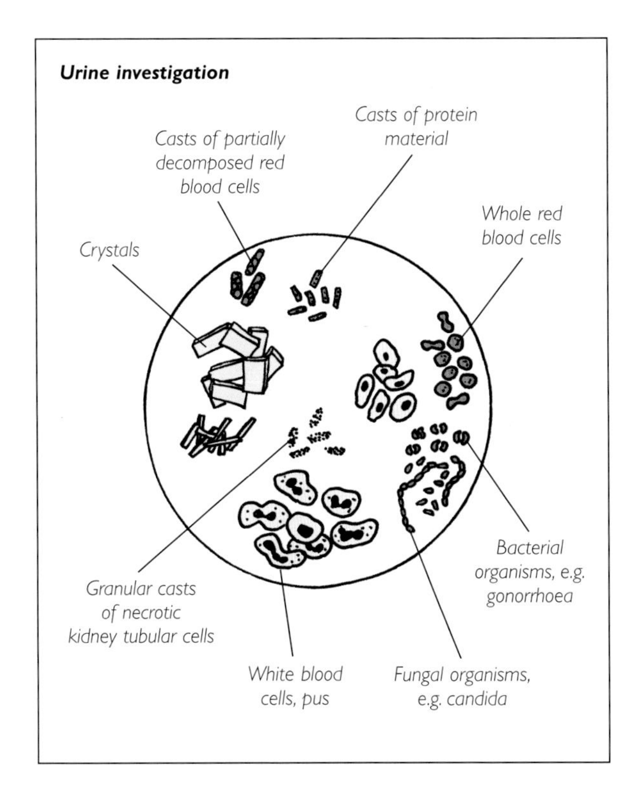

Microscopy of urine may reveal the pathology when investigating kidney disease. The presence of significant numbers of white cells indicates an inflammation within the urinary tract, typically an infection, but also from stones, necrosis or nephritis. The presence of red cells indicates bleeding, which may arise from anywhere between the glomeruli to the urethra. Casts are composed of various cells or materials moulded into a cylindrical shape by passage along the kidney tubules – they may consist of protein leakage, dead cells, decomposed red blood cells. Casts indicate tubular disease within the kidneys. Bacteria may be found within the urine by culture, but can at times be demonstrated by staining the initial urine sample. Crystals may be found in crystal/stone deposition diseases within the kidneys, or from such disease as gout or pseudogout affecting the kidneys.

Related images

p.561-562 Hepatitis
p.222 Fatty liver
p.222-223 Gallstones
p.223 Jaundice
p.133 Liver failure and ascites
p.494 Crohn's disease
p.542 Portal hypertension
p.507 Coeliac disease
p.488-490 Urethritis and complications
p.718 Pyelonephritis
p.115-116 Renal calculi
p.248 & p.250 Renal failure and dialysis
p.75 Psoriasis

LYSSINUM

Original

PRECEDING PAGE. 'Lyssinum and the deluge destruction of Atlantis', by Esther Lane. A rabid dog has entered the mad phase of its infection. The stormy flood damage is part of the final destruction of the previous root race of humanity, Atlantis. Reddish human beings are drowning in the maelstrom. This is indicating the misuse of the forces of Mars-iron, which represent will-power and emotional forcefulness. Indeed, the karma of Atlantis was transferred to several post-Atlantean cultures and civilisations, and the red-skinned race (Native American Indians) was responsible to healing the Mars related karma. Meanwhile extraterrestrial activity is evident above, partly as an attempt to assist the post-Atlantean wave of colonisation into Europe, Asia, Africa and the Americas. However, some alien groups were also negatively involved in the progressive deterioration of humanity during the latter days of Atlantis. The dog species is especially related to Sirian extraterrestrials (see also Lac caninum p.425).

'Lyssinum and medieval treatment of rabies', by Antonia Chetwyn. This painting is based on various themes portrayed in medieval images of rabies, in particular on one manuscript by Apuleius (held at the Vienna National Library). Several wild animals are shown, bats and a squirrel, as carriers of the virus. A rabid dog has been decapitated as an attempt at disease control. A remedy was sought from the collection of its blood. This could have been a realisation that the blood of victims contained antiviral antibodies, and thus provide a therapeutic serum. Several infected humans, with animal bites on their legs, are entering states of paralysis, seizures and madness. At the lower left a physician/healer is attempting to provide a serum to the salivating patient.

Astrology

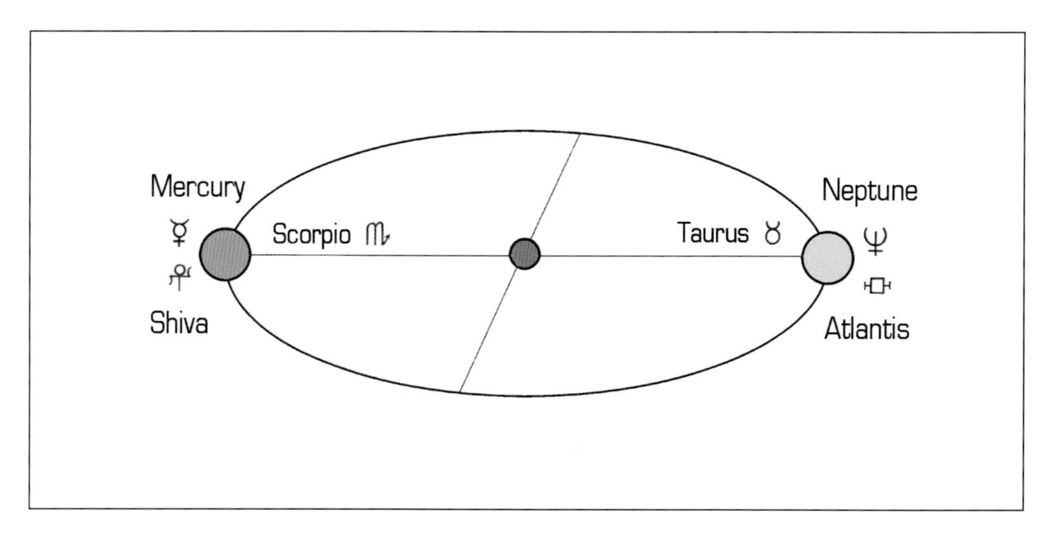

Mercury conjunct Shiva within Scorpio, opposite Neptune conjunct Atlantis within Taurus.

Oriental

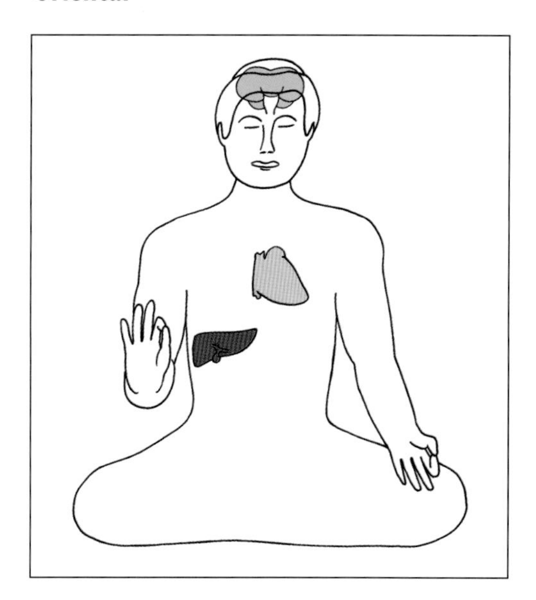

Liver chi stagnation, with phlegm-mist within heart and wind-phlegm stroke of brain.

Particulars

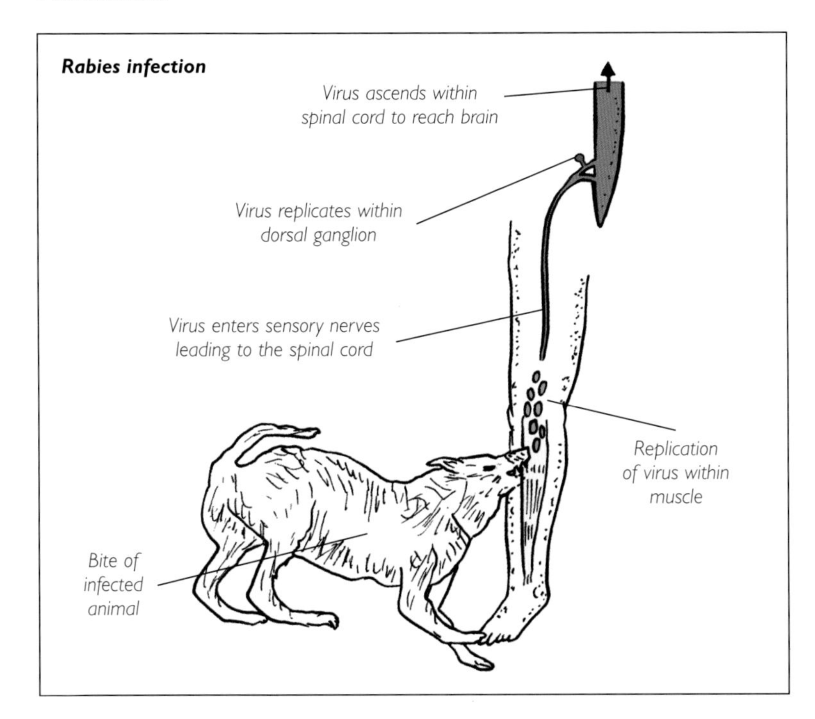

Rabies infection usually occurs from the bite of a rabid animal. The virus is secreted within the saliva of the animal and multiplies within the striated muscle at the site of the bile. Day to months later it infects the peripheral nerves to travel to the dorsal root ganglion nerve cells and spinal cord. Once the virus reaches the spinal cord there is rapid progression of the infection into the brain.

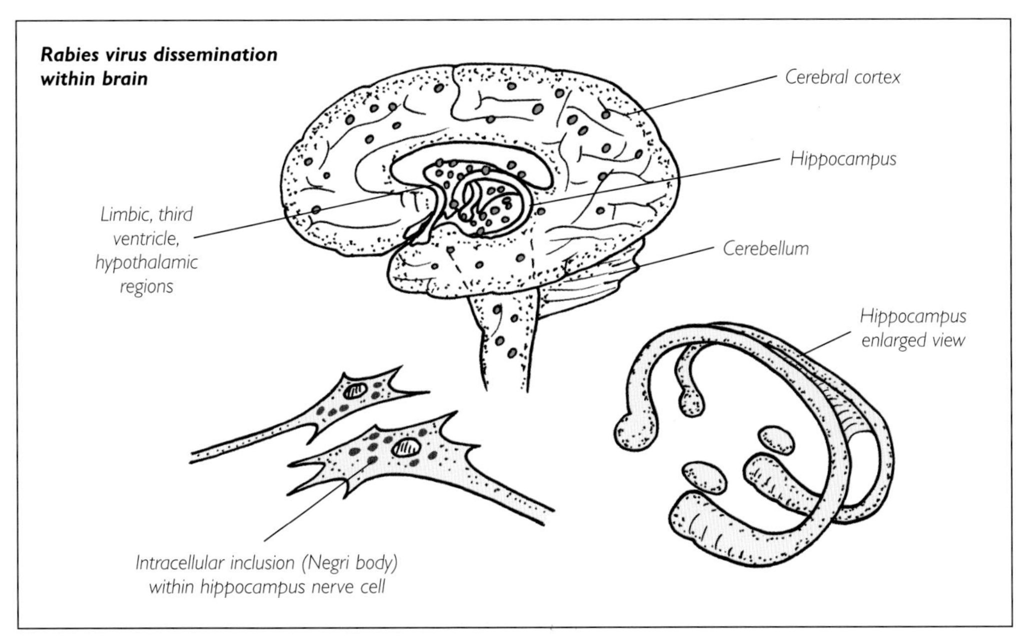

After the initial inoculation, the rabies virus disseminates widely within the brain. It especially affects the central region around the limbus, hippocampus and third ventricle, but also throughout the cortex. Characteristic collections of viral material inside the nerve cells can be found, called Negri bodies, and are shown for cells in the hippocampus in this diagram. From the brain the virus can then travel within the nerves to multiple organs, e.g. the salivary glands and skin.

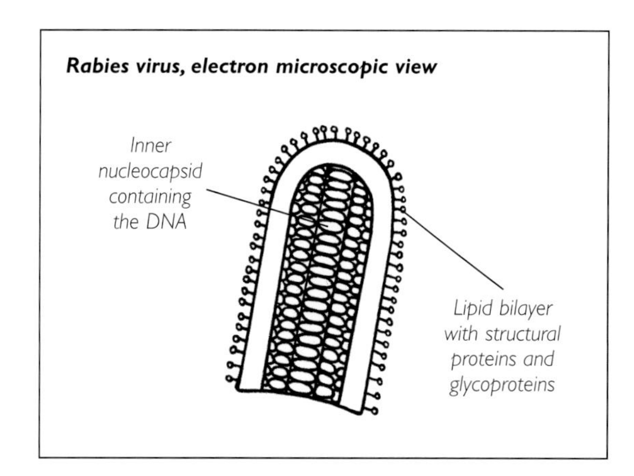

Viruses are very small in size and are obligate intracellular parasites that depend on the host cell for their replication. A virus consists of a genome (the genetic material) composed of DNA or RNA, packaged in a protective shell of protein and a membrane. Rabies virus belongs to the Rhabdovirus family and is bullet-shaped. The outer envelope has spikes of glycoproteins on the lipid-protein envelope. Inside there is the nucleocapsid, coiled into a symmetrical cylinder shape and containing one single-stranded RNA strand.

Related images

p.233-234 Epilepsy
p.232 & p.343 Multiple sclerosis
p.277 Motor neurone disease
p.35 Spinal myelitis
p.278 Spinal cord compression

MAGNESIA CARBONICUM

Original

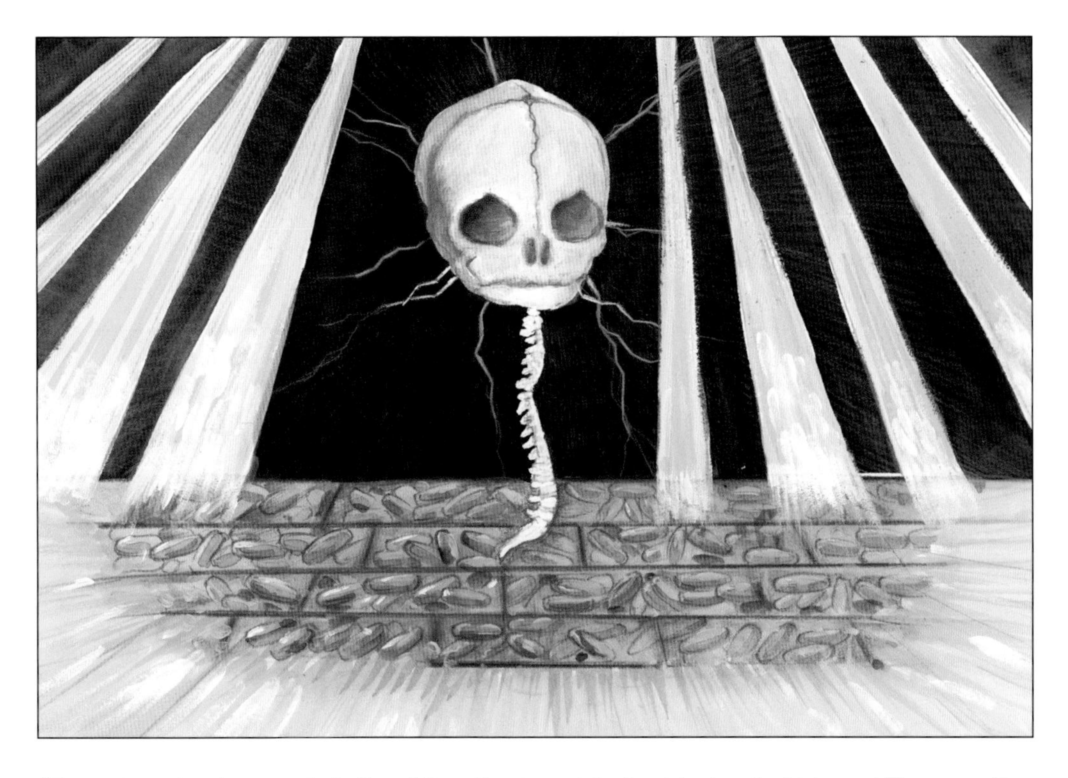

'Magnesia carbonicum and vitality of the etheric metabolism', by Loolie Habgood. The reception and anchoring of light is shown, descending beams of light entering the plant-like epithelial cells below. The cells contain inclusions similar to the green chloroplasts of leaf cells, which use magnesium as the metal carrier within the photosensitive pigment chlorophyll. Bone tissue is created by the magnesium influenced movement of light into calcium phosphate based mineralisation. A fetal skull and vertebral column is shown with electric light radiations to indicate the remedy especially suits the incorporation of mineral in the early years of life. A particular attribute of magnesium is the stimulation of the etheric-based metabolism of the liver. The liver is the plant-like organ within the human; hence its activity should normally be unconscious to the senses. The remedy also stimulates the metabolism and physical-etheric nourishment available within the breastmilk of a lactating mother. Milk is a plant-type of food (see Lac humanum in volume 1, p. 390). The image indicates how the newborn soul still largely resides within its head, the rest of the body is only gradually being grasped over the following few years. The child should remain dim and plant-like in its consciousness during the early phase of life, thus accelerated premature incarnation into the body below the head may cause irritability, exhaustion and hypersensitivity of the senses. This situation is correctable through remedies such as Magnesia carbonicum.

Astrology

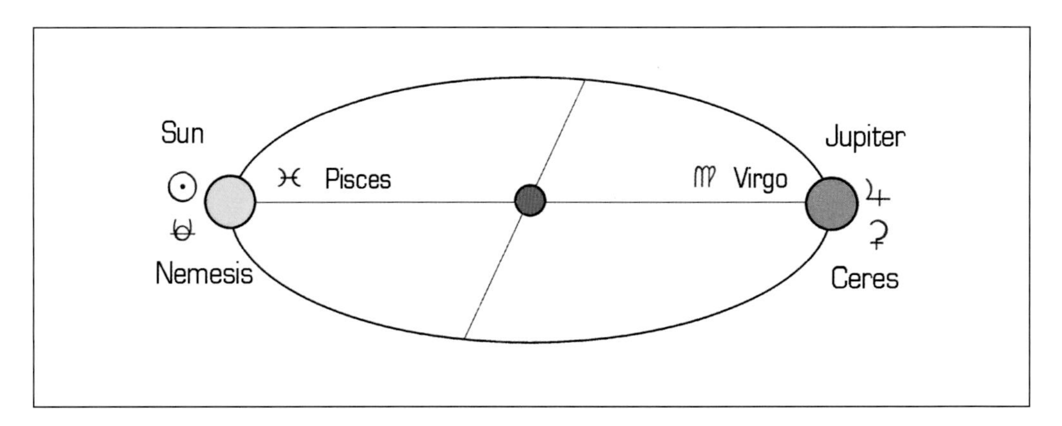

Sun conjunct Nemesis within Pisces, opposite Jupiter conjunct Ceres within Virgo.

Oriental

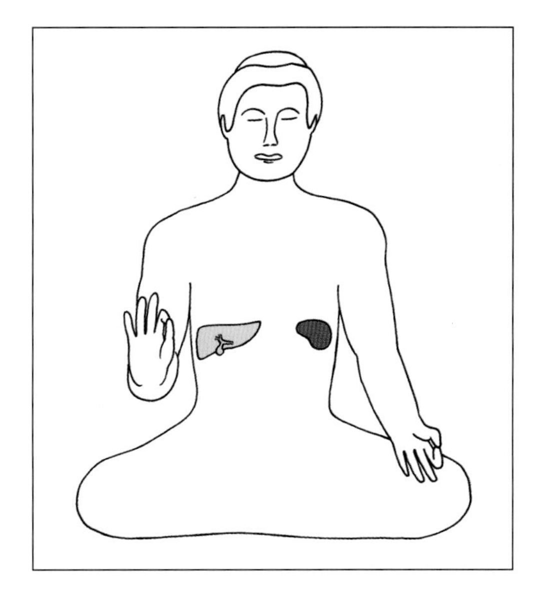

Liver yin/blood deficiency and spleen chi deficiency.

Related images

p.582 Infectious gastroenteritis & p.507 Coeliac disease
p.95 Cystic fibrosis
p.10 Sciatica & Torticollis
p.265 Toothache & p.3 Neuralgia, trigeminal
p.729-731 Hyperthyroidism
p.335 Endometriosis

MAGNESIA PHOSPHORICUM

Original

'Magnesia phosphoricum and warmth activity at the solar plexus', by Katherine Mynott. Radiations of warmth are centred on the solar plexus and its associated organs – liver, gallbladder, stomach, spleen and pancreas. There is an ascent of chi or vital energy from the solar plexus to the chest region, as well as soul-spiritual light from above the head descending into the heart and solar plexus chakras. For instance, from an Oriental medicine perspective, food chi is transformed and transported upward by the spleen to vitalise the cardiovascular and respiratory systems, and liver chi moves upwards to nourish the heart.

Astrology

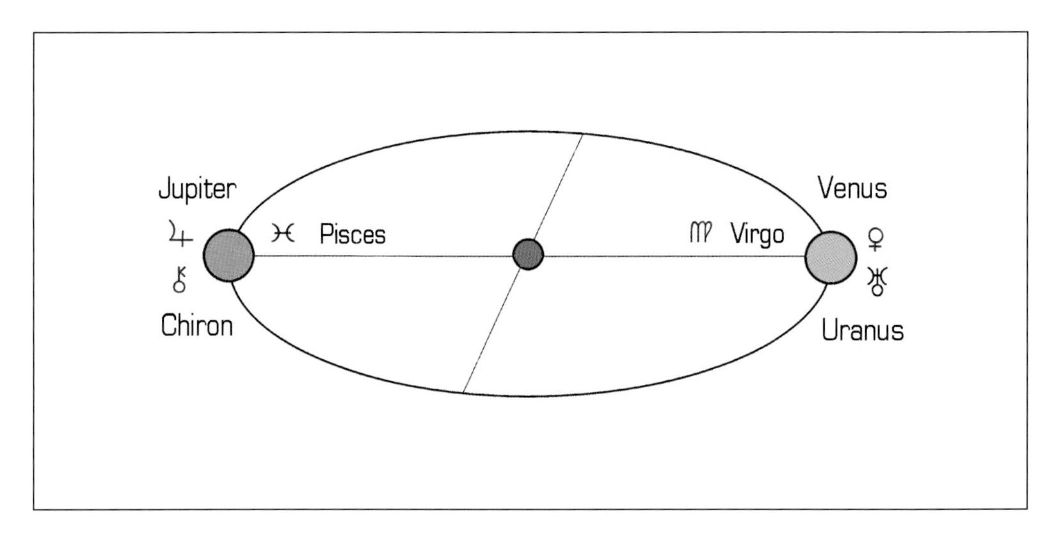

Venus conjunct Uranus within Virgo, opposite Jupiter conjunct Chiron within Pisces.

Oriental

Liver yin/blood deficiency with interior wind affecting muscle.

Particulars

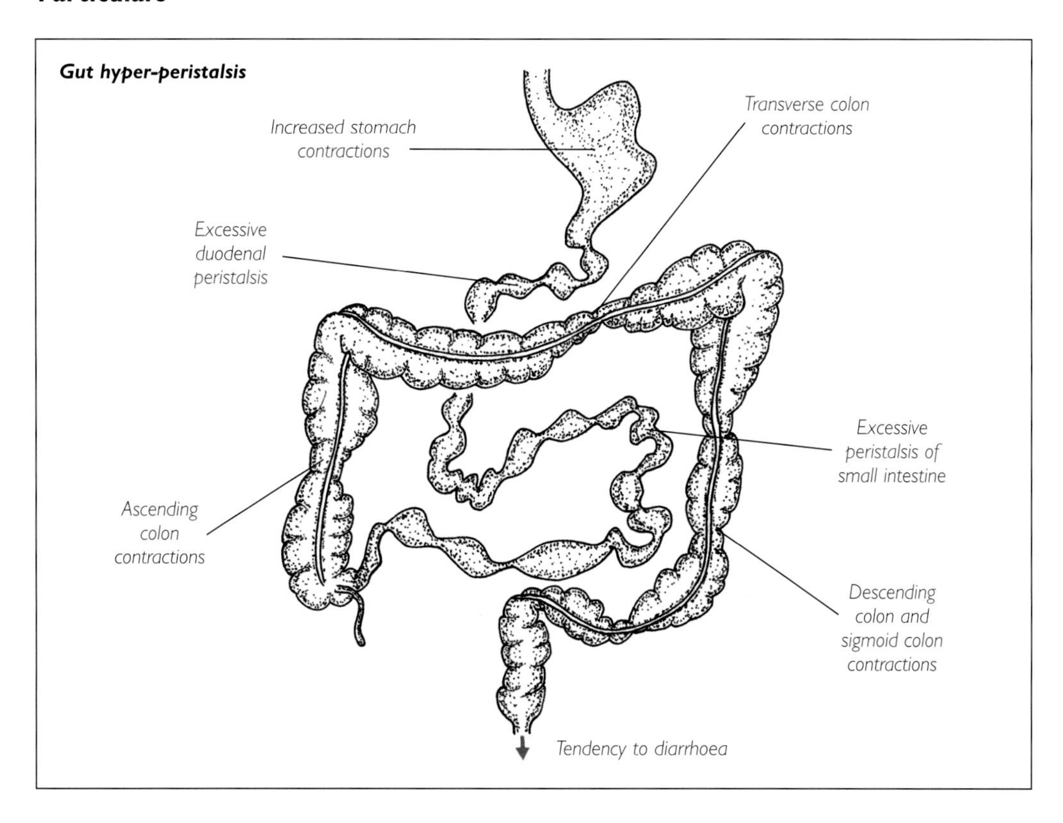

Hyper-peristalsis or increased gut motility is a feature of hyperthyroidism, presenting with diarrhoea. Note that some degree of increased gut spasm and a variable amount of diarrhoea (alternating with constipation) can also occur in irritable bowel syndrome – however not to the widespread extent of peristalsis as shown in this illustration.

Related images

p.219 Pain assessment chart
p.10 Sciatica
p.265 Toothache
p.3 Neuralgia, trigeminal
p.10 Torticollis
p.4 Bell's palsy
p.145 & p.451 Acute angina and infarction
p.527 Headache
p.528 Migraine visual aura
p.335 Endometriosis

MEDORRHINUM

Original

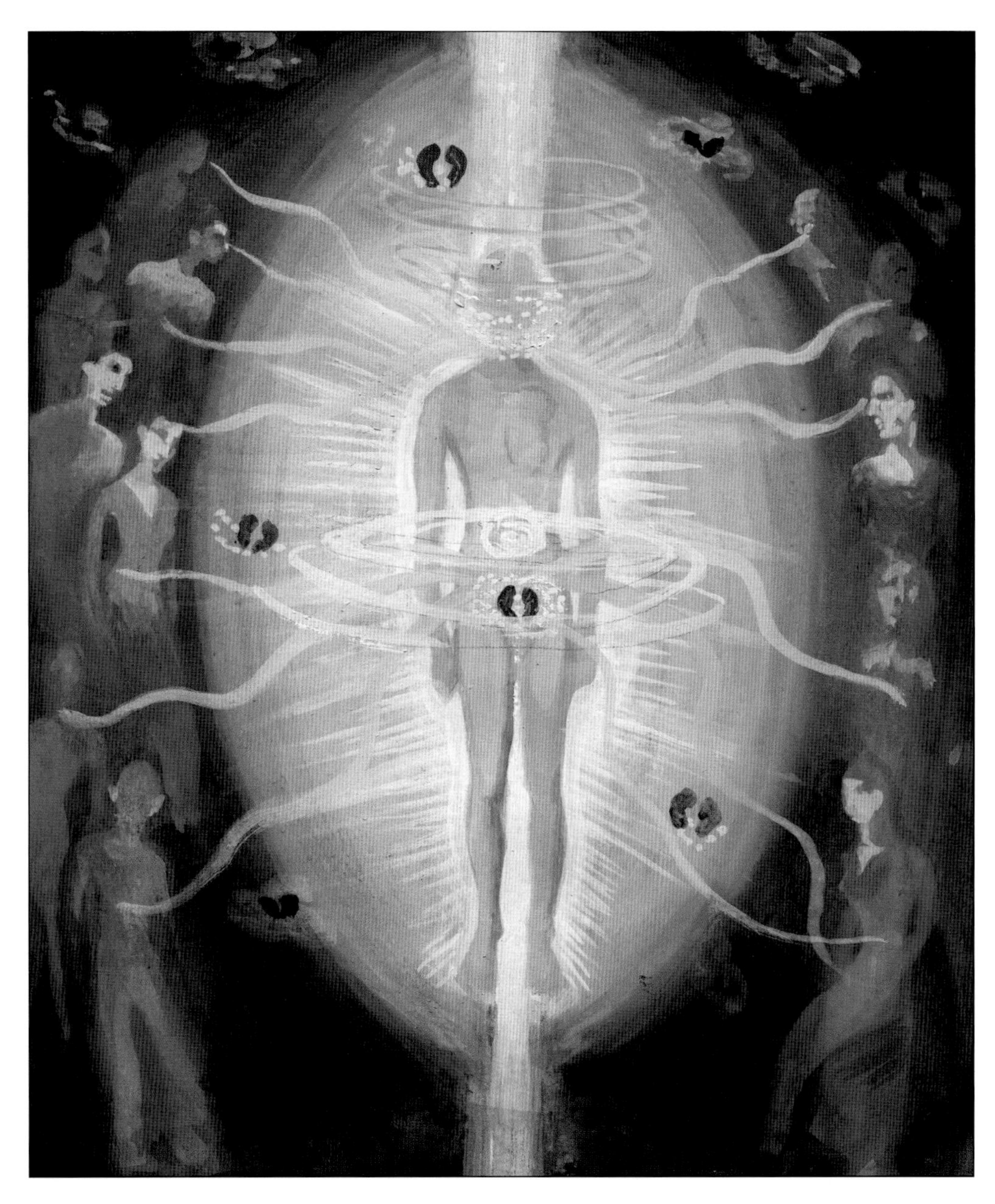

'Medorrhinum and the distortion of the sacral chakra', by Joanna Campion. The central figure is infected by gonorrhoea and the sycotic miasm; hence its aura is filled with etheric mucus. The head appears absent, in keeping with the symptom of feeling empty-headed due to the misty pus clouding the mental clarity and reception of thoughts by the brain. Several individuals gather around the person, with karmic cords attached especially to the sacral chakra – indicating the distortion of the sexual energy. The bacteria are shown as kidney-shaped paired bacilli, note one pair is shown overlying the reproductive region.

Astrology

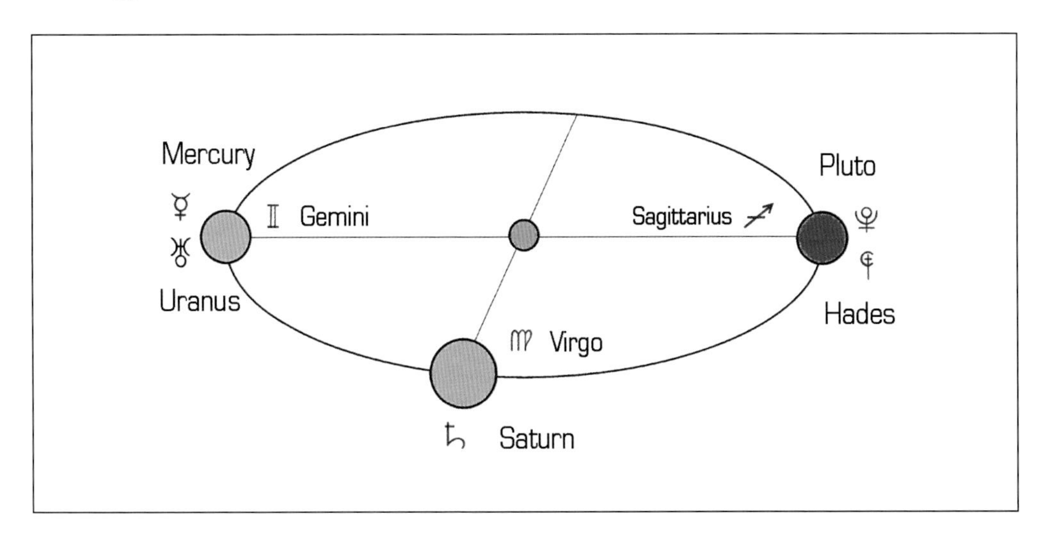

Mercury conjunct Uranus within Gemini, opposite Pluto conjunct Hades within Sagittarius, squared by Saturn in Virgo.

Oriental

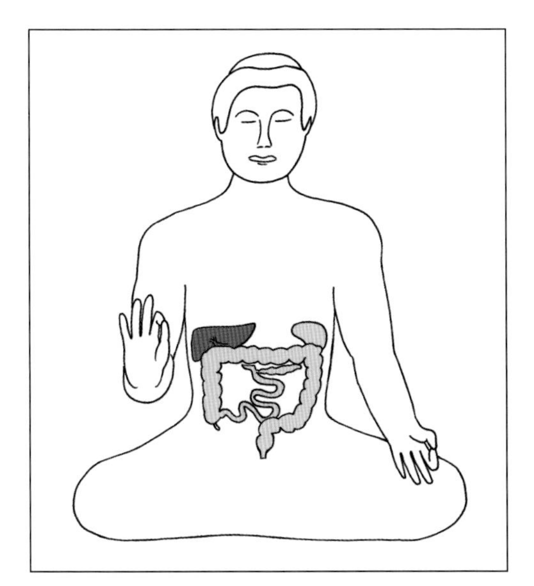

Liver chi stagnation, with damp-heat congestion of spleen and intestines.

Particulars

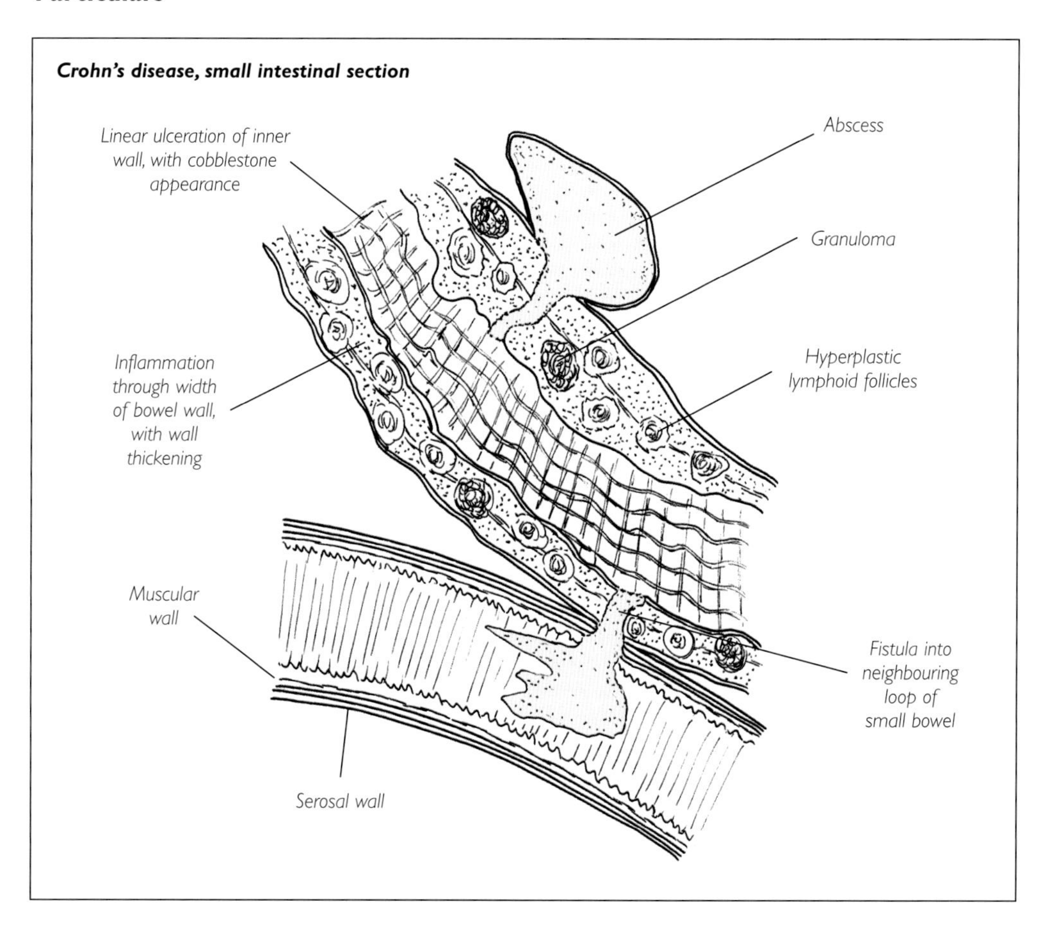

Crohn's disease is one type of chronic inflammatory bowel disease (the other being ulcerative colitis). There is inflammation affecting any part of the digestive tract and spanning the whole thickness of the bowel wall. Therefore fistulae and abscesses outside the bowel often develop. The bowel wall is thickened and oedematous, and malabsorption of food is a significant problem as well as episodes of abdominal pain.

Related images

p.582 Infectious gastroenteritis
p.187 Cystitis
p.718 Pyelonephritis
p.475 Urine microscopy

MERCURIUS SOLUBILIS

Original

C. Lasinio, after Raphael. 'Mercury on his chariot' (1516) engraving, published in Rome. © Wellcome Library, London. The astronomical and youthful Mercury is shown with winged sandals; his caduceus contains the two intertwined serpents and his chariot drawn by cockerels. The cockerel was regarded as the herald of the new day. Other animals associated with Mercury/Hermes were the ram or goat (symbolising fertility), and tortoise (in reference to his invention of the lyre from a tortoise shell). Another mention of the cockerel can be found in the Twelve Keys of Basil Valentine', a work first published in 'Ein Kurtz summarischer Tractat, von dem grossen Stein der Uralten..', Eisleben 1599. A Latin translation of the original text was published as 'Tripus aureus' in Frankfurt 1618. This alchemical manuscript contained 12 illustrated keys for the transmutation of the metals, planets and soul, and included animal imagery. In the second key, winged Mercury is introduced to the Sun and Moon of the first key, as well as two men with swords coiled by a serpent and bird respectively. In the third key, a winged dragon with a coiled tail and forked tongue stands in a mountain-backed landscape. To its left, a wolf or fox runs off with a bird (considered to be a hen) in its mouth, whilst being attacked by a cockerel on its back. The text further explains (in its hidden meaning) that the dragon represents the base of the combat, the Fallen energy of the material plane. Of it is born the fox, representing the wily self. But the blood of the dragon (via the bird within its mouth) must be transformed by the activity of Mercury-cockerel on its back.

Original

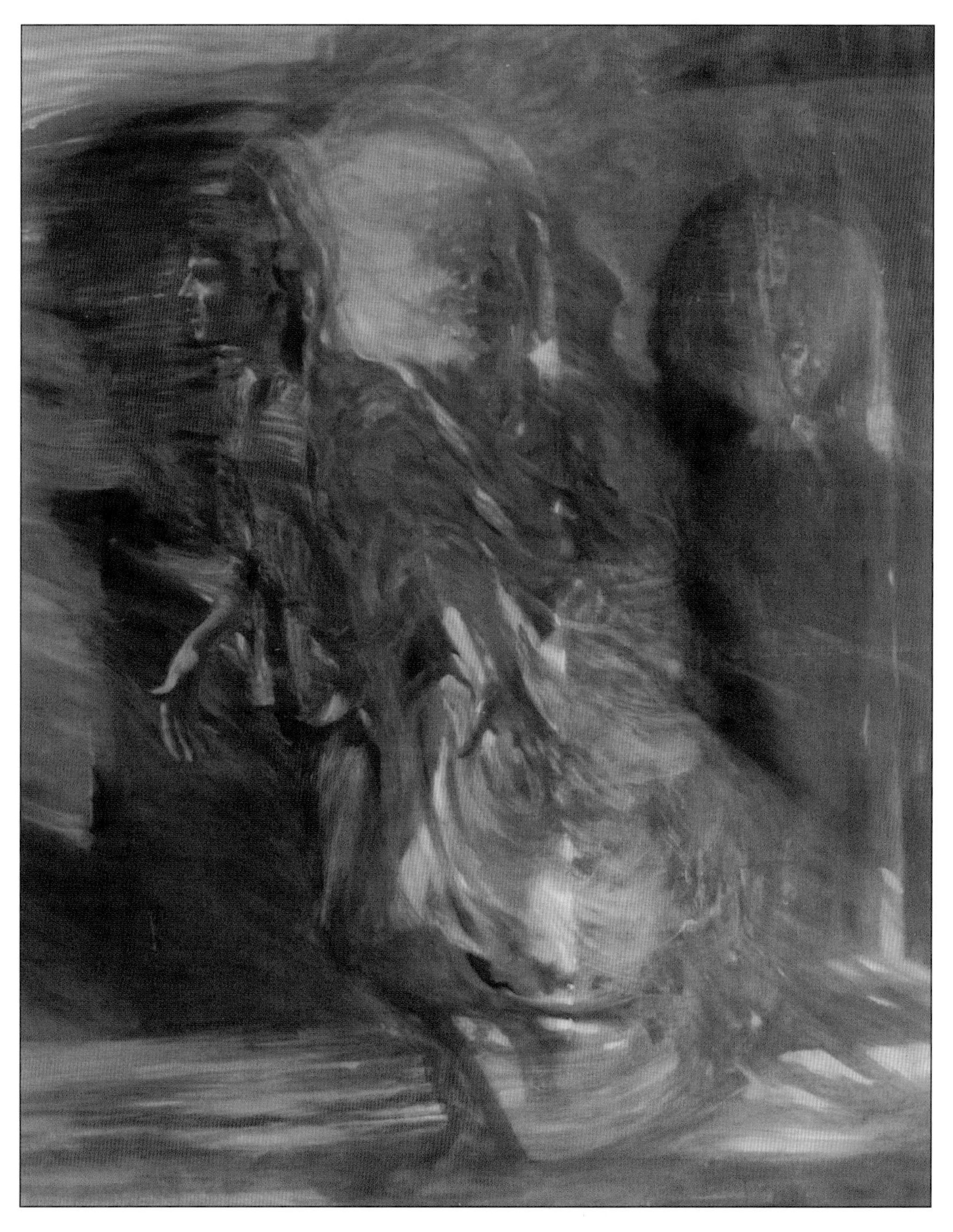

'Mercurius solubilis and parallel realities of the psyche', by Joanna Campion. The artist has also named the painting as 'The Warrior Movement'. An individual is shown along the path of movement in several stages of time-space. Normally the thread of consciousness is maintained with clarity and enough sense of I'ness throughout the multiple experiences of the psyche and across alternate and parallel realities. However, disruption of this ego identity is a basis behind split personality and schizophrenia.

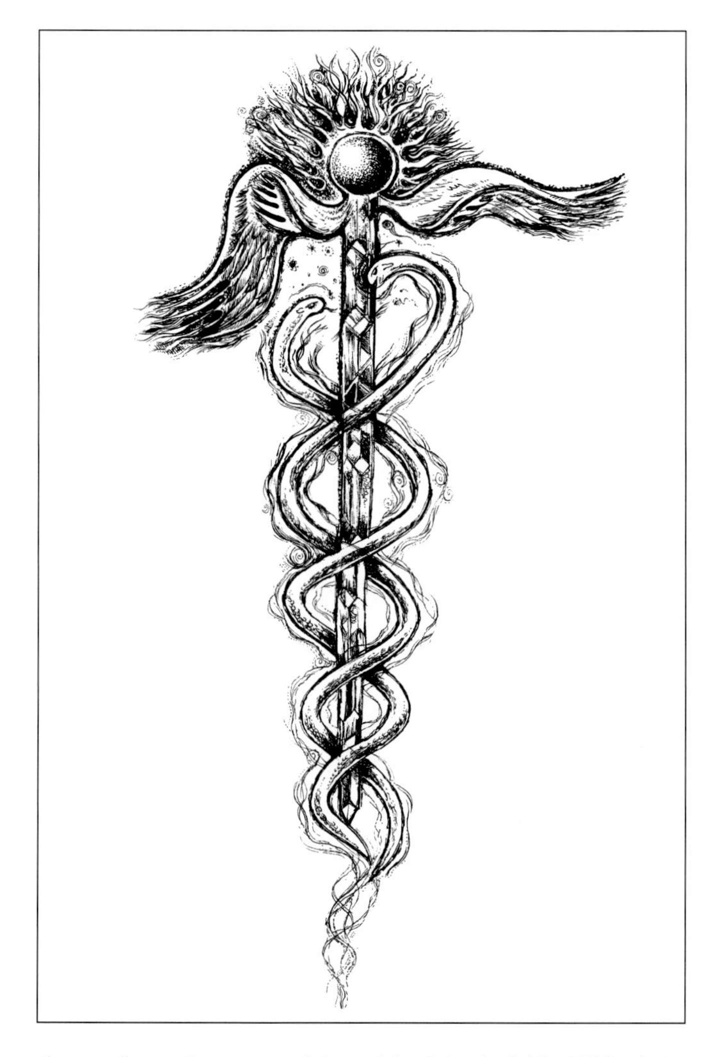

'Mercurius and Caduceus', by Katherine Mynott. This is the wand or rod carried by the mythic god of communication, Mercury. There are two serpents twined upward around it. The upper part features either two small wings or a winged helmet. When overcoming the duality of good or evil, all are manifestations from the 'Absolute All' of universal perfection. Pure light condensed into matter became depicted as evil polarised to the spiritual aspect of light. The snake has represented divine wisdom and perfection, and imbued psychical regeneration and immortality. Through the caduceus was given the power to guide souls into the spiritual realm after physical death, but also the power to bring back life to the 'dead', as resurrection. Energetically the staff symbolises the pranic tube of the soul. This is a column of light about 10 cm in diameter that connects the alpha and omega chakras together and runs along the spinal region of the body. The alpha chakra is an energy centre 15-20 cm above the head that interfaces with the totality and vastness of the spirit of the individual. This chakra conveys the immense amount of information coming to the incarnated soul from all the aspects of its spirit across spiritual reality and beyond time, space and incarnations. The omega chakra is 15-20 cm below the coccyx and interfaces with the rest of the soul's experiences across its incarnational grid. Essentially the column of light between alpha and omega conveys all that a soul is 'up there' to all that a soul is 'down here'. Within this column there is another tube, about 3-4 cm in diameter, called the pranic tube, which carries the specific frequencies of light and other energy required in the particular incarnation at hand. Three waveforms travel within this inner tube, also called the waves of Metatron (who is the king of the archangels and responsible for all light in the universe). These are the electrical, magnetic and gravitational waves. The spinal cord of concentrated nervous tissue is simply the final material manifestation of this pranic tube. The single coiled serpent is revealed in the staff of Asclepias (the Greek god of healing), which represents the healing journey the soul must undergo to return to the divine mercurial state of communication with the spiritual realm. With this transition the staff develops a double spiral where before there was one. Later, on the soul's journey, a triple phase spiralling energy develops which reflects the forces of trinity within the pranic tube of the initiate. Thus the threefold nature of God as Father-Will, Mother-Love and Christ-Wisdom/Child can manifest within the being of the incarnated soul. This is represented in the caduceus by the central rod around which the two serpents are coiled.

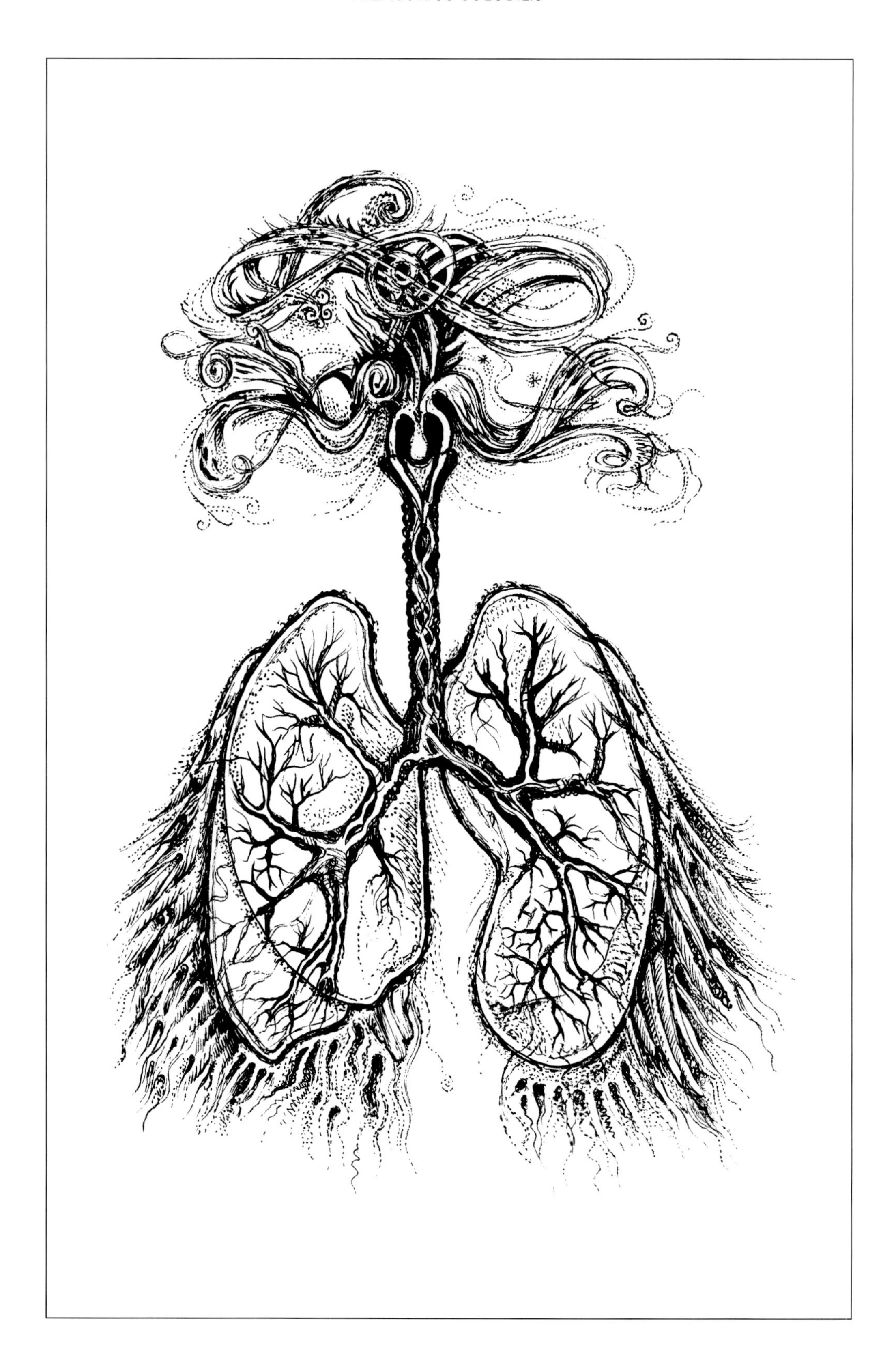

PRECEDING PAGE & BELOW. 'Mercurius and astral incarnation through the lungs', by Katherine Mynott (preceding page) and Yubraj Sharma (below). The preceding image shows the astral body flying into the trachea and descending through the bronchi into the lungs. The lungs provide for the entry of the air organism and through this process the human is intensely and more consciously connected with the environment. Part of the air of the environment becomes the inner world for a moment and inside the physical body. Air is the element conveying astral forces. Thus breathing and the rhythm of respiration reflects the rhythm of the emotions. The below image shows the relationship between the Mercury process and the alveoli. The formation of these end-sacs requires the subtle activity of this metal within the embryo. The formation of hollow spaces or invagination of tissue (which occurs in lung formation to form tubular alveoli) is an astral process. It is the astral body that, by moving into the physical-etheric tissues of the embryo, provides the driving force for the formation of hollowed tubes making up the lungs. Through the lungs, the astral body incarnates. The astral body must then descend and disperse further into the body, and this requires the further activity of the kidney-adrenal system.

Astrology

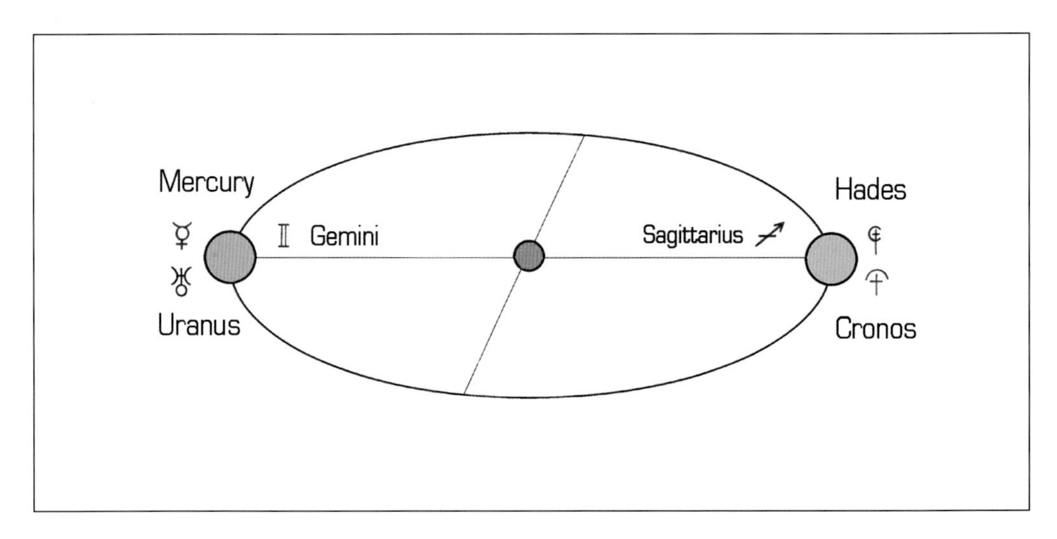

Mercury conjunct Uranus within Gemini, opposite Hades conjunct Cronos within Sagittarius.

Oriental

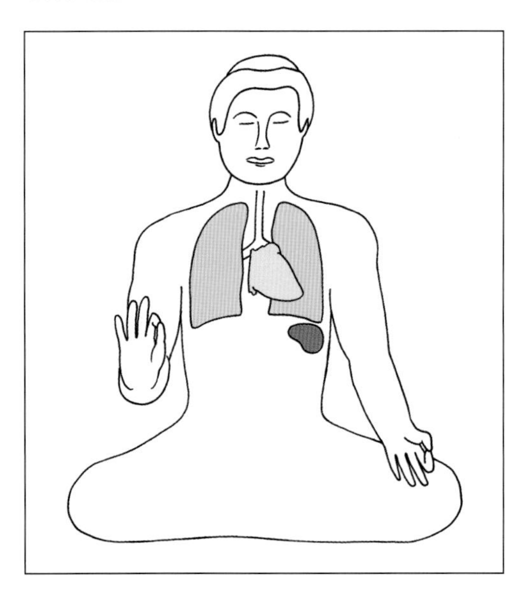

Spleen chi deficiency, with heart blood deficiency and damp-phlegm within the lungs.

Particulars

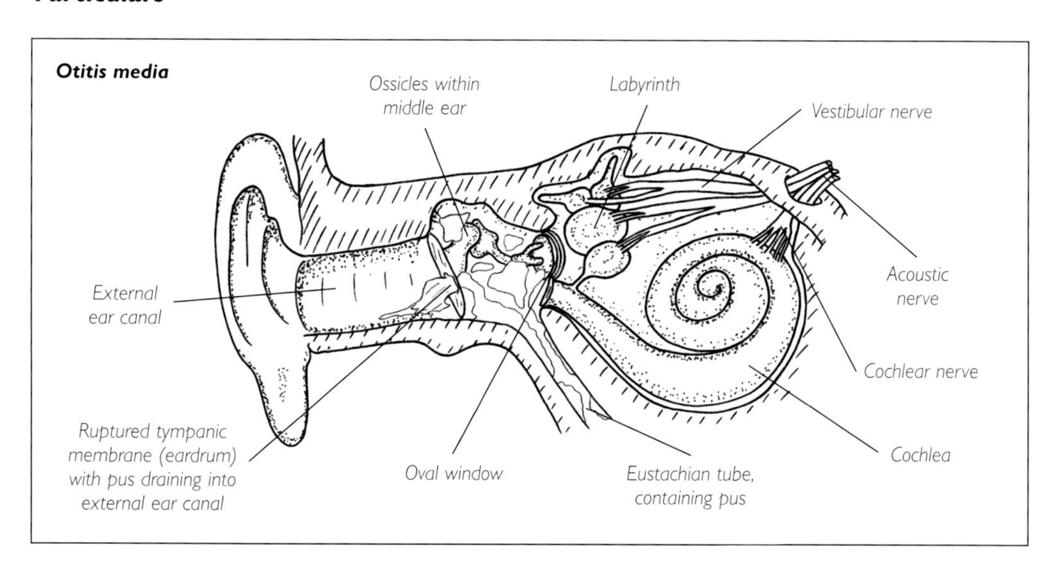

The middle ear is a mucous membrane compartment bounded by the tympanic membrane (eardrum) laterally (toward the exterior) and the oval window medially. The three ossicle bones (malleus, incus, and stapes) form a bony chain to conduct sound waves across the cavity. The Eustachian tube connects the cavity to the pharynx of the mouth/throat. Otitis media is inflammation of the middle ear, usually from an upper respiratory tract infection spreading from the nasopharynx through the Eustachian tube. It can be viral or bacterial. When air is obstructed from circulating into the middle ear through this tube then pain is aggravated, mucus pressure builds up, and with eardrum perforation the pus is discharged.

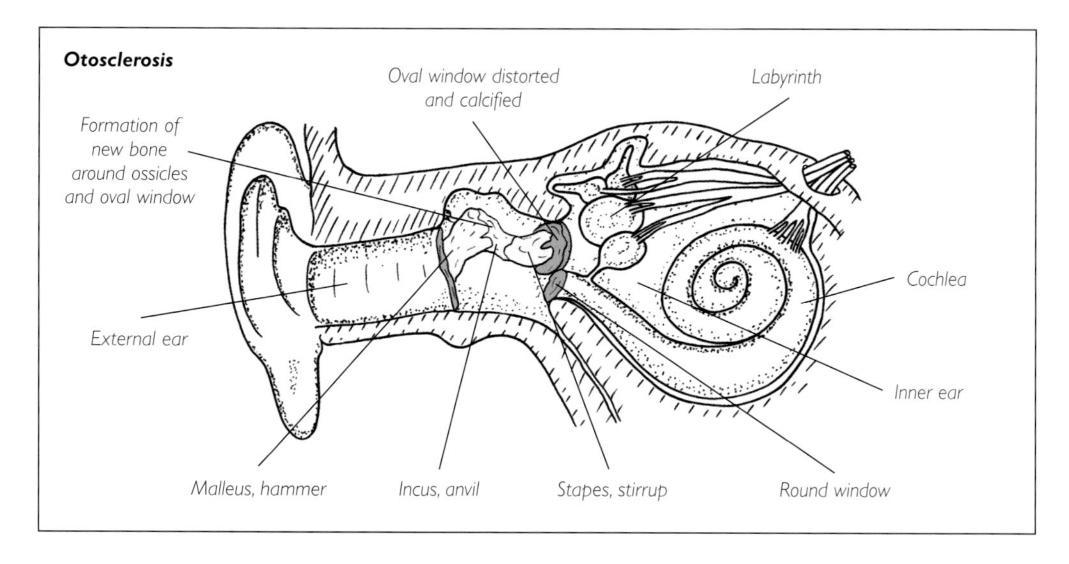

Otosclerosis is characterised by new spongy bone formation about the stapes auditory ossicle and the oval window (the drum between the inner and middle ear compartments). It is an inherited genetic disorder and a common cause of conductive hearing loss in young adults. The most frequent site of bone formation is just in front of the oval window; this bone then infiltrates and replaces the stapes. It may progress to the rest of the ossicles. Bony ankylosis (fixation of the joints between the three ossicles – malleus, incus and stapes) leads to loss of the sound vibration conduction.

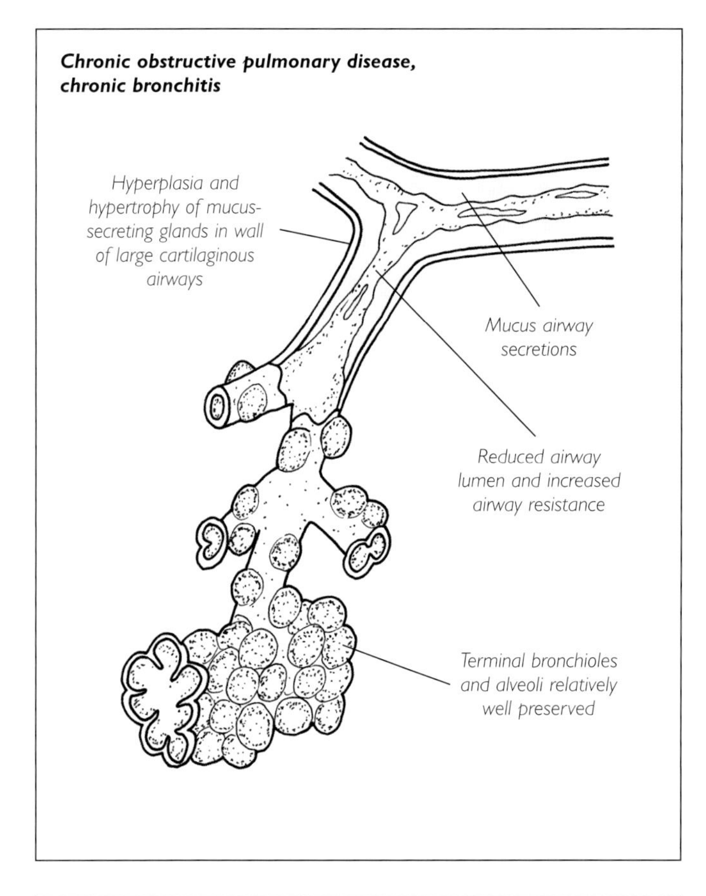

Chronic obstructive pulmonary disease (COPD) consists of a combination of chronic bronchitis and emphysema. Chronic bronchitis is defined by the presence of cough and sputum production for at least 3 months of the year for more than two consecutive years. The mucus secretions from the hypertrophied glandular tissue in the walls reduce the airway lumen, causing chronic breathlessness, cough and sputum with infective exacerbations.

Mercury toxicity through dental amalgam

Mercury enters the dentine and root blood vessels and thence into systemic circulation

Prismatic structure of tooth enamel

Mercury dispersed from amalgam enters the sinusoidal enamel tubes

Tooth enamel is a mineral deposit on the surface of the teeth, and formed by a membrane of cells called ameloblasts. It is composed of a network of pits or channels arranged as sinusoidal (wave-like) prisms or rods. These are packed in vertical rows, i.e. layered next to each other. These enamel channels interconnect the surface to the underlying dentine and thereby the blood vessels of the root and gum regions. Thus a constant flow of nutrients reaches the enamel from the blood, enabling constant regeneration of the enamel. Crowning or filling the teeth with dead inert substance such as metal alloy (e.g. amalgam – a mix of mercury with silver and some tin and copper) will block this nutrient flow. Paradoxically, therefore, the dental treatment accelerates the deterioration of the local tissues. There is also constant chemical leaching of the mercury into the body, with toxic effects over time.

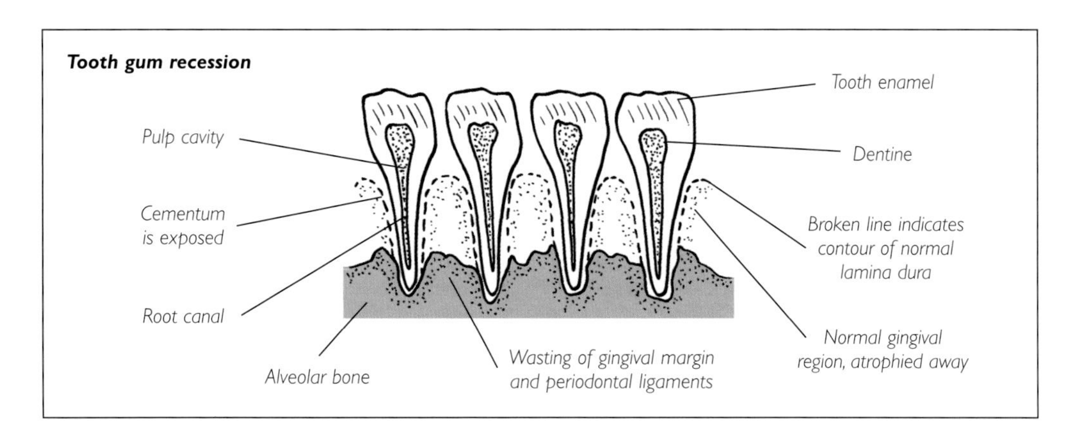

Each tooth has a crown, extending above the gingival (gum line), a neck (at the level of the gum – where the enamel ends and the cementum abuts), and one or more roots buried within the alveolar bone of the maxilla or mandible. There is a fibrous periodontal ligament about 0.2mm thick, between the cementum (which lines the root of the tooth) and the alveolar bone. The cementum is a mineralised material, containing collagen fibres which penetrate the ligament to fuse into the alveolar bone. The gingival (gum) is a mucous membrane which attaches to the enamel and to the underlying alveolar bone. Gum recession and atrophy can be a consequence of severe chronic periodontal disease, with chronic gingivitis, ulceration and infiltration by tumours (e.g. leukaemia), haemorrhagic disorders, scurvy (vitamin C deficiency) etc. There is loosening and potential loss of teeth and alveolar bone.

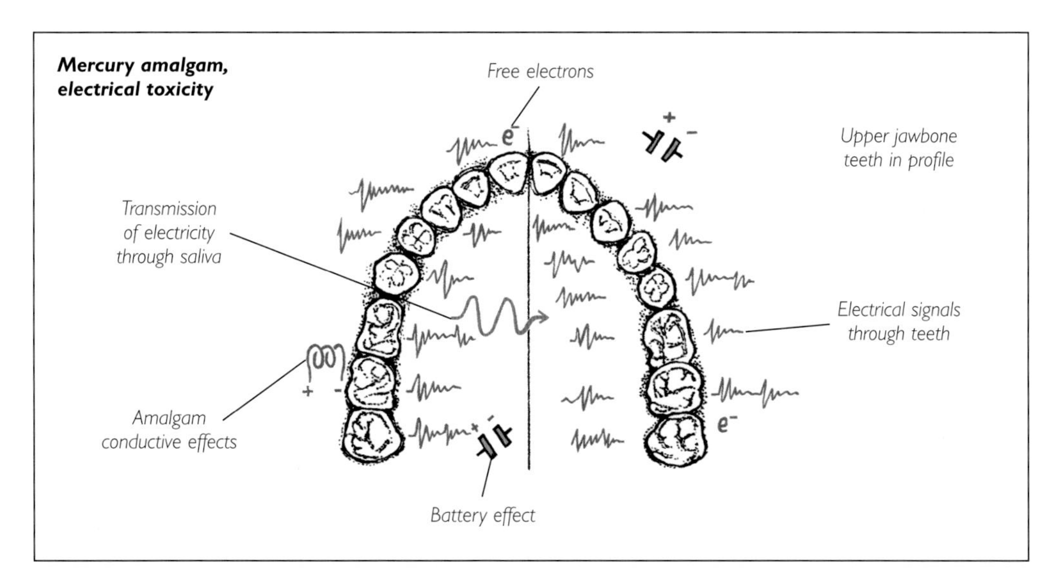

There is an electrical current created by having metal deposits (especially where using metal alloys with induction of galvanic currents) within the mouth. The alkaline saliva functions as an electrolyte medium and the dissimilar metals in an alloy also react with each other. Such electricity can distort nearby nerves and ganglia, causing chronic toothache, muscle tension, neuralgia, headaches, sensory distortion (e.g. visual or hearing) and potentially more serious central nervous disease (e.g. multiple sclerosis). There is also a link between the electrical activity within the acupuncture meridians/acupoints and the teeth. Effectively the teeth contain a morphological reflex map of the whole body. Such biologically natural electrical currents are also distorted by amalgam currents.

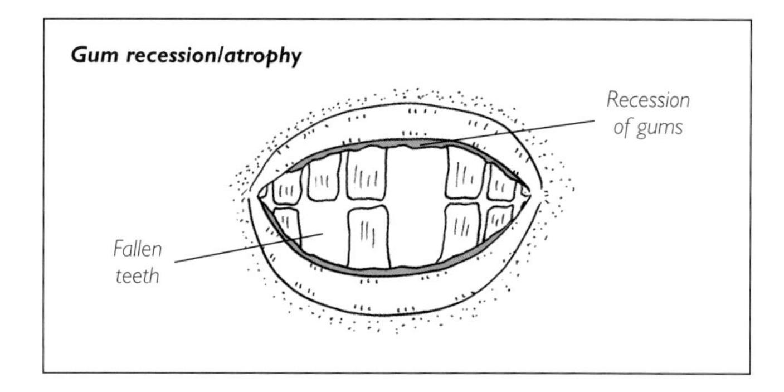

Gum recession and atrophy leads to reabsorption of the underlying alveolar bone. The loss of teeth support and exposure of the tooth roots leads to them falling out. Causes include chronic gingivitis or inflammation, vitamin/nutritional deficiencies (e.g. scurvy), ageing and periodontal disease with poor dental hygiene.

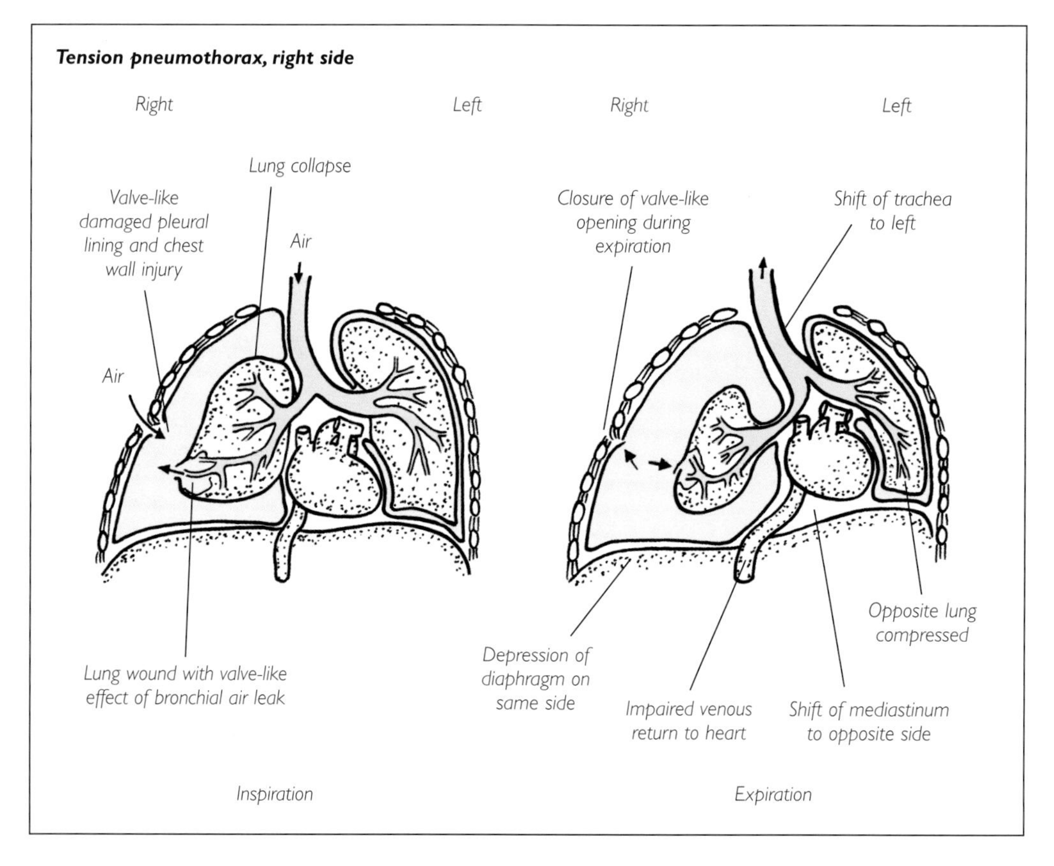

Pneumothorax is air in the pleural space around the lungs. It is the result of chest wall trauma or can occur spontaneously. Unless the visceral pleural lining (inner lining attached to the lungs) is abnormally adherent to the parietal pleura (outer lining) then air can extend to the whole pleural cavity of that hemithorax. Normally the pleural space has a negative pressure compared to atmospheric; hence a pneumothorax causes loss of the elastic recoil pressure of the lungs – causing it to partially deflate. Tension pneumothorax is an emergency situation where, at each inspiration, air enters the pneumothorax, but cannot leave at the expiration. There is a valve-like effect of the injury to the chest wall-pleural lining, or within the lung bronchi in communication with the pleural space. As the pleural pressure rises the lung on the same side is progressively collapsed, the mediastinum or central chest region is pushed to the other side – where the other lung is compressed. The situation requires immediate tapping and relief of the pneumothorax (with underwater-seal drainage of the trapped air).

Tension pneumothorax, right side, chest x-ray

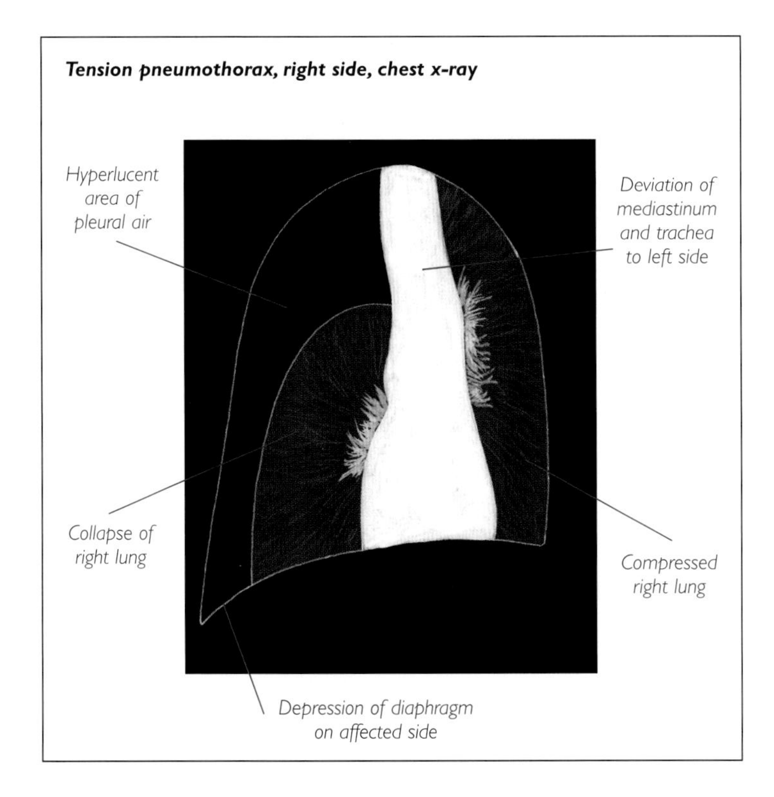

The chest x-ray in a pneumothorax will show the air within the pleural cavity as a hyperlucent area (darker than normal lung tissue) without any lung markings, i.e. no blood vessel or bronchial markings. With a tension pneumothorax the trachea and mediastinum will be pushed to the opposite side and the diaphragm pushed down on the same side.

Coeliac disease

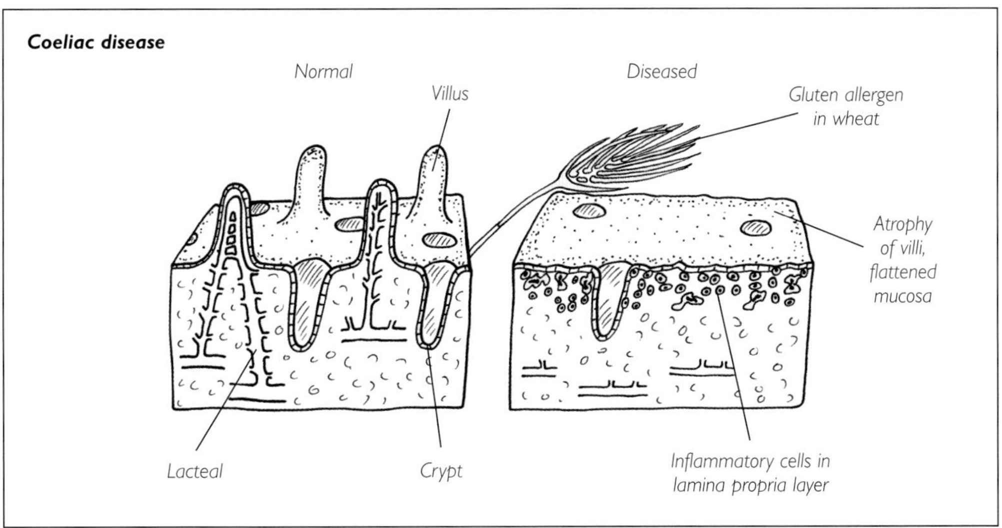

Coeliac disease is a malabsorption disease due to sensitivity to gliadin, a component of the wheat protein gluten. The pathology leads to flattening and thinning of the small intestinal mucosal wall (mostly the distal duodenum and jejunum regions) with subtotal villous atrophy. Normally the tall villi provide a larger surface area for absorption of digested food. There are increased lymphocytes within the epithelial wall. The crypts are preserved and can enlarge with proliferating cells. The symptoms include growth failure in a child, diarrhoea with undigested fats (steatorrhoea), nutritional deficiency (with anaemia) and weight loss. The pathology reverses to normal if gluten is removed from the diet.

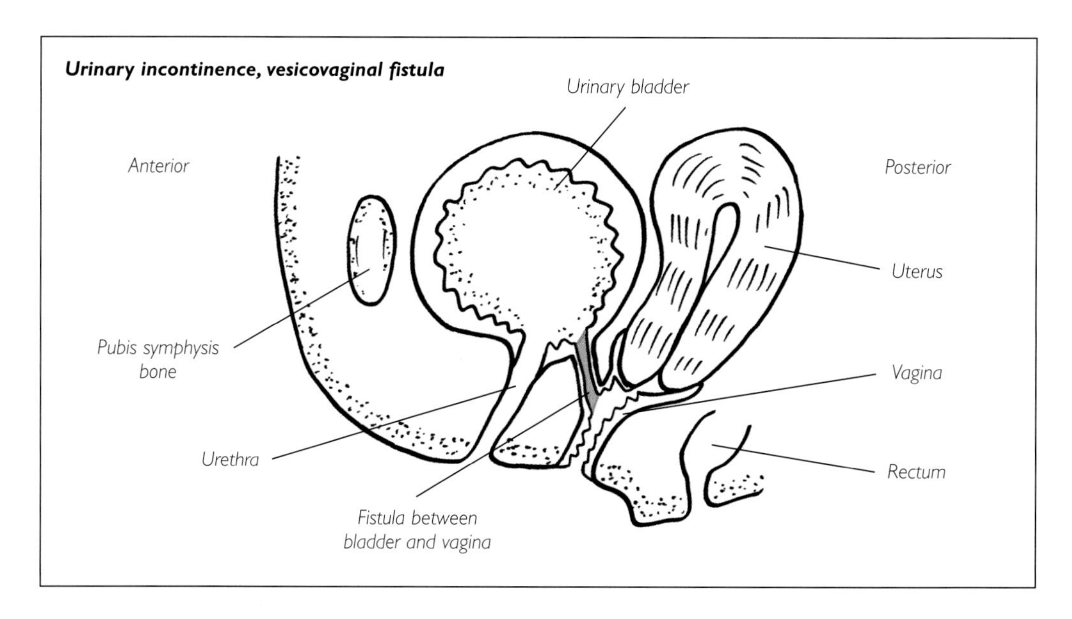

There are a number of types and causes of urinary incontinence (in the female). An example shown here is a fistula, which is an abnormal connection, here between the bladder and vagina and termed a vesicovaginal fistula. Causes of this include congenital abnormalities of development, after trauma during childbirth, surgical trauma (e.g. after hysterectomy or surgery to the neck of the bladder), from a locally invasive cancer (of the bladder or cervix), after radiotherapy and from severe local infection.

Related images

p.198 Emphysema
p.306 Bronchiectasis
p.95 Cystic fibrosis
p.661 Fibrosing alveolitis
p.369 Pneumonia
p.739 Tuberculosis and cavitary disease
p.704-708 Syphilis and miasm
p.519-520 Valvular heart disease
p.232 & p.343 Multiple sclerosis
p.586-587 Poliomyelitis
p.277 Motor neurone disease
p.18 Parkinson's disease
p.586 Muscle wasting
p.35 Spinal myelitis
p.752 Pineal tumour
p.258 Labyrinthitis
p.260 Meniere's disease

MOLDAVITE

Original

'Moldavite and the extraterrestrial support of Earth', by Martin Jezierski. The Earth is not in isolation, as shown here with light radiations to and from the rest of the cosmos, permeating the aura and very substance of the planet. Benevolent aliens look on, watching, waiting and ready to assist in accordance with the Divine Plan. Meteorites stream toward the Earth, providing a route of entry for the impulses of comets and spiritual transformation.

'Moldavite and cloning of the Greys', by Katherine Mynott. Depicted in the foreground are the Greys, the commonest alien race currently shown in popular culture. The channelled story of their race indicated their evolution involved cloning, thus they lost physical and spiritual individuality. Normally the astral body provides unique emotional responses, losing these led to apathy and no real desire to live. Eventually the race lost the power of natural procreation and also the momentum for evolution, causing it to practically die out. The message from these extraterrestrials is therefore timely for modern humanity – to not proceed along a similar path of distortion to the genetic code. Various strands of double-stranded DNA are shown around the group. There is still hope for salvation, as shown by the reception of cosmic and spiritual light at the centre of the illustration.

Astrology

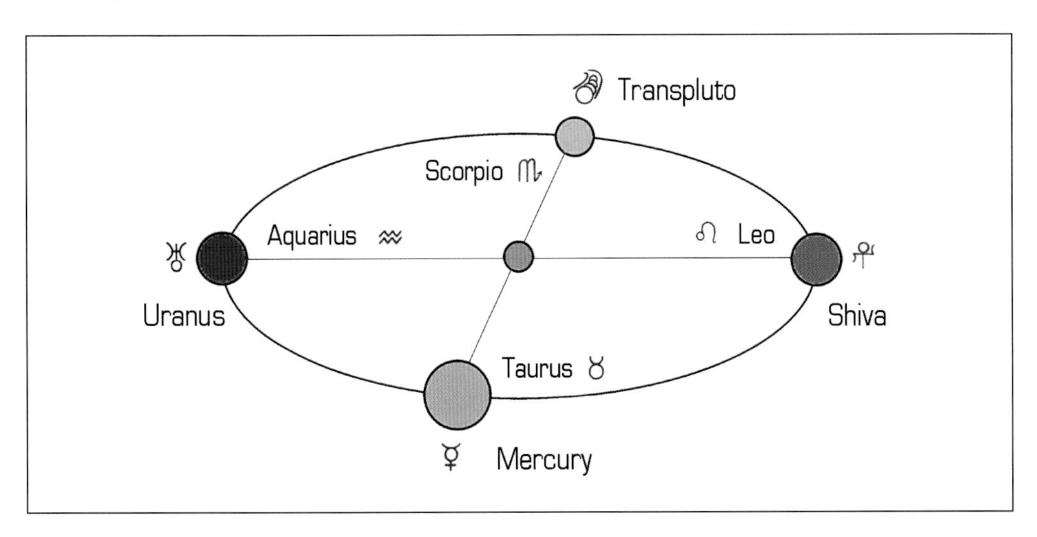

Grand cross, Uranus in Aquarius opposite Shiva in Leo, and Mercury in Taurus opposite Transpluto in Scorpio.

Oriental

Spleen chi deficiency, with external heat invasion of pericardium and phlegm-fire harassing the heart.

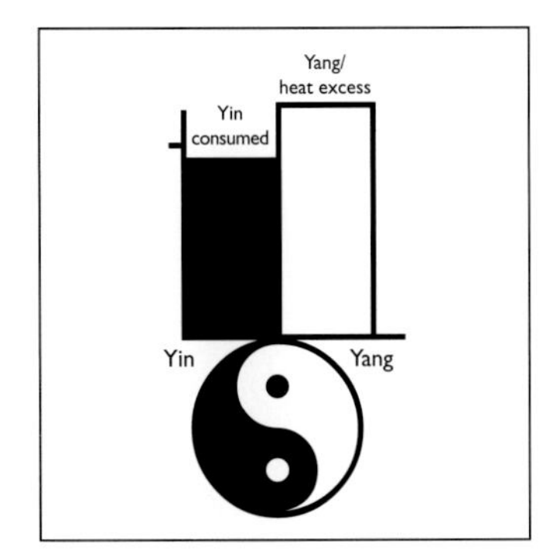

Particulars

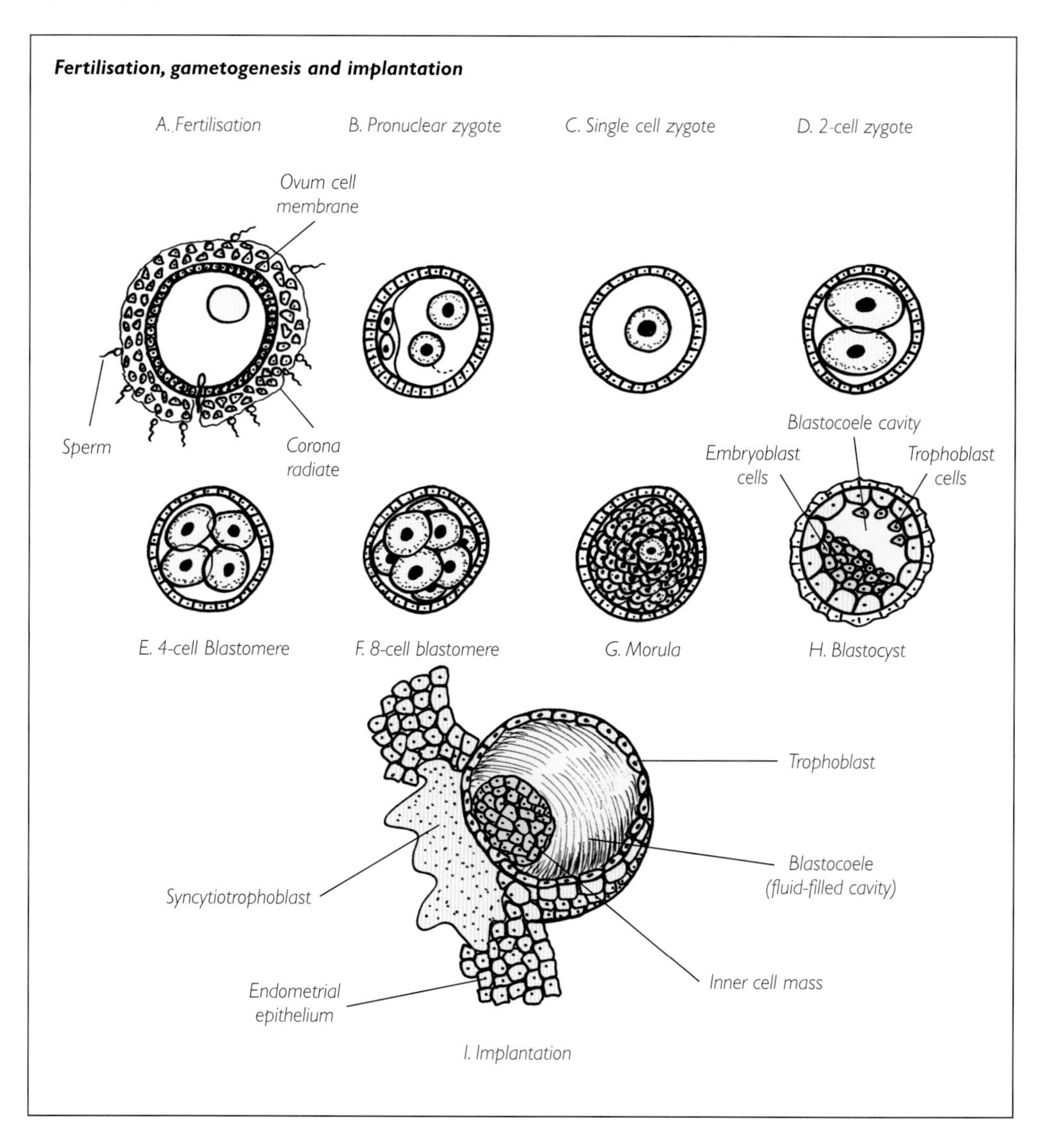

Upon ovulation, the ovum enters the fallopian tube and proceeds toward the uterus. If sperm has reached the ampulla or junction of the tube with the uterus after coitus (within the last 24 hours), then there is a good chance of fertilisation. The activated sperms produce enzymes, which enable one of the sperms to penetrate the corona radiate (comprised of former ovarian follicular cells) and zona pellucida of the ovum. The sperm head can then enter the ovum cell, completing the fertilisation. The head now becomes the male pronucleus (male derived genetic material), the nucleus of the ovum being the female pronucleus. The two pronuclei fuse to form a single nucleus, this then becomes the zygote or new individual entity proper, the zygote undergoes cell division to form a 2-cell stage blastomere, then 4-cells, 8-cells and so on. The morula is a bunch of cells. About 5 days after the initial fertilisation this morula now accumulates fluid into an internal cavity. Cells pushed to one peripheral rim are called the trophoblast, the other end form the inner cell mass. At the 7th day this blastocyst now implants into the uterus. The inner cell mass will further differentiate into the yolk sac and amniotic cavity, and the embryonic disc which will develop into the future embryo proper.

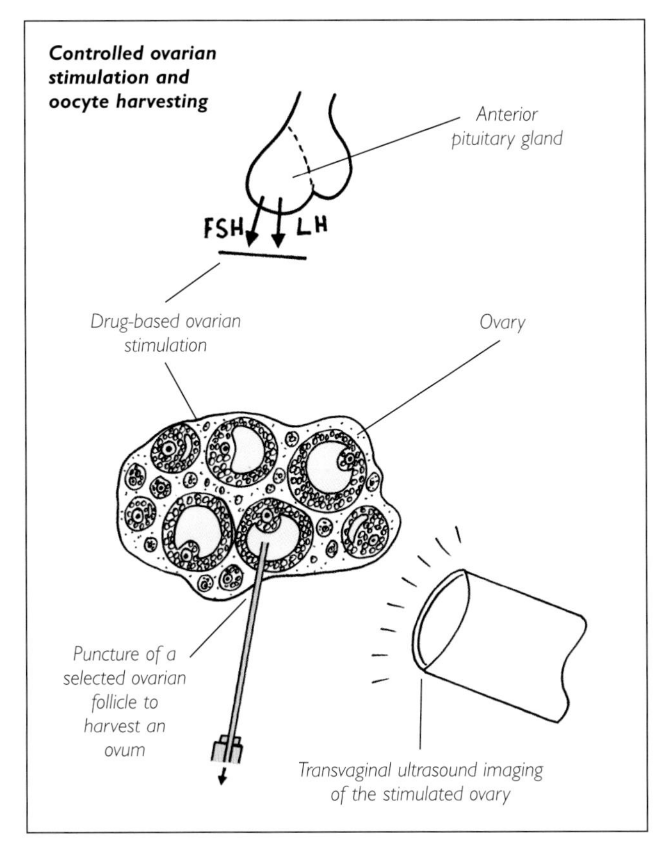

In-vitro-fertilisation (IVF) is the mainstay treatment of assisted reproductive technology. IVF is the mixing of egg and sperm in a dish/container 'in-vitro', i.e. outside the body, followed by incubation in a temperature-controlled, CO_2 enriched environment. If successful, then one or more embryos have been created, and some or all of these can then be inserted directly into the uterus via the cervix. Excess embryos can be frozen for any later use. IVF initially requires controlled ovarian hyperstimulation (COH), in order to develop several mature eggs for harvesting. This is done by using several hormonal drugs in combination. The initial effect is to cause a hyper-secretion or flare of luteinising hormone (LH) and follicle stimulating hormone (FSH) from the anterior pituitary, but then continued drug dosing causes the LH and FSH release to become blocked. Instead further ovarian stimulation is continued by the drug-based gonadotropins (which have LH and FSH-like effects). The endpoint is to retrieve at least several mature oocytes. The ovarian follicles must measure at least 16mm in diameter by ultrasound, and the ultrasound guided probe will aspirate these egg cells. Sperm specimens can now be collected and tested prior to mixing with the eggs.

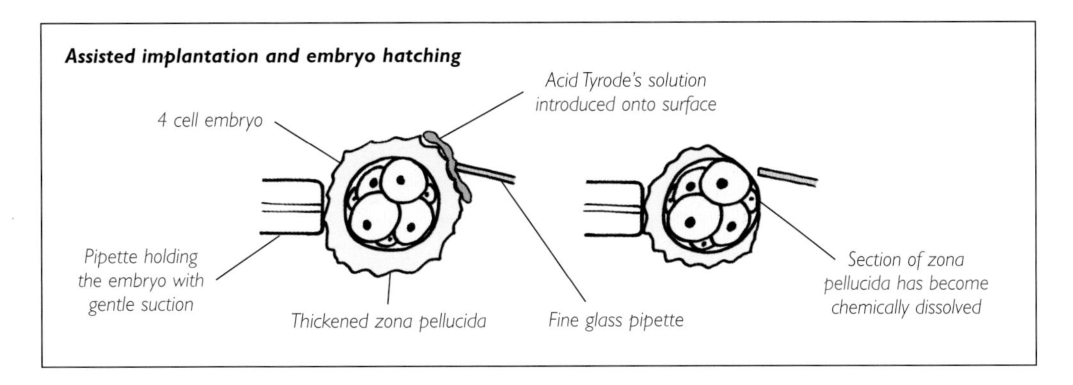

Assisted fertilisation attempts to deal with problems in the union of egg and sperm cell. However, the pregnancy may fail for reasons of improper implantation. At normal implantation the embryonic cells need to break out of the confines of the zona pellucida (the former wall around the ovum) and penetrate the uterine lining. By dissolving part of the zona pellucida lining with an acid solution it has been found that hatching of the embryonic cells and their subsequent implantation is assisted where before this had been difficult.

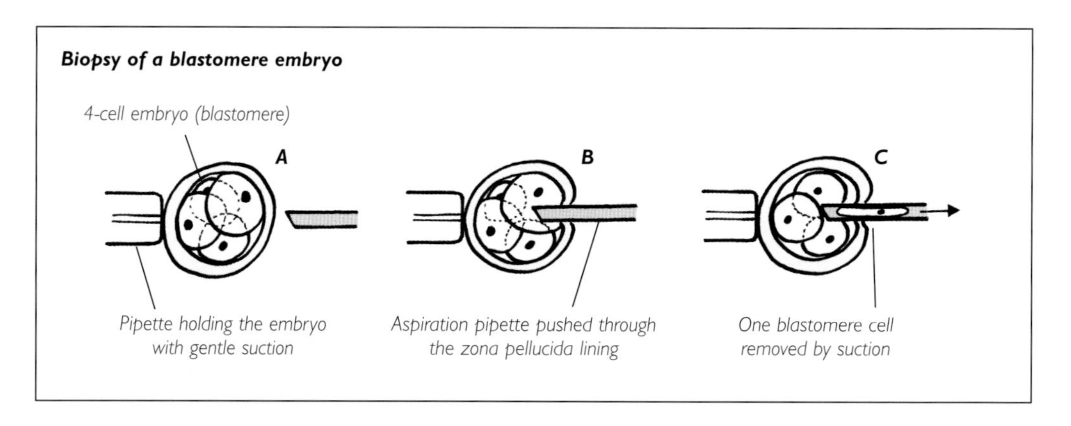

The embryo created by IVF can be biopsed prior to transfer and implantation into the uterus. This may be done, e.g. for genetic diagnosis of any inherited disease. Embryos are usually inserted into the mother to be at 48-72 hours after the initial incubation of the oocytes with sperm, which correlates with the 4 and 8-cell stages of the blastomere (A). The aspiration pipettes punctures the zona pellucida (B) and then draw back one blastomere cell (C).

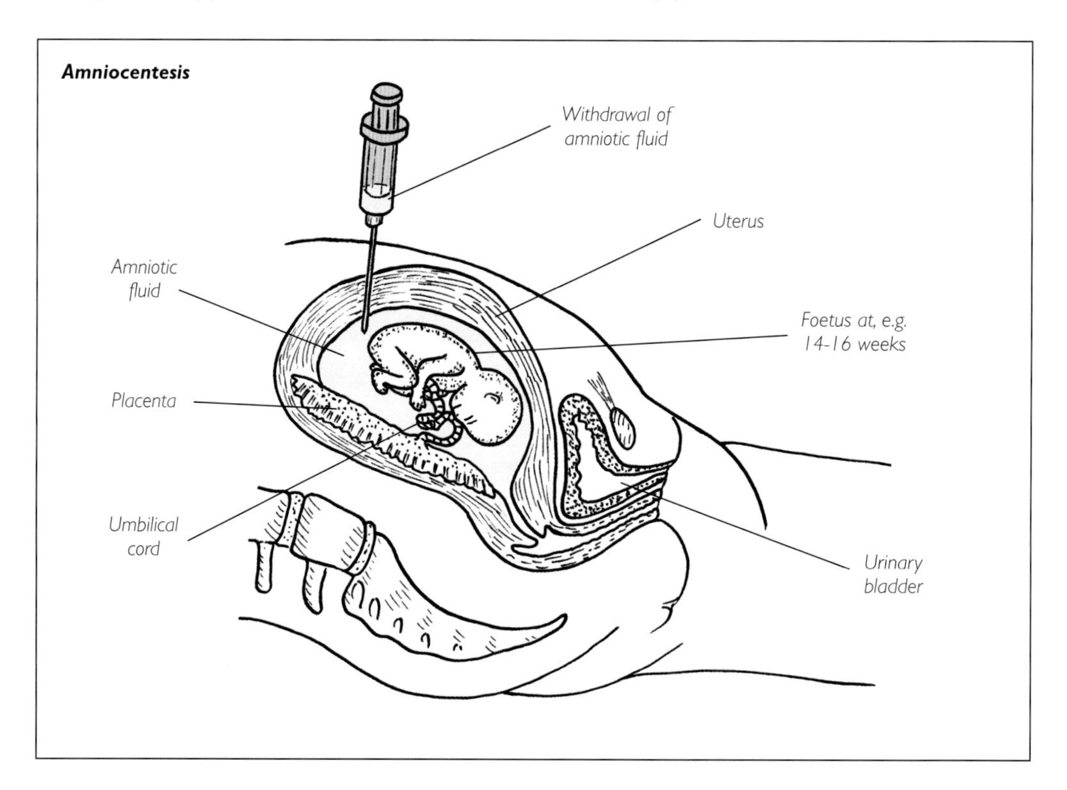

Amniocentesis involves withdrawing some amniotic fluid around the developing foetus, to test for certain genetic disorders (e.g. Downs syndrome, spina bifida, haemophilia) usually at 14-16 weeks of gestation, or to determine foetal maturity/wellbeing near the time of delivery (usually after the 35th week). For the procedure, the position of the foetus and placenta is confirmed by ultrasound, and then a hypodermic needle inserted through the mother's abdominal wall and uterus into the amniotic cavity. About 10ml of fluid is withdrawn. There is about a 0.5% risk of spontaneous miscarriage after the test.

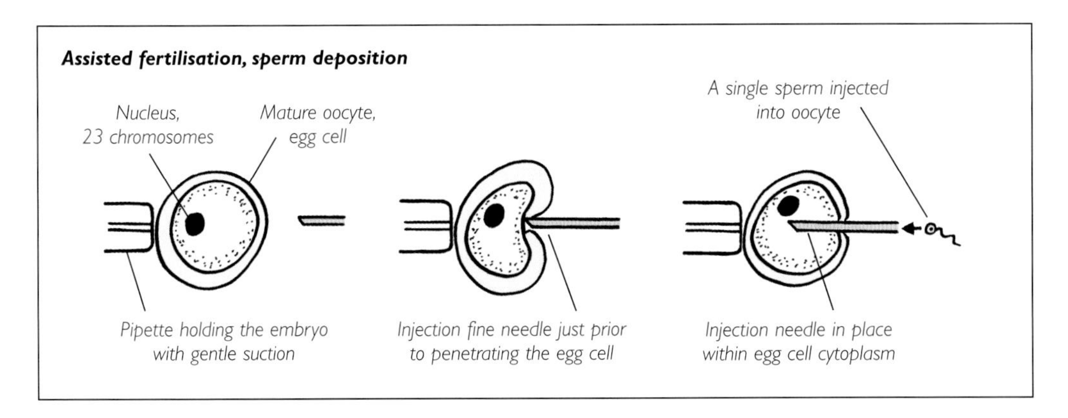

Successful fertilisation requires the entry of a single sperm into an oocyte (egg cell). This sperm must penetrate the cumulus oophorus (of follicular cells) and zona pellucida lining around the egg cell. Various problems can prevent this penetration, such as the presence of anti-sperm antibodies in the female, low sperm concentration, poorly motile sperm or abnormal sperm shapes. A method of assisting this stage of fertilisation is to puncture a hole through the zona pellucida, inserting the needle into the cytoplasm of the egg cell and thereby injecting a single sperm directly into the cell.

Related images

p.186 Burns chart
p.185 Burn
p.215 Electric burn
p.44 Necrotic skin and abscess
p.180 Gastrointestinal bleeding
p.232 & p.343 Multiple sclerosis
p.311 Brainstem stroke
p.586-587 Poliomyelitis
p.277 Motor neurone disease
p.18 Parkinson's disease
p.586 Muscle wasting
p.35 Spinal myelitis
p.364 Syringomyelia
p.752 Pineal tumour
p.258 Labyrinthitis
p.260 Meniere's disease
p.704-708 Syphilis and miasm

NAJA NAJA

Original

'Naja and the Fall of Humanity', by Katherine Mynott. The Fall represents the time of separation of humans from their connection to the spiritual realm, a decision by collective humanity in order to experience limitation, karma and reincarnation. This event occurred during the stage of the Lemurian root race. The axiotonal lines of light from the cosmos were cut, the body no longer nourished by this cosmic light. It led to the body's reliance on earthly-based foodstuffs. In the future humanity will be plugged back into cosmic alignment with their source energy from Spirit. Light from the spiritual realm will permeate the physical cells again, reversing ageing and disease processes. A Guardian angel is shown supporting and facilitating the descent of the human soul. The snake is the key animal representing the sin of the Fall and is shown entwined around the human.

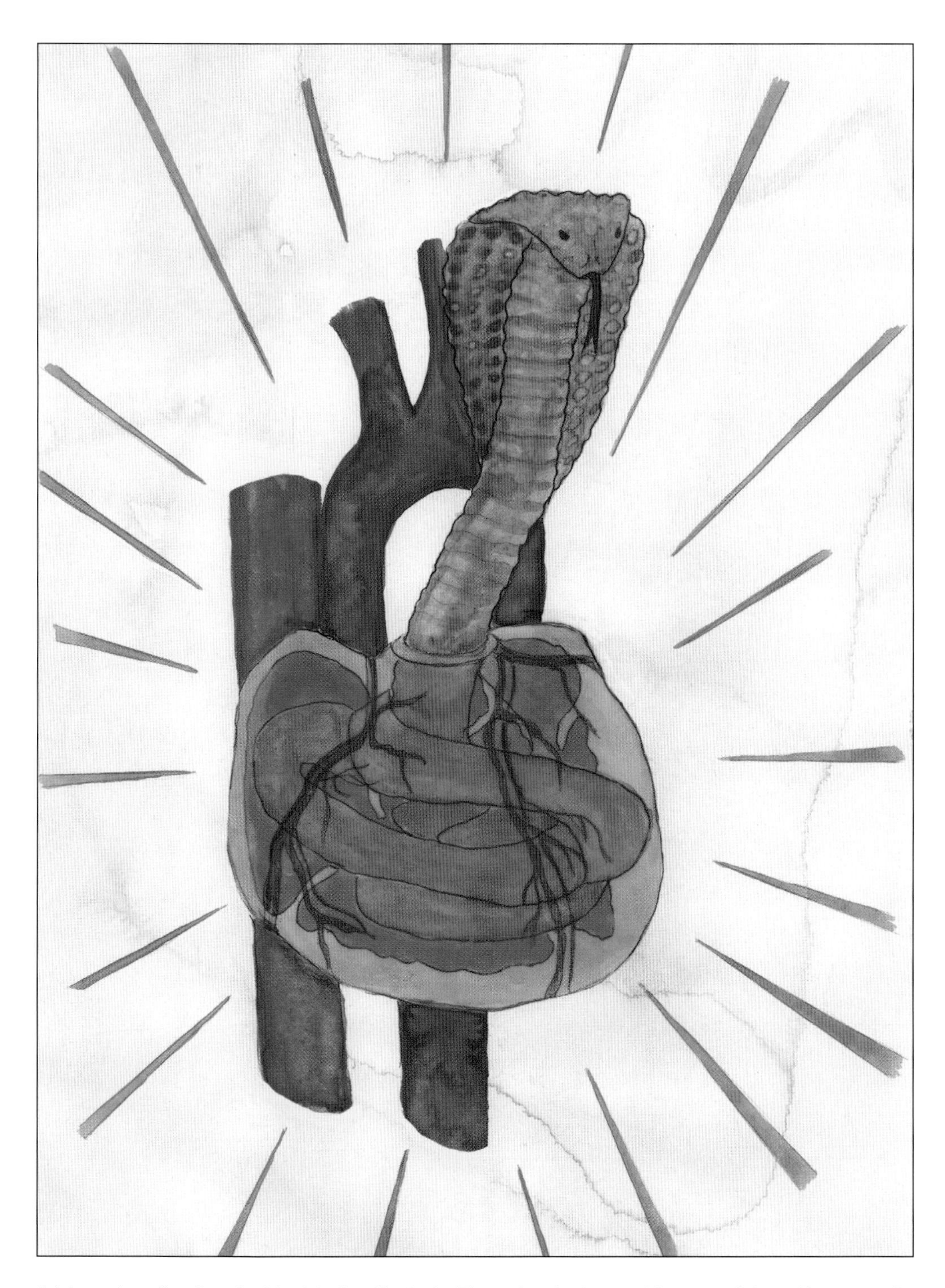

'Naja and cardiac function', by Nadine Kardesler. The cobra is shown rising out of the orifice normally for the pulmonary artery from the right ventricle. The septal walls within the heart have been removed for clarity. Snake remedies are applicable to the treatment of heart conditions, promoting the ego forces into this organ. The rhythmic contraction of the heart also relies on the balance between the parasympathetic (via the vagus nerve) and sympathetic nervous system.

Astrology

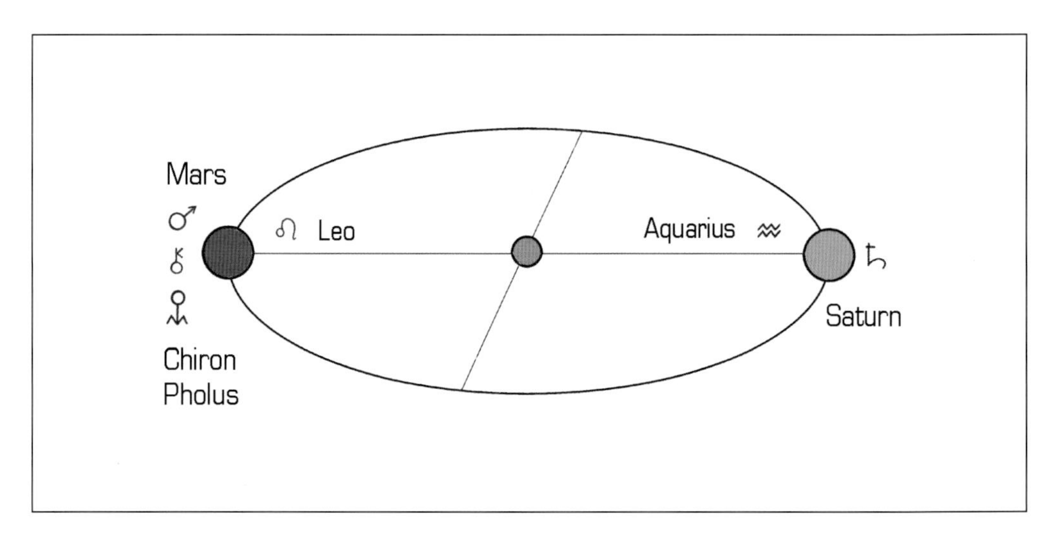

Mars conjunct Chiron and Pholus within Leo, opposite Saturn in Aquarius.

Oriental

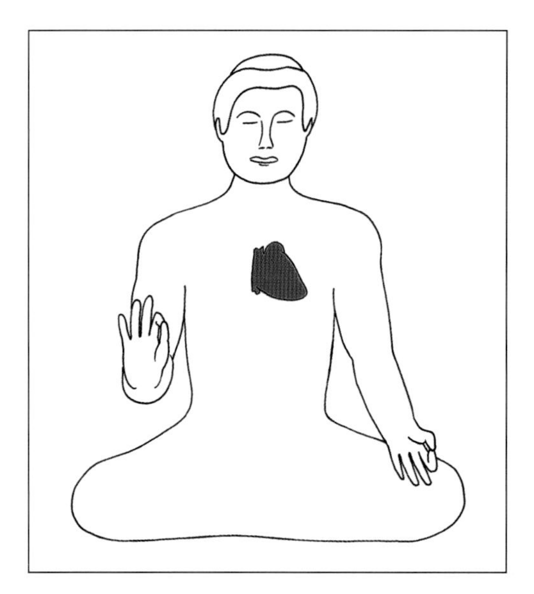

Heart blood stagnation/stasis.

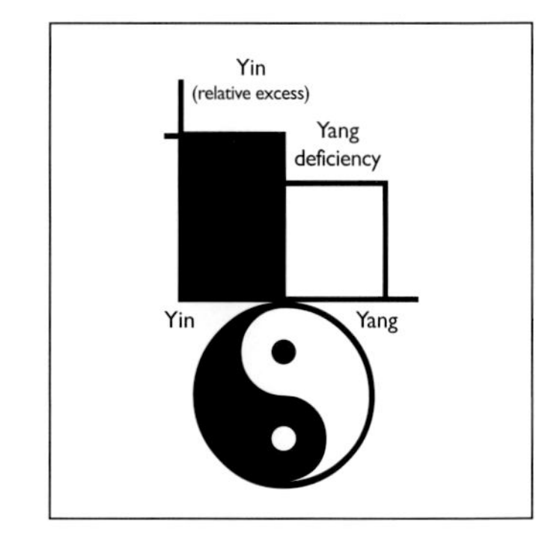

Particulars

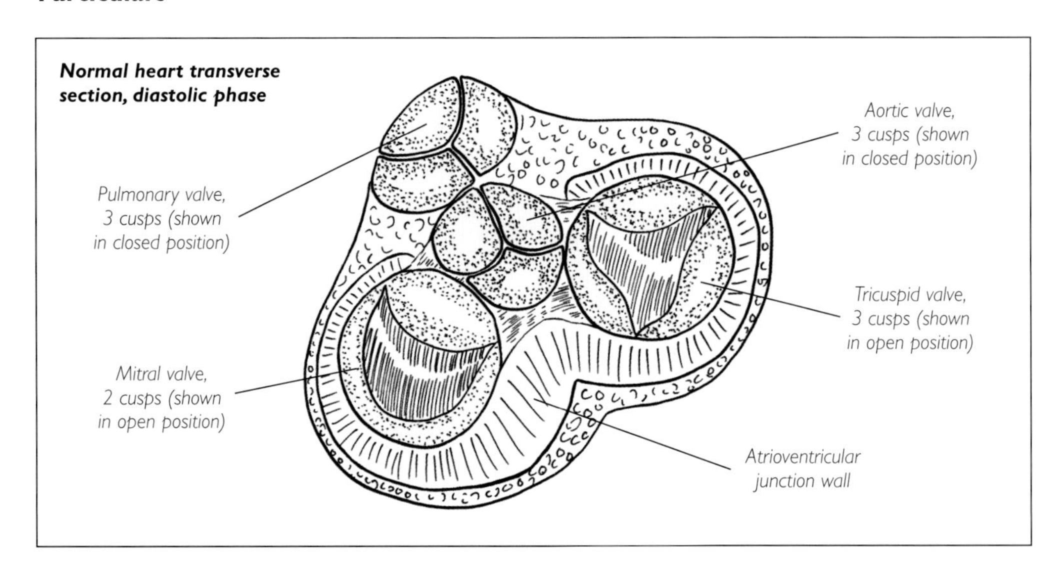

Diastole is the phase of ventricular muscle relaxation with the ventricular chamber filling with blood from their respective atria. Thus the tricuspid valve (between the right atrium and ventricle) and mitral valve (between the left atrium and ventricle) are shown in open position, the valve cusps pulled apart by their papillary muscles. Meanwhile the closed aortic valve and pulmonary valve prevent the exit of blood from the left and right ventricles respectively.

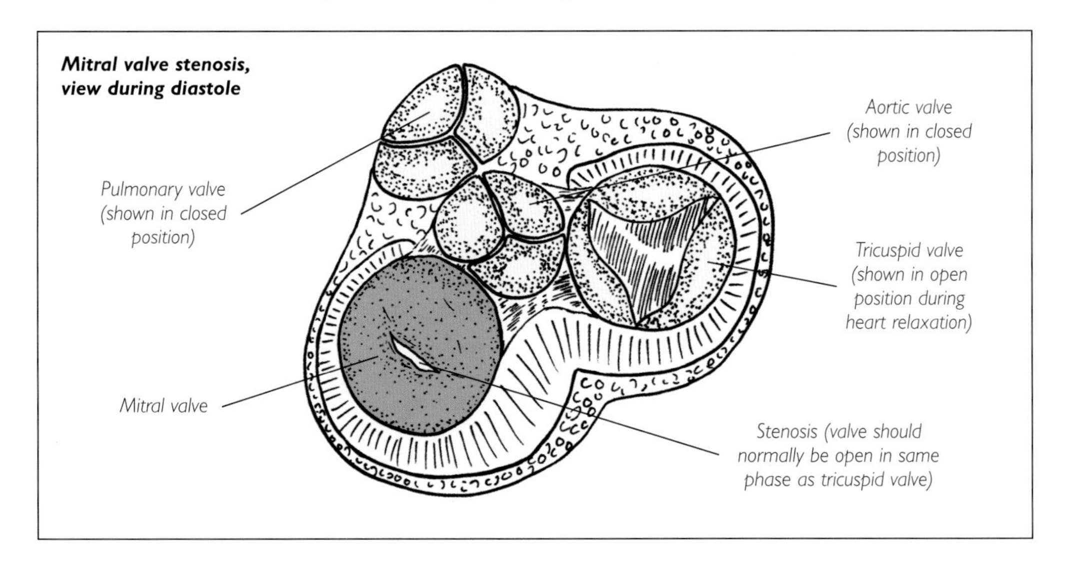

Mitral stenosis is almost always due to rheumatic heart disease, occasionally it is due to rare genetic disorders or ageing calcification and fibrosis. Note that rheumatic fever often leads to two or more heart valves becoming deformed, e.g. tricuspid and mitral stenosis may occur together. The normal valve orifice area is 5cm^2, when reduced to 1cm^2 there is severe stenosis. The left atrium compensates through muscle hypertrophy and dilatation, but increased blood pressure develops in the lung circulation and right side of the heart. Pulmonary odema or fluid congestion occurs and the right heart can fail. The patient often exhibits a dusky pink discolouration over the upper facial cheeks (called the mitral facies/flush).

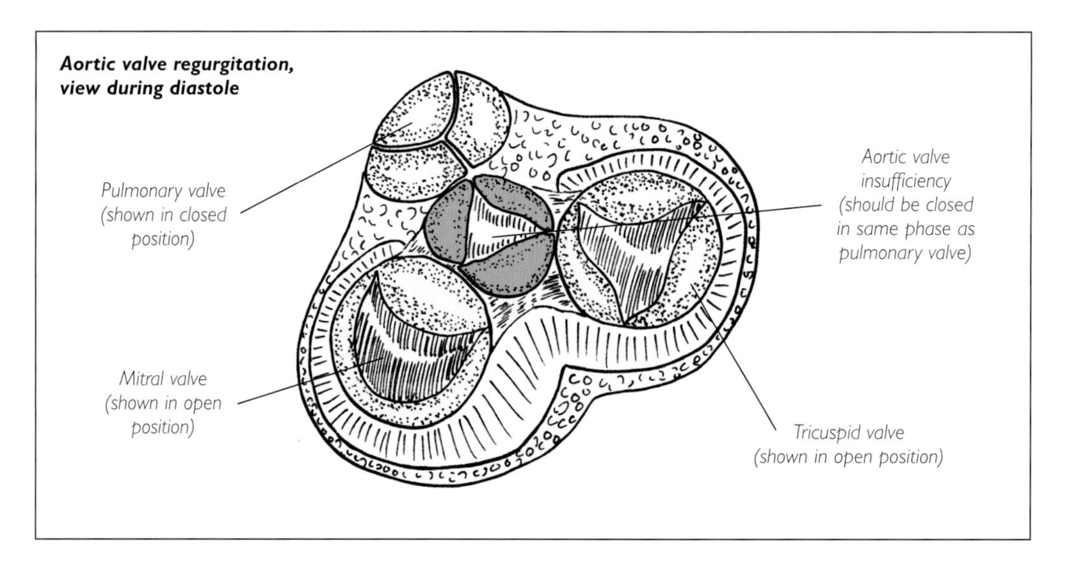

Aortic valve regurgitation is generally due to past rheumatic fever or to infective endocarditis. The valve may also be congenitally abnormal (e.g. a bicuspid valve of two cusps) which predisposes to later disease. There is an abnormal reflux of blood from the aorta back into the left ventricle during diastole (heart relaxation phase). Thereafter the left ventricle enlarges to compensate for the increased volume of blood it accumulates and must pump out. Eventually left ventricular failure can occur, and also angina due to left ventricular muscle strain.

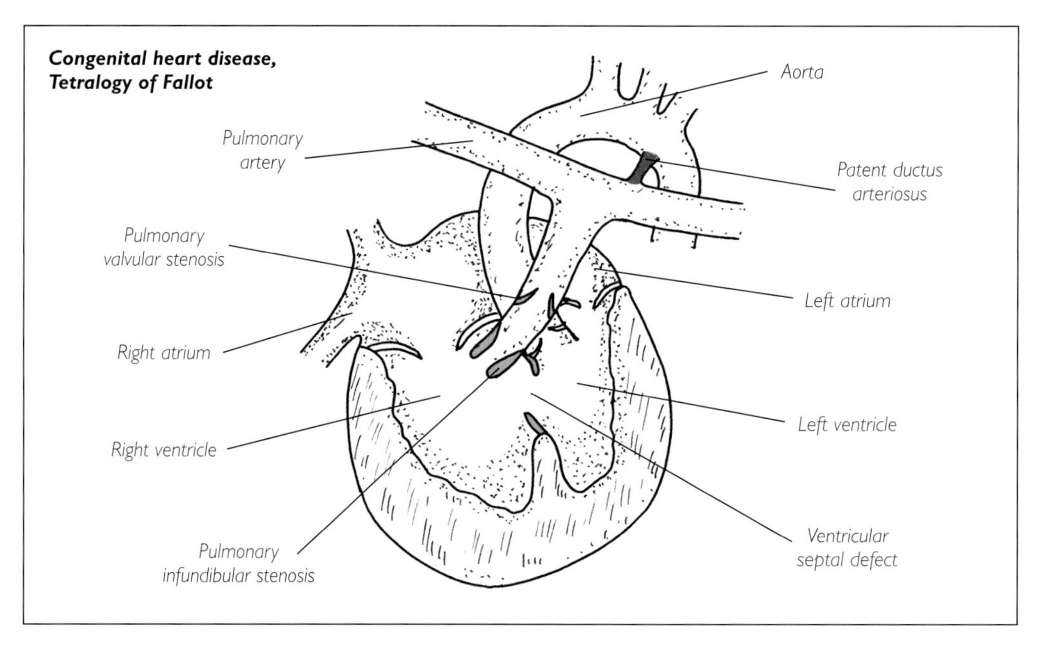

A particular example of congenital heart disease is Tetralogy of Fallot. This is characterised by pulmonary vessel stenosis at two sites as the pulmonary artery leaves the right ventricle. There is an open defect in the septal wall between the left and right ventricles, as well as an open channel between the aorta and pulmonary artery (patent ductus arteriosus). This leads to shunting of blood from right to left heart chambers, and the patient becomes dusky or cyanosed from the lack of blood reaching the lungs.

Related images

p.35 Oesophageal stricture
p.285-286 Cerebrovascular accident
p.311 Brainstem stoke
p.258 Cerebellar tumour and ataxia
p.441 Subarachnoid haemorrhage
p.528 Migraine visual aura
p.145 ECG cardiac ischaemia and infarction
p.281 Endocarditis
p.282 Cardiac muscle sections
p.451 Myocardial infarction
p.81 Post-myocardial infarction aneurysm
p.300 Heart failure, right-sided
p.622 Cervical spondylitis

NATRUM MURIATICUM

Museum

Raphael (school), 'Scenes from the story of Abraham and Lot: the Flight from Sodom' Logge, Vatican © 1990, Photo Scala, Florence. In Genesis 19.17, the angel instructed Lot in fleeing from the city of Sodom with utmost haste: "Escape for thy life; look not behind thee, neither stay thou in all the plain." Lot's wife looked back, and became a pillar of salt. She had hankered after the pleasant things she had left in the city, and looked back with a wishful eye. They had lived a good life in that place, where the soil had provided exceedingly fruitful harvest. But Sodom had become a city full of devils and unclean spirits, sporting and wallowing in filthiness. The people were under the power and dominion of such lustful entities, all their faculties polluted with vile depositions unworthy of human nature. They had hate for God and had incensed His anger. Even those people who outwardly appeared moderate had, within their hearts, collected abominable evil. The Earth could no longer bear such a burden, and God had to send consuming destruction into the place, a dreadful storm of fire and brimstone. By not looking back, Lot and his family would demonstrate they would be disinclined to return to that state. There was nothing in Sodom that was worth looking back on. Those left in the city cried aloud, but none were there to help them, or to afford relief. The decree had gone forth. And the city's destruction was not only swift, but unexpected to its inhabitants. It had started as a fair morning that day in Sodom. All of a sudden fire would search them all out, no matter where they hid within the city, and without exception as to age, gender or condition. The cities of Sodom and Gomorrah (the latter suffering the same fate) would not even be rebuilt, for the very land they stood upon sank and became covered up by the Dead Sea. Christ mentioned in the New Testament scriptures to pay heed to this story and not look backward, but proceed without hesitation or regret toward the Kingdom of God. Blacksliders may end up losing all. By faltering in one's spiritual conviction, the heart and body becomes hardened and the soul put into stupor, as in Lot's wife. Attachment and holding onto memories of the past leads to a crystallised out salt-state.

Pietro Perugino (1445/50-1523), 'Handing of the Keys to Saint Peter' (circa 1482) fresco. Sistine Chapel (walls), Vatican, Rome © 1990, Photo Scala, Florence. The original text of the Apocalypse of St. Peter is lost, however, there are Greek and Ethiopian versions, but which have differences with each other. St. Peter is a decisive member of the apostles and scenes of the life of Christ. He is the key witness to the resurrection of Jesus. In the early stages of the life of Christ, when Peter was still officially known as Simon, Jesus asks the question, "Who do people say the Son of Man is?" (Matthew 16:13-20). The other apostles responded, "Some say John the Baptiser, other Elijah, still others Jeremiah or one of the prophets." Jesus then turned to them and asked directly, "And you, who do you say that I am?" St. Peter/Simon replied, "You are the Messiah, the Son of the living God. Jesus recognised the divine principle working through Simon through this reply and caused his name to change to Peter, stating: "No mere man has revealed this to you, but My heavenly Father.... You are 'Rock', and on this rock I will build My Church and the gates of hell shall not prevail against it." The name change signifies his role with special leadership of the human race, compare with the similar name change conferred on Abram to 'Abraham', Jacob to 'Israel'. Rock refers to the solid foundation upon which the soul qualities are built and carried over into future lives, and upon which a community of souls can evolve. Such qualities include, for example, faith, trust, charity, unconditional love. St. Peter also becomes a visible force protecting the Church and keeping back the power of hell. Jesus also says, "I will entrust to you the keys of the kingdom of heaven. A keymaster in both the Old and New Testament refers to an individual who acts with authority entrusted from the higher plane. Thus Jesus finally states, "Whatever you declare bound on earth shall be bound in heaven; whatever you declare loosed on earth shall be loosed in heaven." This refers to Peter receiving special authority to preserve, interpret and teach the Divine Truth. It is noteworthy that at the end of his life, St. Peter was crucified, but in his humility asked to be crucified upside-down. This could signify his continuing role in safeguarding the journey of souls between the gates of hell as well as heaven. The painting is an example of the responsibility and duty of the salt state, note the phrases, 'pillar of salt' and a 'safe pair of hands'.

Perugino, the artist, reveals masterly use of form and composition. The descending diagonal from Christ to the kneeling St. Peter draws the viewer to the central event. There is equal weight with freedom to the accompanying figures on either side, which are sited well below the horizon line, and include several of the Apostles, depicted with halos. The figures stand gracefully, with pose and elegant demeanour, yet are also standing firmly on the ground. Judas is included (5th figure on the left), and some individuals from Perugino's time, including one said to be a self-portrait (5th from the right side). This central area contains various scenes from the life of Christ, including the Tribute Money on the left. The central background building is a representation of the Temple of Solomon, with Roman style triumphal arches to each side. This Temple was an architectural representation of the inner temple within the human. A future stage of the human race will achieve this as a physical vehicle for Spirit in all its mastery and perfection. Much of this lore was carried into the esoteric wisdom and symbols of Alchemy and Freemasonry. The language of Alchemy is veiled, but contains the spiritual history of the world and humanity. The creator being is known as the Architect of the Universe, and used various Divine Hierarchies to exert His will and imagination into this world. As humanity enlightens and learns to co-create, then the guardianship of such 'gods' lessens. The initial human was androgynous and then hermaphrodite, containing both male and female. It was also plant-like, as yet in a dreamless sleep state without personal will or drive. One half of the human was creatively turned upward for the purposes of building a larynx (the creative word) and brain, to become the image of the Elohim/gods. Certain beings, known as the Angels of the Moon, were involved in maintaining and propagating the human race without the need for sexual reproduction. Other beings, known as the Lords of Mercury, were involved in guiding the creative forces of the brain and mind. However, certain retarded beings deriving from a previous stage of world evolution, known as the Luciferic Spirits, worked from Mars to teach the human race how to act within the physical body for egocentric or selfish reasons, as well as provide the animalistic passionate drives required for sexual expression. Without these Luciferic beings humanity would never have left the sphere of the Moon. The alchemists provided a system of tools to transform the body and named the various spiritual beings in veiled language. Thus, 'Salt' designates the Angels of the Moon, who could influence the fluid movements of the body. A certain amount of salt is necessary to sustain the thinking processes and mobilise the astral body, but excessive salt could induce madness or 'lunacy' (hence the poisoning symptoms of seawater). The fiery Luciferic spirits are designated as 'Sulphur', tying the soul to the subconscious. The 'Mercury' state referred to the Lords of Mercury. A fourth element was also described, 'Azoth', representing the influence of esoteric Neptune and the spiritual fire within the spinal canal of the spinal cord. The body thereby becomes a laboratory for the distillation and refinement of the sulphur process (especially from the reproductive system) into the Salt-Mercury-Azoth state.

FOLLOWING PAGE. 'Natrum muriaticum and support of the Worlds', by Patricia Moffett. Several worlds are shown; these can be either different time stages of the same planet's evolution, or different planets within the universe. An Atlas-like being surrounds and supports each world, acting as a logoic being to supervise and administer the many activities within the planet. There are myriad beings normally evolving and living within any particular world, including nature spirits, elementals, mineral, plant, animal and human-type souls etc. During the youthful evolving stage of a planet the Atlas is also vibrant and vigorous, as shown in the mid-right. However, with progressive density and the weight of karma, both the planet and Atlas appear darker and lifeless, as shown in the lower left. Ultimately a planet may become destroyed, as in the upper left corner, perhaps leading to a new cycle of evolution at a higher dimension of reality.

Original

Astrology

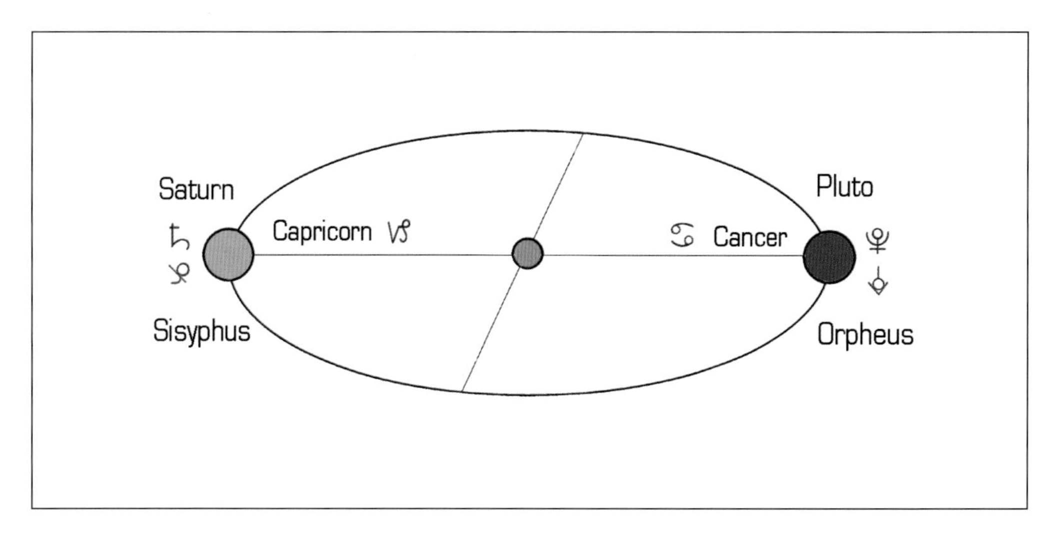

Saturn conjunct Sisyphus within Capricorn, opposite Pluto conjunct Orpheus within Cancer.

Oriental

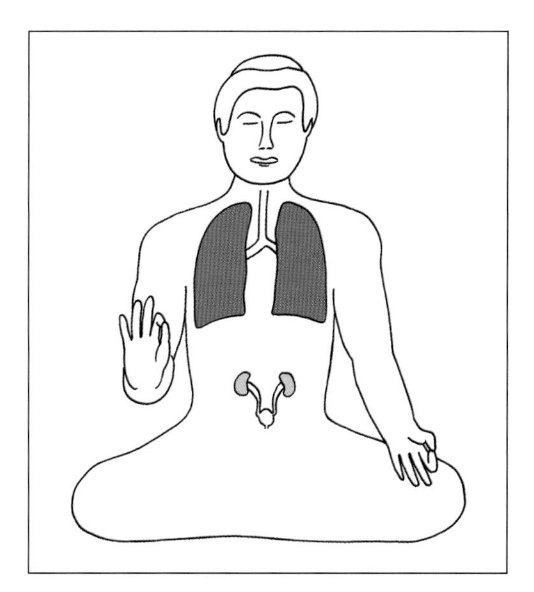

Kidney yang deficiency with lung chi deficiency.

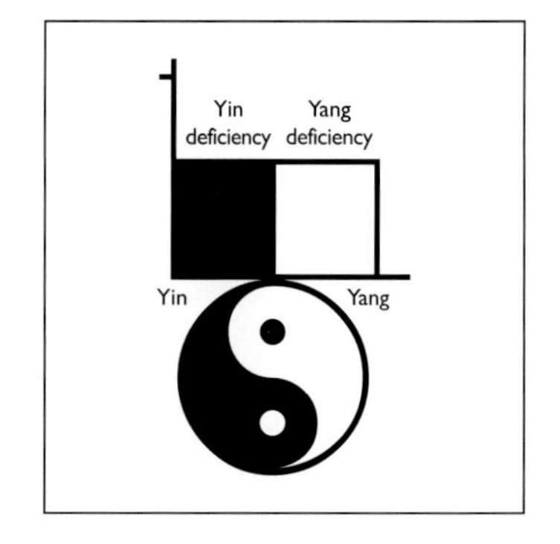

Particulars

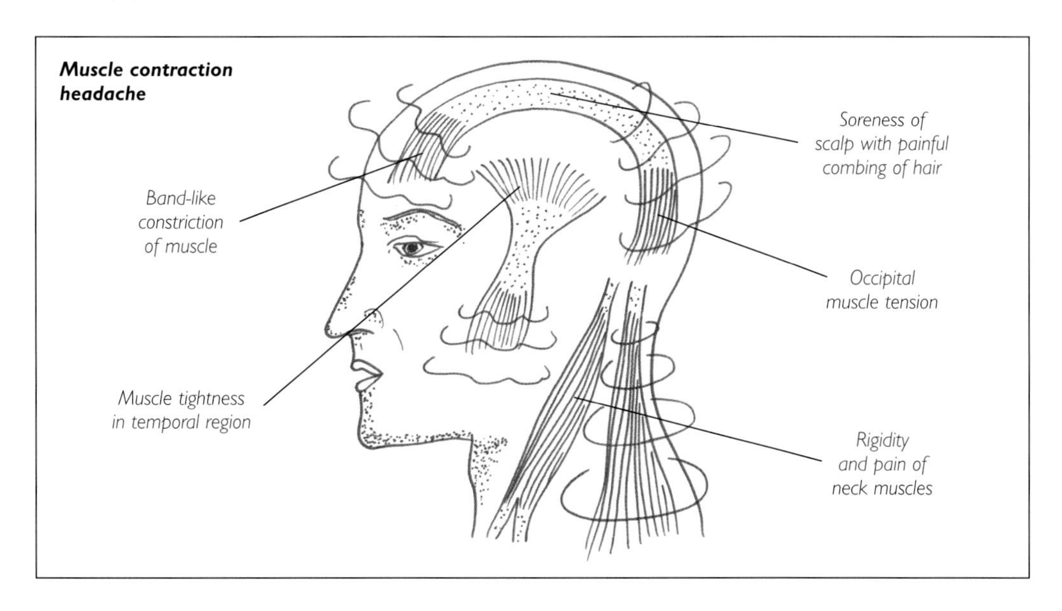

A muscle contraction headache is often caused by emotional tension or stress, although arthritis of the cervical spine and any neck strain will also be a factor in some cases. They can also occur after or in association with classic migraine (vascular) headaches. There is constant contraction of the temporal, pericranial, occipital and neck (nuchal) muscles, which places traction pressure on the pain-sensitive cranial surface nerves. The pain is constant, throughout the head (but concentrated in the forehead, occipital or neck areas) like a dull pressure, band or vise around the head. It may last all day, or persist for a days or weeks without relief.

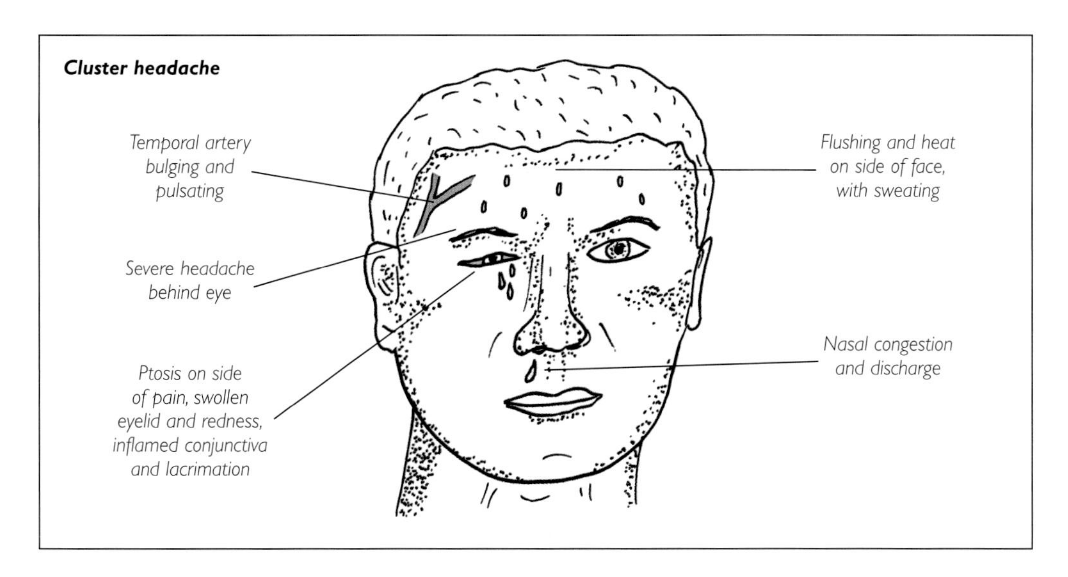

Cluster headaches are classed as a variety of migraine. The pain is often of acute onset, behind or around one eye to affect that side of the face, becoming a severe sharp pain. Attacks usually last only an hour. There is associated facial heat and flushing, weakness of the eye with tears and redness, and nasal discharge. Attacks can recur frequently, especially after a nap and after alcohol.

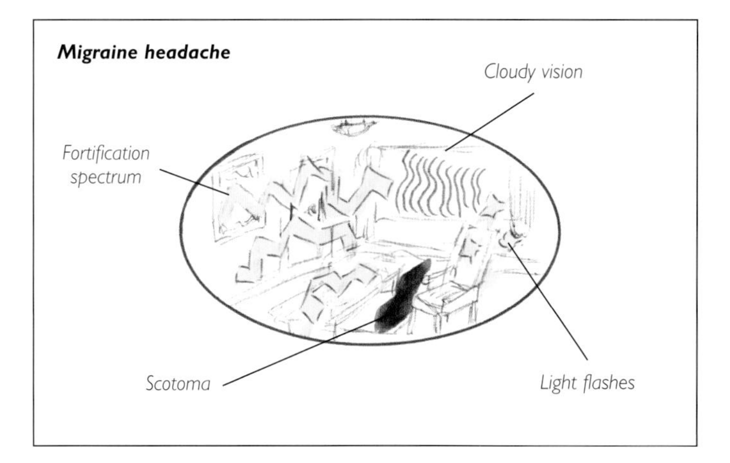

Migraine is a very common cause of recurrent headaches, affecting up to 25% of the population at some period of their life. The onset is usually during childhood. Visual disturbance is typical, with blurred cloudy vision, blind spots or scotomas, scintillating zigzag lines (known as fortification spectrum) and flashes of light as typical symptoms.

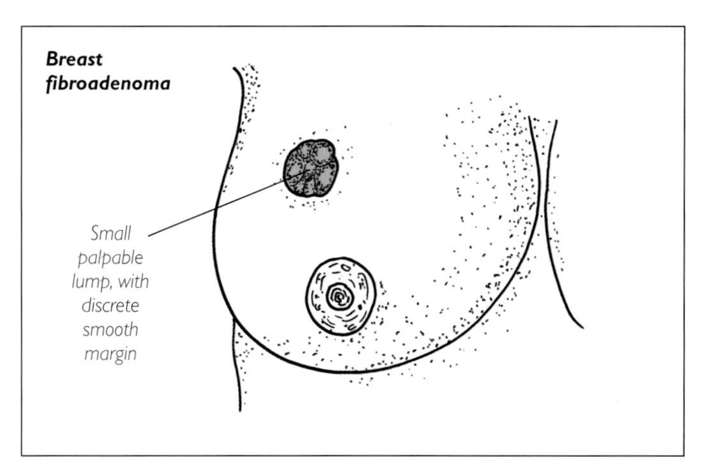

A fibroadenoma is a benign nodular growth, and usually develops out of fibrocystic change in the breast. Fibrocystic disease is characterised by fibrosis of parts of the breast, cyst formation from obstruction of the ducts causing duct dilatation. Fibroadenoma are usually single, presenting as a small firm mobile lumps. It is not considered to convert into a malignancy.

Related images

p.718 Pyelonephritis
p.56 Glomerulonephritis
p.248 & p.250 Renal failure and dialysis
p.593 Adrenal atrophy
p.650 Urinary incontinence
p.300 Heart failure, right-sided
p.574 Hypertension
p.72 Asthma
p.504 Chronic bronchitis
p.198 Emphysema
p.206-210 Cancer and malignancy
p.606-612 Radiation and radiotherapy
p.13 Allergic rhinitis
p.408 Sinusitis
p.318 Iritis
p.562 Herpes virus

NATRUM SULPHURICUM

Museum

PRECEDING PAGE. Hieronymous Bosch (1450-1516), 'The Extraction of the Stone of Madness (The cure of Folly)' (circa 1475-80), oil on board. Derechos Reservados (all rights reserved) © Museo Nacional del Prado, Madrid. The inscription reads, "Master, take away the stone – my name is Lubbert Das." Removing 'stones' from the head was a fairly common operation in medieval times. Such stones were attributed to be the cause of various mental illnesses, madness, epilepsy, melancholy. Much quackery also occurred; with disreputable physicians pretending to cure insanity with a stone palmed into place after a superficial but bloody enough incision was made to the scalp. Referring to someone having 'stones or rocks in his head' became a byword of old for describing them to have mental imbalance. However, Bosch has painted a tulip flower as the object being removed in this patient. In Dutch, the word 'tulpe' means madness. It was common to call someone in a mad crazy state a 'tulip head'. (See continuation of this text on p.533.)

Original

'Natrum sulphuricum and the melancholy of trapped memories', by Nathalie Nahai. Superimposed on the reddish-brown liver is an expanded view of the liver circulation. The liver is segregated into lobules by connective tissue septa. At the corners of these lobules the circulation is organised into triads of hepatic artery (shown as red vessels), portal vein (shown as blue) and bile duct (green). The figures below are sclerosed, twisted and stuck memories or soul parts of the individual. They appear wooden, in keeping with this being the Oriental medicine element related to the liver. Furthermore, a SRP symptom in some melancholic patients is a hard wooden sensation within body parts (see also SRP symptoms of Staphysagria). The stagnation within the subtle bodies leads to physical bile and blood stagnation within the hepatic system – the end-stage of this being endogenous depression or liver cirrhosis depending on the manifestation of disease.

Astrology

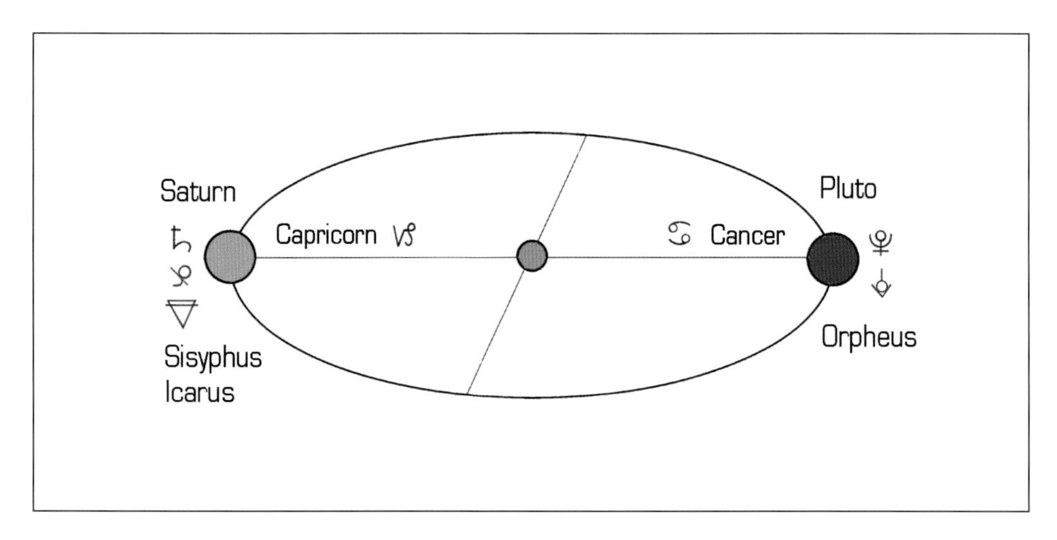

Saturn conjunct Sisyphus and Icarus within Capricorn, opposite Pluto conjunct Orpheus within Cancer.

Oriental

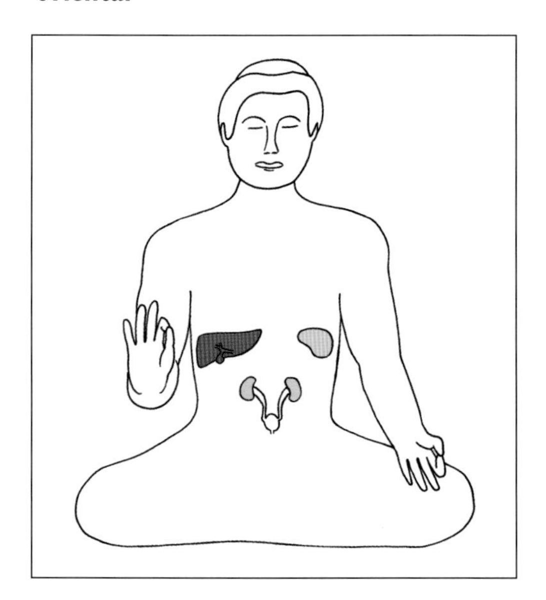

Kidney yang deficiency, with liver chi stagnation and spleen dampness.

Particulars

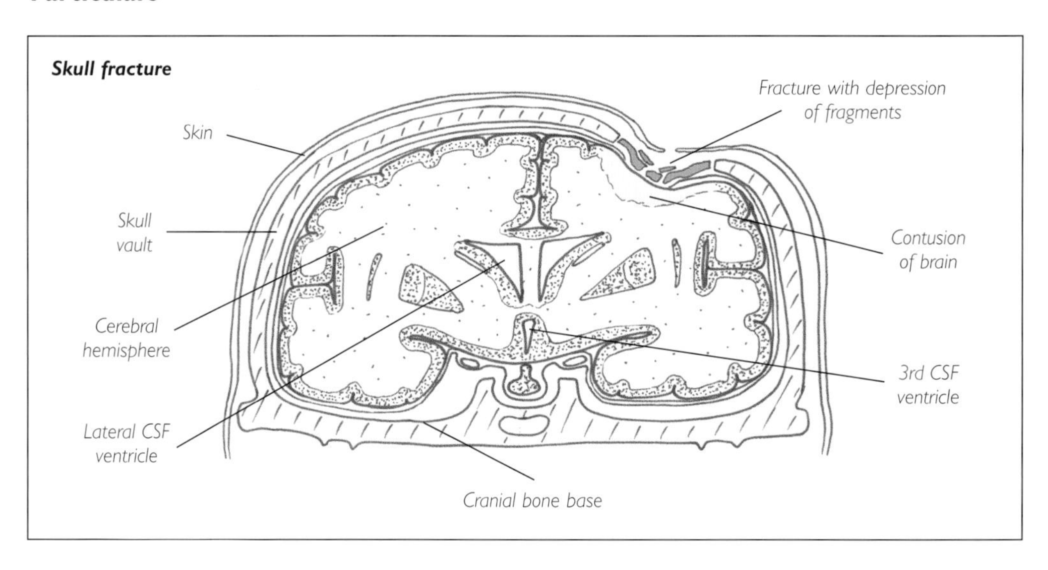

A skull fracture may manifest depression of bone fragments and the skull vault with damage to underlying brain substance. This can then lead to infection (e.g. meningitis), seizures or loss of brain function.

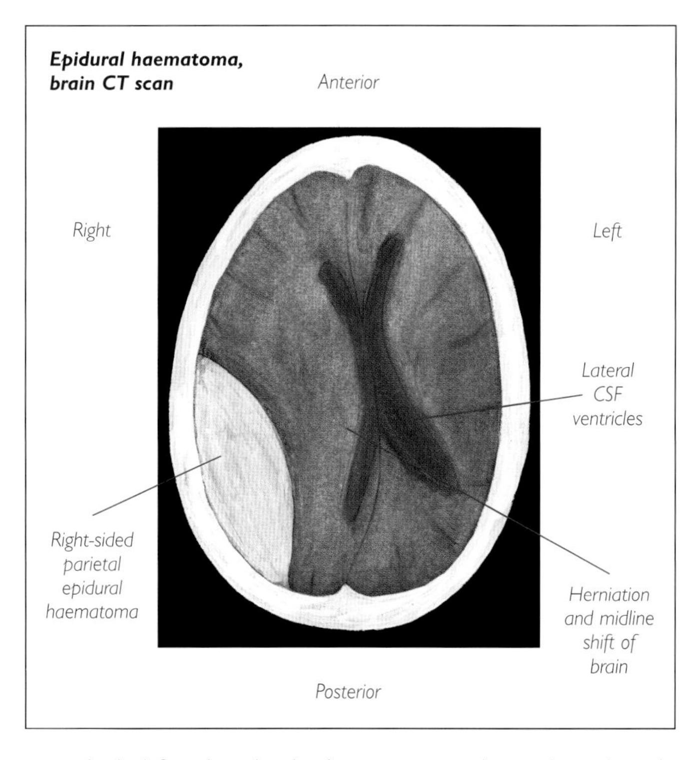

There are many possible problems after a head injury. The most minor is a concussion, with short-term loss of consciousness and amnesia. However, in about 1-3% of major head injuries, there arises an epidural haematoma. There is damage to a blood vessel, such as artery (85%), or meningeal vein or dural venous sinus. Blood becomes pooled, usually at the temporal, frontal or occipital regions. The most common pattern is a temporal fossa epidural haematoma from damage to the middle meningeal artery, usually after a fracture to the temporal part of the skull. The clinical features are usually an initial concussion, followed by a lucid/alert interval and then a rapid deterioration of neurological function. As the haematoma enlarges it pushes the temporal lobe medially, causing parts of the brain to herniate over the tentorial notch. This is revealed by decreasing levels of consciousness, dilatation of the pupil of the eye on the same side as the herniation, and paralysis – usually of the other side of the body. In this illustration there is an epidural haematoma in the right parietal region – revealed as a hyperdense collection just under the skull vault.

Astrology

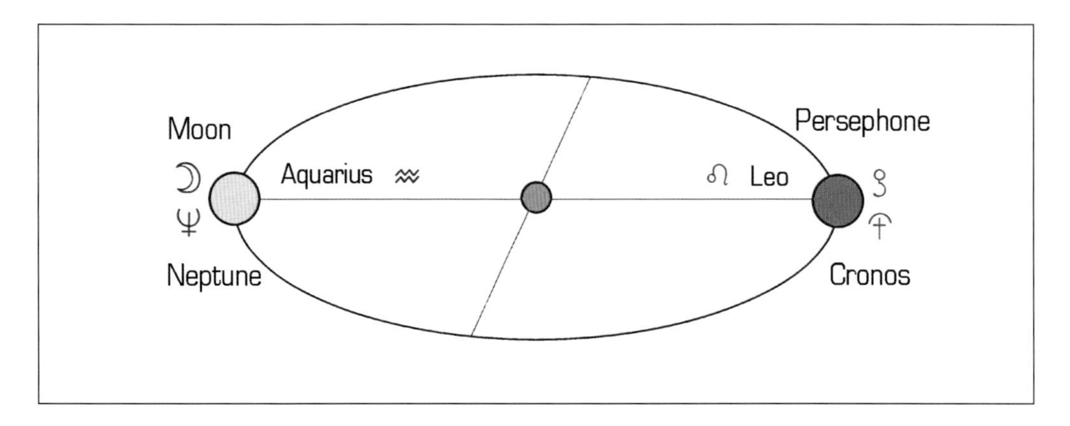

Moon conjunct Neptune within Aquarius, opposite Persephone conjunct Cronos within Leo.

Oriental

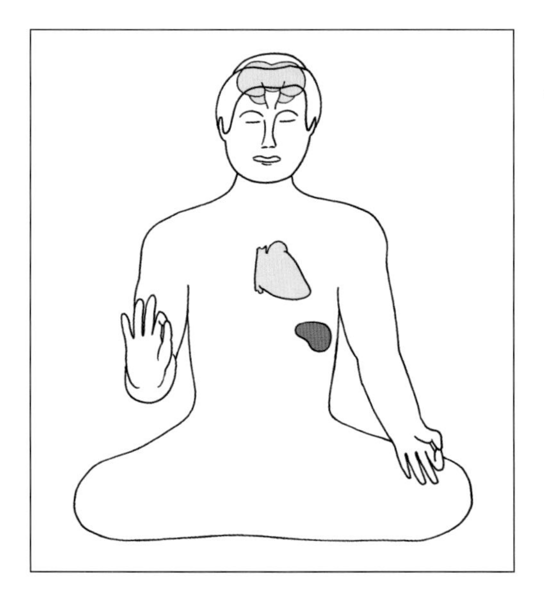

Spleen chi deficiency, with heart blood deficiency. Brain blood deficiency and shen floating.

Related images

p.264 Multiple extrasystoles/ectopic beats
p.91 Sinus bradycardia
p.91 Bradycardia with conduction block
p.527-528 Headaches
p.642 Pre-eclampsia

NUX VOMICA

Original

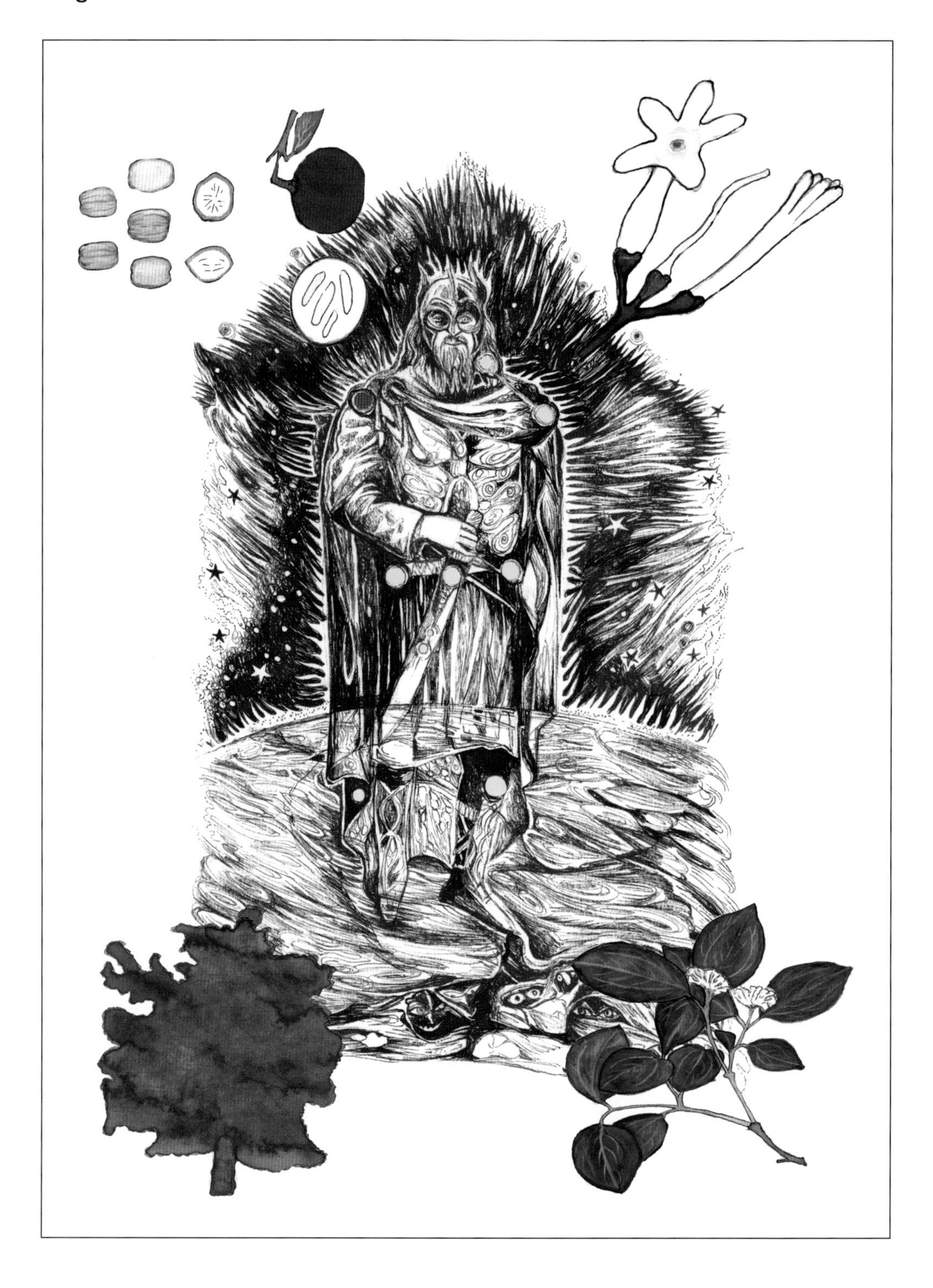

PRECEDING PAGE. 'Nux vomica, the warrior and the constellation of Orion', by Katherine Mynott (Orion) & Nadine Kardesler (plant parts). The Orion star system is shown in the background: the central belt stars (Mintaka, Alnilam, Alnitak) with dangling sword, and the major stars of (left to right) Betelgeuse and Bellatrix above, Saiph and Rigel below. Orion traditionally represents warrior energy, and several channelled teachings of the extraterrestrial races from these regions indicate their civilisations had undergone much by way of conflict resolution. In the foreground are various aspects of the plant, i.e. the tree/shrub, flowering twig, expanded flower view, cut and whole seeds and fruits.

The stars of Orion are also described in Latrodectans, p.449. Orion was equated with the god Osiris in ancient Egyptian mythology, the constellation regarded as his dwelling place (Sirius in Canis Major was the dwelling place of his wife Isis). Orion rose with the spring equinox Sun and claimed rulership of the world. However, as hundreds of years went by, they noted that less and less of the constellation Orion rose before the dawn on the equinox morning. The effects of precession caused the god to slip lower and lower in the sky. The Egyptians thus knew that their immortal god was moving into the whirlpool of the underworld, known as a journey into the Duat. The constellation Orion contains the bright red star Betelgeuse, in his right shoulder. Remarkably, Taurus (the next constellation to herald the equinox dawn) also contains a bright red star – Aldebaran. So, as Taurus replaced Orion/Osiris, the natural heir to the solar throne appeared as his son, Horus. Osiris became the god of the underworld and afterlife, whilst Horus ruled the new world order. This mythology surrounding the precessional movement of Orion is a prefiguring of Christ. God is immortal, but as the god dies, he promises us an afterlife in his presence. The following pyramid text captures this Egyptian concept. 'You sleep that you may wake, You die that you may live.'

The constellation Orion is an archetype of a male god, in contrast to the circumpolar Ursa Major and Minor constellations, which never set and represent the goddess. Thus goddesses may fade, but remain immortal. The male gods of the equator and ecliptic must, however, resort to the hero's journey into the underworld. The ancient Greeks regarded Orion as a giant, described as an unwelcome admirer of Artemis. Artemis created a giant scorpion which stung Orion in the foot, causing him to go blind. But he regained his sight by watching the sunrise. This myth reflects the astronomical movements of the constellations. Thus in the north, as the Scorpion rises, Orion appears to flee by setting. Another version of the story describes Artemis appreciating the advances of Orion but was tricked into accidentally killing him. He swam out to sea (i.e. the constellation slips into the sea) where Artemis mistook him for driftwood and tried out some target practice. Greek myth thereby echo the Egyptian, the Orion stories have in common the death or blinding of Orion and then being re-born through some involvement with the Sun. This is also in keeping with the homoeopathic profile of Nux vomica, which particularly needs the regeneration of sleep (indicating the descent into the subconscious).

Of the stars of Orion, the brightest star is Rigel (although not labeled as the alpha star); the other stars in descending order of magnitude are: Betelgeuse, the armpit; Bellatrix, the left shoulder; Mintaka, Alnilam, Alnitak (three belt stars); Saiph, the right thigh; and Thabit, within the sword. In the field of vibrational essences, the star remedies from Orion, such as Mintaka, can treat an aggressive or animalistic nature, where there is an overemphasis of the physical at odds with spiritual development. Channeled information within the spiritual community often indicate the extraterrestrial races of the Orion system experienced many wars. This included genetic and biological warfare. They developed powerful aggressive tendencies and powers so as become better fighters. They markedly altered and controlled their worlds. However, the karmic consequences included long periods of depression, suicides, and disease. Eventually there was a transformation of solidarity, cooperation and an energy of love, similar to the Christ on Earth. The race learnt to channel their aggressive tendencies into peace, strength and happiness. There is particular influence of Orion into the planet Mars of our solar system, a planet with a powerful influence on humanity towards hostility, hatred and anger. This channeled information also resonates with the Martian nature of Nux vomica.

Astrology

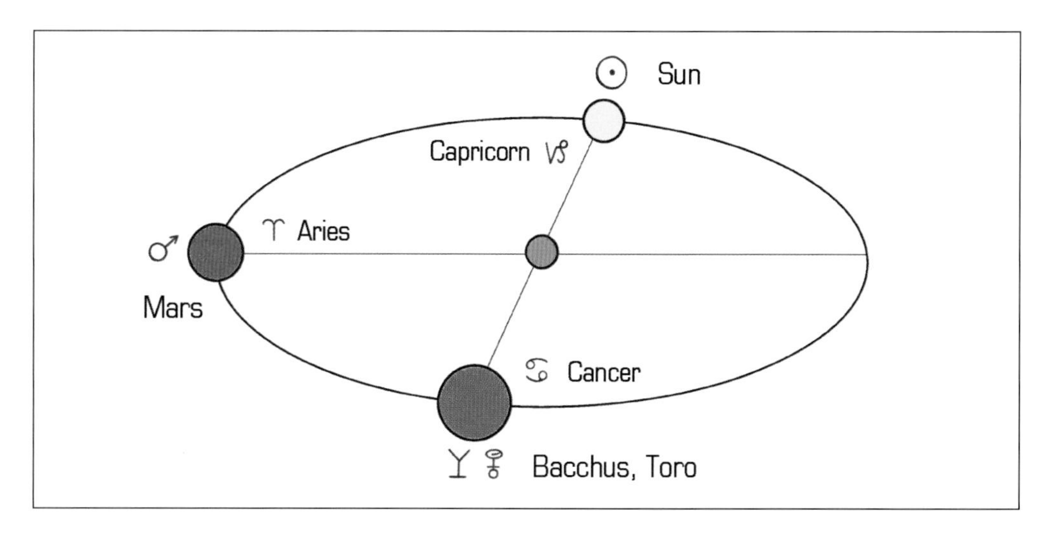

Sun in Capricorn opposite Bacchus conjunct Toro within Cancer, squared by Mars in Aries.

Oriental

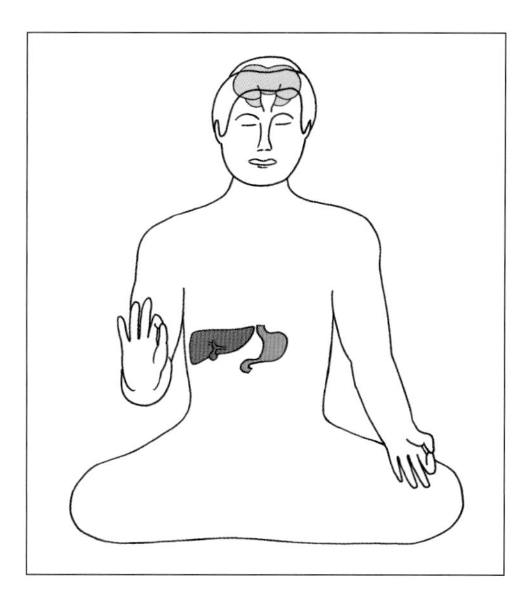

Liver chi stagnation, with stomach heat and interior wind rising to brain.

'Opium somniferum and separation of the thread of consciousness', by Esther Lane. This picture is based on a painting by Gustave Doré, 'Composition of the Death of Gérard de Nerval'; he may have used both opium and cannabis for inspiration. In our illustration, the more solid human figure represents the physical body collapsing towards the Earth, whilst the lighter more buoyant astral body just behind it is separating and being carried upwards by the soul. Slightly above these is the skeleton, representing the Grim Reaper/Death about to escort the soul/astral body into the spiritual realm above – should the separation of the bodies become complete.

Astrology

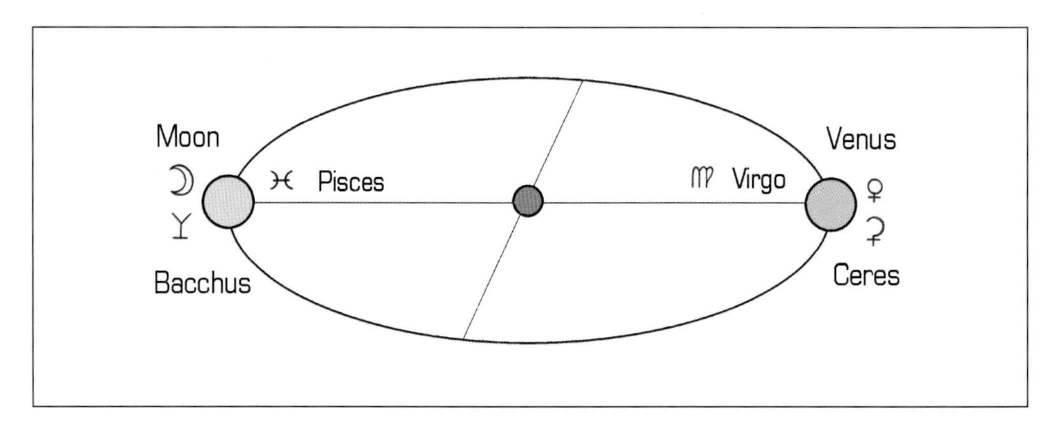

Moon conjunct Bacchus within Pisces, opposite Venus conjunct Ceres within Virgo.

Oriental

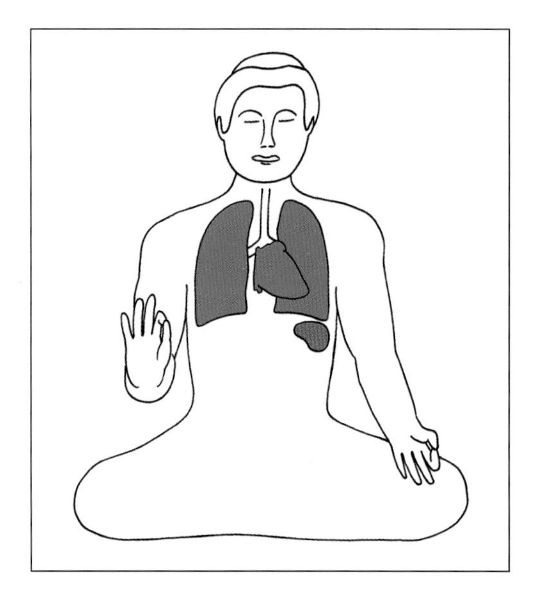

Spleen chi deficiency and yang collapse of lungs.

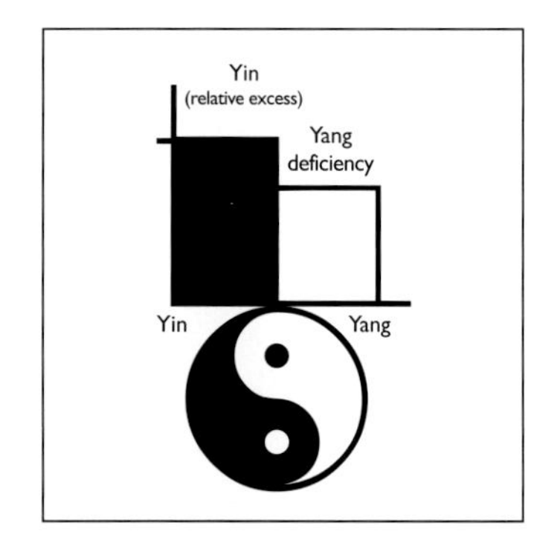

Related images

p.202 Glasgow coma scale & p.532 Skull fracture head injury
p.55 Encephalitis & p.54 Meningitis
p.214 Bladder atony, flaccid paralysis
p.158 Meconium ileus & p.159 Hirschsprung's disease
p.19 Constipation with faecal impaction
p.443 Respiratory distress syndrome, newborn & p.50 Sleep apnoea
p.95 Cystic fibrosis & p.28 Supplementary oxygen therapy

PETROLEUM

Original

'Petroleum and evolution of the genetic code', by Nadine Kardesler. From an underground pool of crude oil rises a column of petroleum to the surface of the planet, reminiscent of the extraction of crude oil through drilling. Spirals of DNA and individual chromosomes mingle around and within this oil column, and some aspects of cell division (mitotic and meiotic) are shown below. Mermaids swimming within the pool and apes looking on from the corner symbolise ancient stages of human evolution (although these are strictly speaking cast-off aspects of the human form rather than directly ancestral).

Astrology

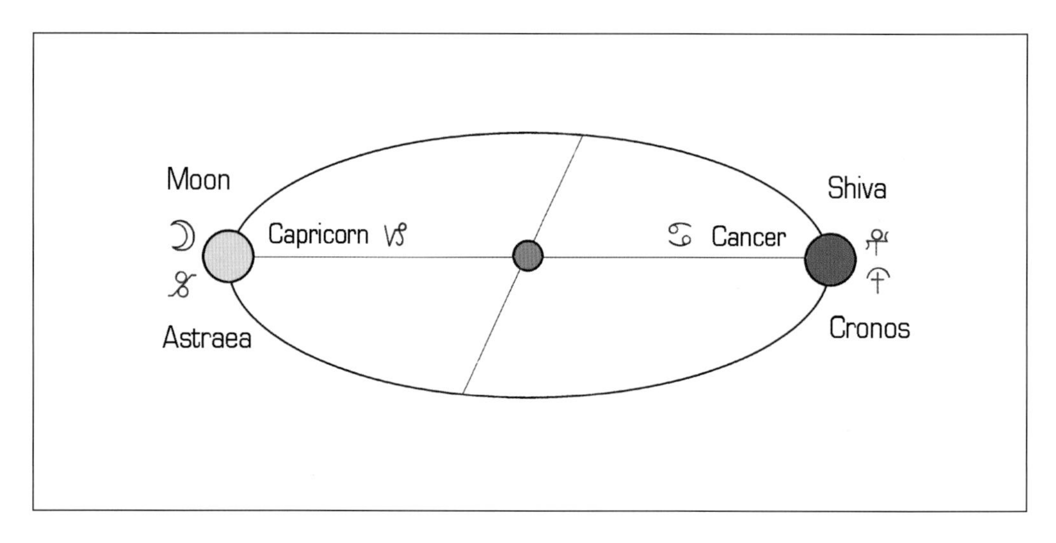

Moon conjunct Astraea within Capricorn, opposite Shiva conjunct Cronos within Cancer.

Oriental

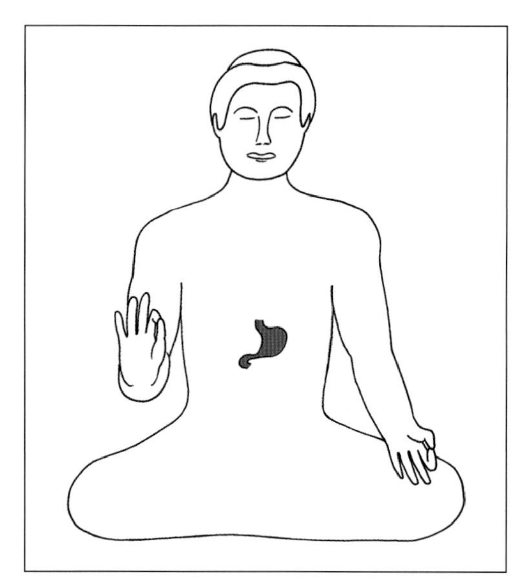

Retention and stagnation within stomach.

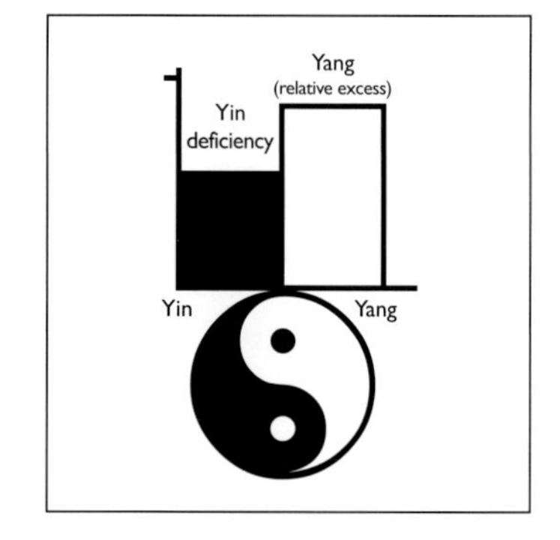

Particulars

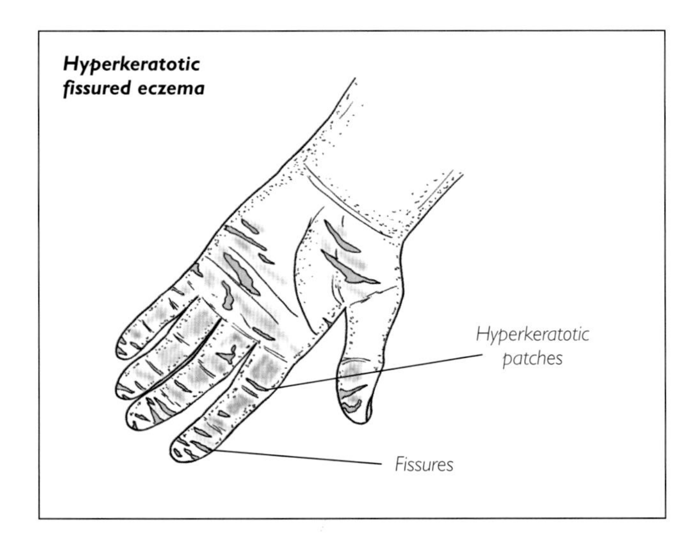

This is an uncommon form of eczema, not necessarily atopic/allergic in nature, but often related to mechanical friction, contact with chemical toxins and an underlying tendency to skin scarring or psoriasis. There are intensely itchy hyperkeratotic patches of eczema with fissures, on the palms and fingers.

Related images

p.527-528 Headaches
p.258 Labyrinthitis
p.260 Meniere's disease
p.541 Peptic ulcer
p.582 Infectious gastroenteritis
p.494 Crohn's disease
p.562 Herpes virus
p.71 Eczema
p.75 Psoriasis
p.619 Shingles

PHOSPHORICUM ACID

Original

'Phosphoric acid and the karma between humans and Promethean-Luciferic beings' by Antonia Chetwynd. A depiction of the energy of fallen light is shown. Above is the spiritual realm, containing sacred structures and temples of light. In the shadowy Earth realm below are several depictions of humans karmically linked to each other. Angels are also present, attempting to protect the human race with their light, but in doing so they become bound up with the Fall of humanity.

FOLLOWING PAGE. 'Phosphoric acid and the Fall of spiritual beings into darkness', by Siobhan McGillicuddy. The Promethean descent of light and fire back to humanity facilitated the evolution of the human soul out of karma and forgetfulness. The descent of a Promethean-Luciferic being into the shadow realm of Earth and humanity is shown, by the central figure diving to connect back to the fallen human below. The figure rising to the spiritual world (of temple structures) at the upper left represents the human ascension process. Furthermore, certain spiritual beings are able to evolve into higher cosmic realms by virtue of the lower Luciferic spiritual beings choosing to sacrifice themselves to assist the evolution of humanity.

Original

'Phosphorus and the Promethean descent of Light' by Nathalie Nahai. The scene on Earth below is long after the Fall of humanity, with progressive densification of the race (typical of late Atlantis). Mankind is huddled cold and lost in the darkness. Prometheus is descending from the spiritual realm with his fire-brand, forging a link of light between the two realms. This middle dimensional region (lit up with lightning) is equivalent to the astral plane.

Astrology

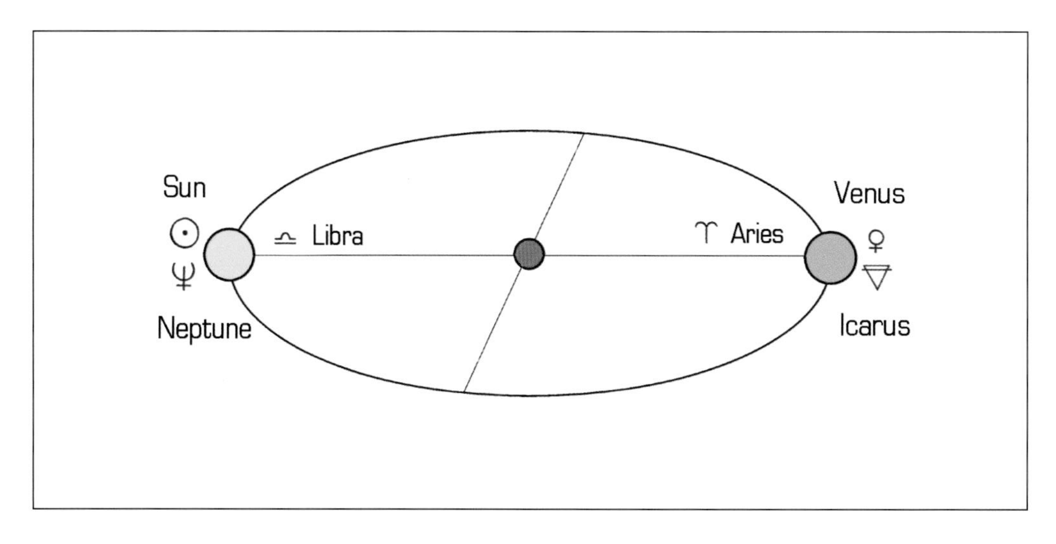

Sun conjunct Neptune within Libra, opposite Venus conjunct Icarus within Aries.

Oriental

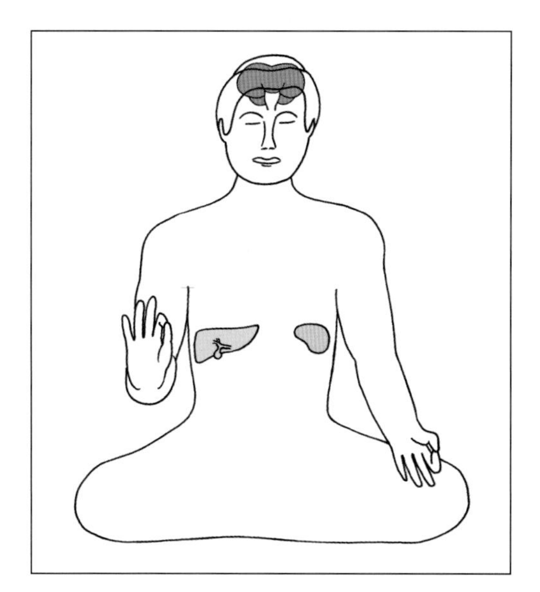

Liver yin/blood deficiency with chi invasion to spleen. Liver yang/heat rising to brain.

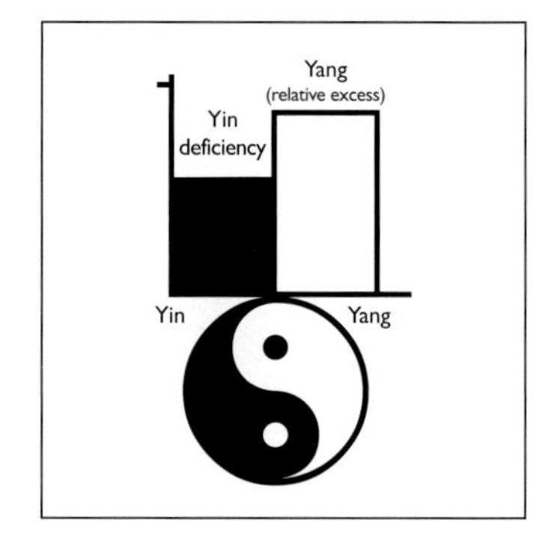

Particulars

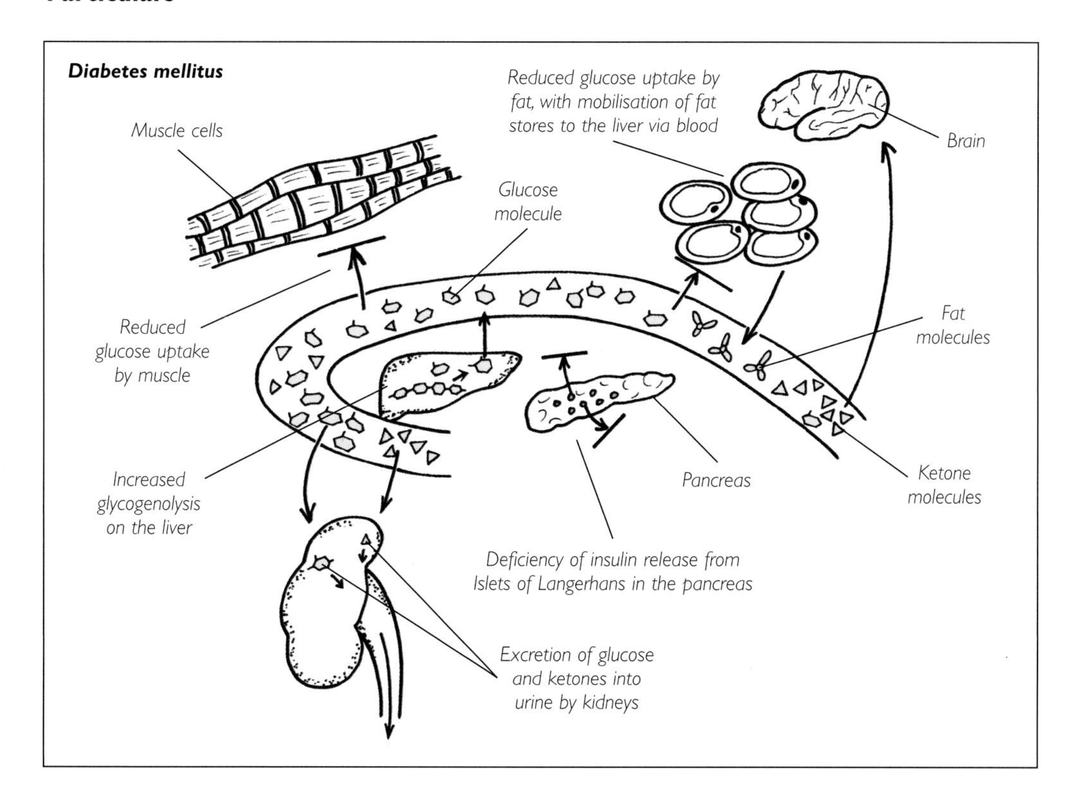

Insulin deficiency occurs in diabetes mellitus. There is failure within the insulin producing cells at the Islets of Langerhans in the pancreas. The insulin sensitive tissues (skeletal muscle, heart, adipose/fatty tissue, liver etc.) therefore show a much slower uptake of glucose from the blood. Furthermore the liver increases its rate of glucose release into the blood from glycogen stores. Therefore blood glucose levels rise greatly. The glucose derived from a meal cannot be manoeuvred into the body cells at a rapid enough rate, which further increases blood glucose after meals. The kidney tubules exceed their capacity for glucose re-absorption and so lose glucose into the urine, which 'drags' water with it to cause frequency of urination. Weight loss and thirst occur with dehydration. The reduced glucose supply within the body cells causes them to utilise proteins as an energy source, which eventually leads to the build-up of ketones, a metabolic by-product. In the fat tissues, fatty acids are excessively released into the blood and further processed in the liver into ketones. Without insulin replacement, there is the risk of coma as the body becomes acidotic, dehydrated and severely imbalanced in minerals.

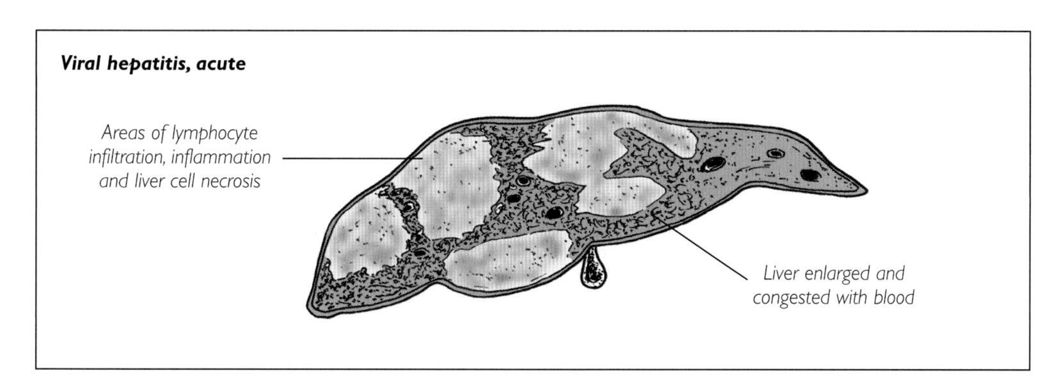

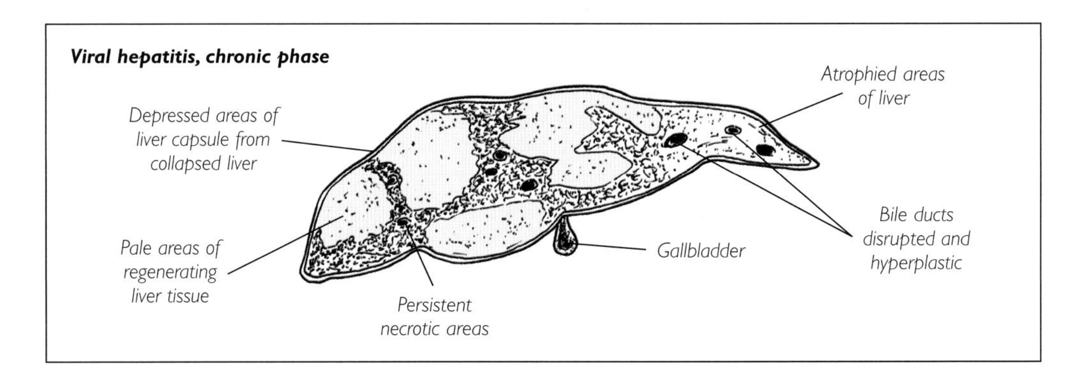

The usual cause of hepatitis (liver inflammation) is viral infection, such as hepatitis virus A, B or C. In the early stage the liver is mild-moderately enlarged and congested with blood, as shown by the first image (p.561). The liver cells (hepatocytes) become swollen, a white cell lymphocyte infiltration develops in the organ and there are scattered areas of cell death (necrosis). The symptoms may be mild (nausea, fever and loss of appetite) or more severe (jaundice and potentially fatal liver failure with bleeding, ascites and fits). All being well, healing and regeneration of liver cells occurs. However, the liver may become smaller, yellowish or greenish in colour and with depressed areas of outer liver capsule from underlying atrophy, as shown in the second image above. If full recovery does not occur then there is the possibility of chronic hepatitis, cirrhosis, liver failure or liver cancer.

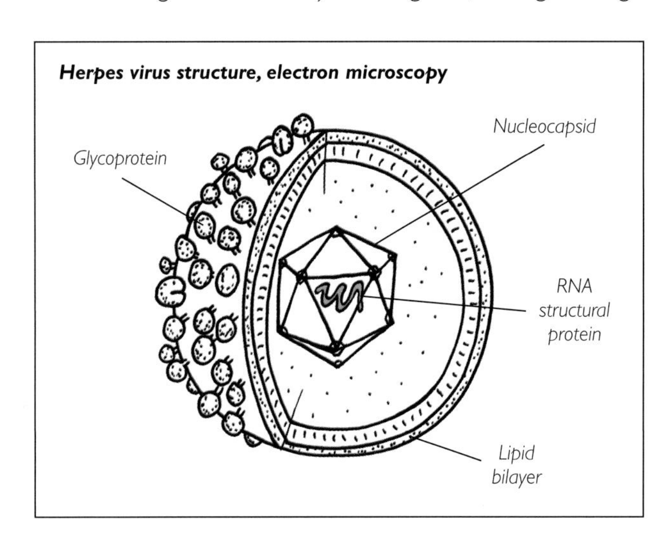

Herpes virus is an example of an enveloped virus. There is an external protein and lipid lining, covered with glycoproteins. Inside is the nucleocapsid containing the genetic material, a coil of RNA in this case.

Related images

p.180 Gastrointestinal bleeding
p.288 Immune thrombocytopenic purpura
p.222 Fatty liver
p.222-223 Gallstones
p.223 Jaundice
p.133 Liver failure and ascites
p.541 Peptic ulcer
p.293 Wilson's disease
p.470 Pancreatic failure
p.737 Tubercular type fever
p.171 Rickets

PHYTOLACCA DECANDRA

Original

'Phytolacca decandra and densification within gel matrix', by Nadine Kardesler. The blossom and fruit are both shown on the plant. Surrounding it is a watery medium typical of the Old Moon environment. However, mineralisation of the world is developing, as shown by the woody structures suspended within the colloid.

Astrology

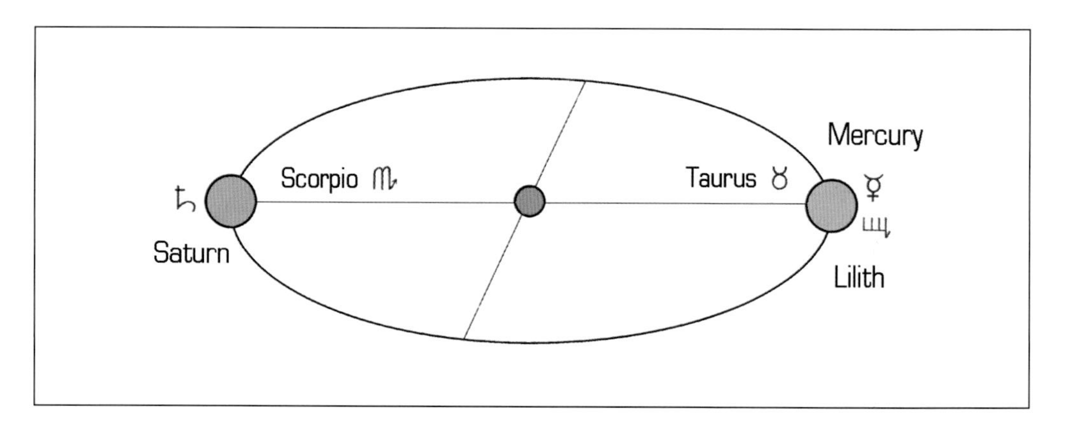

Mercury conjunct Lilith within Taurus, opposite Saturn in Scorpio.

Oriental

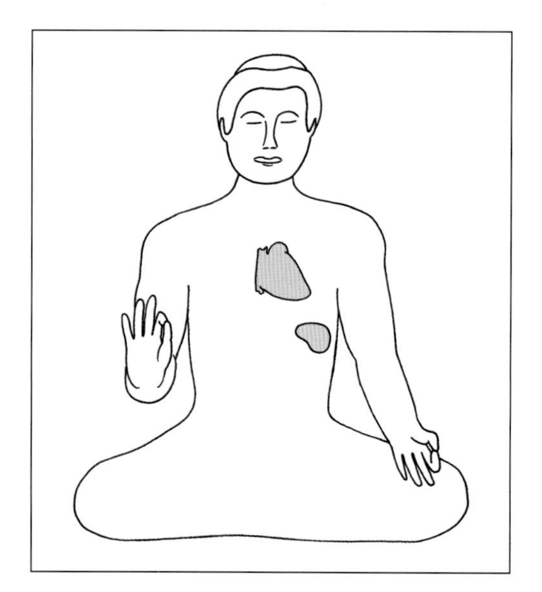

Phlegm-damp obstruction of spleen and heart.

Related images

p.347 Polymyalgia rheumatica & p.619-620 Tendonitis
p.166 Ligament sprain & p.621 Capsulitis, frozen shoulder
p.619-624 Rheumatoid arthritis
p.434 Mastitis & p.371 Breast abscess
p.528 Breast fibroadenoma & p.209 Breast cancer
p.41 Posterior pituitary tumour
p.265 & p.503 Toothache and abscess
p.4 Croup, p.103 Tonsillitis & p.501 Otitis media, glue ear

PLATINUM METALLICUM

Original

'Platina and the higher subtle bodies', by Loolie Habgood. The human figure on the planet surface represents the physical body; the soul/spiritual body is depicted as a flowing radiating body above. In the heart centre of this latter body shines a cross to represent Christ forces. At its head is a Star of David, representing the union of upper and lower triads of self, and above is shown an 'All-seeing Eye' within the cosmic pyramid of Godhead. However, in this illustration the spiritual body is not well aligned with the physical body but floating above. The physical body is therefore shown slightly also lifted off the Earth surface, leading to a sanguine or overly detached mood.

Astrology

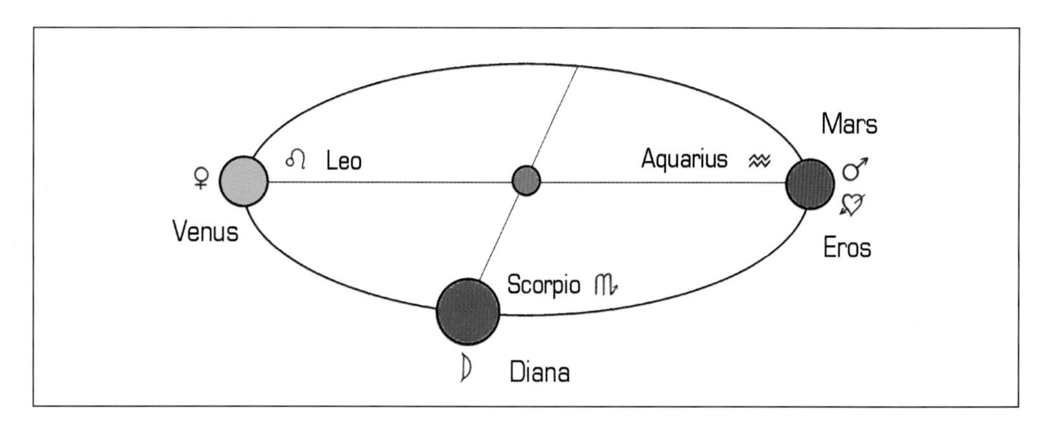

Venus in Leo opposite Mars conjunct Eros within Aquarius, squared by Diana in Scorpio.

Oriental

Kidney yin deficiency with empty-fire blazing within heart.

Related images

p.420 Cancer of vulva
p.57 Ovarian inflammation
p.210 Ovarian cancer
p.335 Endometriosis & p.490 Pelvic inflammatory disease
p.420 Candidiasis
p.335 & p.427 Polycystic ovary
p.512-515 Assisted and artificial reproduction

PLUMBUM METALLICUM

Museum

Francisco de Goya Y Lucientes (1746-1828), 'Saturn devouring one of his Sons', mural transferred to canvas. Derechos Reservados (all rights reserved) © Museo Nacional del Prado, Madrid. The mythological scene of the god Saturn/Cronos is devouring the children he created, fearing they would otherwise dethrone him (it was prophesised that the only way Saturn could die was through one of his sons). This also symbolises how time (which Cronos/Saturn represents) devours all things that it creates. The story also illustrates the cycle of life, that all things end with destruction. The scene is shown in a startling and savage manner. Saturn seems to appear out of a shadowy black background, his eyes are huge and bulging to show his madness. Saturn even appears horrified and revolted by his own act. He has already eaten his son's head and right arm and he digs his fingers into the backbone as he is about to eat the left arm. Colour is only really shown by the splashing red blood from the consumed body. Saturn and his son are both depicted in a human form, their godly status is not revealed, emphasising that the same disturbing cannibalism could occur in the mortal realm. Historically, in 1823, an absolutist monarchy became established again in Spain, and Goya went into hiding and then self-imposed exile in France, where he remained to the end of his life. He suffered some disease that affected his vision, hearing and balance sense, and then to develop madness. Early theories of the cause of Goya's madness suggested that Goya may have suffered from lead poisoning. More recently it is suggested he suffered from Vogt-Koyanagi-Harada, or uveomeningoencephalytic syndrome. This is an autoimmune disorder that specifically affects the visual and cochlear pigment stemming from the neural crest cells of the embryo.

Original

'Plumbum and the rings of Saturn', by Katherine Mynott. The ancients knew of Saturn's rings, despite modern astronomy proposition that such knowledge would have required telescope observation unavailable at that time (the telescope purportedly invented in the 17th century). Thus the ancient Chaldeans, Egyptians, Greeks and Romans all described the rings. Archaeological finds from ancient Mexico include an engraved wooden panel showing the solar system planets, Saturn is recognisable with its rings. The statue of the god Saturn in the Roman Capitol had bands around its feet, and philosophers at that time described the god as being bound by chains. Egyptian mythology could equate Osirus as Saturn, and he is described as swathed (bound up) by Isis (representative of Jupiter and later Venus). In Babylonian lore the god Tammuz represents Saturn and is called 'he who is bound'. In the Zend-Avesta the being of Pairiko is the Saturn equivalent, and is held by a two-fold bond and then a three-fold bond. Indeed the planet was subsequently found in the 17th century to be encircled by two groups of rings, one larger than the other, with a space between. Even more so, a third ring was observed around Saturn in 1980. Greek myth tells of Jupiter driving Saturn away and placing him in chains, thus Aeschylus writes in Eumenides "He [Zeus] himself cast into bonds his aged father Cronus". The esoteric concept of the ring-past-not refers to the circle or bounding frontier to consciousness and the subtle bodies, beyond which there is unity but within which there is the delusion of separateness. As a being evolves, it stretches past its own comfort zone and beyond this ring-past-not. However, it is not an actual material boundary, rather it is a barrier in consciousness. Nonetheless, Saturn was regarded by the ancients as the boundary to personal identity. Beyond Saturn is the stretching of consciousness into transpersonal and collective identity, as demonstrated by the influences of Uranus, Neptune, Pluto and others beyond.

'Plumbum and the Fire beings of Saturn', by Iona Mackenzie. The nature of Old Saturn and of the Saturn beings is warmth and fire. A representation of such beings is therefore shown, streaming out from the ringed Saturn planet towards the Earth. The planet's ring is a cosmic reflection of the Ring-Past-Not within human consciousness. This is the sense of a border or definition provided to the lower self, without which there would be excessive spaciness from the wider cosmos and Higher Self overly permeating the lower self.

Astrology

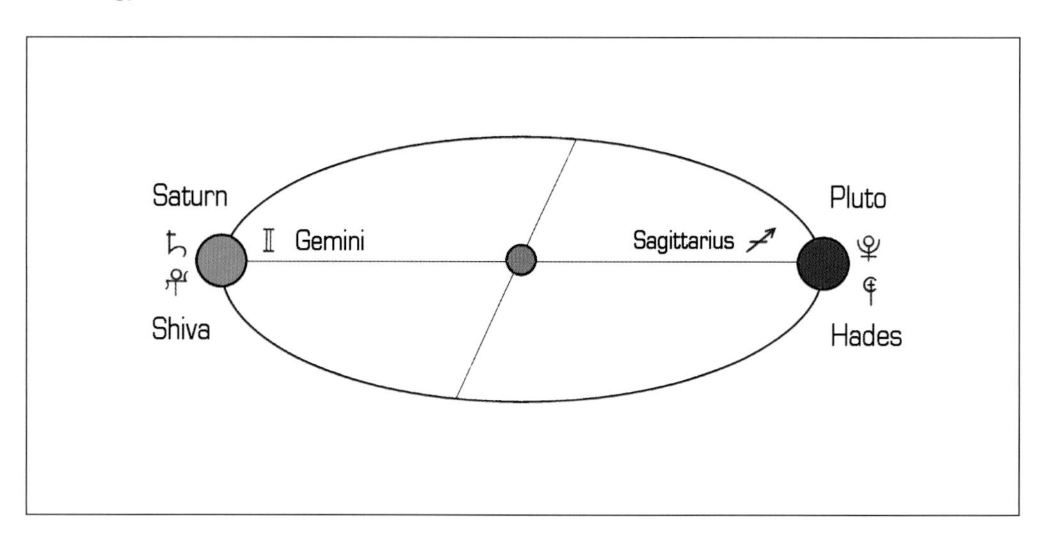

Saturn conjunct Shiva in Gemini, opposite Pluto conjunct Hades within Sagittarius.

Oriental

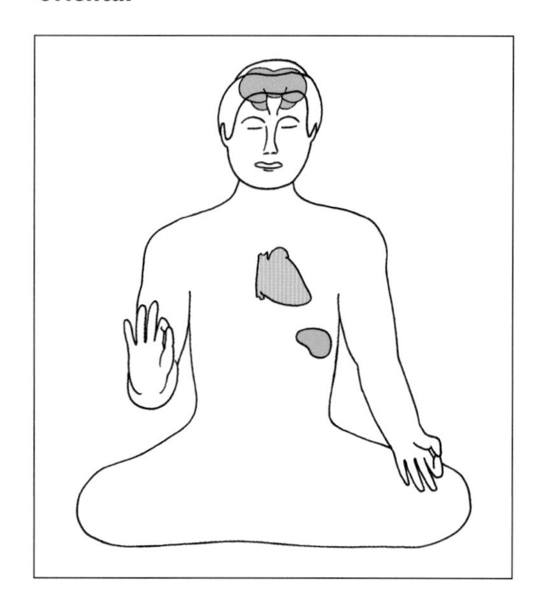

Spleen yang deficiency, with phlegm obstruction of heart and phlegm-wind misting the brain.

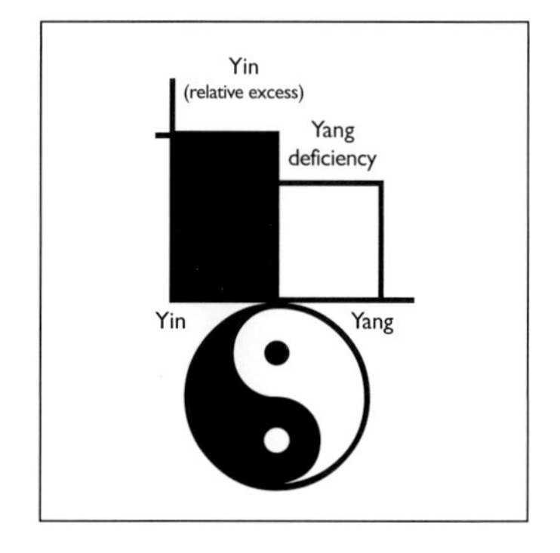

Particulars

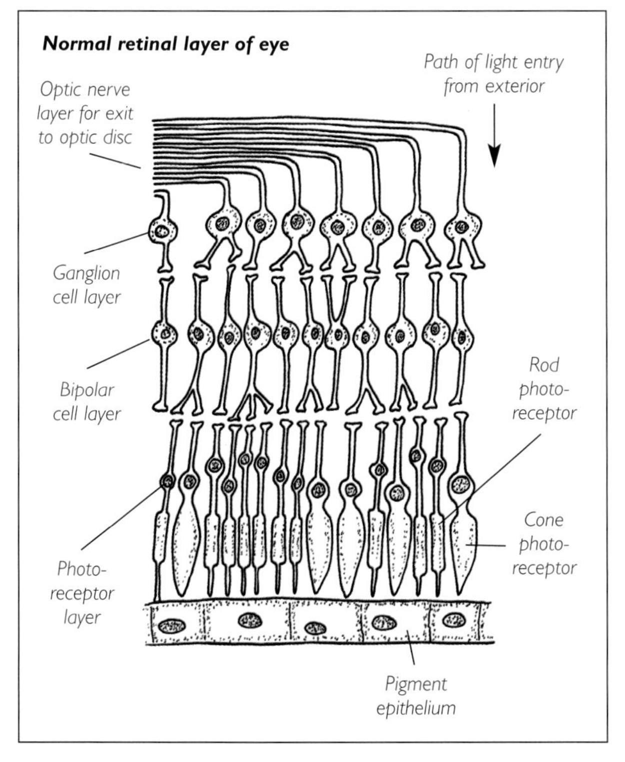

The retina lines the posterior three-quarters of the eyeball. There are blood vessels on its anterior surface (above the optic nerve fibres, not shown in this diagram). The optic disc is the site for eventual exit of the optic nerve from the eyeball. The retina comprises a pigment epithelium, containing melanin pigment, which absorbs stray light rays to thus prevent scattering and reflection of light within the chamber. The light is sensed by the photoreceptor layer, which transduces the light into nerve impulses – rods perceive shades of white-grey-black, and cones provide colour vision. The bipolar and ganglion cells are nerve layers to transmit these signals out through the optic nerve.

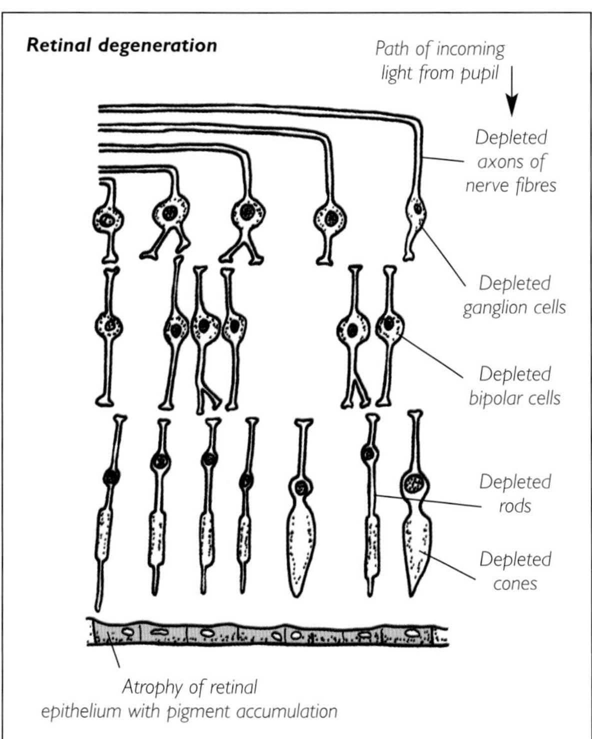

There are a wide variety of genetic disorders that underlie retinal degenerative conditions, such as mutations in the genes responsible for the production of rod/cone photo-pigments. Thus a family history of the disease is typical. The most common retinal degenerative disease is Retinitis pigmentosa (see p.322). Symptoms usually begin with night blindness and constriction of visual fields (tunnel-type vision), leading to progressive deterioration in sight. There is loss of retinal photoreceptors (rods and cones) and accumulation of pigment (mostly melanin) within the retinal epithelium, especially at the peripheral zones of the retina. Central vision (based on projection to the cone-rich macula) may be preserved until later in life, when macular degeneration leads to eventual blindness.

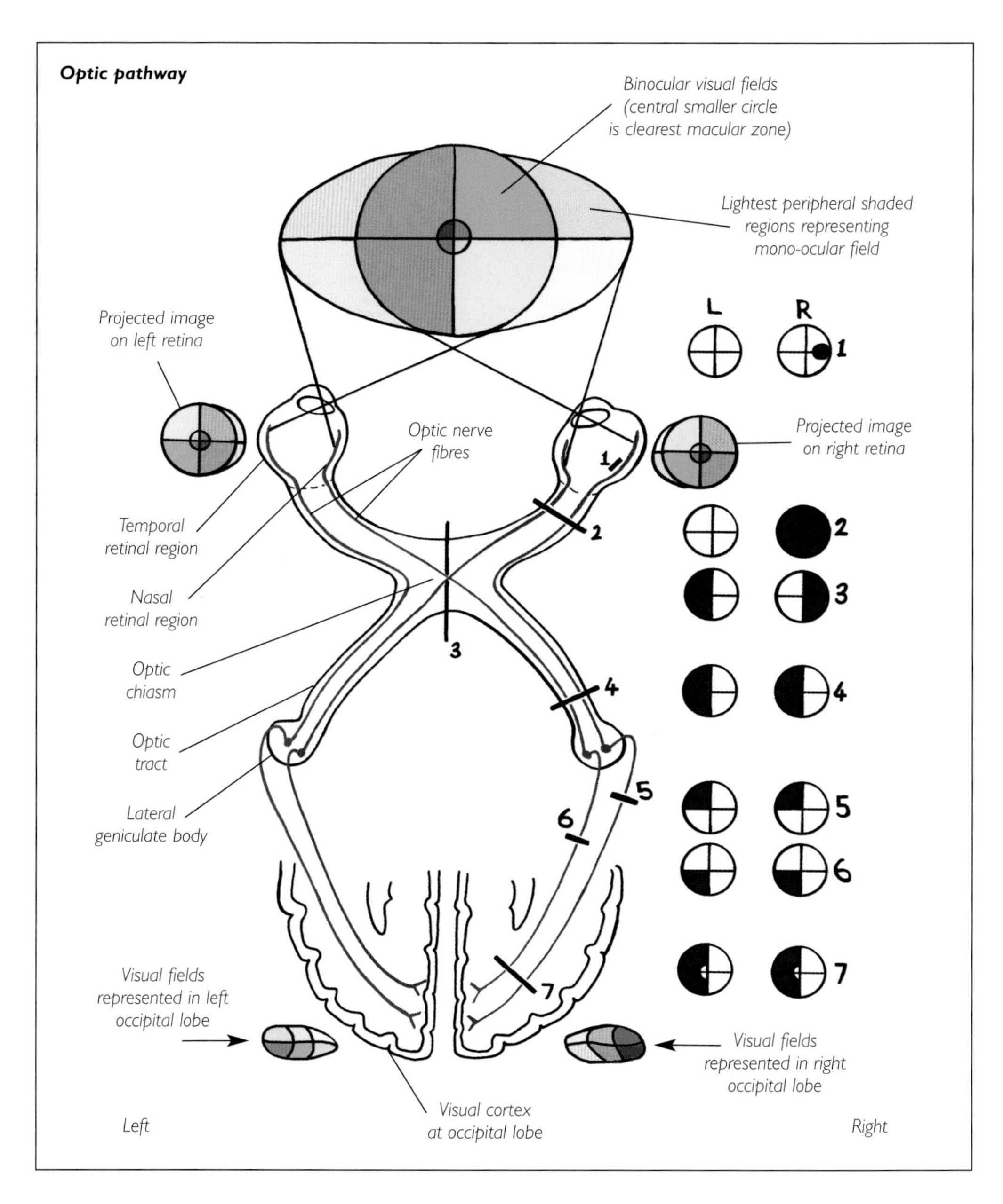

The visual pathway extends from the surface of the eyes to the occipital visual cortex. The lens causes the image on the retina to be an inverted representation of the real object, (i.e. are swapped left to right and upside down). The impulses are then transmitted down the optic nerve. The optic chiasm is a partial crossing over of the optic nerve fibres and is sited just in front of the third ventricle/hypothalamic region. Nerve fibres from the nasal part of the retinas on both sides cross over to travel with the nerve fibres of the uncrossed temporal nerve fibres. The fibres then travel down the optic tracts on each side to reach the lateral geniculate bodies, and from here continue down the optic radiations to the occipital lobes on each side. This visual data is arranged topographically. The net effect of all this is that the left occipital lobe creates an image of the right visual field, and the right occipital lobe creates an image of the left visual field. The sharpest image derives from the macula of the retina, and this is located to the central-posterior part of the occiput, and by a larger proportional amount

Astrology

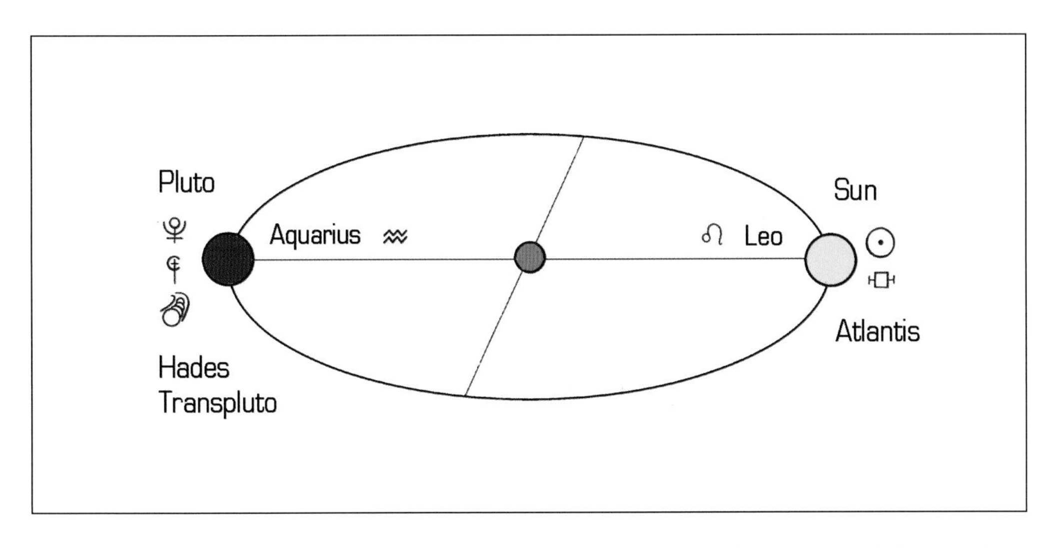

Sun conjunct Atlantis within Leo, opposite Pluto conjunct Hades and Transpluto within Aquarius.

Oriental

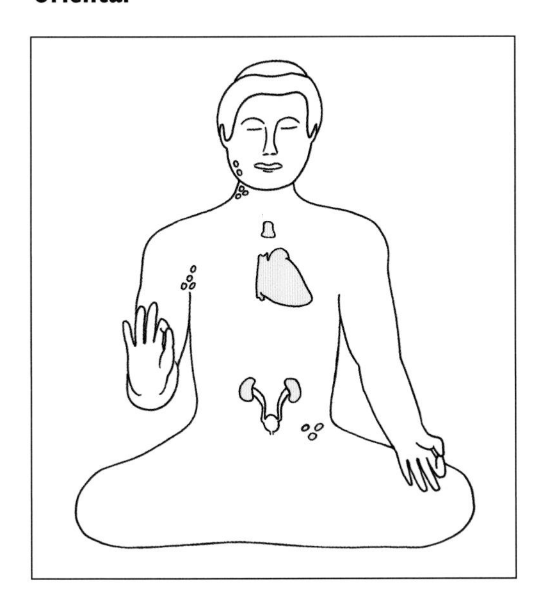

Yin collapse within kidneys, heart, defence chi/lymph nodes, thymus gland.

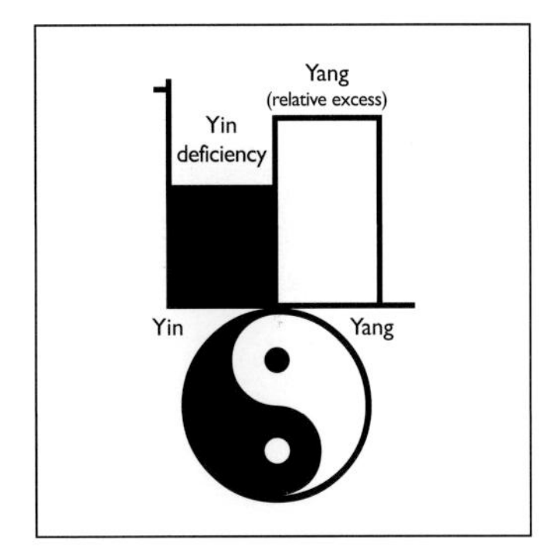

Particulars

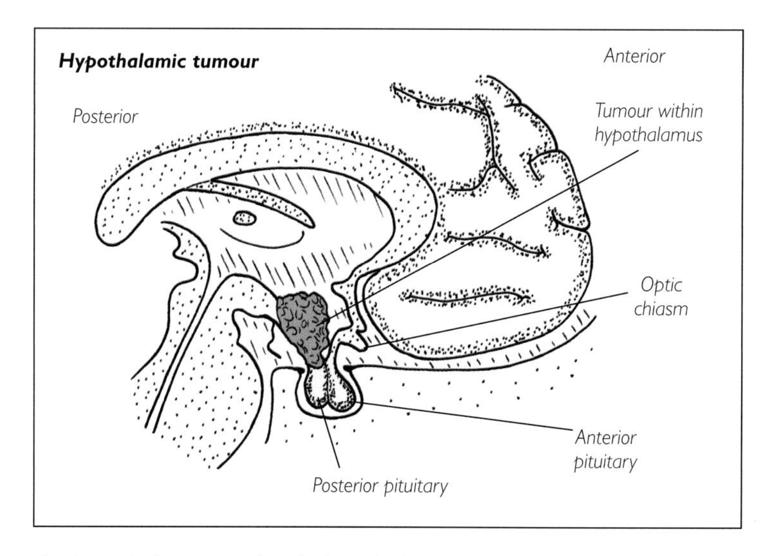

A tumour within the hypothalamus could arise from a tumour growing and spreading from the pituitary gland or its stalk, or arise out of the hypothalamus itself. The destruction of normal hypothalamic endocrine cells lead to hormone disturbance with e.g. obesity, fatigue and/or diabetes insipidus. There may be hypopituitarism with reduced thyroid, adrenal and gonadal function – the regulatory effect of the hypothalamus on the pituitary being deranged. There can be pressure on the optic chiasma with disturbed vision (see Bitemporal hemianopia p.573). Other features are headaches in the brow area.

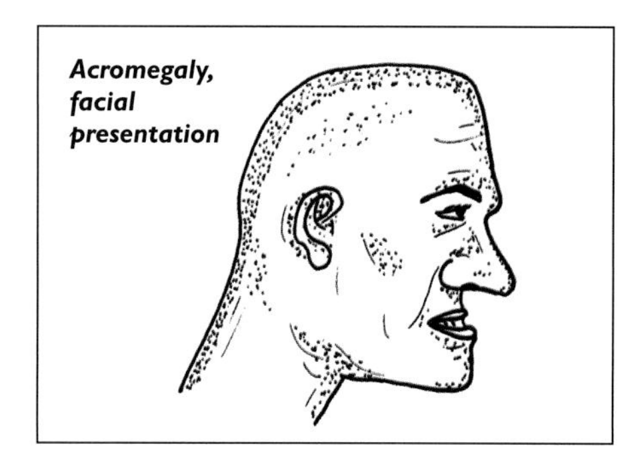

Acromegaly is due to excessive growth hormone secretion by the anterior pituitary gland, either by a benign tumour (adenoma) or general gland hypersecretion. The skeleton and viscera become enlarged, with obvious bigness and coarseness of facial features, especially the lips and nose. The tongue enlarges, as do the nasal sinuses and the jaw becomes projectile. There is irregular thickening of the bones, a tendency to osteoarthritis, high blood pressure, cardiac hypertrophy and a risk of cardiac failure, diabetes and nerve compression syndromes.

Related images

p.376 Bone marrow suppression
p.375 Autoimmune disease
p.206-210 Cancer and malignancy
p.606-612 Radiation and radiotherapy
p.186 Burns chart & p.185 Burn, p.215 Electric burn
p.44 Necrotic skin and abscess
p.586 Muscle wasting
p.103 Tonsillitis
p.729-732 Thyroid disease
p.752 Pineal tumour & p.40-41 Pituitary tumour
p.96 Growth chart
p.512-515 Assisted and artificial reproduction

PODOPHYLLUM PELTATUM

Museum

William Heath (also as pseudonym Paul Pry), (1795-1840), 'Thames water or Monster soup' coloured etching with watercolour 1828 © Wellcome Library, London. The image is evocative of gastroenteritis contracted after ingestion of contaminated food or water. A lady has discovered the quality of the Thames water under a magnifying glass, which causes her to drop her tea-cup in horror. The top title reads: "Microcosm dedicated to the London Water Companies. Brought forth all monstrous, all prodigious things, hydras and organs, and chimeras dire." The bottom title reads: "Monster Soup commonly called Thames Water being a correct representation of that precious stuff doled out to us!" The image probably referred specifically to the water distributed by the Chelsea Water works. London had experienced cholera outbreaks in 1831 and 1832, eventually attributed to the contaminated water. Complainants stated that the water taken from the Thames at Chelsea was 'charged with the contents of the great common-sewers, the drainings of the dunghills and laystalls, the refuse of the hospitals, slaughterhouses, and manufactures.' Nonetheless, a London Commission, appointed in 1827, suggested that no treatment was necessary for the contamination.

Original

'Podophyllum peltatum and nerve-catabolic control of the gastrointestinal system', by Caroline Hamilton. The plant is shown growing amidst loops of small and large bowel. Note the flower actually appears beneath the level of the leaves, indicating the descent of the metabolic forces of the plant (within the blossom) towards the nerve-sensory system (within the root). Catabolic forces from the ego and astral bodies can permeate into the metabolic and digestive processes through the descending nerve fibres, shown in yellow above.

Astrology

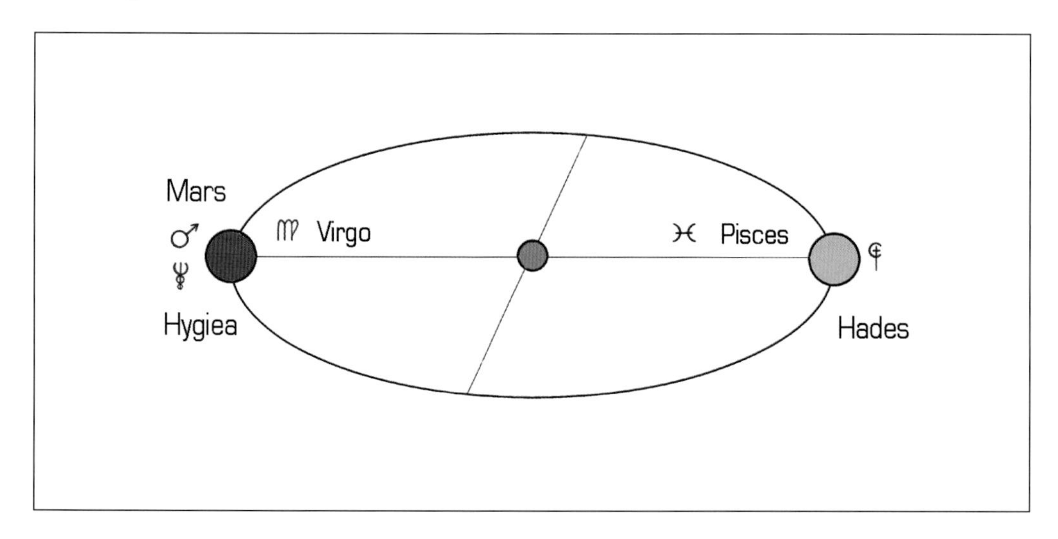

Mars conjunct Hygiea within Virgo, opposite Hades in Pisces.

Oriental

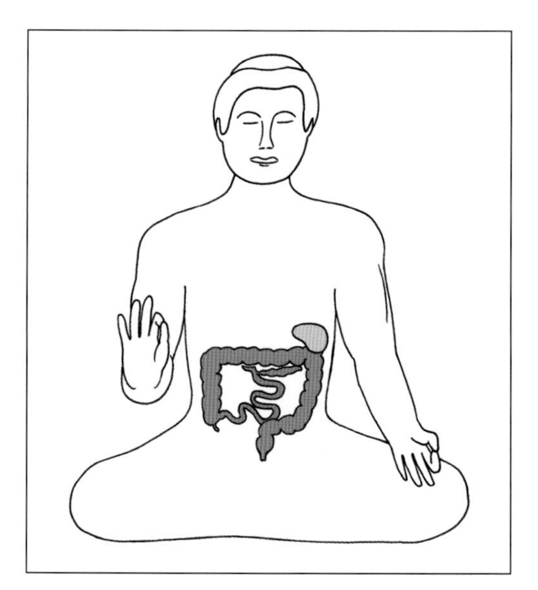

Spleen dampness with damp-heat invasion/congestion of intestines and pancreas.

Particulars

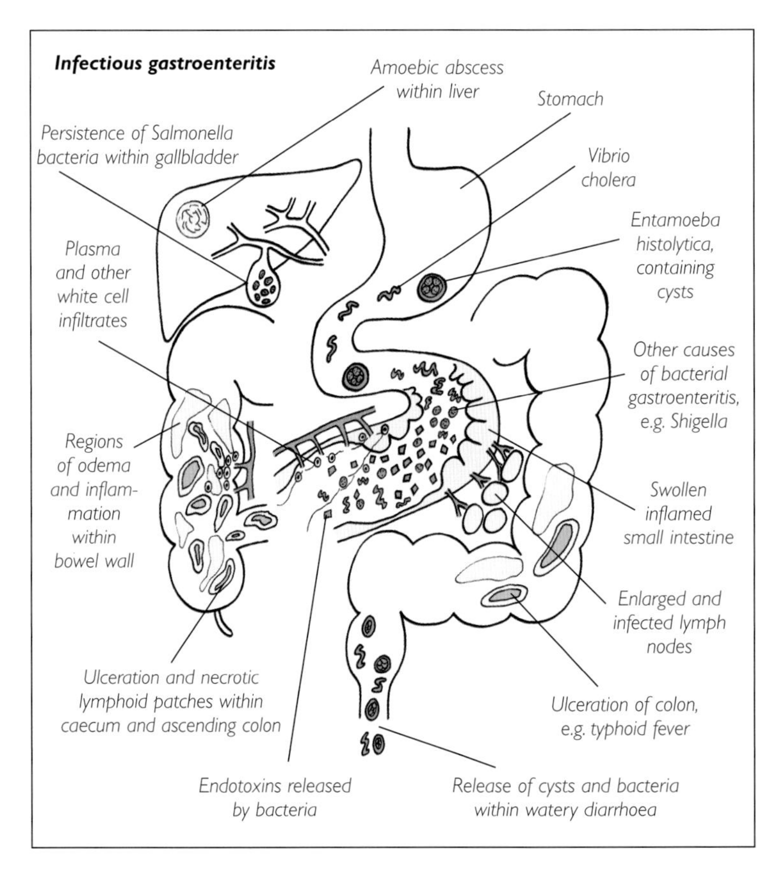

Various types of microbe can infect the gastrointestinal tract, i.e. viruses, bacteria, protozoa and worms. During an infection some organisms remain within the gut lumen and release endotoxins that damage the epithelial surface, often causing severe fluid excretion into the lumen with watery diarrhoea, e.g. vibrio cholerae, the cause of cholera. Other organisms invade the gut wall and trigger inflammation therein, with white cell infiltration, e.g. bacillary dysentery. A third type of pathology is invasion of the microbes through the gut wall into the bloodstream, e.g. typhoid fever caused by Salmonella typhimurium. This particular bacteria can persist within the gallbladder after the initial infection, causing a carrier status. Haemorrhage can occur from the gut wall ulceration or blood vessel damage, e.g. in Escherichia coli or typhoid fever. Lymphoid tissue within the gut wall (Peyers' patches) can also become necrotic and ulcerated, and neighbouring lymph nodes enlarged. In infection by Entamoeba histolytica, the cause of amoebic dysentery, the amoebae within a cyst are ingested within food and the amoebae set free within the gut after digestion of the cyst outer wall. Large numbers of amoebae are found in the diarrhoea, as well as invading the gut wall and causing amoebic abscess in the liver.

Related images

p.494 Crohn's disease
p.507 Coeliac disease
p.485 Irritable bowel syndrome and hyper-peristalsis
p.222-223 Gallstones & p.222 Fatty liver
p.648 Femoral hernia & p.472 Inguinal hernia
p.461 & p.463 Uterine prolapse
p.4 Bell's palsy
p.3 Trigeminal neuralgia
p.527-528 Headache

POLIOMYELITIS

Museum

LEFT. Egyptian polio stela 'Magician and leech' © Ny Carlsberg Glyptotek, Copenhagen (AEIN 134). An Egyptian stela is showing deformation from infantile paralysis. The most likely cause is poliomyelitis infection. The inscriptions identify the doorkeeper as Roma, his wife Imaya and her son Ptah-em-heb, worshipping the goddess Astarte during the reign of Amenophis III 1403-1365 BCE. This stela is generally recognised as the oldest known representation of polio. Its find spot is unknown, but was acquired in Egypt in the 1890's.

FOLLOWING PAGE. 'Poliomyelitis and the incorporation of ape genes into humans', by Iona Mackenzie. The ape creature below has a poorly developed cerebral brain, flattened and atrophied. Within its kidneys lurk primordial stem cells (in oriental medicine the kidneys are the source of marrow substance for the brain). Stages of human embryogenesis are shown from its kidneys to brain, symbolising the evolutionary link between ape and human species (from fertilised egg cell, blastocyst, foetus to a still quite immature form superimposed on the ape brain). Above, three phases of world evolution are shown; at the top is the Earth-Moon planet prior to Moon separation, with human souls electing to temporarily leave for neighbouring planets to avoid the cataclysmic event of Moon separation. In the 2nd phase the Moon is splitting off the Earth, followed by the finally completed orbiting Moon as satellite. At this 3rd stage human souls are returning to the Earth. A reddish cell is being transferred at each phase, shown descending into the ape's kidneys and symbolising the polio cell as retention of stuck soul energy bound to Old Moon forces (i.e. energy that did not properly experience separation from the Moon permeated Earth).

Original

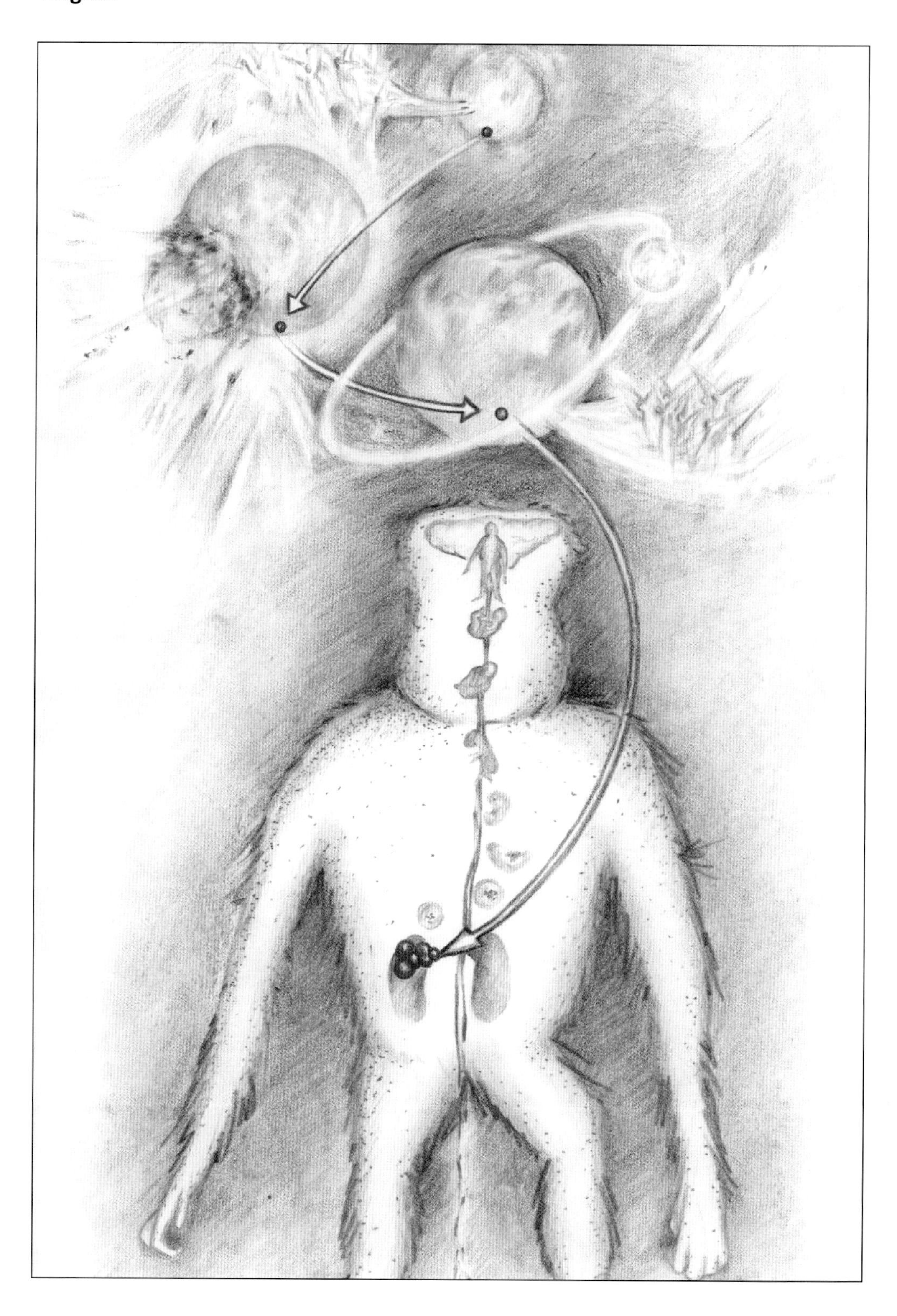

spoken like one of the foolish women, if we have received good things at the hand of God, why should we not receive evil? In all these things Job did not sin with his lips.' The subject thereby reinforces the faith in God despite all hardship, pains or trials and tribulations of life.

Blake depicts a vengeful Satan with arms outstretched, standing on Job's supine body and pouring boils from a vial with his left arm whilst shooting arrows at him from his right. Job has lifted his hands up and head backward as if in agony. His wife weeps at his feet. The background is dramatic, with a setting sun amidst dark swirling clouds. The arrows are the opposite of those of the cherub Cupid, who promotes sensuality and sexual union. Satan's arrows instead cause sexual damnation and destruction of the physical organs. Although the subject is used for Psorinum to illustrate the background miasm of skin disease, it is also in keeping with leprosy, syphilis, various other venereal diseases and modern problems such as AIDs and Kaposi's sarcoma.

William Blake (1757-1827), 'The House of Death' colour print finished in ink and watercolour on paper. © Tate, London 2004. This is an illustration for part of Book XI of John Milton's poem 'Paradise Lost', who Blake considered as England's greatest poet. 'Paradise Lost' was originally issued in 10 books (chapters) in 1667, then Books 7 and 10 were split into two parts to make 12 Books in the second edition of 1674. Archangel Michael hovers above, showing a dejected Adam standing on the right. He is witnessing the misery and suffering that befalls Man now that he has eaten the forbidden fruit from the Tree of Knowledge in the Garden of Eden. This is Death's cave – before this event Man had not experienced death, but lived in eternal youth. The story tells of the Fall from grace of

Adam and Eve. In many ways there is a sympathetic characterisation of Satan, which several Romantic poets, including William Blake, considered to be a hero within the epic – for inciting rebellion against the 'tyranny' of Heaven. To quote the relevant section pertaining to Blake's painting, Adam states: "But have I now seen Death? Is this the way I must return to native dust? O sight of terror, foul and ugly to behold, Horrid to think, how horrible to feel!" To whom thus Michael. "Death thou hast seen in his first shape on Man, but many shapes of Death, and many are the ways that lead to his grim cave, all dismal; yet to sense more terrible at the entrance, than within. Some, as thou sawest, by violent stroke shall die; by fire, flood, famine, by intemperance more in meats and drinks, which on the earth shall bring diseases dire, of which a monstrous crew before thee shall appear, that thou mayest know what misery the inabstinence of Eve shall bring on Men." Immediately a place before his eyes appeared, sad, noisome, dark; a lazar-house it seemed; wherein were laid numbers of all diseases; all maladies of ghostly spasm, or racking torture, qualms of heart-sick agony, all feverous kinds, convulsions, epilepsies, fierce catarrhs, intestine stone and ulcer, colick-pangs, demoniack phrenzy, moaping melancholy, and moon-struck madness, pining atrophy, marasmus, and wide-wasting pestilence, dropsies, and asthmas, and joint-racking rheums. Dire was the tossing, deep the groans; Despair tended the sick busiest from couch to couch; and over them triumphant Death his dart shook, but delayed to stroke, though oft invoked with vows, as their chief good, and final hope. Sight so deform what heart of rock could long dry-eyed behold? Adam could not, but wept, though not of woman born; compassion quelled his best of man, and gave him up to tears"

This is a clear description of the formation of miasmatic disease, with much psoric overtones of dejection and despair of recovery. Nonetheless, death was a necessary evil consequent with the Fall of humanity from Paradise. Death provided a route back into the spiritual realm (albeit the astral plane) and for souls to travel back and forth between material lives. Without death the human soul would become overly bound by its karma and biography on Earth. Indeed, in an earlier section of the same chapter, Milton writes: "Created him endowed; with happiness, and immortality: that fondly lost, this other served but to eternize woe; till I provided death: so death becomes his final remedy; and after life, tried in sharp tribulation, and refined by faith and faithful works, to second life, waked in the renovation of the just, resigns him up with Heaven and Earth renewed." This illustrates that upon true death of the lower self, that part of the soul bound by karmic reincarnation, there is a second death and second life. This is the rebirth of the redeemed soul within the spiritual plane, when it reconnects back to its most lofty spiritual nature. A hidden or esoteric message is that the human race will at that future stage of evolution be able to partake of the fruit of the Tree of Life, which imparts immortality, total body rejuvenation and the clearing of all diseases. For this reason, the Elohim or founding gods ordered the primordial humans to vacate the Garden of Eden, lest they acquire both knowledge and immortality prematurely, before they undergo the journey of karmic reincarnation on Earth. Until then, disease and death is imprinted into the physical-etheric body at each incarnation. In Ayurvedic medicine an individual is born with a limited number of available breaths, and in Oriental medicine a limited number of heartbeats. Should these quotas become used up, then death ensues forthwith. Furthermore, the constitutional strength of an individual is dictated by the jing or essence chi, largely stored within and around the kidney-adrenal system, and functioning as the pre-natal Hara. This pool of energy should ideally be clear of ancestral disease and also become aligned to the power centres of the Earth (planetary Hara) as an indication that the person is in harmony with the electromagnetic, gravitational and subtle fields of the planet – but this is at present hardly ever the case. Depletion of the Hara centre is also typical of the psoric state.

Original

'Psorinum and collapse of the warmth organism', by Lorraine Spiro. The human is clearly debilitated and near-dead, lying in the crucified position sometimes observed in this remedy. He appears imprisoned within the shadowy chamber, unable to free himself from some apathetic state. The greyish pallor indicates anaemia and cyanosis (poorly oxygenated tissues). There is a desperate lack of metabolic warmth, indicated by the dwindling fires of the sulphurous realm. The warmth activity within the adrenal hormonal system is especially dwindled, with little medullary and cortical function (deficient release of adrenaline and corticosteroid respectively). Very little light penetrates into the dismal situation, also suggestive of the scanty light metabolism within the physical cells (with deficient ATP energy stores and hypoglycaemia). The victim lies helplessly as a gigantic scabies mite is burrowing into his lower leg, some of its eggs shown collecting behind. These eggs are normally released into the skin, causing unbearable itching.

Astrology

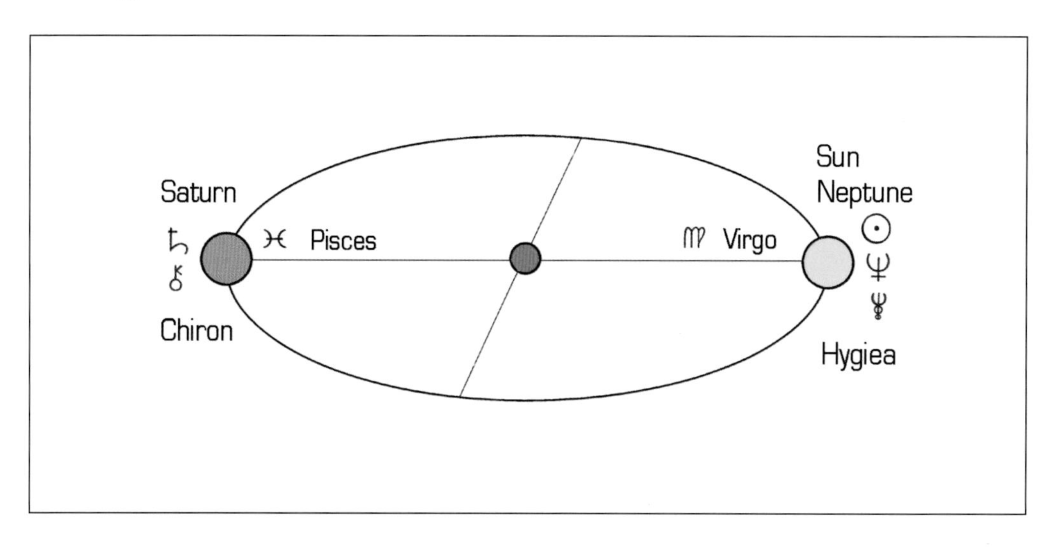

Sun conjunct Neptune and Hygiea within Virgo, opposite Saturn conjunct Chiron within Pisces.

Oriental

Chi deficiency of spleen and lungs.

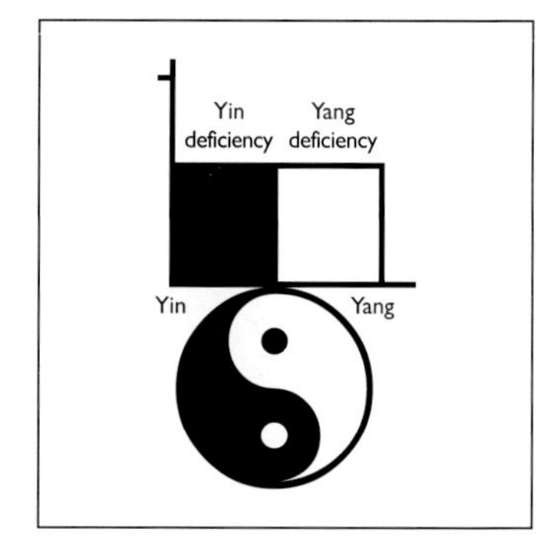

Particulars

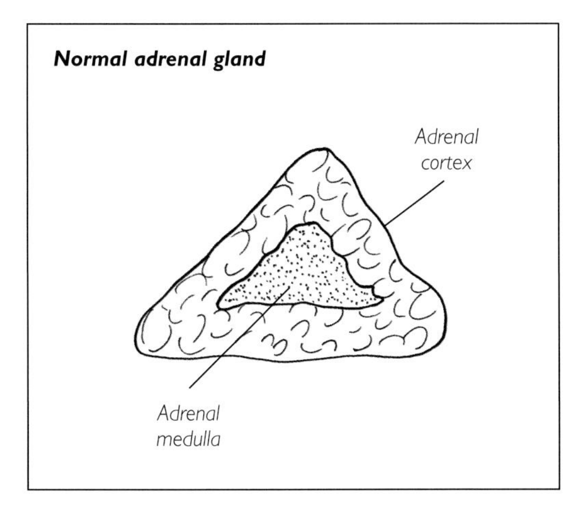

The adrenal glands are comprised of an outer cortex and inner medulla. The cortex produces glucocorticoids (involved in carbohydrate, protein, fat metabolism, immune regulation and hypersensitivity responses), mineralocorticoids (involved in sodium and potassium balance at the kidneys) and androgens (involved in sexual differentiation in puberty, protein metabolism and libido). The adrenal medulla produces catecholamines (adrenaline and nor-adrenaline) which are involved in control of blood pressure and sympathetic nerve system responses.The cortex normally makes up 75-90% of the gland.

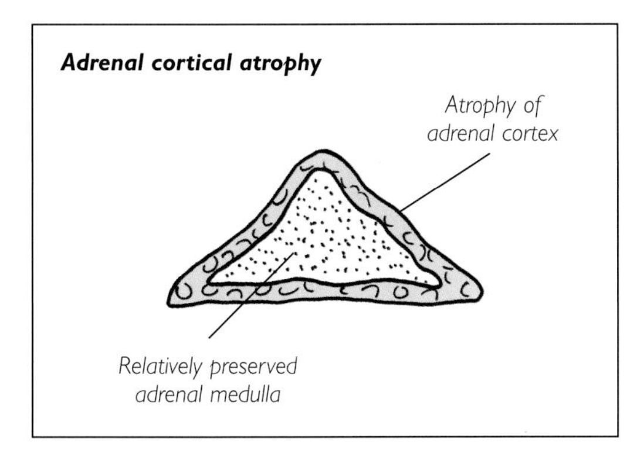

The adrenal cortex makes glucocorticoids (e.g. cortisol), mineralocorticoids (e.g. aldosterone) and androgens. The medulla makes catecholamines (e.g. adrenaline). Mineralocorticoids are involved with the renin-angiotensin system (via the kidneys) and antidiuretic hormone (from the posterior pituitary) for regulation of the blood volume and blood pressure. Glucocorticoids regulate the immune system, with anti-inflammatory actions, carbohydrate, fat and protein metabolism. Acute features of the adrenal cortex can lead to immunosuppression, septicaemia, shock and collapse. Chronic under-functioning with cortical atrophy is often autoimmune triggered, from tuberculosis secondary to pituitary failure or from chronic administration of steroid drugs. This leads to muscle wasting, vomiting and digestive weakness, anaemia, dehydration and chronic immunosuppression. There may also be hyperpigmentation of the skin.

Related images

p.527-528 Headaches
p.504 Chronic bronchitis
p.198 Emphysema
p.50 Sleep apnea
p.28 Supplementary oxygen therapy
p.71 Eczema
p.411 Acne vulgaris
p.75 Psoriasis
p.103 Tonsillitis
p.376 Bone marrow suppression

PULSATILLA PRATENSIS

Original

'Pulsatilla and congestion of Old Moon', by Loolie Habgood. The slightly drooping large-flowered plant lies within a watery but heavy etheric sphere of Old Moon, when the Moon was still permeating the Earth. Large microbial-like white cells and mucus drift within this medium. However, warmth activity is an attempt to assert the Ego forces of individuality, as represented by the Sun and the volcanic eruption in the background. The constellation of Andromeda (lower asterism) and Pegasus (the square-shaped cluster above) overlie this scene.

'Pulsatilla and the female submerged', by Joanna Campion. A woman wades in a lake or sea, being a portrayal of the feminine nature of the remedy and its yin/watery state.

Astrology

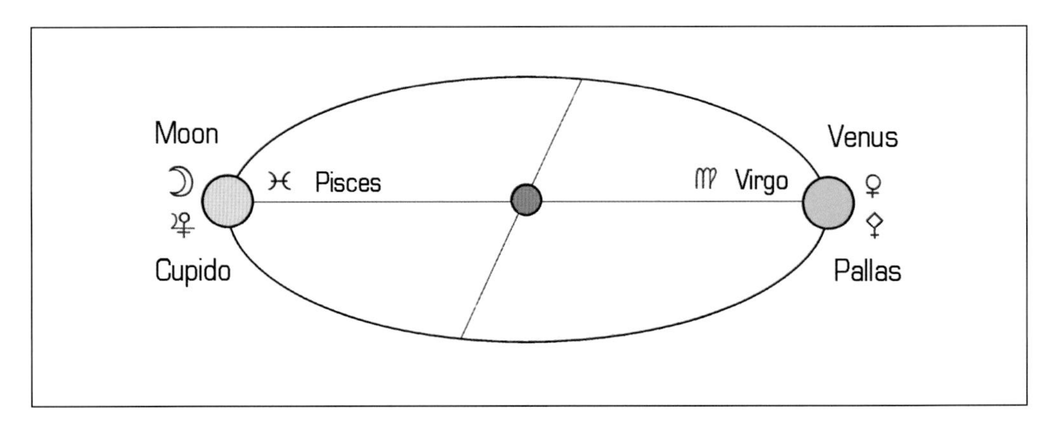

Moon conjunct Cupido within Pisces, opposite Venus conjunct Pallas within Virgo.

Oriental

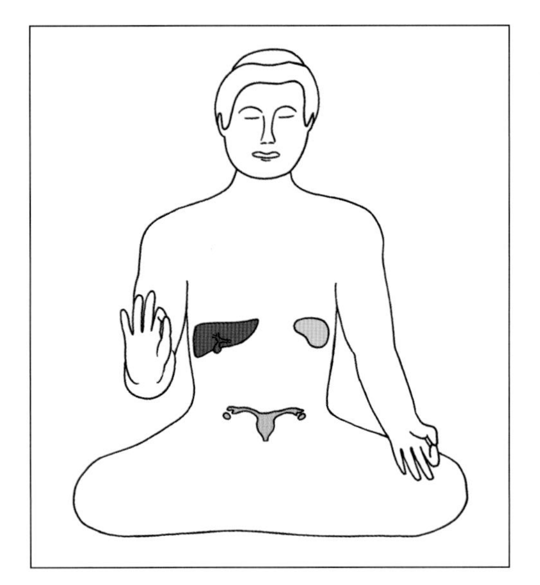

Liver chi stagnation, with spleen cold-dampness and cold-damp invasion of lower burner/uterus/gonads.

Related images

p.57 Ovarian inflammation & p.335 Endometriosis
p.420 Candidiasis & p.335 & p.427 Polycystic ovary
p.742 Tubercular orchitis & p.473 Orchitis
p.360 Mumps
p.408 Sinusitis & p.501 Otitis media, glue ear
p.13 Allergic rhinitis & p.56 Conjunctivitis
p.758 Varicose veins & Venous ulcer
p.527-528 Headaches

PYROGENIUM

Original

'Pyrogenium and the crisis of homoeostasis', by Yubraj Sharma & Kathyrn Eastman. The hypothalamus is shown above, in this case with five collections of ganglion nerve centres (star-shaped due to the radiations of nerve axons) serving homoeostatic functions. Blood tributaries normally transmit regulatory hormones to the anterior pituitary gland just below. However, this is shown lying in a cup of greenish mucus (representing the congested sella turcica); the pus is so excessive that it spills out into a sea of mucus below. Various white cells (neutrophils, basophils, eosinophils and macrophages) are shown stuck within this infected zone.

Astrology

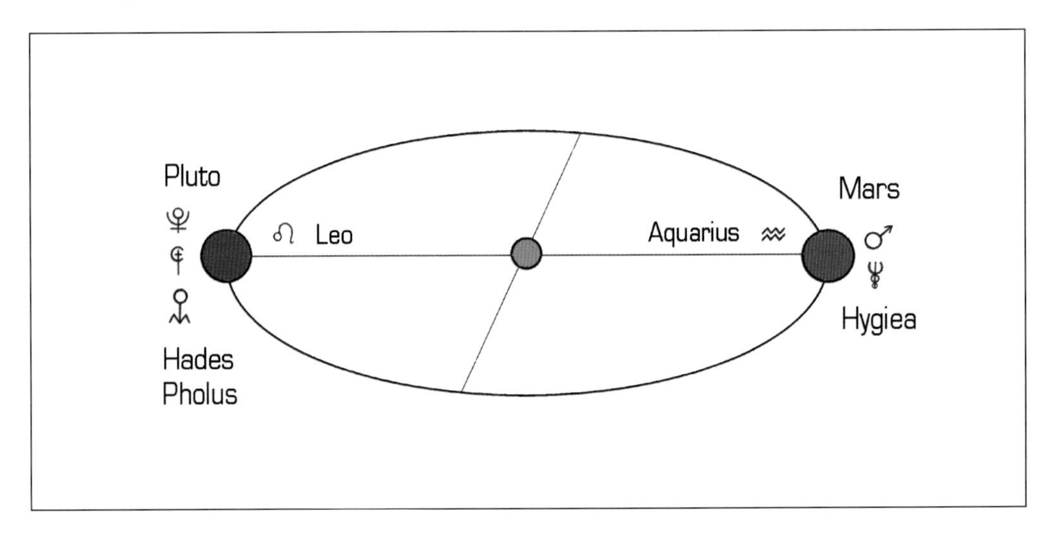

Mars conjunct Hygiea within Aquarius, opposite Pluto conjunct Hades and Pholus within Leo.

Oriental

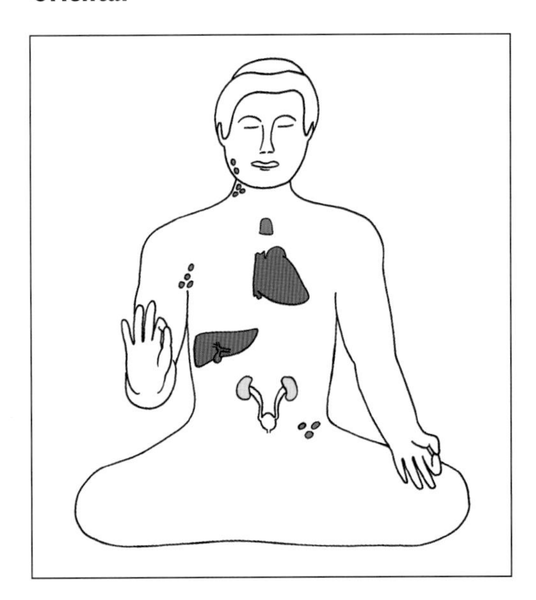

Kidney yin deficiency, with yang collapse of defence chi/lymph nodes and thymus gland. Phlegm-fire or heat invasion of liver and heart.

Particulars

Temperature and pulse chart

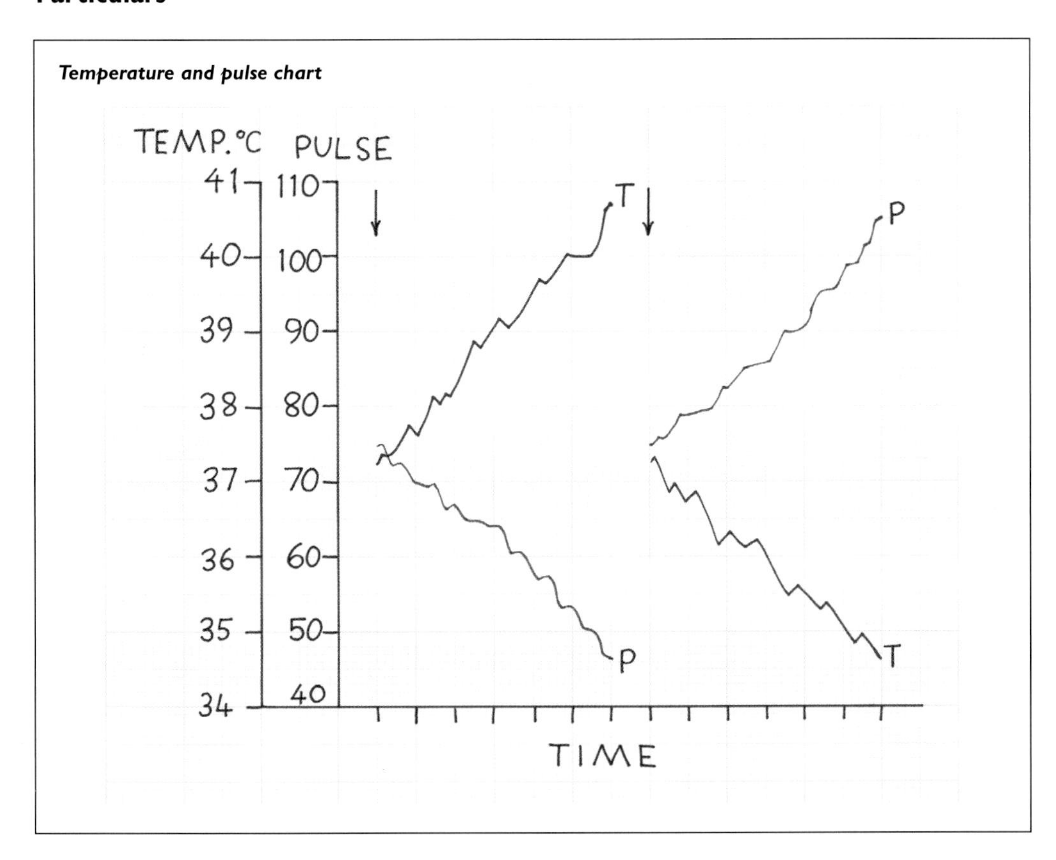

Pyrogen is characterised by a disparity of the pulse and temperature during an infection. The left-hand trace shows a rising fever yet associated with a falling pulse (bradycardia). The right-hand trace shows a rising pulse (tachycardia) with a falling temperature (hypothermia) during an infection.

Related images

p.376 Bone marrow suppression
p.375 Autoimmune disease
p.206-210 Cancer and malignancy
p.606-612 Radiation and radiotherapy
p.186 Burns chart
p.185 Burn & p.215 Electric burn
p.44 Necrotic skin and abscess
p.586 Muscle wasting
p.103 Tonsillitis
p.729-732 Thyroid disease
p.752 Pineal tumour
p.40-41 Pituitary tumour
p.96 Growth chart
p.512-515 Assisted and artificial reproduction

QUERCUS ROBUR

Museum

Tintoretto (1518-1594), 'Road to Calvary' (1566-67) oil on canvas. Scuola Grande di San Rocco, Venice © 1999, Photo Scala, Florence. The artist has shown the subject in an entirely different manner than usual, merging several versions of the Gospels and using a double-diagonal composition. The ascent is along a steep angle. The thieves are in the shadowy lower section, whilst Christ is placed in full light against the sulphur-coloured sky shot with pink. A soldier is holding the rope tied around Christ's neck, with pious women around. Christ is shown carrying his own cross, as described in St. John, and not carried by Simon of Cyrene for him (as described by the other Evangelists). The two criminals are also shown carrying their crosses, a detail only found in the Gospel of St. Luke. The burden of carrying the Cross of Matter is used to illustrate the similarly burdened Quercus remedy state.

Original

'Quercus robur and megalith power', by Loolie Habgood. The deep root system mirrors the equally powerful branch and foliage above. Lightning strikes the tree through the Mars forces. The tree is sacred to Druidery, as shown by the megalith series of dolmen stones around it. An expanded view of acorn fruiting is shown in the lower right corner.

Astrology

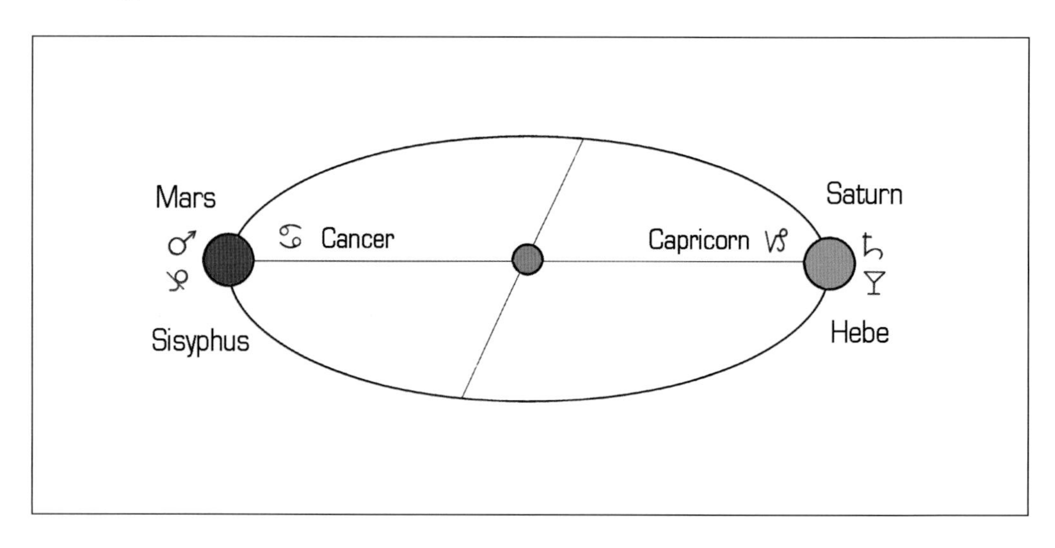

Mars conjunct Sisyphus within Cancer, opposite Saturn conjunct Hebe within Capricorn.

Oriental

Spleen yang deficiency with lung chi deficiency.

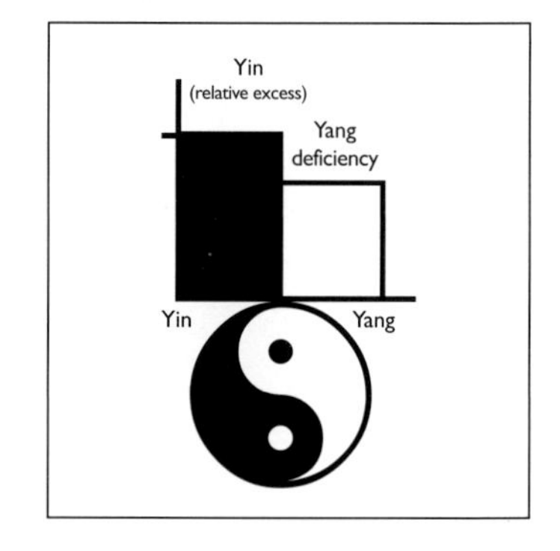

Particulars

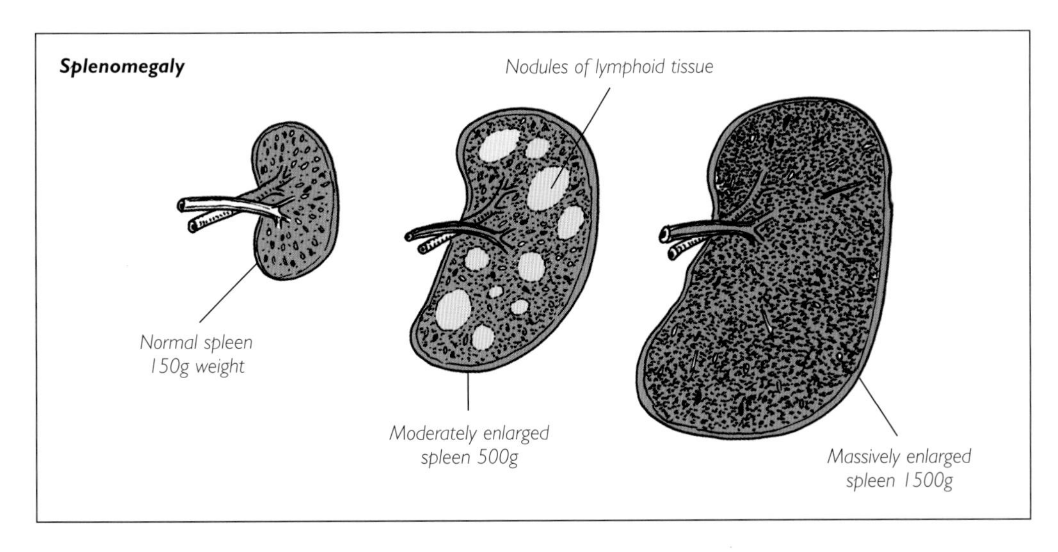

Enlargement of the spleen may occur from increased numbers of white cells or red blood cells. Causes include infections (e.g. malaria, glandular fever), congestive heart failure, liver cirrhosis, amyloidosis, tumours (e.g. lymphoma, leukaemia) and haemolytic anaemia. In the examples depicted, the moderate enlargement shows nodules of white lymphoma tissue. The massive spleen shows uniform white and red cell congestion in an example of chronic leukaemia.

Related images

p.288 Immune thrombocytopenic purpura
p.227 & p.229 Malaria
228 Pernicious anaemia & p.327 Anaemia
p.561-562 Hepatitis & p.222 Fatty liver
p.222-223 Gallstones
p.223 Jaundice & p.133 Liver failure and ascites
p.470 Pancreatic failure
p.156 Worm gut infestation
p.420 Candidiasis & p.582 Infectious gastroenteritis
p.462-463 Uterine prolapse
p.648 Femoral hernia & p.472 Inguinal hernia
p.507 Coeliac disease
p.180 Gastrointestinal bleeding
p.494 Crohn's disease
p.541 Peptic ulcer
p.593 Adrenal atrophy
p.54 Hydrocephalus
p.129 Pericardial effusion
p.95 Cystic fibrosis
p.504 Chronic bronchitis
p.306 Bronchiectasis

RADIUM BROMATUM

Original

'Radium bromatum and radioactive meltdown', by Antonia Chetwynd. A spectacular example of the damage caused by severe exposure is shown, the victim literally melting bodily and his blood decomposing. In the background the mushroom-cloud of a nuclear explosion is shown.

Astrology

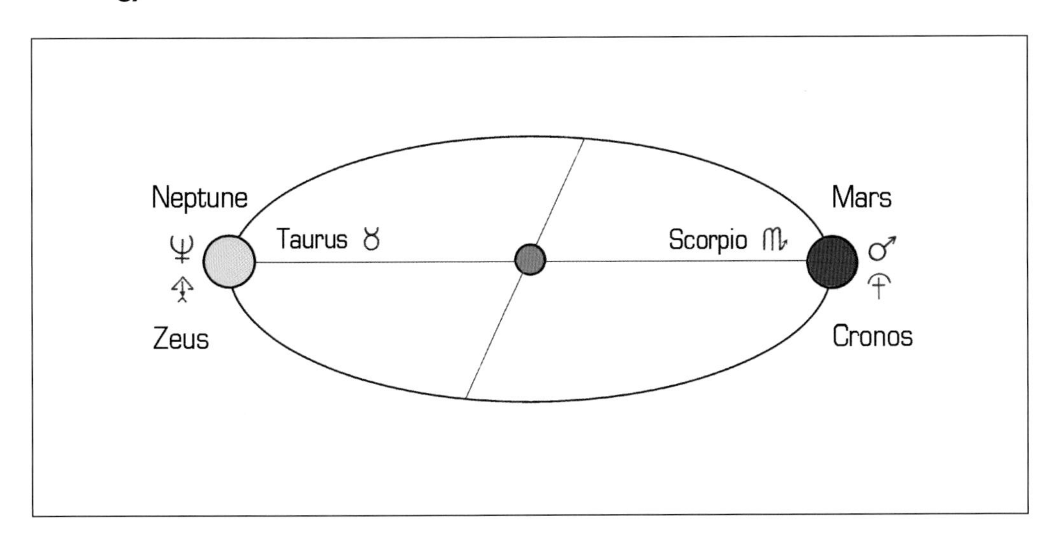

Mars conjunct Cronos within Scorpio, opposite Neptune conjunct Zeus within Taurus.

Oriental

Kidney yin deficiency, with fire-heat congealing the heart.

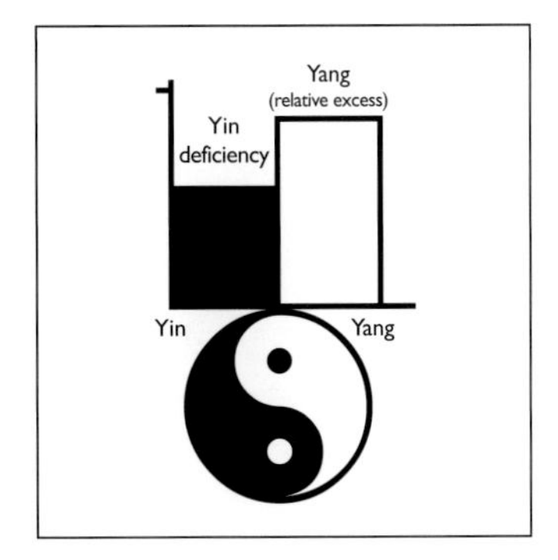

Particulars

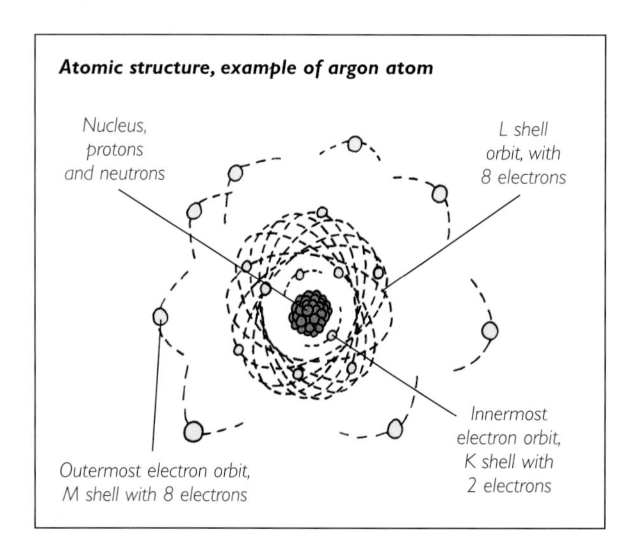

The atom is regarded by science as the basic component of matter, the popular model for its structure being of a 'planetary' makeup with orbits around a central structure. This is not the same as the esoteric perspective. However, in the scientific model, the core nucleus is composed of two particle types – the protons (with a positive charge and mass of unit 1) and neutrons (with no charge but a mass of unit 1). The mass number of an atom is the sum of all the proton and neutron mass numbers. The atomic number is the number of protons, and defines the type of element that material becomes within the periodic table of elements. Electrons orbit the nucleus, arranged in orbital shells termed K, L, M etc. Each shell has a limit to the number of electrons it may contain, and the inner shells become occupied first. The innermost K shell can only hold 2 electrons, the L shell up to 8, the M shell up to 18, and so on. The electrons provide the atom (and therefore the element) with its chemical or bonding properties with other atoms. Electron shells seek to become completely full. The inert elements therefore do not easily chemically react with substances because their electron orbits are filled to capacity. An example of the Argon atom is shown in this diagram. Electron orbits also have a binding energy associated with them, which is greater the nearer to the nucleus the orbit is.

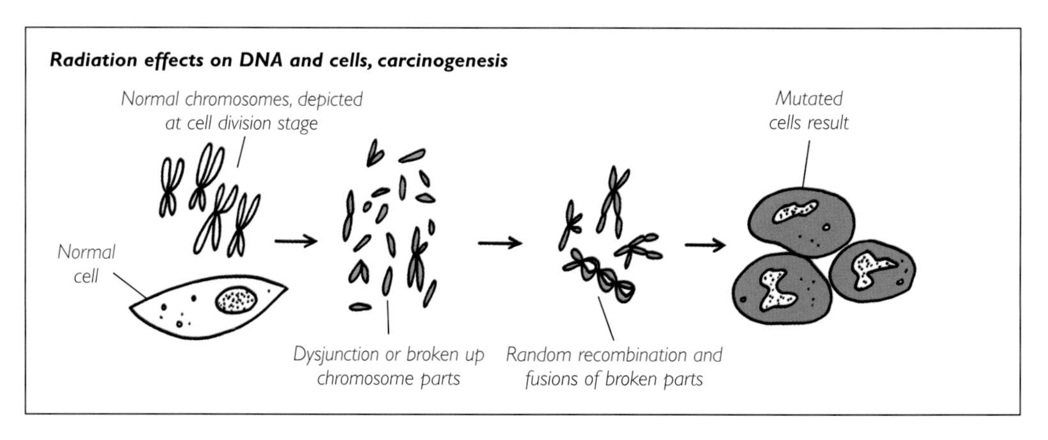

Radiation has an ionising effect to damage the chromosomal DNA, especially during the phases of cell division – when the DNA must duplicate and is thereby vulnerable. The damage can range from a single gene mutation to severe extensive chromosome destruction. These can include breaking of the chromosome, deletions of part and translocations (one part of the chromosome relocating or transferring to another part of that same or another chromosome altogether). Those tissues that have rapid cell turnover or cell proliferation are especially vulnerable to ionising radiation, i.e. bone marrow, the gastrointestinal mucosal lining and the skin. A particularly serious consequence (other than death of the tissue) is the formation of cancers from the mutated final cells being produced. Sources of radiation that have been implicated in particular cancer formations (carcinogenesis) include sunlight (ultraviolet portion especially) for skin cancers such as melanoma, nuclear fallout or nuclear reactor leakage for leukaemia, medical radiotherapy for sarcomas and leukaemia, uranium mining for lung cancers and so on.

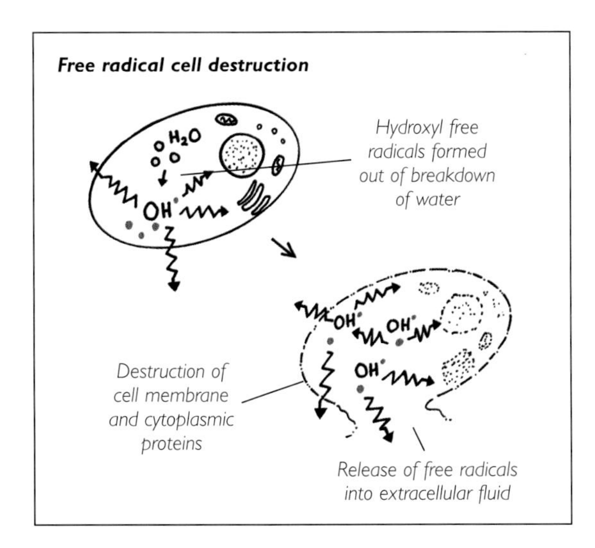

There are various means by which a cell can be destroyed, or destroy itself. Free radicals is one such method, these are molecules with a single unpaired electron in their outer atomic orbit. They react fiercely with many other molecules such as the lipids of cell membranes, structural proteins and the DNA/chromosomes. Chemical notation depicts free radicals by a dot above the chemical symbol. The main radicals are hydroxyl radical (OH.) and superoxide radical (O_2). The former is formed by the hydrolytic breakdown of water, e.g. through radiation. Free radicals are generated within vacuoles and utilised by neutrophils and macrophages to help kill microbes. The overall effects are therefore to promote inflammation, scavenge necrotic/dead tissue, to take part in radiation damage of tissues, the ageing process and so on. Antioxidants (e.g. vitamin E) are a group of chemicals which can remove excessive free radicals.

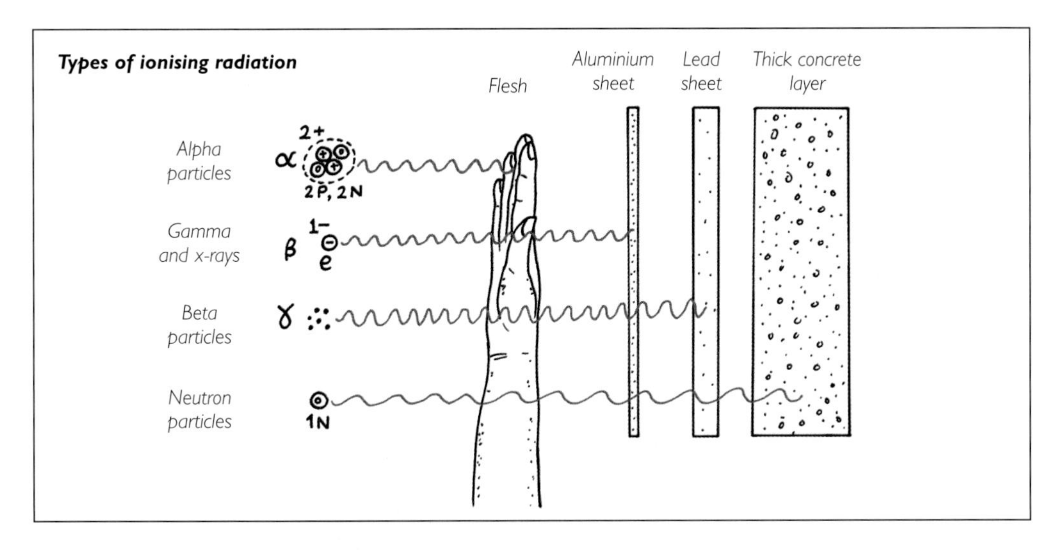

Incoming radiation can occur in two forms – as rays or as particles. The term ionising refers to the property of this radiation to produce electrically charged particles, called ions, in the material that it strikes. Ions can then have various biological effects where that material is living. There are several types of ionising radiation. Alpha particles (α) consist of two protons and two neutrons, i.e. are type of atomic nuclei. They are positively charged (by virtue of the protons). Being relatively large in size they easily collide with matter and lose their energy quickly. Their penetrating power is therefore low and they can be stopped by the first layer of skin or a sheet of paper. Beta particles (β) are fast moving electrons ejected from atoms. Being much smaller they can penetrate human flesh, and 1-2cm of water, but are stopped by a sheet of aluminium (of a few millimetres thickness). X-rays and gamma rays (γ) have wave or light-like properties. They are similar to each other, except that x-rays are artificially produced. They have great penetrating power, being able to pass through the human body, but not through a thick barrier of concrete, lead or water. Neutrons are very penetrating particles, usually derived from the splitting (or fusion) of various atoms within a nucleus reactor. They penetrate the body but are stopped by thick concrete or water.

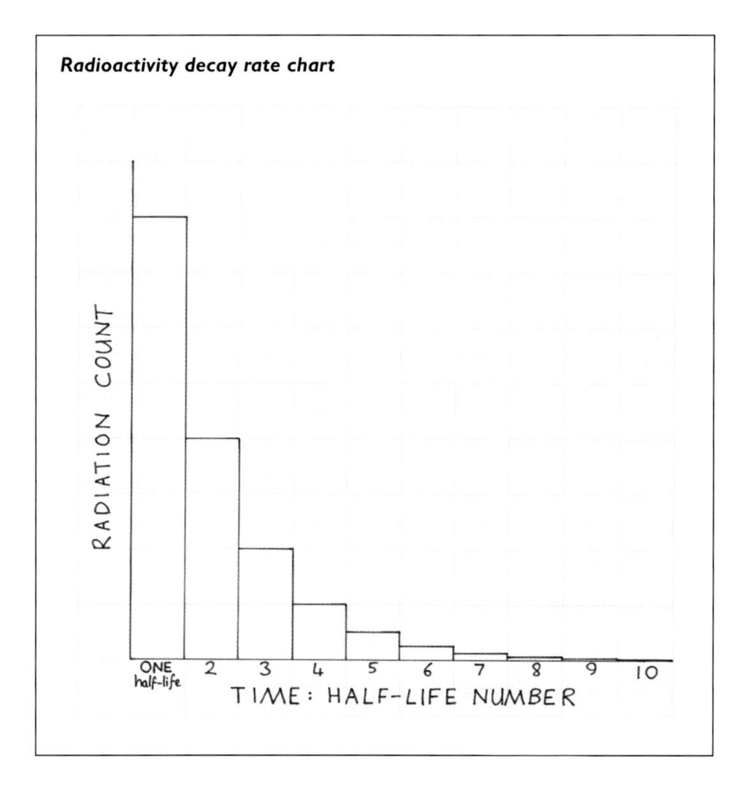

The atoms in a radioactive substance decay randomly but overall with a characteristic net decay rate. The half-life is the time taken for half the atoms of a radioactive substance to decay. It can range from a fraction of a second to millions of years, depending on the particular radioactive element. Thus after two half-lives, the total radioactivity level in the substance is one-quarter of the original, after 3 half-lives it is one-eighth etc.

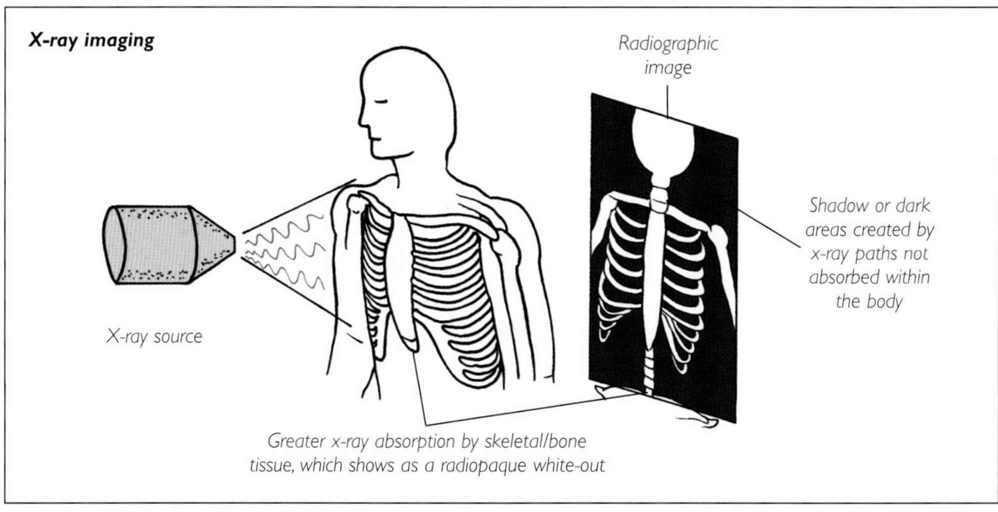

The principle behind diagnostic x-ray imaging is that the radiograph (or final image) is composed of the shadows created when all or part of a beam of x-rays are absorbed by body parts. Hence those x-rays that are not absorbed by the body will reach the detector. The image will reveal all the radio-opaque (x-ray absorbing) objects in the ray path. However, there is no differentiation between body parts in front and behind each other, i.e. overlapping will occur in the line of the x-ray path and only a flat planar image of the body is produced. The most x-ray absorbed part of the body is the skeleton, which therefore shows as the whitest, i.e. with the least shadow. An extension of this technique is CT scanning, where a computer calculates a cross-sectional image of the body.

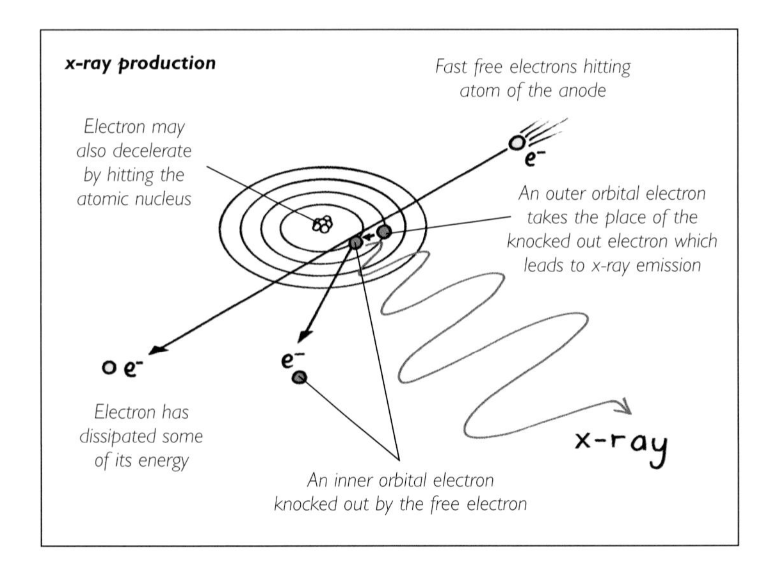

X-rays are produced by an x-ray tube. This structure produces free electrons (e.g. by passing an electrical current through a fine filament of tungsten). Electrons are negatively charged and are caused to travel (very fast) toward a rotating anode (a positively charged electrode). X-rays are produced when these fast electrons suddenly slow down upon hitting the anode target. When charged particles, such as these electrons, suddenly change velocity, then it causes them to emit radiation. This can be precipitated by the electron hitting the larger positively charged atomic nuclei. The other means of x-ray production is when the high energy incoming electron knocks out another electron already present and bound within the orbits of the atoms within the anode. This leaves a vacant spot, which is then filled by the shift of an electron from an outer orbit, causing an x-ray emission.

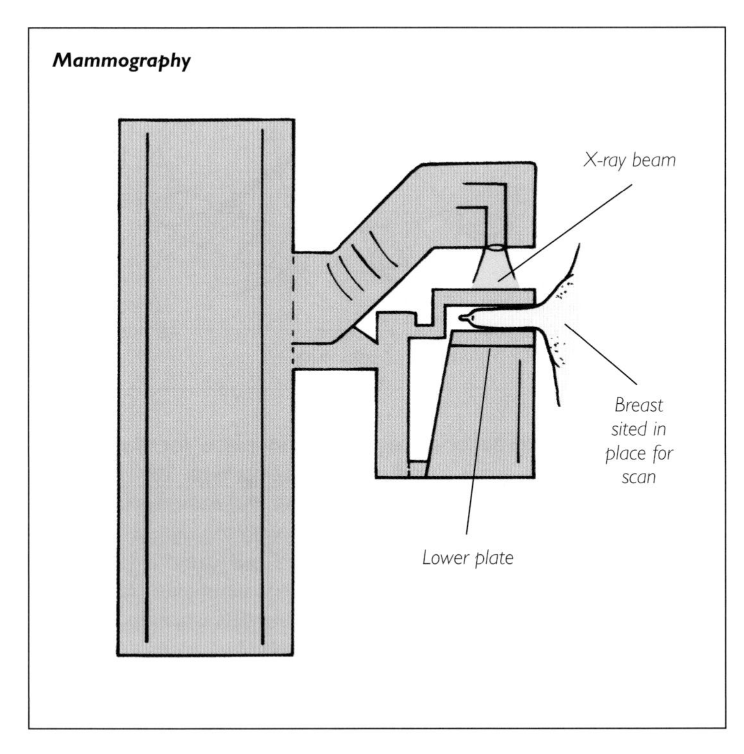

Mammography attempts to detect breast tumours at their early stages. It may be able to detect a tumour 1-2 years before a lump is palpable. The breast is positioned between the two plates and compressed to thin out the breast tissue to several centimetres thickness. X-rays are transmitted through the breast and captured on the film-screen cassette on the lower plate. Shielding the equipment and the woman wearing a lead apron helps to reduce the radiation dose to the rest of the body. Suspect lesions may show as an area of increased radio-opacity (whiteness), there may be pockets of calcification and/or cyst formation visible. However, such calcification is microscopic and therefore requires a second mammogram scan at higher resolution and magnification (undertaken for suspicious lesions). Furthermore, generally, no medical conclusion can be reached as to the presence of malignancy without a biopsy.

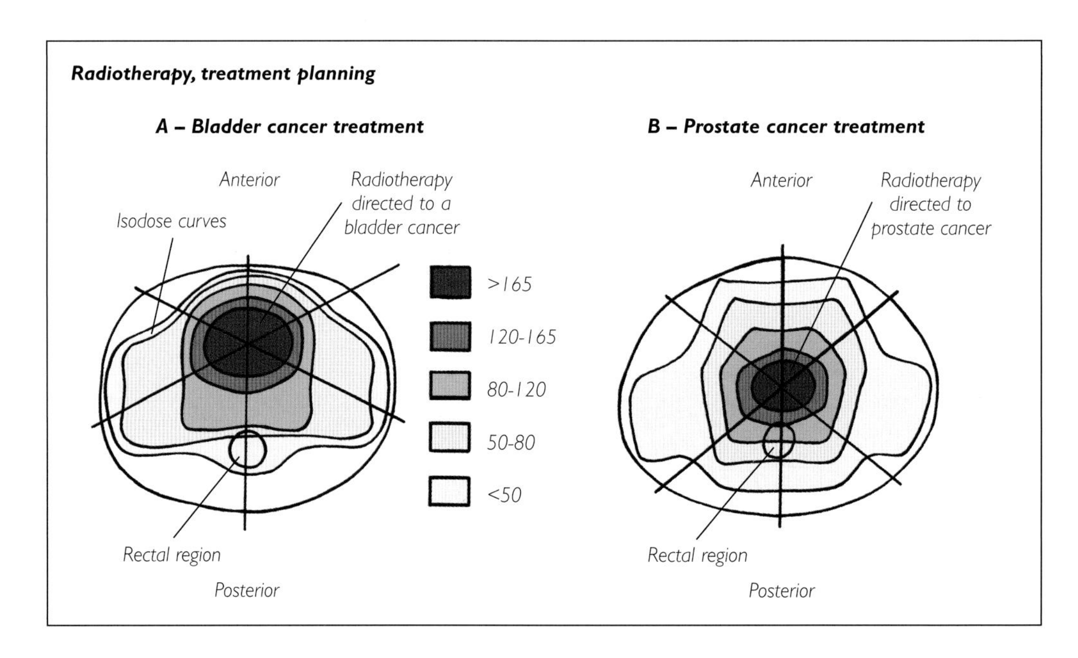

Radiation doses during radiotherapy of cancer must be titrated to find a balance between providing lethal doses to the cancer but minimising side effects to surrounding tissues. A radiation isodose curve can be plotted to map out the cross-sectional doses. Radiation is therefore focused at the highest doses of this map into the centre of the tumour, with progressively reducing doses of radiation toward the periphery. An example (A) of radiotherapy to the urinary bladder is shown with relative sparing of the rectum where the dose remains low (below the 60 isodose curve). In (B), however, radiotherapy is being used to treat prostate cancer; hence the rectum is much closer and the anterior half of the rectum receives a higher dose within the 80-120 isodose band. The symptoms within the rectum could become haemorrhage, inflammation and necrosis.

Related images

p.270 Gout and pseudogout
p.339 & p.660 Osteoarthritis
p.619-624 Rheumatoid arthritis and deformities
p.172 Osteogenesis imperfecta
p.171 Osteoporosis
p.172 Osteomalacia
p.691 Paget's disease
p.721 Lichen planus
p.207-208 Malignant melanoma
p.75 Psoriasis
p.71 Eczema
p.186 Burns chart
p.185 Burn
p.215 Electric burn
p.746 Radiation damage renal nephrosclerosis

RANUNCULUS BULBOSUS

Original

'Ranunculus bulbosus and the Old Moon ribcage', by Caroline Hamilton. The world as Old Moon is indicated by the backdrop of a huge moon, in a stage of early or partial separation from Earth. The plants are growing within a watery etheric ground, not yet solidified. The atmosphere is milky; the clear night sky of stars would not have visible to beings upon Earth. In terms of the description of Genesis within the Old Testament, this stage would be indicated by the first day separation of the 'waters from the waters just before the appearance of 'dry land'. The gathering together of denser fluids led to the formation of the Moon, enabling the rest of the Earth planet to become lighter. The skeleton of early humans was not yet properly mineralised, the bones still as a gel-like matrix. A therapeutic relationship to the ribcage is shown by these anatomical structures around the plants. The pink-red heart organ is shown within the ribcage; but the blood cells have only just developed red haemoglobin. The red colour change occurred in parallel with the formation of the planet Mars from out of the Sun. The milky nature of this primordial world has now become internalised as the latex fluid within plants of this botanical family.

Astrology

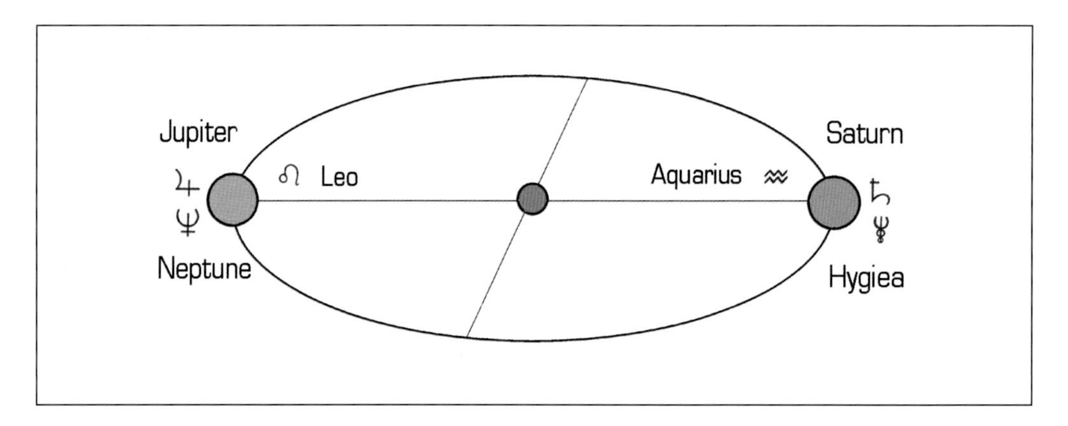

Jupiter conjunct Neptune within Leo, opposite Saturn conjunct Hygiea within Aquarius.

Oriental

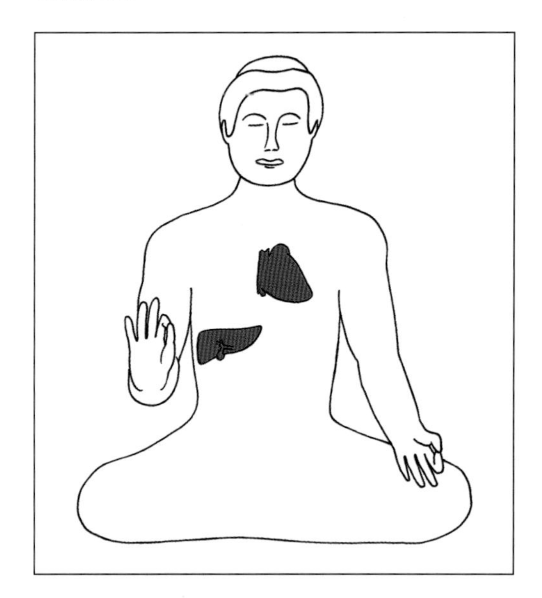

Liver and heart blood and chi stagnation.

Related images

p.222 Fatty liver & p.223 Jaundice
p.133 Liver failure and ascites
p.470 Pancreatic failure
p.574 Peripheral neuropathy
p.369 Pneumonia
p.130 Pleurisy and pleural effusion
p.619 Shingles & p.562 Herpes virus

RHODODENDRON CHRYSANTHUM

Original

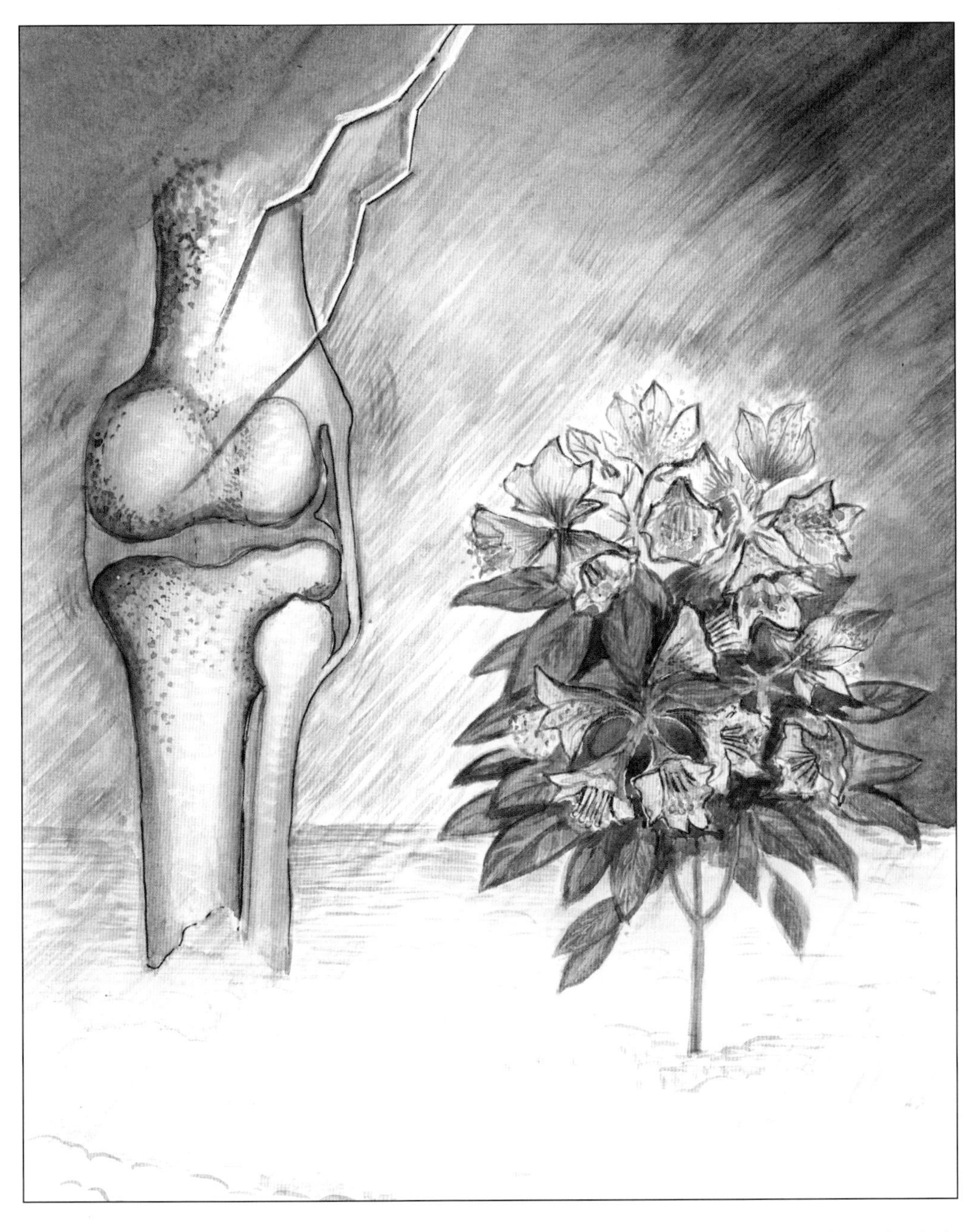

'Rhododendron chrysanthum and cold-damp joint invasion', by Loolie Habgood. The shrub is growing within a snow-covered landscape, amidst a thunderstorm. A knee joint is juxtaposed, the rain incessantly beating against this structure. The Ego forces attempt to clear the cold and damp pathogenic factor invasion through stimulation of inflammatory heat, hence the lightning strike.

Astrology

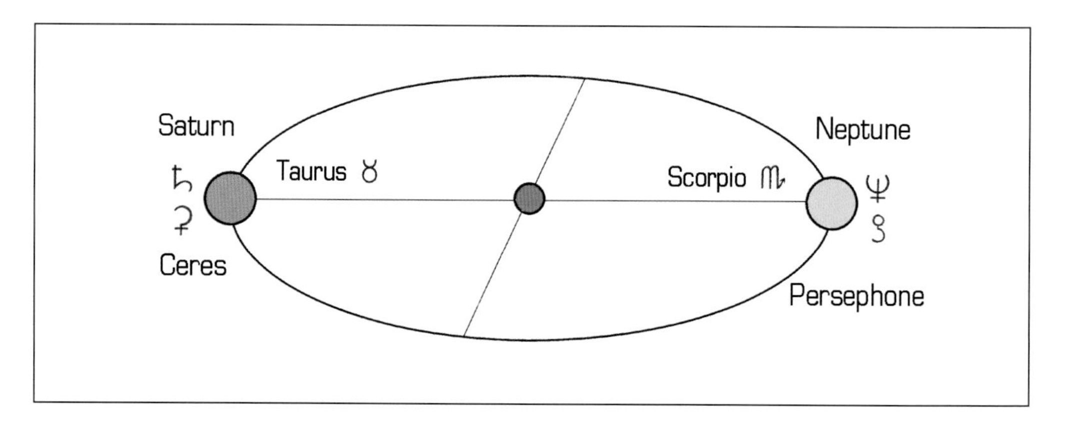

Saturn conjunct Ceres within Taurus, opposite Neptune conjunct Persephone within Scorpio.

Oriental

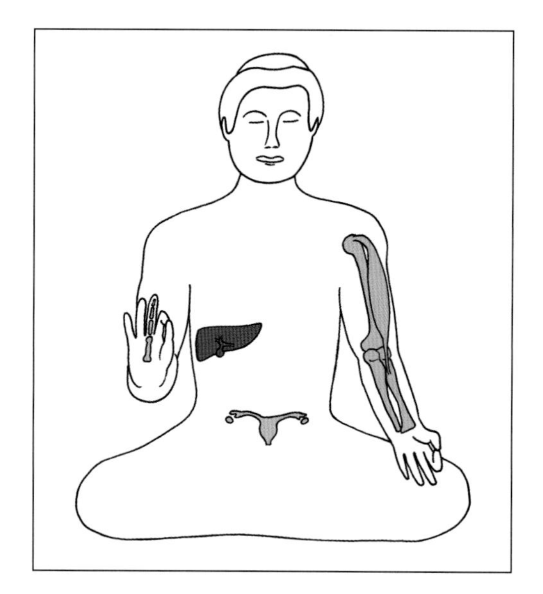

Liver chi stagnation from cold invasion, with cold-damp painful obstruction syndrome of bones and joints. Cold invasion of uterus.

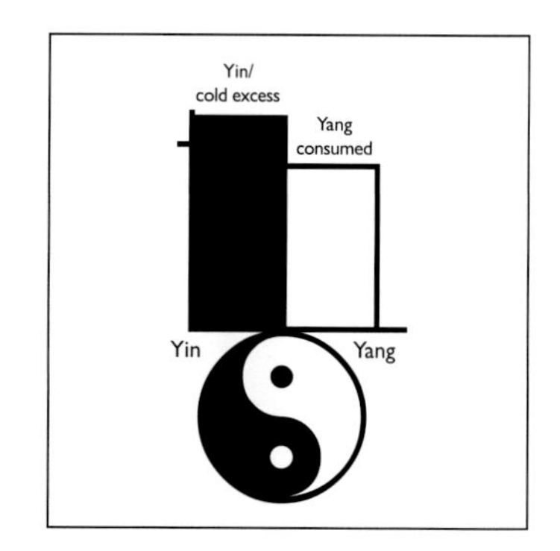

Related images

p.619-624 Rheumatoid arthritis and deformities
p.339 & p.660 Osteoarthritis
p.347 Polymyalgia rheumatica
p.742 Tubercular orchitis & p.473 Orchitis
p.360 Mumps
p.472 Scrotal hernia
p.721 Testicular cancer

RHUS TOXICODENDRON

Original

'Rhus toxicodendron and astral spasm' by Esther Lane. The plant is shown creeping up the helpless victim, who is suffering intense pain as it constricts his astral and physical body. The joints react with inflammation at the initial sclerosis or hardening of the Ego within the musculoskeletal system, as indicated by the reddish glow at various sites.

Astrology

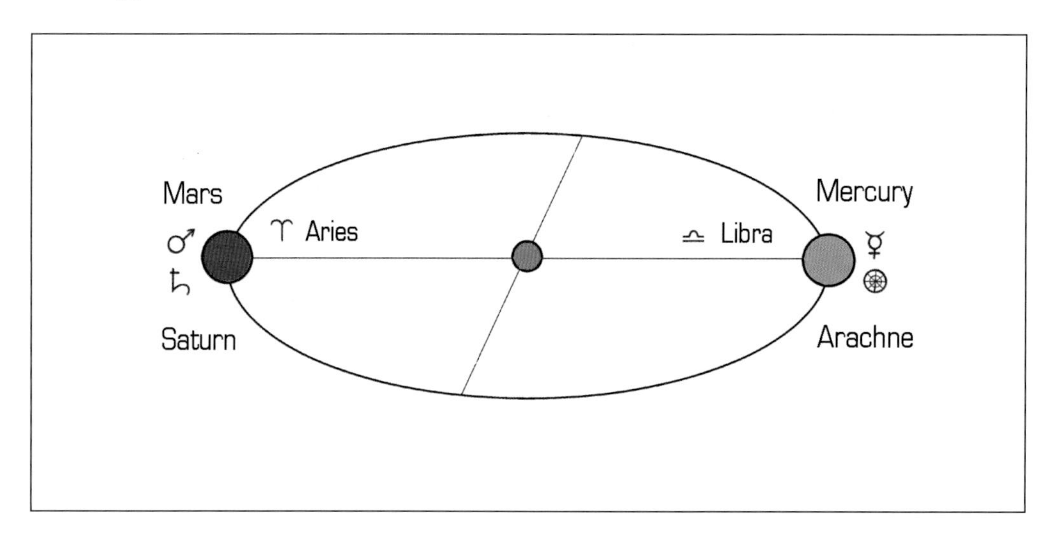

Mars conjunct Saturn within Aries, opposite Mercury conjunct Arachne within Libra.

Oriental

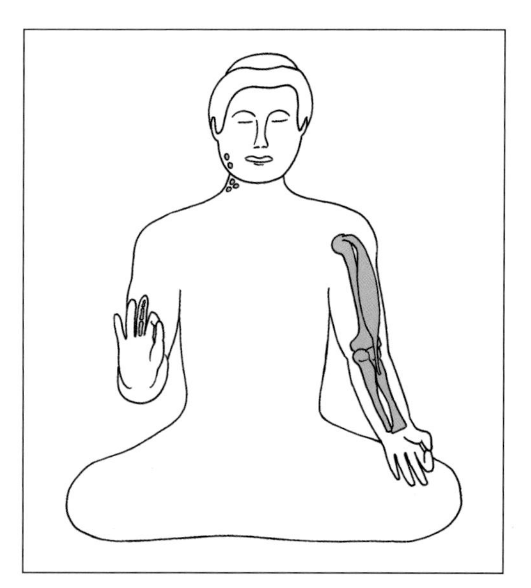

Wind-cold invasion and painful obstruction syndrome of bones, joints, defence chi/lymph nodes.

Particulars

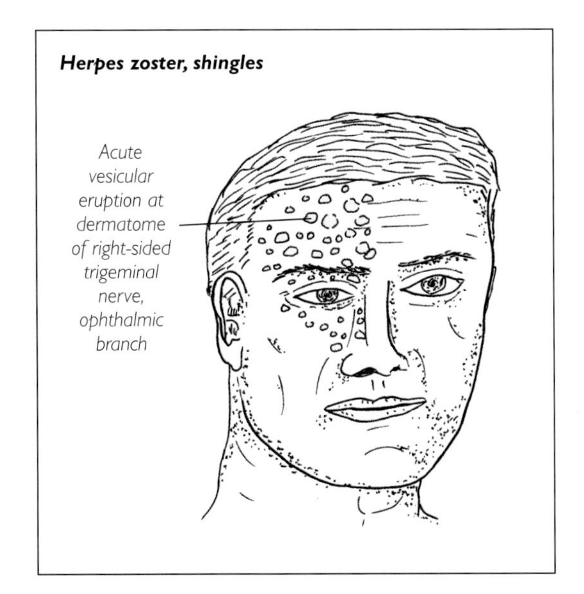

Herpes zoster is a disease presenting in adults, with a painful vesicular rash (blistering) generally affecting one or a few adjacent dermatomes only. A dermatone is the skin region supplied by a particular spinal root nerve. The varicella (chickenpox) virus had been lying latent within the posterior root ganglion, and may reactivate from e.g. local trauma, radiotherapy or other causes of immunosuppression. The virus then travels along the sensory nerve fibre to the skin or mucosal surface where it multiples. Skin epidermal vesicles then erupt, continuing the virus and acute inflammation. A common site for this activation-eruption is the ophthalmic branch of the trigeminal (V) cranial nerve, as depicted here. Serious damage to the eye may occur. Sometimes intense pain persists long after the acute eruption has healed.

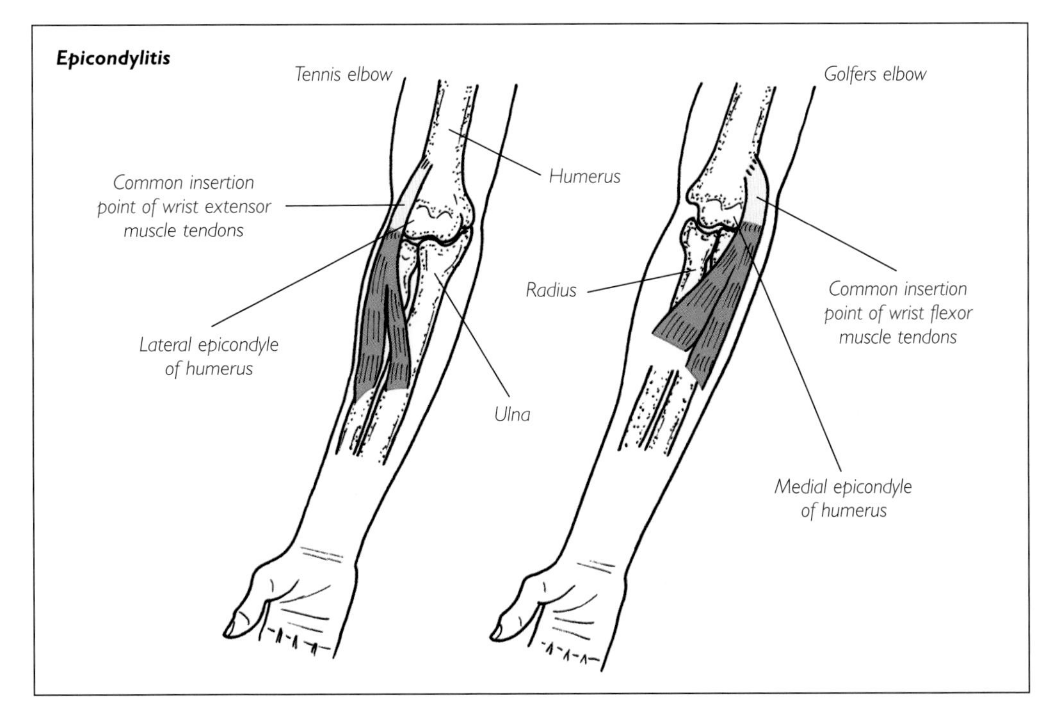

Pain in the elbow is commonly due to epicondylitis where inflammation occurs at the insertions of the tendons into the bone. Tennis elbow refers to the problem occurring at the lateral epicondyle of the elbow, where the muscles extending the wrist are attached to the bone. Golfer's elbow refers to where the inflammation has developed at the medial epicondyle, where the muscles attached are those that flex the wrist. There is local tenderness and pain is aggravated when using the affected muscles, e.g. holding a heavy bag for tennis elbow or carrying a tray for golfers elbow.

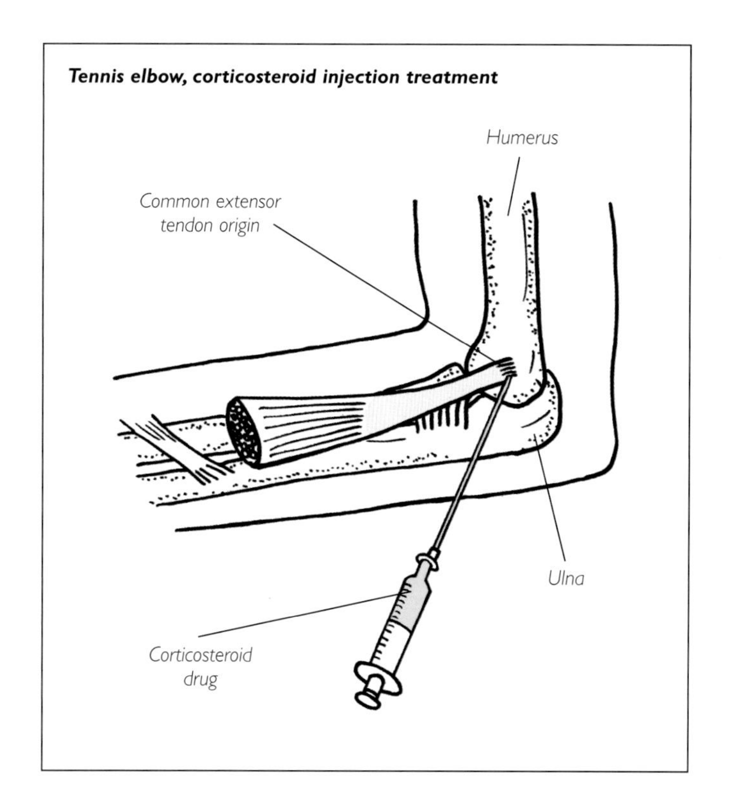

A typical allopathic treatment for inflammatory pain at tendon insertion or joint capsule points (such as golfer's elbow, tennis elbow, frozen shoulder-capsulitis, tenosynovitis-repetitive strain injury, and carpal tunnel syndrome) is an injection of corticosteroid. This has anti-inflammatory effects. However, the effect is often short-lived. Side effects of this treatment can include localised osteoporosis, skin thinning and depigmentation, infection into the joint and tendon rupture.

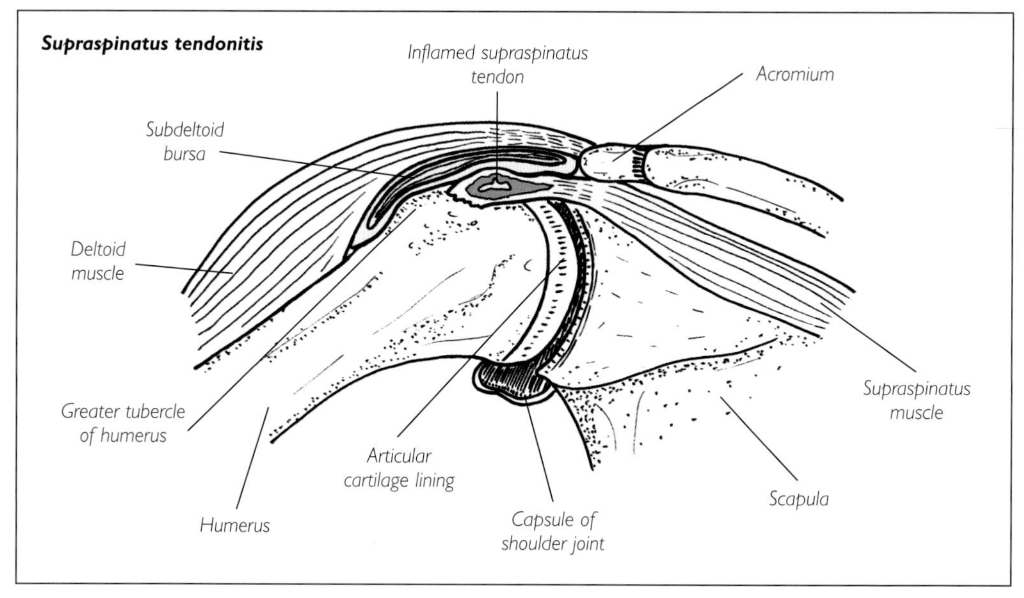

Tendonitis of the shoulder joint typically involves inflammation and degeneration of the supraspinatus tendon. This leads to secondary inflammation of the subdeltoid bursa. Calcium deposits occur in the degenerated tendon, which further aggravate the symptoms. There is shoulder pain, especially on abduction movements (swinging the arm laterally outwards and elevating the arm). This movement pinches the damaged supraspinatus tendon between the greater tubercle of the humerus, the acromium and the coracoacromial ligament. The image shows the arm partially abducted.

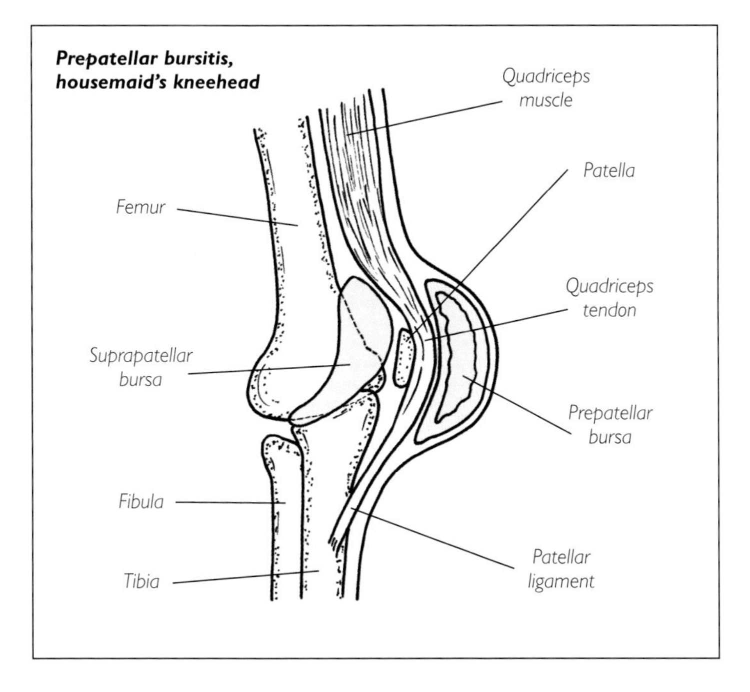

Bursitis is an acute or chronic inflammation of a bursa, which is a sac-like pouch sited to relieve friction of the moving parts of a joint. Bursae are lined by synovial membrane and contain a fluid similar to the synovial fluid found inside the joint. They lie between tendons and bones; muscles and bones; ligaments and bone; and within the joint articular capsules themselves. Bursitis could be caused by, for example, trauma, infection or rheumatoid arthritis. Repeated friction causes chronic bursitis with the accumulation of fluid. Symptoms are pain, swelling and restricted movement. Pre-patellar bursitis occurs at the bursa between the patella and the skin surface, and is related to repeated pressure from a crouched position on one's knees (e.g. scrubbing the floor).

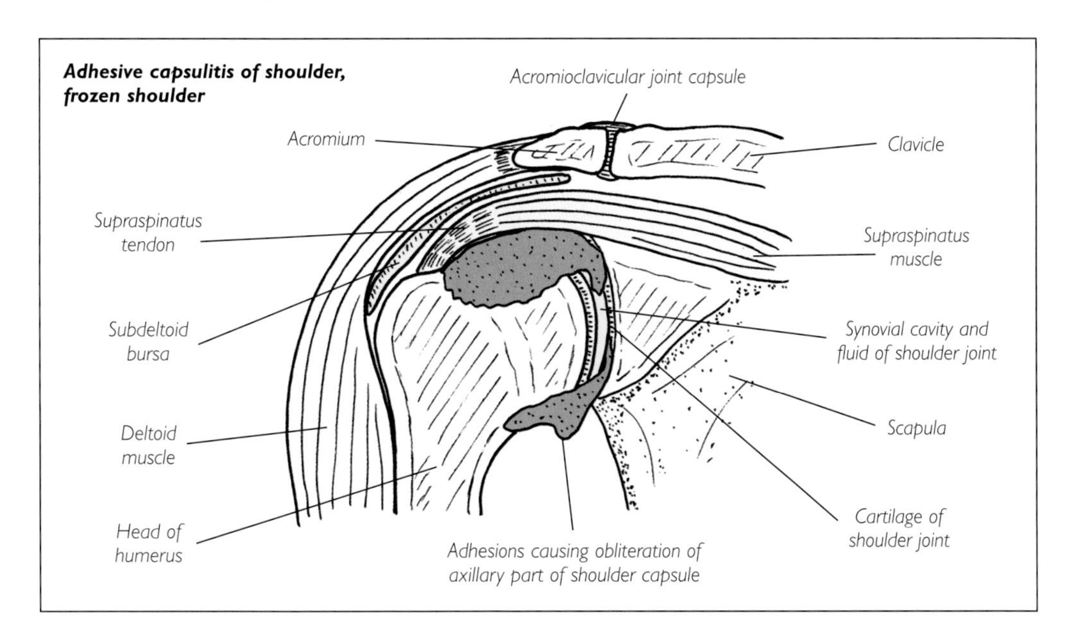

Adhesive capsulitis is also called adhesive bursitis and frozen shoulder. There is shoulder pain with limitation of both active and passive movement. Immobilisation of the shoulder after an injury or an episode of bursitis (inflammation of the bursa) may precipitate the problem. A chronic inflammation then sets in the shoulder joint capsule, synovial membrane and rotator cuff (musculotendon region). This leads to adhesions forming between the folds of the capsule and between the head of the humerus and the capsule (but without adhesions in the subdeltoid bursa).

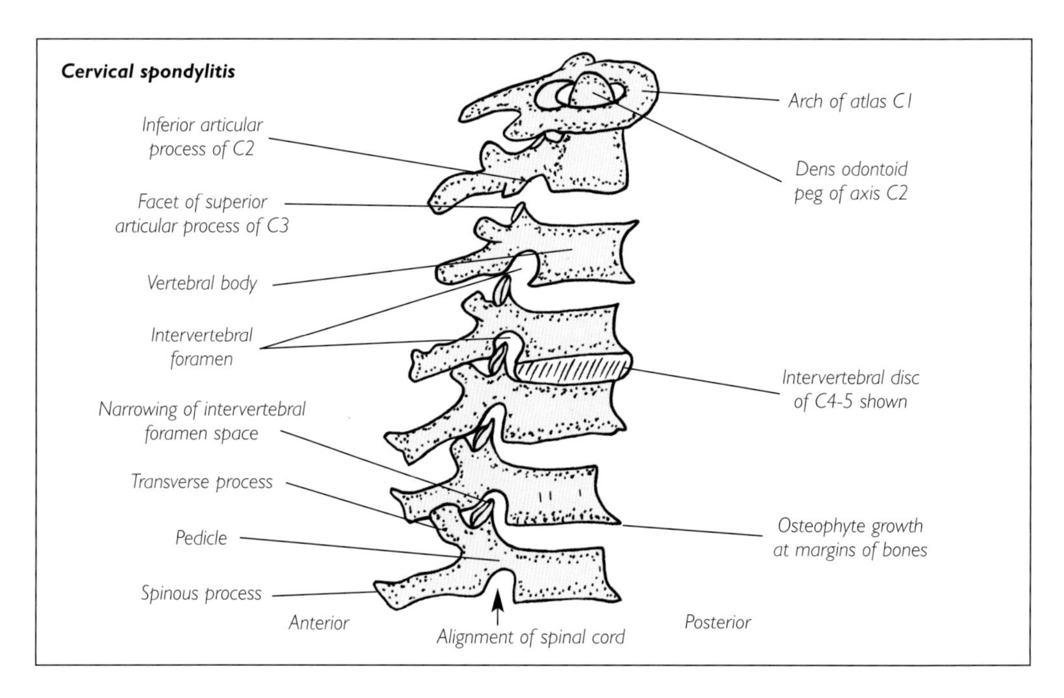

Cervical spondylitis is osteoarthritis of the cervical vertebrae. There is degenerative change with cartilage damage to the facet joints between the vertebrae. Bone is exposed at the joint surfaces, leading to cyst formation as the bone degenerates. Osteophytes (extra bony spurs at the margins of bones) form around the various joints, including at the intervertebral disc margins. There is generally pain and stiffness. Neurological symptoms may develop from compression of spinal nerves as they exit from the more limited intervertebral foramen spaces.

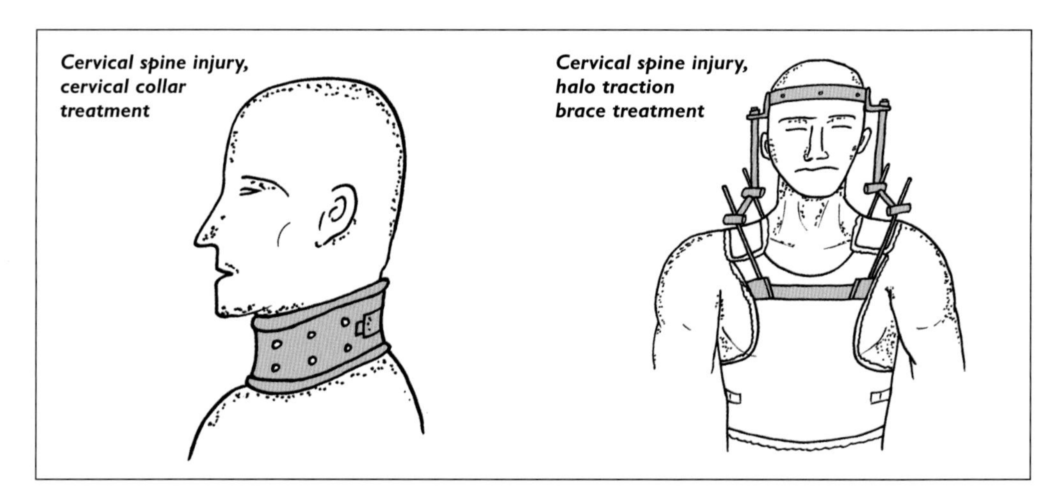

Treatment of a cervical neck injury requires emergency evaluation of potential or actual spinal cord injury. Further complications are to be prevented. If the spinal cord is not damaged, and the injury is only to the surrounding soft tissues of the neck (e.g. a whiplash injury) then a soft cervical collar with pain relief may be all that is needed. Where cervical vertebral fracture and/or spinal cord injury has occurred, then the spinal column needs to be realigned, usually requiring skeletal traction. An example of a halo traction device is shown here, where the tongs have been fixated to the skin to limit mobility of the neck.

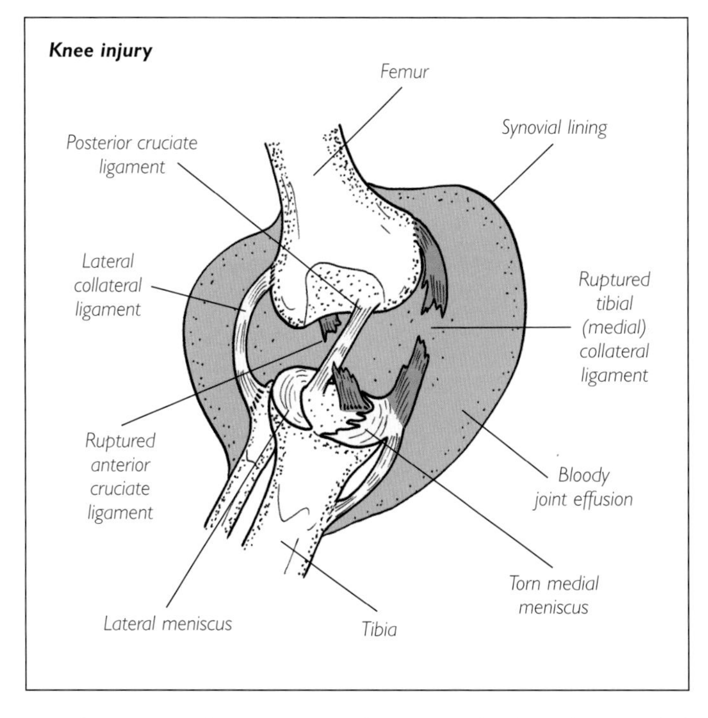

Knee injury

The knee joint is normally a very secure joint, bound together by multiple strong ligaments. However it is also subject to many types of injuries with great strain imposed on the ligament attachments, especially in sports activities. An example of an injury is shown here, which may have been caused by a contact blow to the lateral side of the knee whilst the person is running and his foot is fixed on the ground (e.g. a football or rugby tackle). The knee is bent inwards or medially in relation to the fixed tibia, which has ruptured the lateral/tibial collateral ligament. He has also torn and detached the medial meniscus, which is attached to this ligament. The anterior cruciate ligament normally prevents backward (posterior) displacement of the femur with hyperextension of the knee joint; it has also ruptured in this case. Haemorrhage into the joint space is inevitable, causing an acutely hot, swollen, painful knee with loss of effective movement.

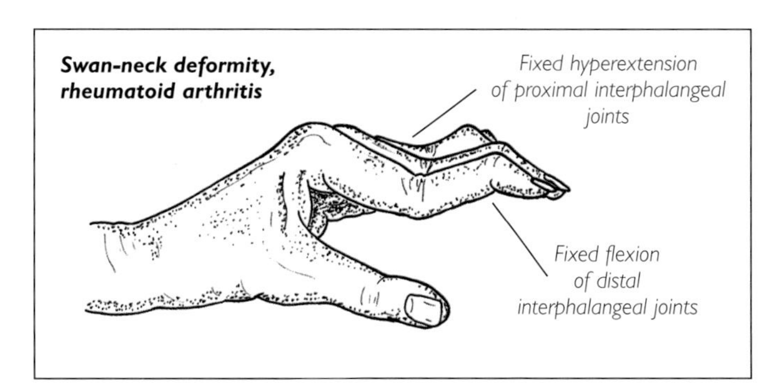

Swan-neck deformity, rheumatoid arthritis

Swan-neck deformity in rheumatoid arthritis is characterised by hyper-extension of the proximal interphalangeal joint and flexion of the distal interphalangeal joints. All these and other deformities markedly reduce hand function.

Boutonniere's deformity, rheumatoid arthritis

Fixed flexion of proximal interphalangeal joint

Fixed hyperextension of distal interphalangeal joint

Swan-neck deformity in other joints

Rheumatoid arthritis has many devastating affects on the hand. Boutonniere's deformity is characterised by flexion of the proximal interphalangeal joint and hyper-extension of the distal interphalangeal joints, there is damage to the joint capsules, lengthening and deformities of the tendons to the fingers. The soft tissue contraction and joint stiffness ensures it becomes a fixed deformity.

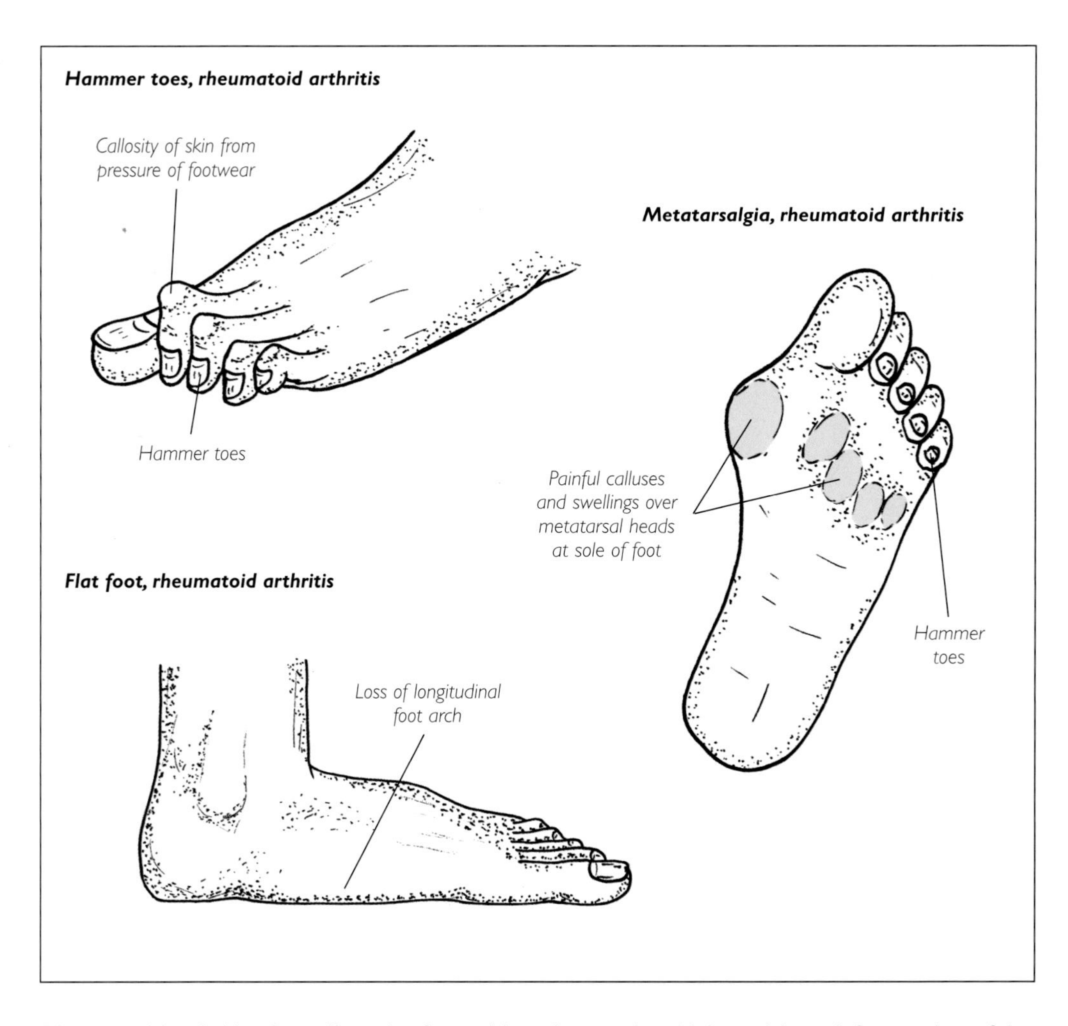

Rheumatoid arthritis often affects the foot, with various and multiple problems. Inflammation of the metatarsal joints leads to swelling of the synovial joint linings, damage to the small intrinsic muscles supporting these joints and deformation of the tendons. The result is descent of the metatarsal joints, such that the heads of the bones become prominent at the sole of the foot. Walking becomes painful, with a sensation as if walking on marbles. The foot also becomes broader and hammer-toe deformities develop in the smaller toes. Inflammation further back at the mid- and hind-foot causes a flattening of the normal foot arch with consequent loss of flexibility, i.e. a flat foot. The ankle often deviates outwards into a valgus position.

Related images

p.145 & p.451 Angina & myocardial infarction
p.278 Spinal cord compression vertebral fracture
p.339 & p.660 Osteoarthritis
p.619 Shingles
p.562 Herpes virus
p.71 Eczema

PRECEDING PAGE. 'Two Shiva devotees', gouache drawing. © Wellcome Library, London. The Shiva devotees are adept at extracting the poison from a scorpion bite, for which they use small stones. There is a story called the 'Saint and the Scorpion' worth recounting: One day a saint was bathing in a river, whilst his disciple sat waiting at the bank with his clothes and rosary. The saint happened upon a scorpion struggling in the water's current and lifted the creature in his palm to carry him to shore. However, the scorpion stung the saint's hand, causing him to suffer a sudden severe pain radiating up the arm. However, the saint did not drop the scorpion, but continued towards the riverbank. The alarmed disciple did not say anything at first. After a few steps, the scorpion again bit the saint, which caused even worse pain and a struggle to remain upright. This time the disciple cried out, "Put him down Guruji! He will only sting you again. Leave him to his fate; your kindness will not help him!" Nevertheless, the saint ignored the warning and continued walking. Nearly at the bank, he was stung for a third time and this time the intense pain exploded in his chest and nervous system, causing him to collapse in the water, although he retained a blissful smile on his face as he did so. The disciple dragged him to shore – and he was still smiling and holding the scorpion safely in his hand. As soon as it had reached the dry land, the scorpion scurried away. After the saint recovered consciousness, the disciple asked, "Guruji! How can you still smile, that wretched creature nearly killed you." Said the saint, "You are right… But he was only following his dharma, his nature. It is the scorpion's dharma to sting, and it is the dharma of a saint to save its life. He is following his dharma, and I am following mine. Everything is thus in its place. That is why I am so happy."

LEFT. Ferdinand Landerer, after Martin Joachim Schmidt. 'Witch brew', etching. © Wellcome Library, London. A witch is shown placing a scorpion into a pot in order to make a potion. Scorpions are especially related to the astrological sign Scorpio, and are both potent ingredients in a magical spell. Talismans and amulets in the shape of a scorpion are also used as protective devices against magical attack.

Original

'Scorpion and venom within the central nervous system', by Esther Lane. A gigantic scorpion sits next to a human, whose tail is ready to release venom into the brain and spinal cord juxtaposed with it. High above is the All-seeing Eye of God within a pyramid, symbolising the nature of the nervous system as a mirror or receptacle for thoughts deriving from the spiritual plane.

Ernest Board, 'The Abbaye of Saint Antoine'(The Abbey of Saint Anthony), oil on canvas. © Wellcome Library. London Pilgrims suffering from ergotism or St. Anthony's fire are shown approaching the abbey infirmary at the Sologne, France. Here the relics and bones of the saint have been preserved, and acted as curative talismans for the condition.

Original

ABOVE. 'Secale cornutum and fall of angels into hellfire', by Katherine Mynott. A fallen angel lies prostrate and seemingly irredeemable within a realm of hell. Demons rise out of sulphurous pools, dragons rage overhead. The red horns of the demon are the typical shape of the blacker coloured fruit of secale. The small-sized mushroom stage is shown growing in the foreground.

LEFT. 'Secale and infection of rye grain', by Yubraj Sharma. The blackish fruiting bodies of the ergot fungus have replaced some of the rye kernel.

Astrology

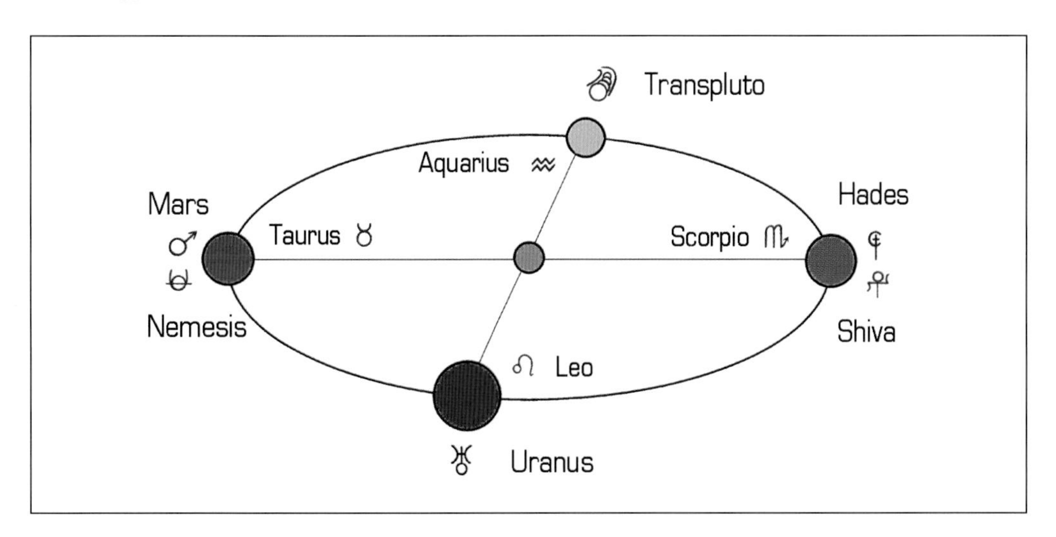

Grand cross, Mars conjunct Nemesis within Taurus opposite Hades conjunct Shiva within Scorpio, and Uranus in Leo opposite Transpluto in Aquarius.

Oriental

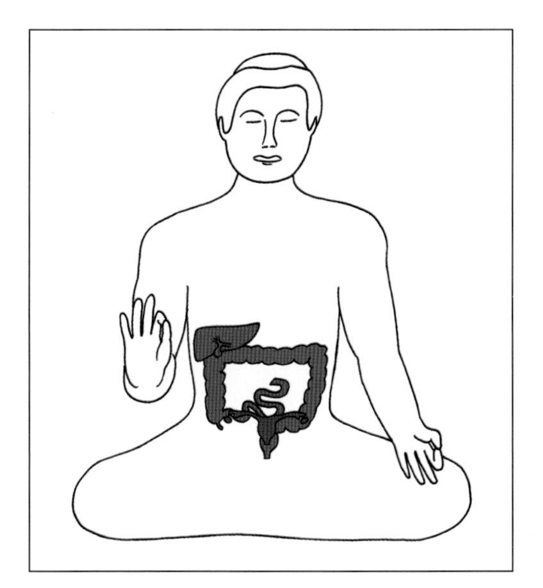

Stagnation of liver and intestines, with blood stasis of uterus/gonads.

Particulars

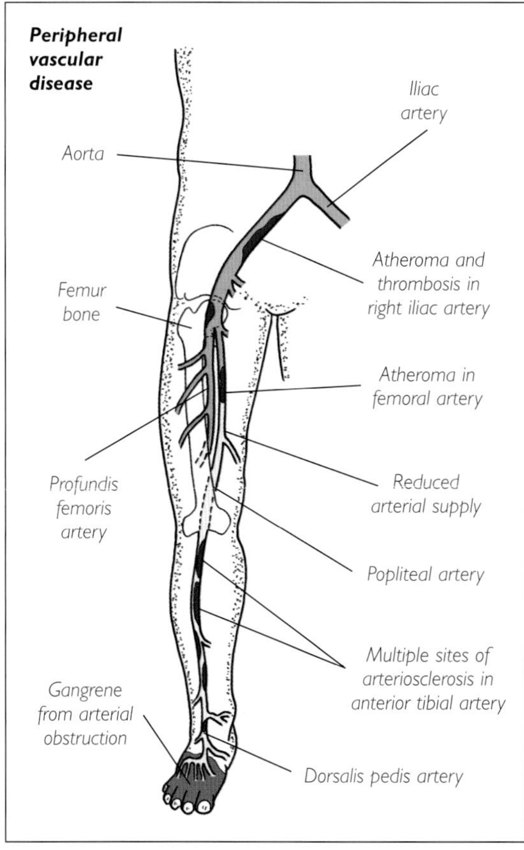

Atherosclerosis is the usual cause of obstruction to the peripheral arteries to the limbs in patients over middle age. Risk factors include hypertension, high cholesterol, smoking and diabetes. There are segments of occlusion and stenosis (narrowing) in the large- and medium-sized arteries, such as the abdominal aorta, iliac arteries proximally, the femoral and popliteal arteries, and the more distal tibial and peroneal arteries (this last artery not shown for clarity). The typical symptom is intermittent claudication, a pain (aching or cramping) and fatigue in the leg muscles precipitated during exercise and relieved with rest. The pain occurs distal to the sites of obstruction, hence buttock to thigh pain occurs in patients with disease in the aorta and iliac arteries. Calf claudication occurs in femoral-popliteal disease. Severe and deteriorating disease leads to pain even at rest, and also at night when the legs are lying horizontally (as gravity no longer assists the arterial circulation). Other signs are that the pulses (such as at the dorsalis pedis artery in the foot) may be reduced or absent, muscles may atrophy, hair is lost, and the skin becomes cold and pale. Finally ulcers and gangrene may develop.

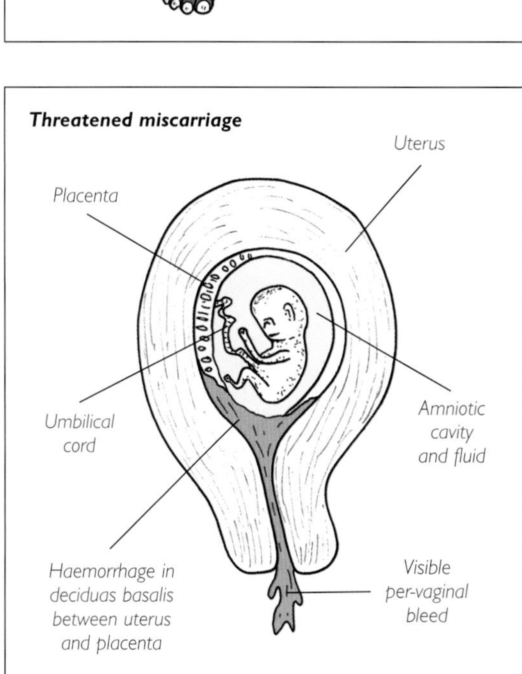

Miscarriage is the expulsion of the dead products of conception, technically before 24 weeks of gestation. Initially bleeding occurs in the deciduas basalis layer between the placenta and uterus. There is local necrosis and inflammation. The gestational sac acts as a foreign body and initiates uterine contractions and cervical dilatation. The expulsion may complete over the next few days of lochial flow. A threatened miscarriage may reverse back to continued and normal pregnancy, or become inevitable and complete. Miscarriage becomes inevitable if there is sufficient blood loss or the cervix becomes sufficiently dilated. Any bleeding (usually painless) before the 24th week may signify threatened miscarriage. Bed rest is usually advised and an ultrasound performed to ensure the foetus is still alive.

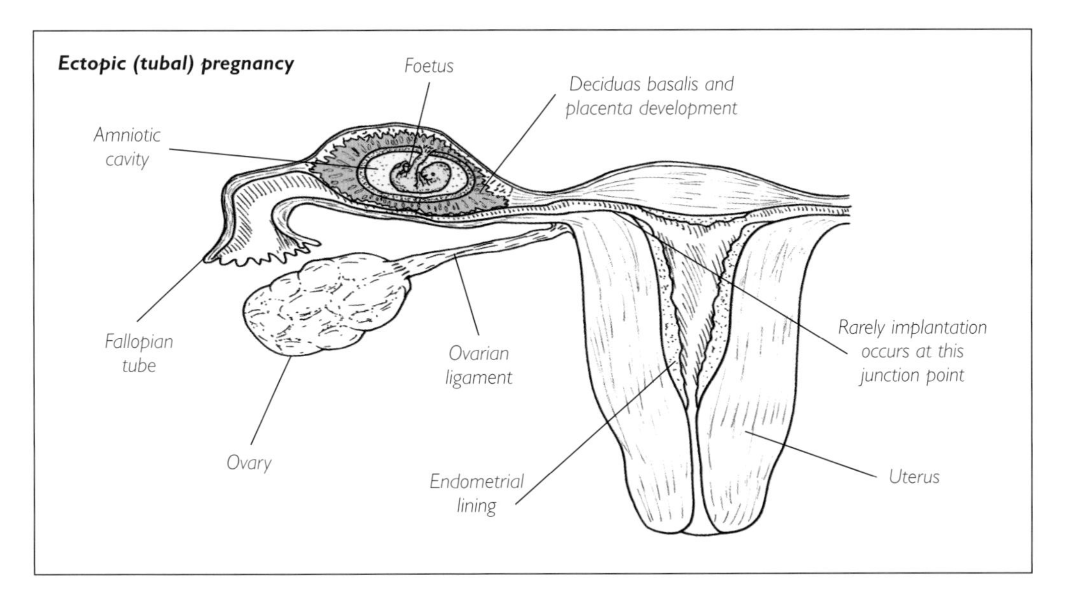

An ectopic pregnancy is characterised by implantation of the fertilised egg cell outside of the uterine cavity. The commonest site is along the ampulla of the fallopian tube (as shown here). Less commonly it is at the junction of the fallopian tube with the uterus. The deciduas basalis tissues around the foetus and placenta are unable to properly develop. Erosion of the fallopian tube will lead to rupture, with heavy bleeding, local peritonitis (with abdominal pain, internal and per-vaginal bleeding). Very rarely the embryo and placenta re-implants within the peritoneal cavity after rupturing out of the tube, where usually it would die nonetheless (although rare cases have survived). Risk factors for ectopic pregnancy are prior salpingitis (causing partial blockage of the fallopian tube), pelvic inflammatory disease, endometriosis scarring and the presence of an intrauterine contraceptive device.

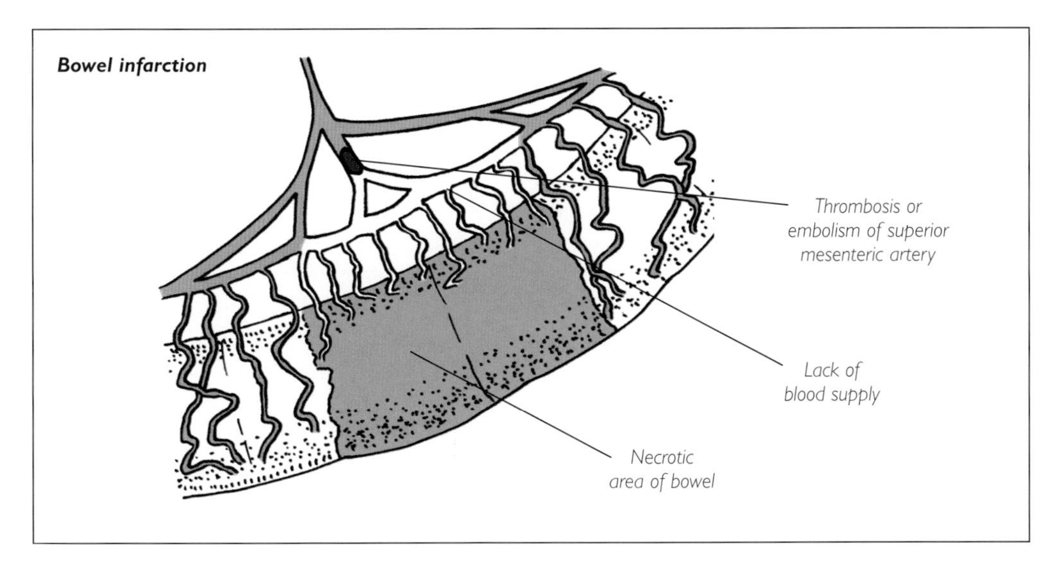

Obstruction of the blood supply to the bowel can develop upon thrombosis at the site of arteriosclerosis of the artery, or after an embolism originating from the left side of the heart or aorta. The result is necrosis, gangrene and secondary bacterial infection of the bowel, with the risk of sepsis and death. Symptoms include severe acute abdominal pain and fever.

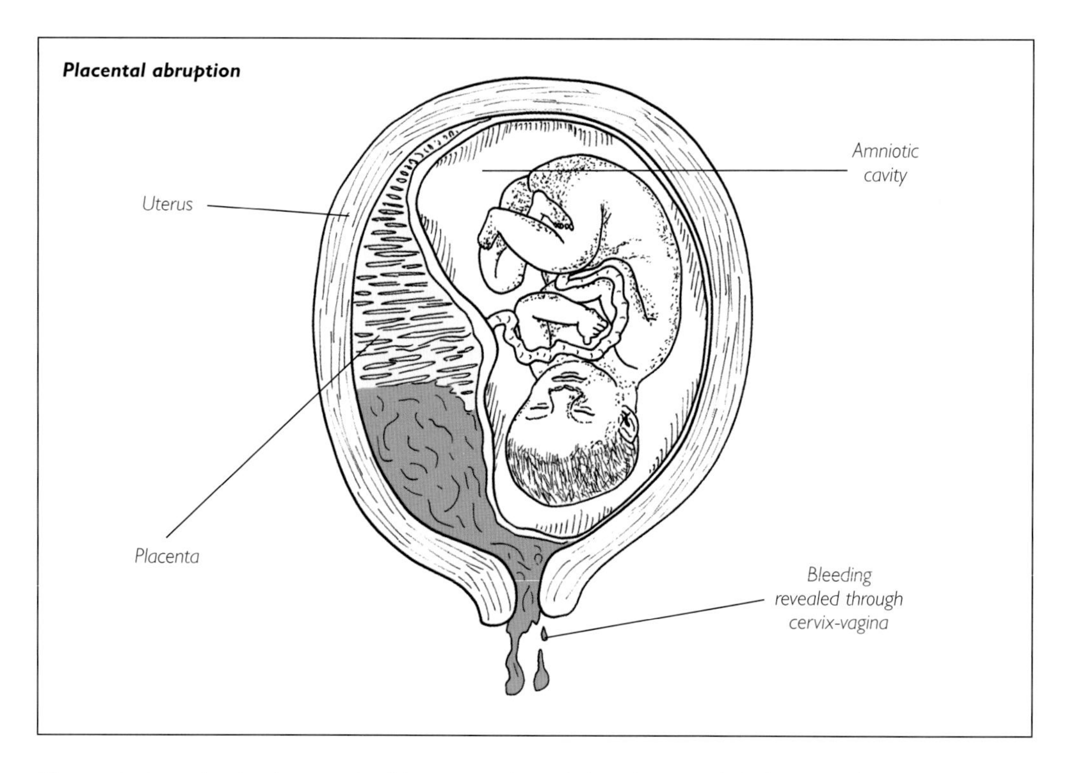

Placental abruption is characterised by separation of the placenta (which was otherwise normally sited within the uterus) from the uterus. It usually leads to blood visibly leaving through the vagina, but sometimes the blood remains concealed between the placenta and uterus. Risk factors for abruption include folic acid deficiency, multiple pregnancies, anaemia, pre-eclampsia (hypertension) and trauma. Other symptoms are abdominal pain. In severe cases the foetus may die, and the mother develop shock and renal failure.

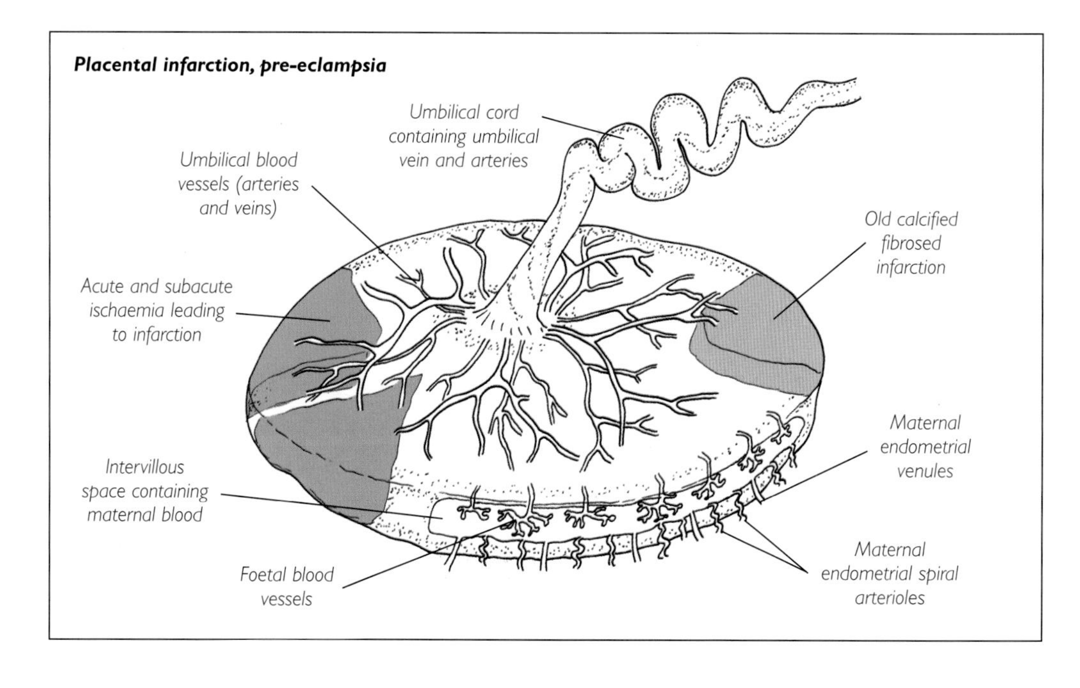

Hypertension during pregnancy can cause pre-eclampsia and eclampsia during the last trimester. It more often develops in first pregnancies than in subsequent pregnancies. Pre-eclampsia is characterised by hypertension, proteinuria and odema, and in the most severe cases there are convulsions. The kidneys become damaged, such that protein leaks during filtration into the urine. Disseminated intravascular coagulation can occur, where both widespread clotting and bleeding occurs, especially in the liver, brain and kidneys. Eclampsia is characterised by fits, accelerated hypertension and odema of the brain. In the placenta there is greatly reduced maternal blood flow to the placenta and the maternal spiral arteries never fully dilate. These arteries are therefore smaller than normal and keep their musculoskeletal wall. In the normal pregnancy the trophoblast of the embryo (the tissue surrounding the embryo) invades the maternal arteries to destroy their musculoskeletal walls. The arteries thereby become dilated channels for the maternal blood to interface with the foetal-placental blood vessels. These changes therefore do not occur in pre-eclampsia. Instead the maternal spiral arteries develop necrosis as they become infiltrated by macrophages and thrombus. Parts of the placenta lose blood supply to the point of triggering infarction. In this diagram this is shown in the acute stage and also a later calcified end-stage of scarring. Sometimes haemorrhage also occurs around the placenta.

Related images

p.180 Gastrointestinal bleeding
p.288 Immune thrombocytopenic purpura
p.758 Venous ulcer
p.490 Pelvic inflammatory disease
p.239 Complete miscarriage
p.239 Incomplete miscarriage
p.239 Retained products after labour
p.242 Dilatation and curettage
p.574 Hypertension
p.574 Peripheral neuropathy
p.343 Multiple sclerosis
p.35 Spinal myelitis
p.44 Necrotic abscess

Continuation for Hieronymous Bosch, 'The Temptations of Saint Anthony' (p.636).

The pious hermit St. Anthony is subjected to all manners of temptations and tortures. Evil lurks everywhere. There is a raging inferno in the background, awaiting those who succumb to evil. Bosch depicts the Saint as unable to defeat the demons plaguing him; indeed they appear to be intimately associated to him. A dead tree and tree branches at the upper right corner represents the Tree of Death (ruled by Satan), as opposed to the Tree of Life within the Paradisical realm. Ghastly animal-human hybrids abound, as images of horrific Atlantean genetic mutilation and manipulation. Many of the humans residing within this underworld realm are clothed and represented as members of the established Church – and clearly either impotent in defeating the monsters or actually relishing in this state. Only the Fallen Adam and Eve, shown at the right side standing within a dark oily pool, are shown with any dignity or grace. They hold a sacred chalice, indicating the opportunity yet remains to become redeemed.

SEPIA OFFICINALIS

Museum

PRECEDING PAGE. Albrecht Durer, 'Melancholia I' (1514). © Copyright The Trustees of The British Museum. Melancholy is shown surrounded by the instruments of her temperament. This print is based on the writings of Marsilio Ficino, 'Libri de Vita Triplici' (On the Threefold life) and Agrippa von Nettersheim's 'De Occulta Philosophia'. Both books described various types of melancholy – a Saturnine disease often affecting geniuses. This state is characterised by the heaviness of memory and the weight of time's passing. The personality has so separated from the soul as to forget how to transcend the material nature of linear space and time. Ficino distinguished between white-bile melancholy (related to brilliancy of thought) with black-bile melancholy (related to mania and depression). Agrippa described 'Melancholia imaginativa' (particularly affects artists), 'Melancholia rationalis (affects scientists and medics), and 'Melancholia mentalis', (affects theologists and philosophers). This drawing is an example of 'Melancholia imaginativa'. The winged woman sits low and slumped close to the wall, her wings are constrained by the hourglass above her. Esoteric lore often depicted the state of Fall from Grace of humans as the falling of winged angels, indicating the divine but trapped aspect within every human. She is leaden, under the heavy Saturn influence of being earthbound. Her body is frozen, she is morbid with a darkened face and only her eyes wander with a bright intelligence. Note how dark discoloration (especially under the eyes) is typical of certain states of adrenal exhaustion (Addison's disease). Around her everything is in disarray, as if her apathetic state prevents her from organising her life. Her counterpart is the young putto, who is dozing after studying some grammar, which triggers a melancholic reaction. Indeed, mental concentration can deplete available reserves of energy in those with adrenal-kidney and spleen chi deficient states. Nonetheless, the keys hanging from her left side represent power, the purse at her feet represent wealth. The stone block appears like a crystal with pentagonal and triangular surfaces, but is actually a cube with its opposite corners cut off. It rests on one of these truncated corners, thus actually revealing the instability of the geometry of her etheric body. The ram sleeping at her feet is representative of the constellation Aries, which normally activates the forces of individualisation and will-power with clarity and zeal. Aries rules the head centre, and here has become inverted at her feet (which is normally ruled by Pisces). The woman's wreath is braided from two watery plants, watercress and water ranunculus, which are traditionally used to treat the dryness caused by melancholy. The magic square is a Jupiter instrument utilised to counteract the malefic influence of Saturn. In mythology, Jupiter/Zeus caused the downfall of his father Saturn/Cronos. This represents a future stage of the human race (seventh root race, far into the future) when each human awakens fully to their mastery and spirit potential, enabling a restoration of the powers of spirit within the body. This will involve a Jupiterian initiation to overcome the karmic laws of Saturn.

FOLLOWING PAGE. 'Sepia officinalis and the Old Moon shepherd of egg cells', by Lorraine Spiro. A moonlit scene of fog and sea is evocative of an earlier stage of humanity, when the ovum egg cells (shown as red-walled cells at the ocean floor) as yet developed within a primordial sea. Indeed, this is reflected by the current model of human embryogenesis, whereby the primordial germ cells (eventually developing into the sperm or egg cells depending on gender) largely arise from the yolk sac wall outwith the embryo, rather than from within the embryo itself. In Genesis, the faculty of sexual reproduction is provided to Adam and Eve (rather than from some innate part of the physical body), with the proviso that they use such a power responsibly. Subsequently, any misuse of sexual energy can cause loss of germ cells, i.e. infertility. In the painting, cuttlefish are shown as shepherds tending to the eggs, their consciousness submerged and dreamy. During Old Moon, the densest phase was a gel or suspension of fluid with solid particulate matter. Creatures were therefore typically composed of watery bodies, with weak mineralisation of the skeleton. An inkjet can be seen streaming from the posterior of the far cuttlefish. In the sky above are depicted the constellations (superior to inferior) Cassiopeia, Andromeda and Aurigae.

Original

SILICA

Museum

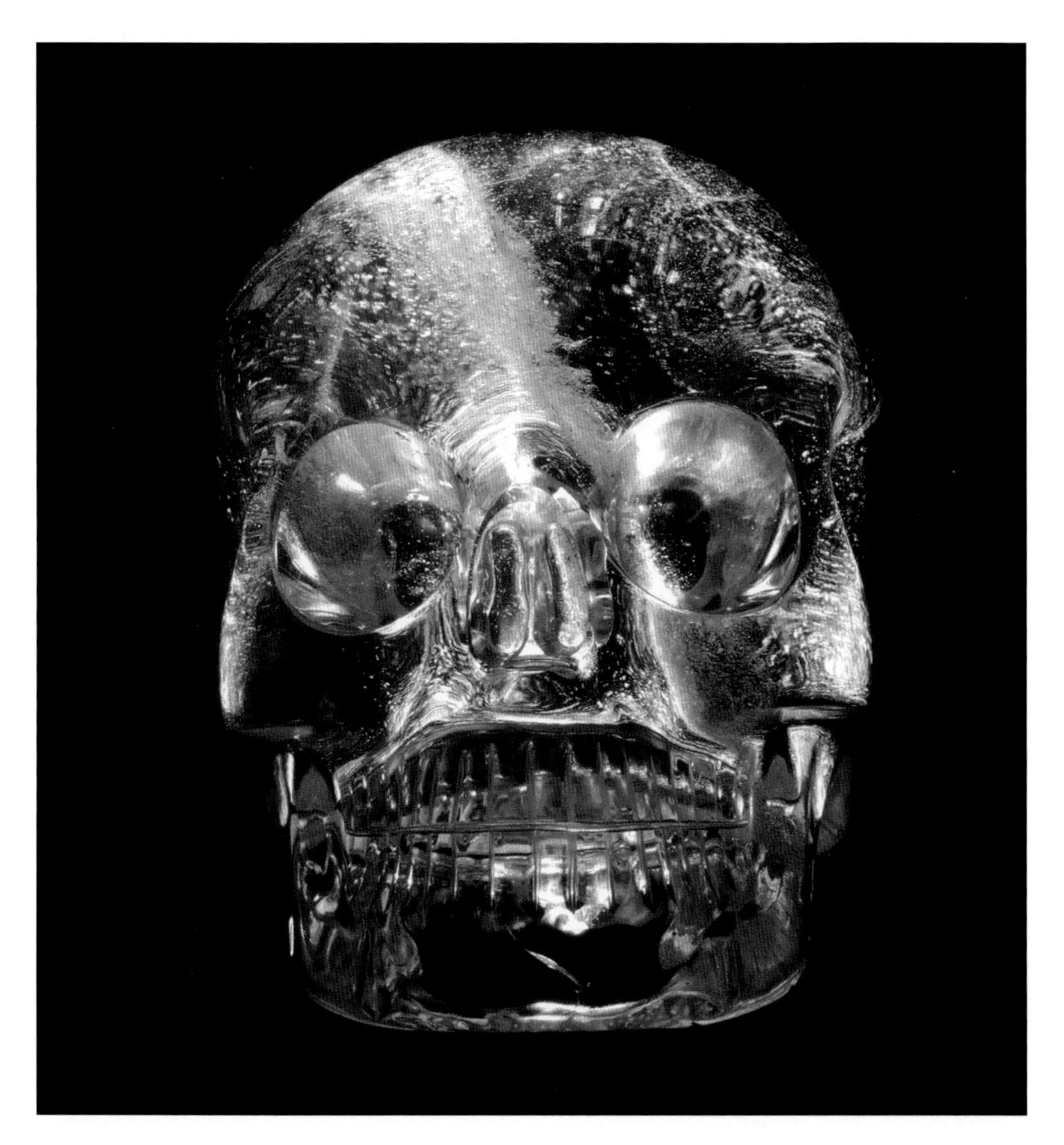

'Rock crystal skull', © Copyright The Trustees of the British Museum (Ethno 1898-1). According to Native American legends, there are 13 crystal skulls from the ancients, life-size and with movable jaws such that they can sing or talk. Other legends also foretell of 52 skulls in various sacred sites throughout the world. Collectively they contain vital information pertaining to world and human evolution, and when brought together into one place will activate this transmission. The legend derives from the Mayans, Aztecs (and their modern descendants in Central America), and various North American tribes (including the Pueblo and Navajo of the south-west and Cherokee of the north-eastern USA. In relation to the Mayans, due to their role as sacred calendar-keepers, there is also a particular timing to this gathering of energy. Thus 21st December 2012 is the activation of a phase known as the Thirteen Heavens. Note there are 13 gods in the 'upper realm' in the mythology of the Maya. There is still scientific uncertainty as to the authenticity of the known purportedly ancient crystal skulls so far. These include the Mitchell-Hedges skull. Another is at the Smithsonian Institute, Washington DC. One is housed at the Musée de l'Homme, Paris. One skull is set into a ornamental cross, and the association between the two objects to represent Golgotha, the site of the crucifixion of Christ. Some of the skulls are anatomically very accurate, although do not include joint suture lines of the vault plate bones. Others have very stylised features, distorting the normal anatomy. In comparison to the Mitchell-Hedges skull, the British Museum skull is slightly less than life-size at 25cm height and of slightly cloudy quartz. It appears to be cut from a single block of quartz. There is less fine anatomical detail, such as at the teeth sockets or eye sockets. The jawbone is not detachable. Initially the opinion at the Museum was probably of Aztec origin, c. 300-1500 ADE. The current opinion is that it is a modern European production, probably 19th century, the source of the block of quartz thought to be Brazil. It is of course not possible to date the skull using carbon-dating. Useware analysis involves scanning electron microscopic examination of a mould cast of the skull surface for evidence of tool marks from, e.g. a jeweller's wheel. One opinion is that the jeweller's wheel was not introduced to the Americas until after the arrival of Christopher Columbus (1492). Such 'wheel-marks' were found on its teeth.

Some have prismatic qualities (such as the Mitchell-Hedges) whereby, if the sun's rays are allowed to fall at a particular angle on the occipital area, then they will become condensed to result in a beam of light emitting from the eyes, nostrils and mouth. This focus of light can be used to start a fire. Some tests were performed on the Mitchell-Hedges skull at Hewlett-Packard's computer/crystal labs in California in 1970. These confirmed the quartz was of natural earth origin, not synthetic quartz. Study of the interior patterns indicated the whole skull had been carved from one single block, even though this would have been a very difficult process to accomplish due to uncertainty of fracturing or internal fault lines when carving from a large block. It would have needed a block three times the size of the final skull to start with. There were no markings indicative of modern power tools on magnified view of the surface, i.e. it appeared to have been made by hand. The particular quartz used had piezoelectric properties, i.e. pressure upon the skull induces an electric current. Conversely applying an electric current will cause slight changes to its shape. As with other piezoelectric quartz (used as the substrate for modern electronics) there is a axial orientation to this property, such that the electricity must travel along one of 6 directions, in other directions it behaves as an insulator. The skull can hold an electrical charge, in keeping with its said function of storing knowledge. The focusing of light is due to an incredible optical axis of the skull, enabling light to travel quicker in one direction than another. If this were polarised light then the skull will also rotate this light as it is passed through. The programming of, and retrieval of such 'computer-like' information is utilised by many psychics who have worked with the skulls. Channelled information concerning the skulls has implicated their origin as even preceding the Maya, and deriving from Atlantis and from extra-terrestrial technology. Furthermore, there is increasing evidence of enormous crystal deposits at the Earth core seams. The high temperatures with low gravity at this region are especially favourable to growing anisotropic quartz with piezoelectric properties. This is in keeping with the ancient belief that the crystal skulls can communicate with a natural Earth grid within and around the planet (also referred to as 'Grandmother Spider' web by native American tribal peoples).

Original

LEFT. 'Silica and the cosmic window', by Selina Swayne. The hexagonal shape of quartz is evident. The starry realm and galactic clustering above the crystals indicate the nature of silica as an interface between the sphere of Earth and cosmos, providing for a window of communication.

BELOW. 'Silica and the geometry of God', by Rishav Shah. In the ancient Greco-Roman, Gnostic and Freemason teachings God is the supreme architect of a perfect geometrical cosmic order, bound with love between all things. This image is based on an illustration by V. Weigel, Introductio hominis, in Philosophia Mystica (Neustadt 1618). To quote from Utriusque Cosmi, volume II (Frankfurt 1621) by R. Fludd: "The Oneness of God is expressed in the visible, elemental world, by the polarity of rest and movement as the fixed and the drawing legs of the compass. The two are linked by 'the bond of love or justice'." In many branches of alchemy and philosophy, geometry is described to exist even before the creation of manifest things, deriving from the spirit of God and being His divine image and proportion. Thus there is a higher order behind numbers and shapes. In Freemasonry, the compass symbolises higher reason and, along with the set-square, is laid across the Bible. Used with the plumb tool the corner stone of the Temple of Jerusalem can be laid (as a human divine body image and similitude of the body of God).

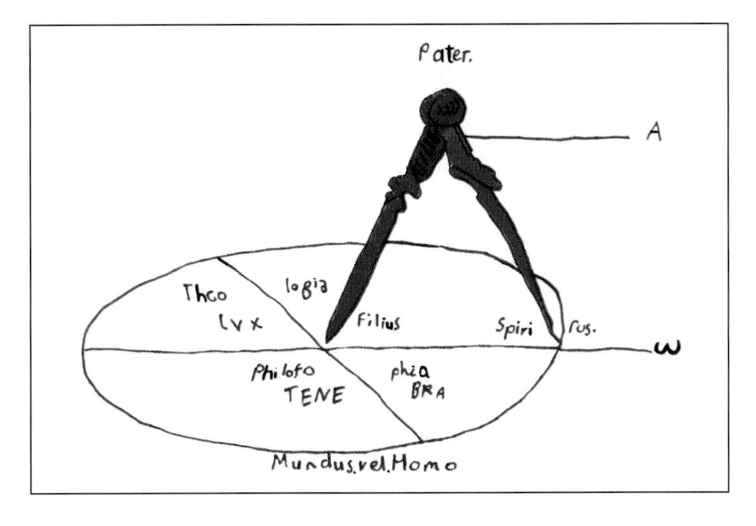

'Silica, Man + Machine', by Joanna Campion. Machine-human combinations are now a reality rather than the stuff of science fiction. Here, an angelic human (note his wings) has become hybridised with computerised implants at both arms and pelvis – symbolising the fall of the spiritual aspect of being into binary/digitalised technology.

Astrology

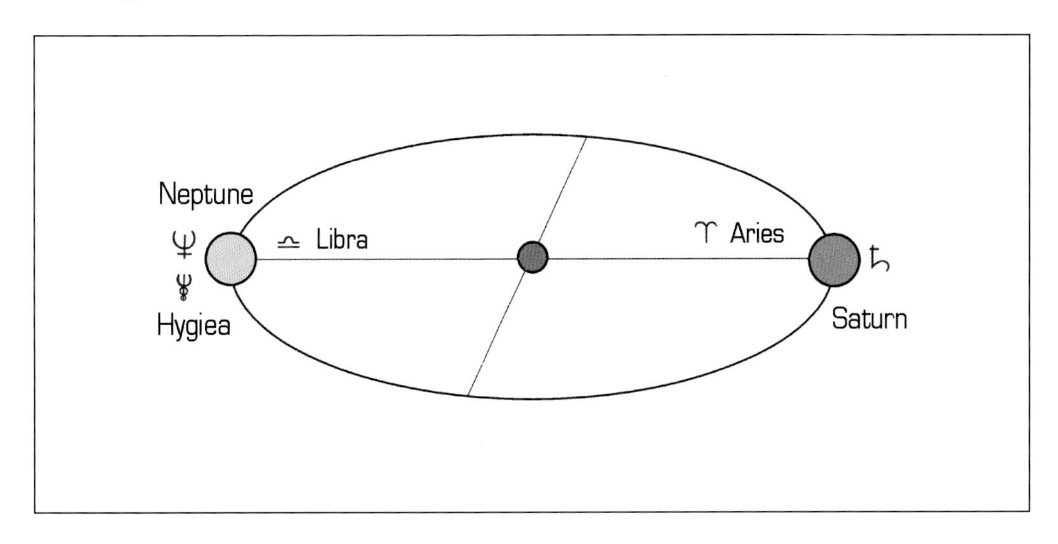

Saturn in Aries opposite Neptune conjunct Hygiea within Libra.

Oriental

Spleen yang deficiency with lung chi deficiency.

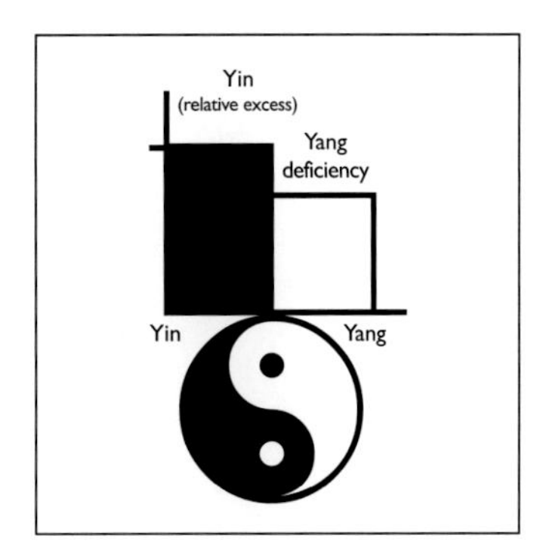

Particulars

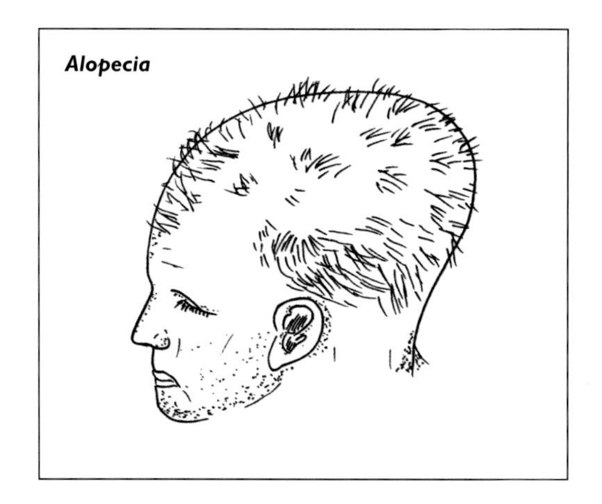

Hair loss can be of a non-scarring nature where the scalp skin looks normal, or scarring – where there is permanent loss of the hair follicles. There are many causes of alopecia, including adrenal androgen hormone imbalances (typically a male frontal recession), polycystic ovarian syndrome in women, autoimmune damage to the follicles (alopecia areata), or from cellulitis. The example shown is typical of an autoimmune cause.

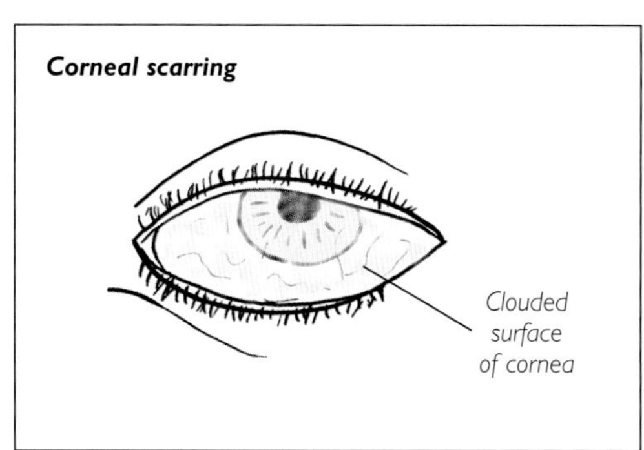

Corneal scarring can be the result of severe and chronic purulent conjunctivitis. This can especially be in the background of Stevens-Johnson syndrome, a disorder of severe immune mediated vasculitis (inflammation of the small blood vessels), often triggered from an allergic reaction to drugs. Other risk factors are other autoimmune diseases (e.g. Reiter's syndrome, rheumatoid arthritis), after radiation therapy and from chemical injuries to the eye (e.g. acids or alkalis). The results are adhesions of the eyelids to the eyeball, fibrosis of the surface of the conjunctiva and scarring with ulceration of the cornea. Cataracts often also form in the lens. Vision progressively deteriorates.

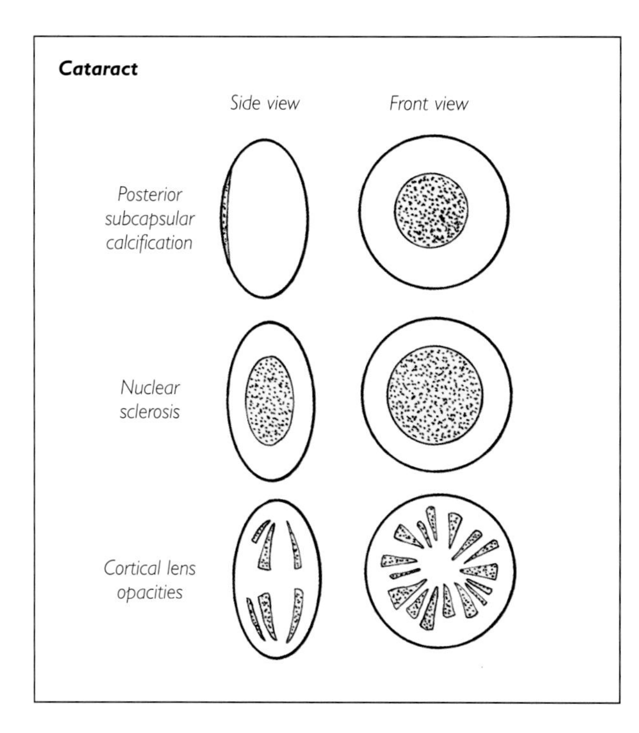

Cataracts are opacifications in the crystalline lens of the eye. They are a major cause of visual loss and blindness. Common causes include diabetes mellitus, nutritional deficiencies (such as of riboflavine), genetic disease, toxic or drug damage (especially steroids), trauma, after eye surgery or ultrasound/radiation exposure. Local eye disease, such as glaucoma, viral infection or retinal detachment, may also trigger cataract. Three types of cataract are shown. The posterior subscapular site of calcification is at the margin, whereas the nuclear sclerosis arises within the centre of the lens. Scattered regions of calcification appear in the cortical cataract example.

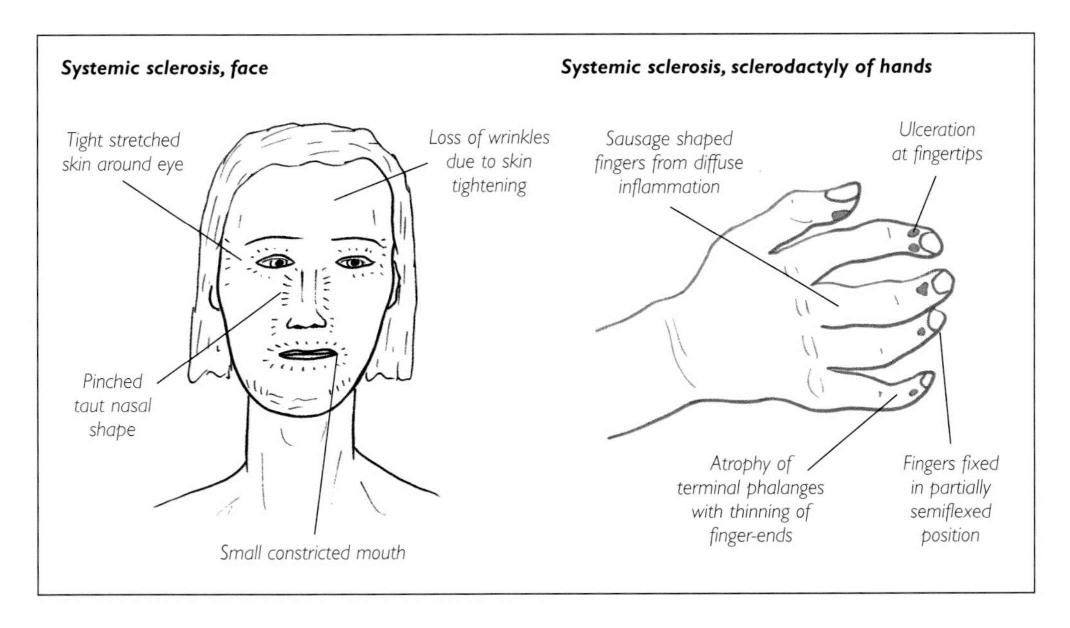

Systemic sclerosis (scleroderma) is characterised by hypertrophy and hyperplastic distortion of collagen fibres, vascular damage and auto-immune mediated inflammation. There is widespread damage to the skin, heart, lungs, kidneys, muscles, joint synovial lining and gut (especially the oesophagus). Symptoms include fever and weight loss. In the skin there is thickening, tightening and rigidity of the tissues, with a small constricted mouth, narrowed lips and skin atrophy. The fingers become fixed in a partially flexed position from the tight skin and tissues, the terminal phalanges atrophy and the fingertips can ulcerate. A serious consequence is damage to the glomeruli of the kidneys, with progressive and end-stage kidney failure.

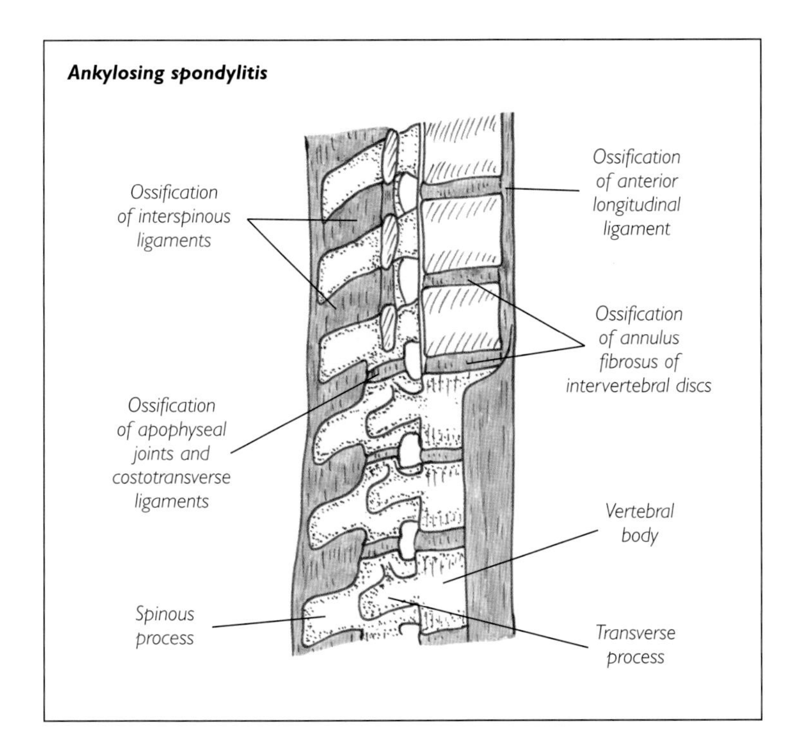

Ankylosing spondylitis is a type of spinal arthritis, mostly affecting young men. There are calcium bridges between the vertebral bodies that eventually rigidify the spine. The sacroiliac joints initially become inflamed. There is then inflammation spreading to the synovium of the various vertebral joints, destroying articular cartilage and triggering calcification into the joints and ligaments. Stiffening of the rib to vertebral joints will also reduce chest expansion and limit breathing.

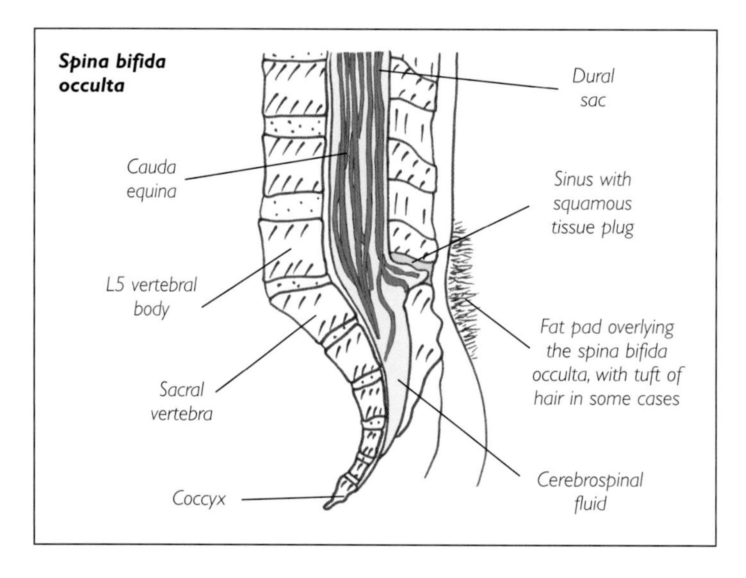

Spina bifida involves a congenital failure of fusion of the midline parts of the spinal column, and there is a wide spectrum of pathology. In spina bifida occulta there is failure of bone fusion, but without any abnormal displacement of the spinal cord. It is usually without significant neurological symptoms. Overlying the area of absent bone may lie a fat pad, sinus tract (which can sometimes extend to open to the skin) and/or a tuft of hair growth.

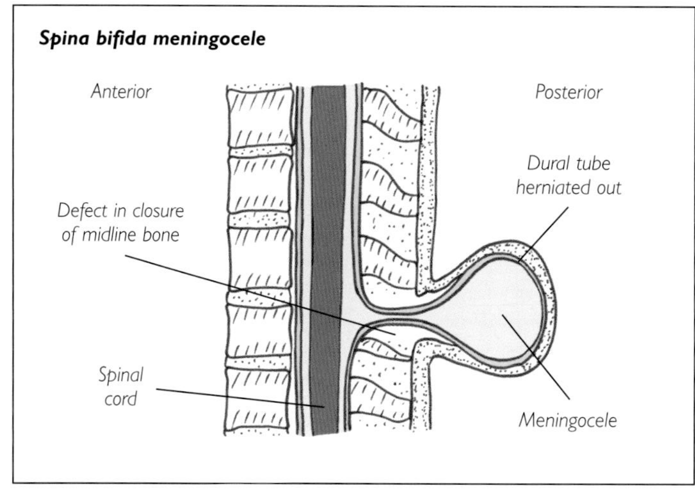

The extent of neurological symptoms is defined by the degree to which the spinal cord is displaced from its normal alignment. A meningocele is the least severe form of displacement. A cyst of subarachnoid CSF develops from meningeal tissues and extrudes through the defect in the vertebral column. A large lump will be clearly apparent protruding from the skin, this could be surgically resected and the defect closed by a dural graft.

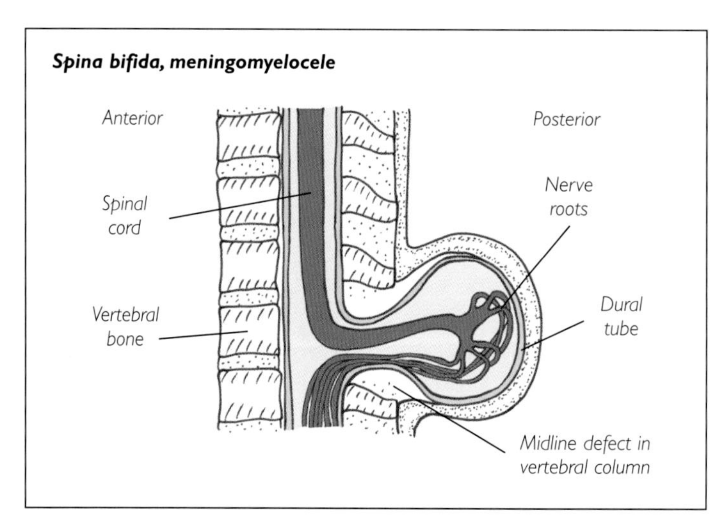

A more serious defect is the meningomyelocele, where the spinal cord and/or nerve roots have protruded through the posterior bone and skin defects. Nerve dysfunction can be severe, especially the more superior the problem is above the sacrum. Features can include paraplegia, loss of bowel and bladder control. Hydrocephalus is often also an associated feature.

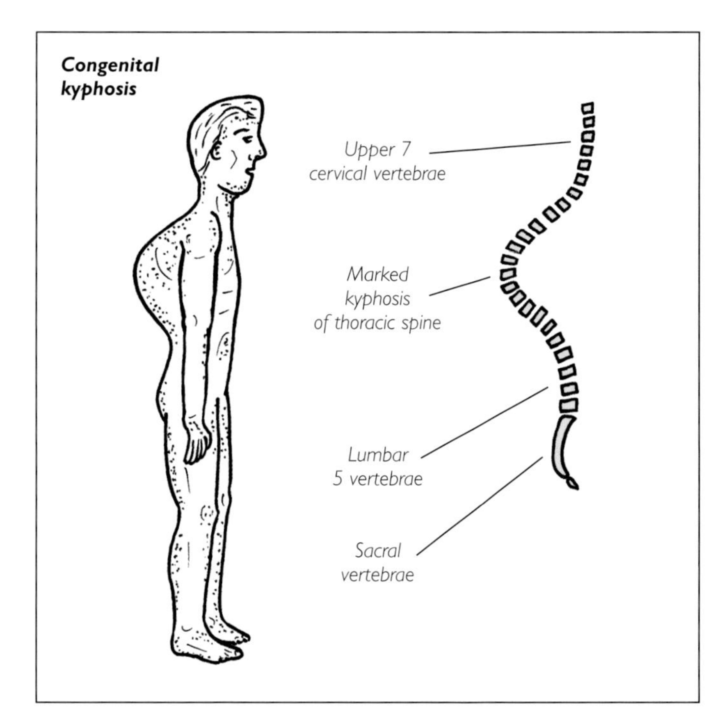

Congenital kyphosis is an embryologic distortion of the anterior-posterior growth of the vertebrae, whereas congenital scoliosis is a lateral growth distortion. A combined deformity, kyphoscoliosis can also occur. These disorders can sometimes be associated with neurological problems, such as paraplegia. Nerve damage is especially common when the kyphosis or kyphoscoliosis also features a rotation and dislocation of the spine – as this causes twisting of the spinal cord. In severe kyphosis, the hump is abruptly angled and the spinal cord can become fixed and damaged at the apex.

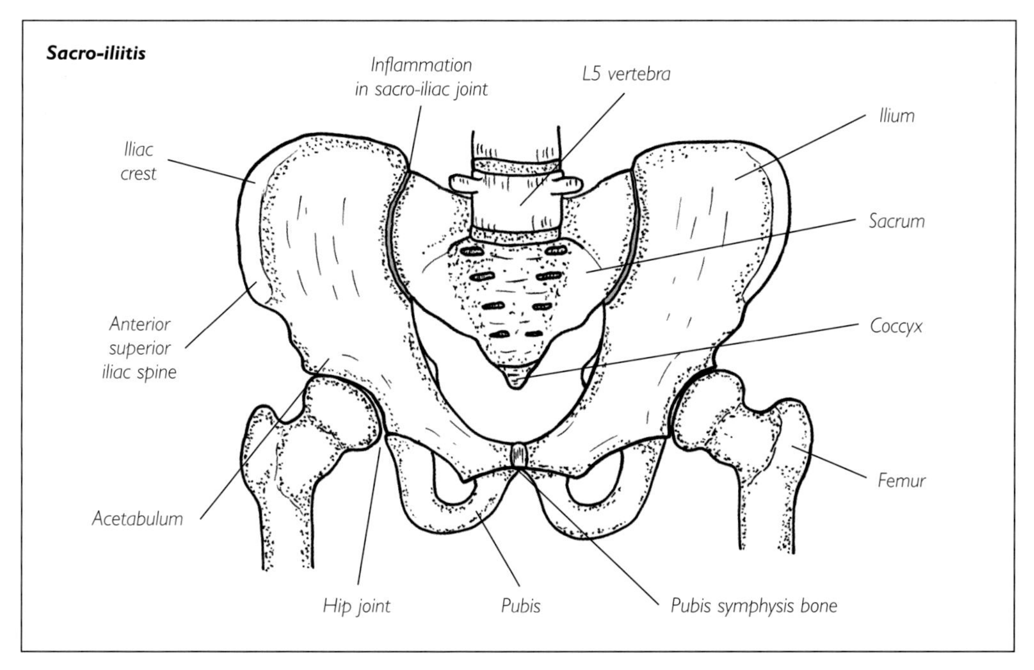

Sacro-iliitis is inflammation at the joint between the sacrum and pelvis (ilium) and can be unilateral or bilateral. There is pain and tenderness at this location in the back, it is associated with a variety of arthritis disorders known as seronegative spondyloarthropathies (not having the same serum antibody profile as rheumatoid arthritis). Examples of these are psoriatic arthritis, reactive arthritis, ankylosing spondylitis and enteropathic arthritis (associated with ulcerative colitis or Crohn's disease of the bowel).

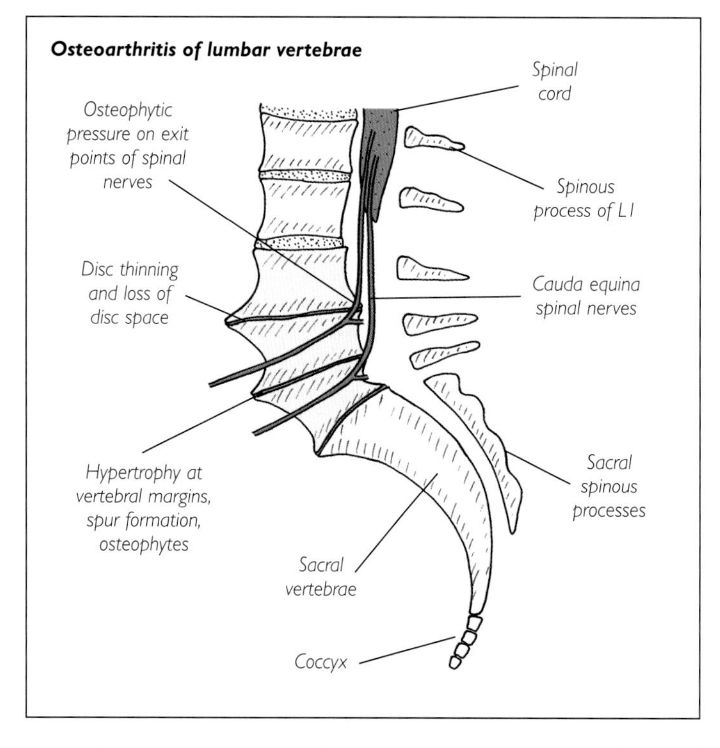

Osteoarthritis is a non-inflammatory disease of deterioration of the joint cartilage and formation of new irregular bone at the joint margins (bony spurs known as osteophytes). It is especially common in the spine. The intervertebral discs lose water and proteoglycans, with fibrous brittle changes in the inner nucleus pulposus and outer annulus fibrosus. The disc becomes thinner and cracks in the outer annulus can cause herniation of the inner core outwards. The vertebral bodies on each side are compressed toward each other with osteophytes at the edges. The facet joints between the vertebrae lose cartilage and develop osteophytes as well. Compression and irritation of the nerve roots is then a frequent occurrence, with pain, numbness or weakness in the nerve distribution (e.g. sciatica along the back of the leg).

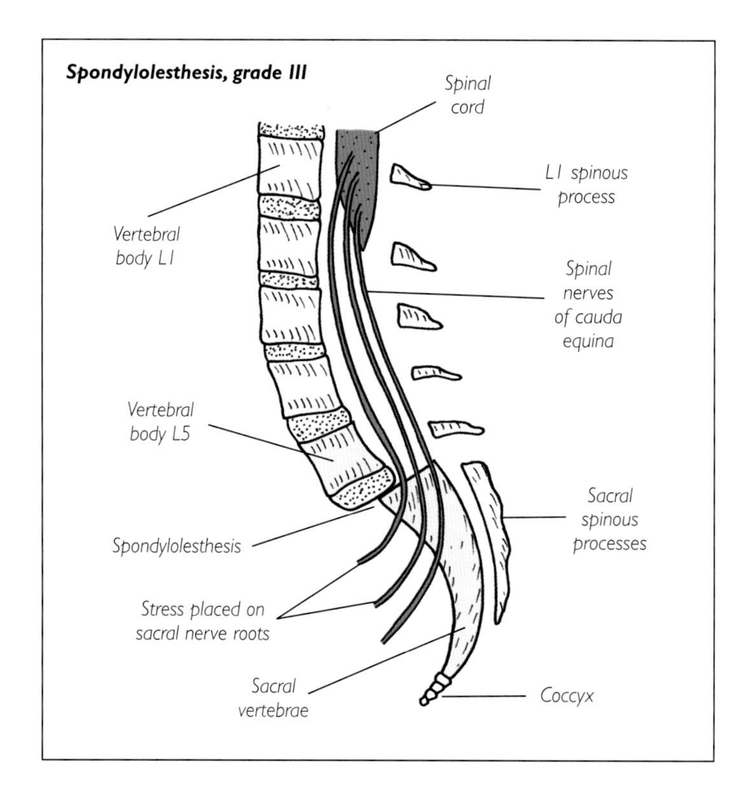

Spondylolysis is characterised by the destruction of the joints between the vertebral bodies (usually between L5 and S1), either by stress fractures or congenital abnormalities of bone development. Spondylolesthesis then results, where typically the L5 vertebral body slips forwards out of alignment from the sacral vertebrae below. There may be no symptoms, but pain, distortion of hip and leg movements and nerve root compression (with e.g. motor or sensory problems to the pelvis and legs) can result. Stabilisation of the spinal area may be needed with a brace, cast or by surgery.

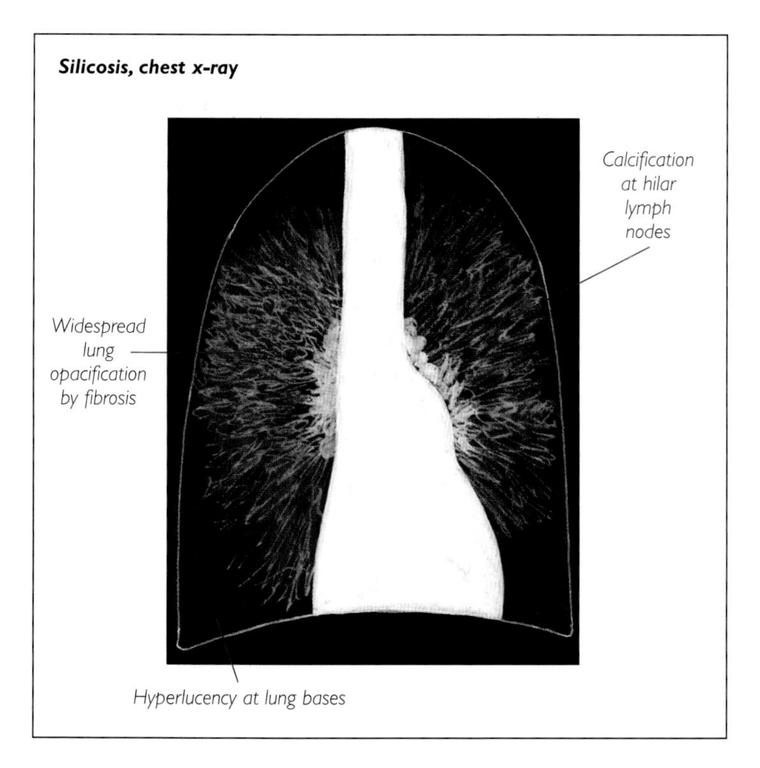

In this chest x-ray of severe lung silicosis there is shown extensive fibrotic opacification (whitening) of the lung tissue, with calcification at the hilar lymph nodes. Note the disease relatively spares the lung bases, which therefore appear dark or hyperlucent.

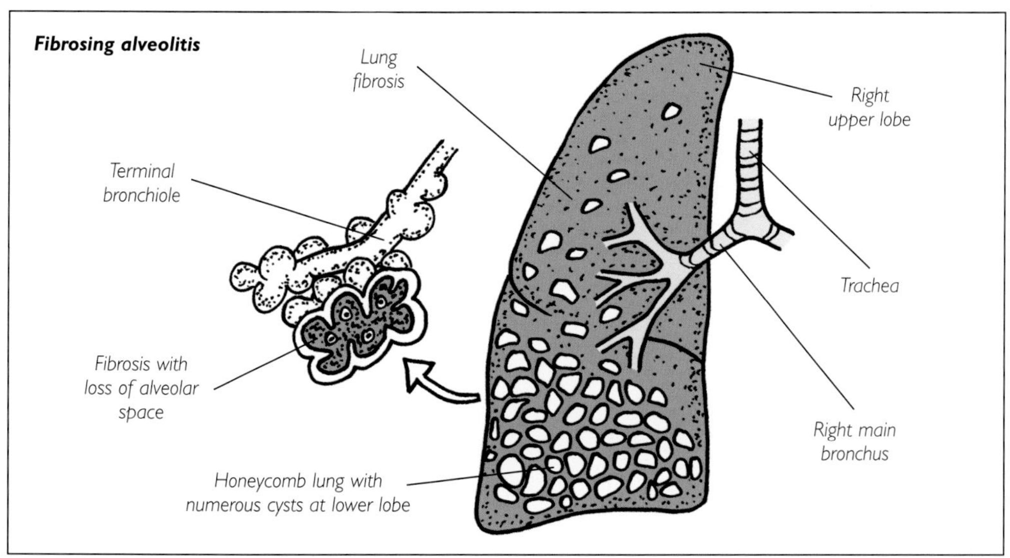

Fibrosing alveolitis (also called interstitial pulmonary fibrosis) is a group of diseases leading to chronic and progressive lung failure and secondary right-sided heart failure. There are many causes, e.g. autoimmune connective diseases (such as rheumatoid arthritis, systemic sclerosis), drugs (such as amiodarone), and certain viral infections. There is inflammation within the alveoli and small airways (bronchioles), mostly autoimmune in nature. This leads to fibrosis, loss of the alveolar spaces and cystic destruction of the lungs – especially at the lower lung lobes. There is a restrictive defect of respiration with hypoxia (low arterial oxygenation) which causes hypertension of the pulmonary arterial supply and right-sided heart strain with failure.

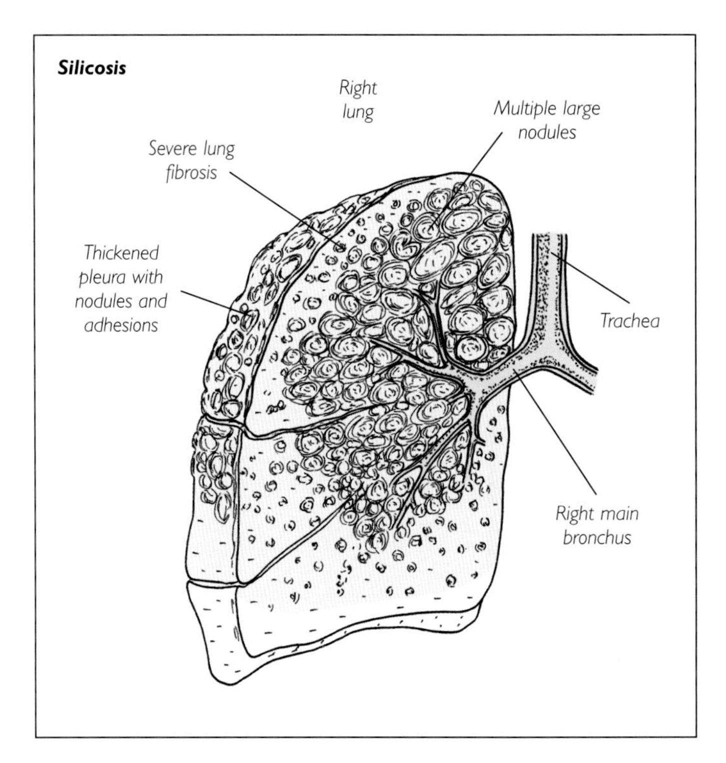

Silicosis is an occupational disease, e.g. in ceramic manufacture (flint), various building industries (use of sandstone). Free silica particles have been inhaled and deposited within the lungs. Nodules are formed by the inflammatory reaction of phagocytic macrophages and a fibroblastic cell reaction to lay down fibrous material. Large nodular masses can form – particularly within the upper lobes (and with cystic or bullous changes in some cases). There is breathlessness on effort, cough and chronic sputum, the risk of secondary infections, pulmonary arterial hypertension and heart failure in the long-term.

Related images

p.96 Growth chart
p.98 Genital underdevelopment
p.40 Anterior pituitary tumour (for growth hormone deficiency)
p.574 Peripheral neuropathy
p.571 Retinal degeneration
p.501 Otitis media, glue ear
p.501 Otosclerosis
p.265 & p.503 Toothache and abscess
p.408 Sinusitis and nasal polyps
p.505-506 Tooth gum recession
p.103 Tonsillitis
p.90 Subdiaphragmatic abscess
p.490 Urethral abscess
p.368 Abscess, buttock
p.164 Scoliosis
p.172 Osteogenesis imperfecta
p.171 Osteoporosis
p.411 Acne vulgaris
p.507 Coeliac disease
p.19 Constipation, faecal impaction
p.375 Autoimmune disease
p.527-528 Headaches

SPIGELIA ANTHELMIA

Original

'Spigelia and dynamic of the rhythmic system', by Caroline Hamilton (plant) & Katherine Mynott (organ system). The liver, which is the seat of the etheric body and the metabolism, is closer to the earthly realm. A pyramid within this organ symbolises its connection to sacred etheric Earth energy. The brain (the seat of activity of the nerve-sensory system) is receiving a down-pouring of light to symbolise its function as a clear mirror for receiving the thoughts of the higher self. The heart and lung system are wrapped with wings to symbolise their rhythmic nature. There is a tidal ebb and flow from the chest that provides an interface between the metabolic and nervous system at this region. Thus, each time the heart contracts (systole) and the lungs inhale, they open to the impulse of the nerve-sensory system. Each time there is heart relaxation (diastole) and lung exhalation, there is an opening to the metabolic system. The plant Spigelia is juxtaposed with an image of the rhythmic system, to indicate its therapeutic effect at this region. Should metabolic toxicity affect the heart then cardiomyopathy (heart muscle damage) is the usual problem. On the other hand, nervous tension or stress leads to spastic heart contraction and the pattern of angina. Ultimately, effective therapy of heart disorders also requires strengthening of the Ego or Self within the heart, enabling this 'I' to control the astral and etheric body into harmonious action.

Astrology

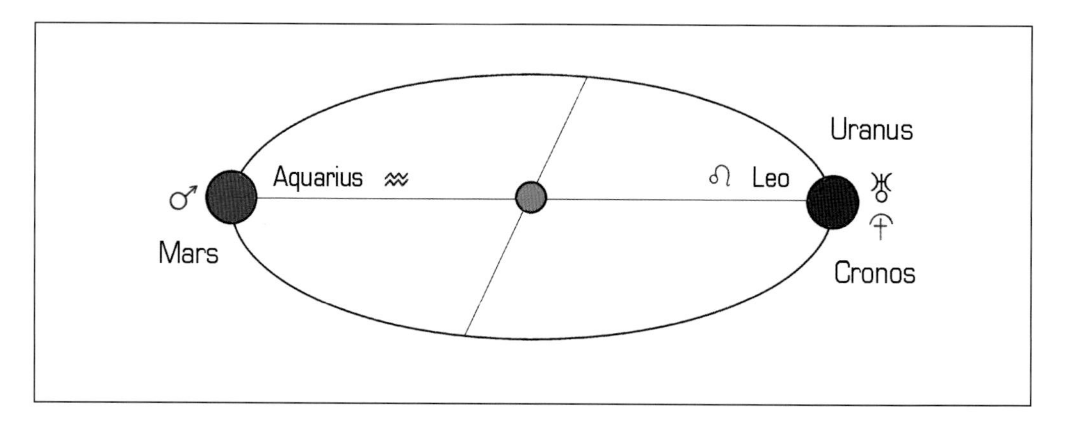

Mars in Aquarius, opposite Uranus conjunct Cronos within Leo.

Oriental

Spleen chi deficiency, with phlegm-fire harassing heart and rebellious chi of heart.

Related images

p.227 Periodic malarial fever
p.144 Coronary artery disease & p.144, p.147 Angiography and angioplasty
p.145 & p.451 Angina and acute myocardial infarction
p.299 Atrial fibrillation & p.82 Pacemaker ECG
p.264 Multifocal extrasystoles/ectopic beats & p.300 Heart failure, right-sided
p.383 Ventricular arrhythmias
p.148 Restrictive pericarditis & p.129 Pericardial effusion
p.3 Trigeminal neuralgia & p.4 Bell's palsy
p.527-528 Headaches, p.319 Glaucoma, p.318 Iritis
p.442 Retinal detachment & p.232 Ptosis, oculomotor nerve damage

SPONGIA TOSTA

Original

'Spongia and stellar geometry', by Caroline Hamilton. Several types of sponges are shown upon the sea-floor, some being depiction of ancient forms from the Archean and Cambrian periods of world evolution. They include Hydroconus (Coralomorph class, reddish forms on far right), Nochoroicyathus (of Archaeocyath class, orange tubular forms on far left), Cambrocyathellus (Archaeocyath, bluish tree-like forms in the background), Leucettusa lancifer (a modern calcareous sponge, the greenish squat vase-like forms at front left), Euplectella (Venus flower-basket tubular form, a Hexactinellida glass sponge, greenish tubes on front right) and Niphates digitalis (Desmosponge class, front middle with the geometries at its mouth). It is this last class containing the source of the homoeopathic remedy, the Bath sponge. Above the seabed is a swirling mass of cosmically ordered information, arranged around a central universal point and symbolised by geometrical shapes and symbols – the corporeal manifestation of which is provided for by the sponge. Some of these glyphs represent astrological planets and bodies (such as asteroids) and zodiacal signs. Others are symbols used in alchemy, representing the divine nature of minerals. The hexagonal nature of silica is indicated as a channel of six-sided molecules connecting the cosmos and sponges. In this manner, the sponge has enabled the descent and organisation (into an etheric matrix) of spiritual and cosmic blueprints. Without this activity, the subsequent body forms within evolution would not be able to developmentally progress further.

Astrology

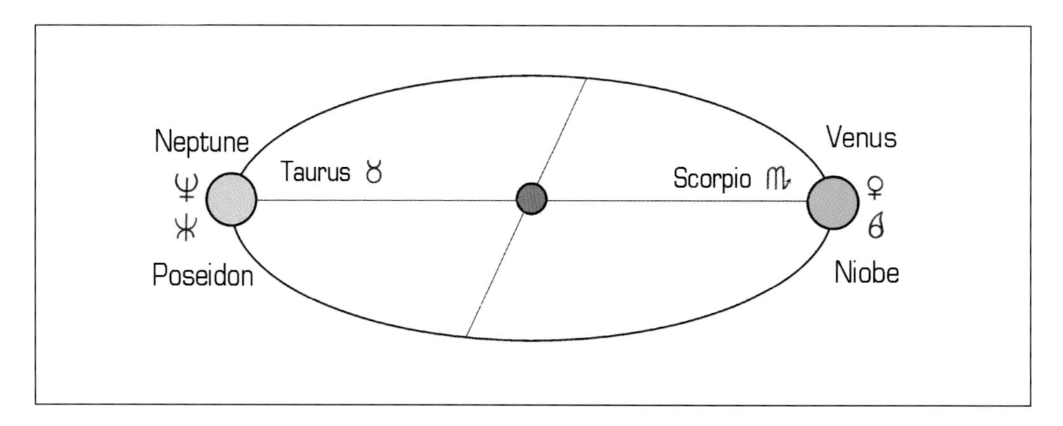

Venus conjunct Niobe within Scorpio, opposite Neptune conjunct Poseidon within Taurus.

Oriental

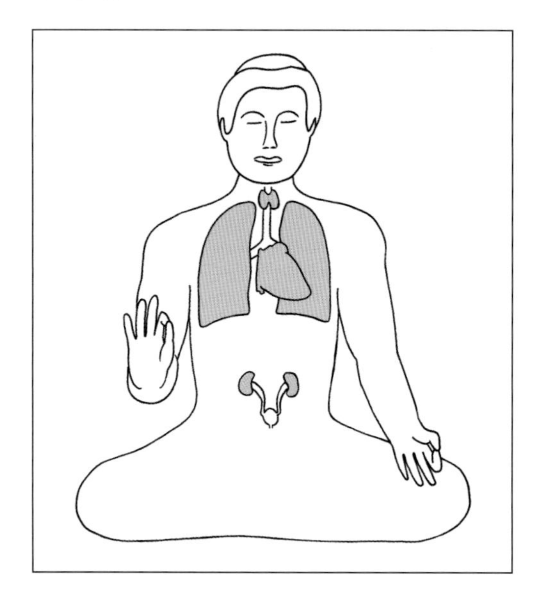

Kidney yang deficiency, with water overflowing within heart, lungs. Damp-phlegm in throat/thyroid.

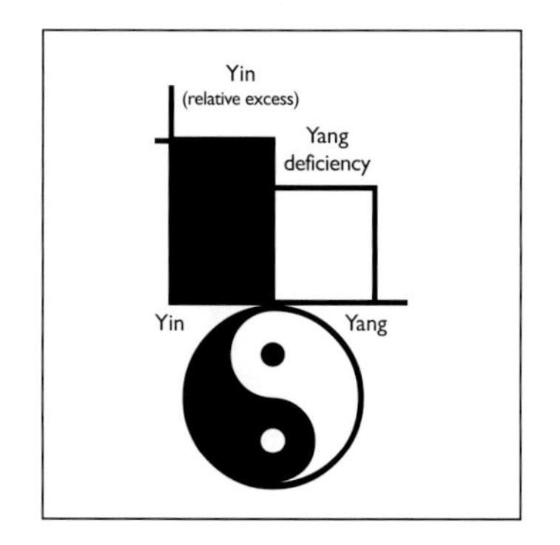

Related images

p.729-732 Thyroid disease & p.375 Autoimmune disease
p.4 Croup, p.72 Asthma
p.145 & p.451 Angina and acute myocardial infarction
p.299 Atrial fibrillation & p.300 Heart failure, right-sided
p.301 Ankle odema & p.300 Pulmonary odema
p.473 & p.742 Orchitis
p.98 Genital underdevelopment & p.97 Undescended testes

Original

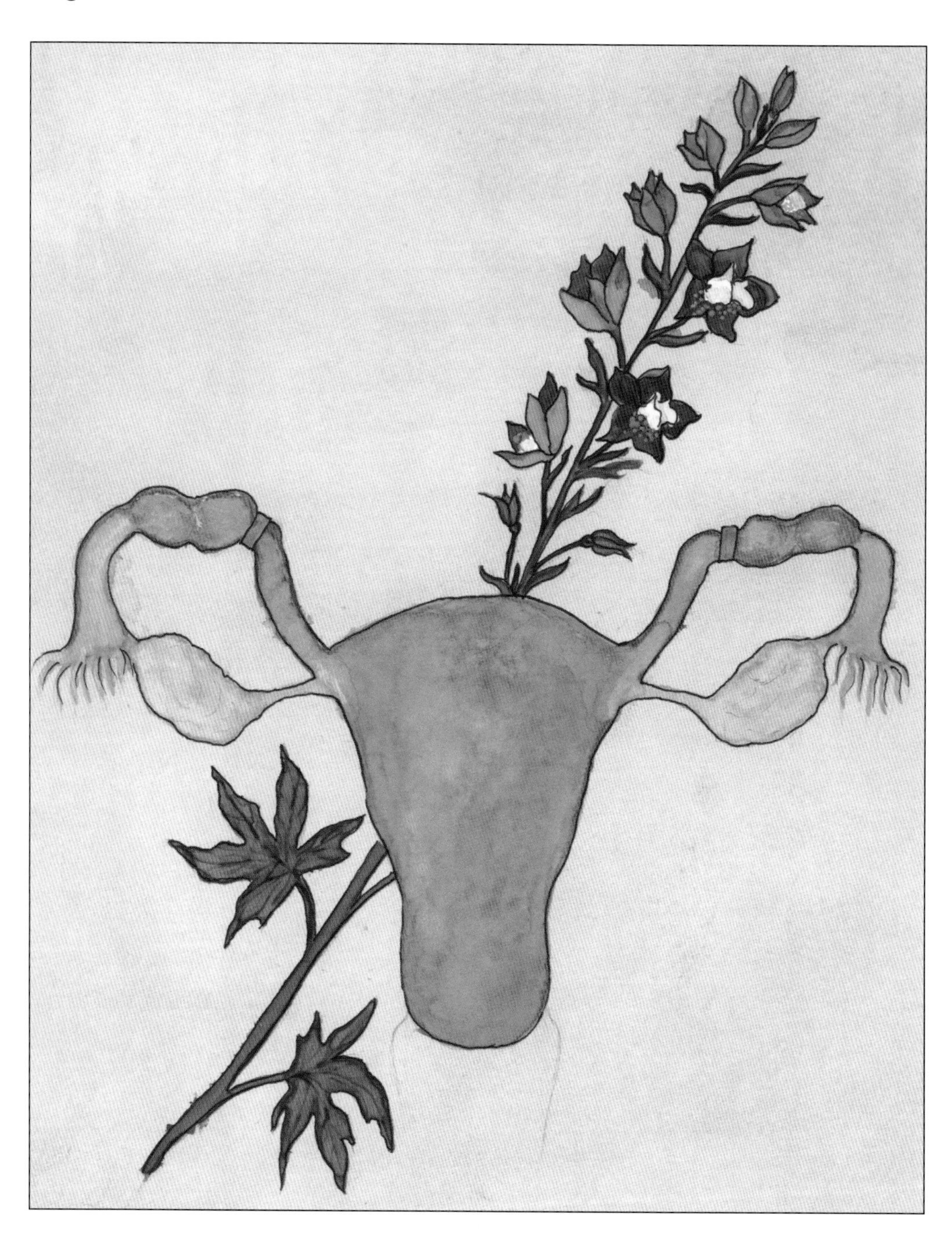

'Staphysagria and clipping of female fertility', by Nadine Kardesler. The plant is depicted alongside the female reproductive system; note the central uterus with adjacent fallopian tubes with ovaries (the ovary is supported on the uterus by the ovarian ligament as shown). The therapeutic indication of the remedy for obstruction of the sacral chakra and female fertility is indicated by the bilateral clips placed at the fallopian tubes.

'Staphysagria and the Abduction of Persephone', by Antonia Chetwynd. Persephone was the beautiful daughter of the Greek goddess Demeter, who ruled over crops and fertility. Hades/Pluto had snatched her away; his brother Zeus doing nothing to prevent the kidnap and so in effect giving the girl to the Lord of the Underworld. The only being that had heard anything was Hecate, a guardian sorceress to the Underworld, and Lord Helius the Sun had witnessed the event. Eventually Demeter (shown on the left imploring the Heavens for the return of her daughter) found out the details, and in her anger and grief she retaliated by causing wasting of the harvests. Eventually Zeus and the other gods appealed to Hades to release Persephone, but the Dark Lord tricked the girl into eating food of Hades, shown as pomegranate fruit. It was eventually agreed that Persephone would reside one-third of the year as Queen in Hades, the other two-thirds with her mother – during which the Earth is fertile again.

STRAMONIUM

Museum

Rockwell Kent (1882-1971), 'Nightmare'. © Philadelphia Museum of Art: Print Club of Philadelphia Permanent Collection, 1949 (1949-45-1). Kent's art depicted humanity in some heroic pose, interpreting life's destiny and existential meaning. Humanity is shown struggling to capture ultimate reality or penetrate some dark mystery. The painting evokes the Bottomless Pit or Abyss, also known as Soul-Well. The person is falling into this hellish place. This portal belongs to the dark forces (the Beast, Satan, Devil etc.), a pit with no bottom (deriving from the Greek 'abussos' of 'a'– not, & 'bussos'– bottom) with souls in purgatory. Parallel realities from here travel into individual personal subconscious. In Revelations it is said: 'And the fifth angel sounded, and I saw a star from heaven fallen unto the earth: and there was given to him the key to the pit of the abyss. And he opened the pit of the abyss; and there went up a smoke out of the furnace; and the sun and the air were darkened by reason of the smoke of the pit.' In Cabbalistic lore the Abyss is the Qliphoth, containing the husks or shells of waste material that cycles of evolution periodically shed. Thus Luciferic forces are the retarding Moon-based beings that have remained behind with general world and human evolution, to provide the resistance against which spiritual evolution proceeds. Such creatures are the laggard spiritual beings left over from previous cycles of humanity.

FOLLOWING PAGE. Francisco de Goya, 'The Sleep of Reason produces Monsters'. © Philadelphia Museum of Art: The Smith, Kline, and French Laboratory Collection, 1949 (1949-97-9). The text caption from the 'Prado' etching version is: "Fantasy abandoned by reason produces impossible monsters: united with her, she is the mother of the arts and the origin of their marvels." This is plate 43 of the Caprichos, a set of 80 prints covering various dark subjects such as abuse, witchcraft and superstition. It is a self-portrait, and revealed the mood of the final years of the artist's life, as a dreaming man surrounded by phantoms. Goya became deaf after a serious illness in 1792, and he became increasingly isolated from others. His works show him to have entered the brink of madness.

El sueño
dela razon
produce
monstruos.

Original

'Stramonium and trapped souls in the realm of shadow', by Caroline Hamilton. Soul fragments are shown stuck within a lower astral plane and subconsciousness, either between or during earthly lives. The plant assists their release, also indicated by the spiralling light shown ascending through its centre. Expanded views of a fruit exterior and cross sectional are shown in the corners.

Astrology

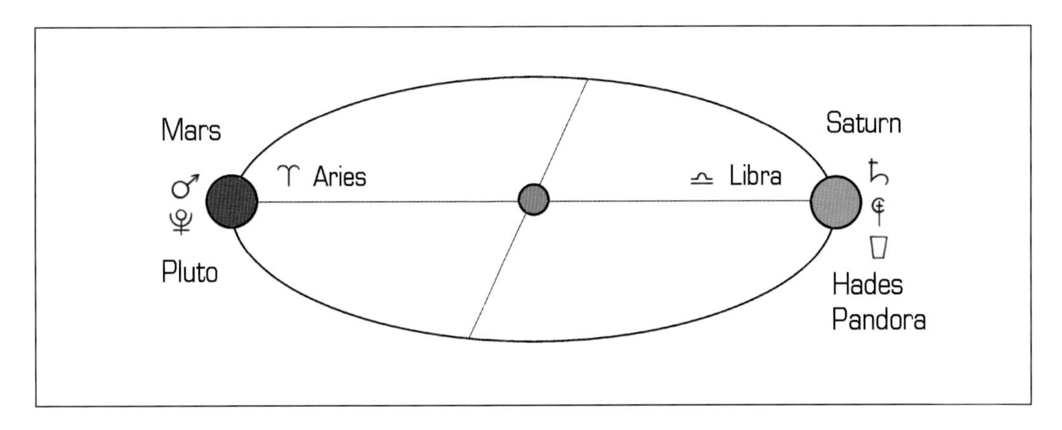

Mars conjunct Pluto within Aries, opposite Saturn conjunct Hades and Pandora within Libra.

Oriental

Liver heat, with interior wind affecting the brain and muscles.

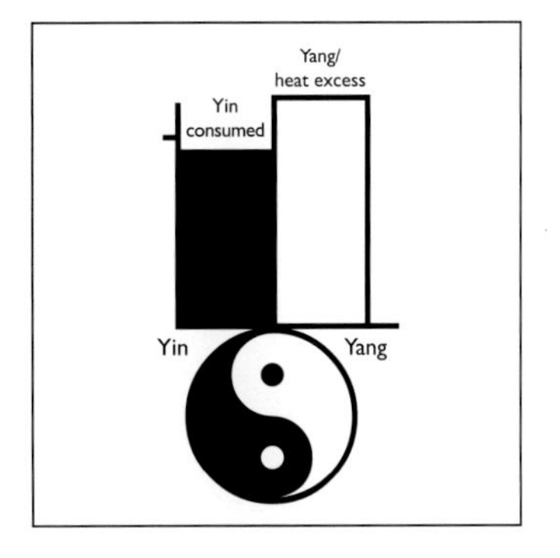

Related images

p.233-234 Epilepsy
p.10 Torticollis & p.233 Squint
p.479-480 Rabies infection & p.18 Parkinson's disease
p.232 & p.343 Multiple sclerosis & p.35 Spinal myelitis
p.277 Motor neurone disease & p.586 Muscle wasting
p.285-286 Cerebrovascular accident & p.202 Glasgow coma scale
p.578 Hypothalamic tumour, p.752 Pineal tumour & p.40-41 Pituitary tumour
p.528 Migraine visual aura

SULPHUR

Original

'Sulphur and descent of human warmth into the subterranean realm', by Katherine Mynott. The warming nature of sulphur is evident in the fire, lava and radiations of heat throughout this illustration. The higher aspect of sulphur above has descended into human bodily form at the base.

Astrology

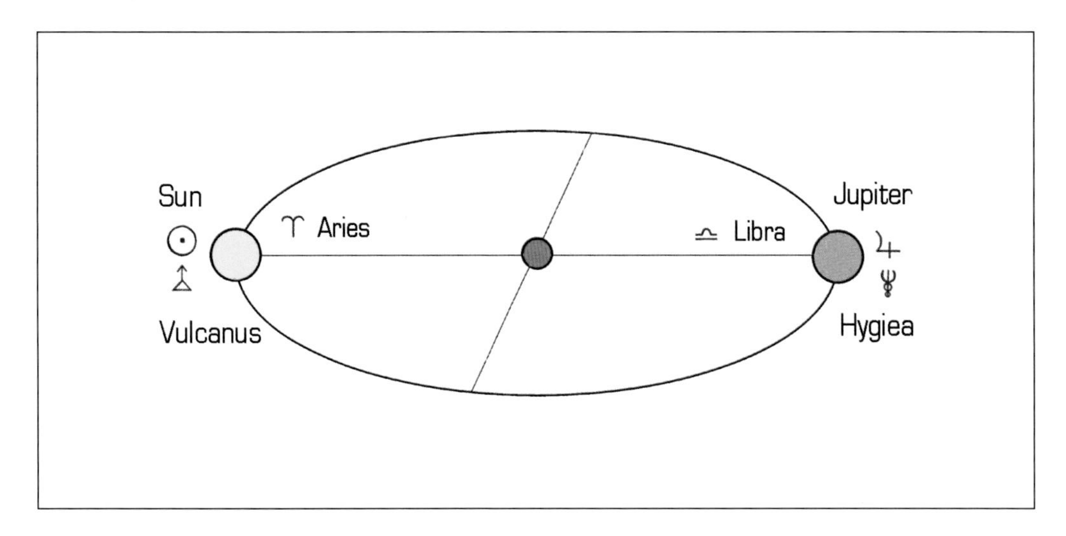

Sun conjunct Vulcanus within Aries, opposite Jupiter conjunct Hygiea within Libra.

Oriental

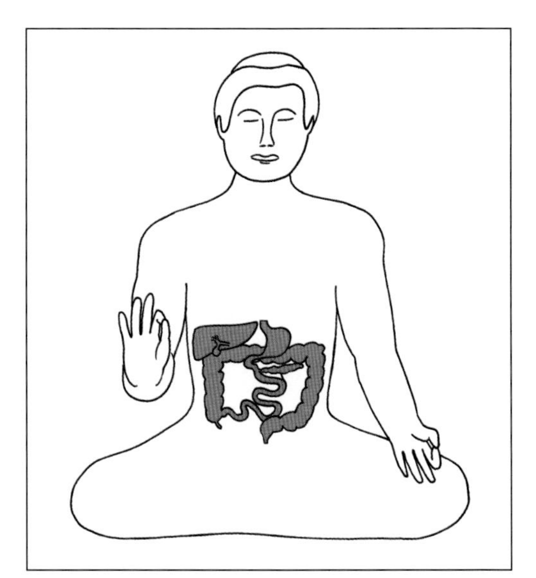

Stomach fire, with damp-heat within intestines and liver, gallbladder.

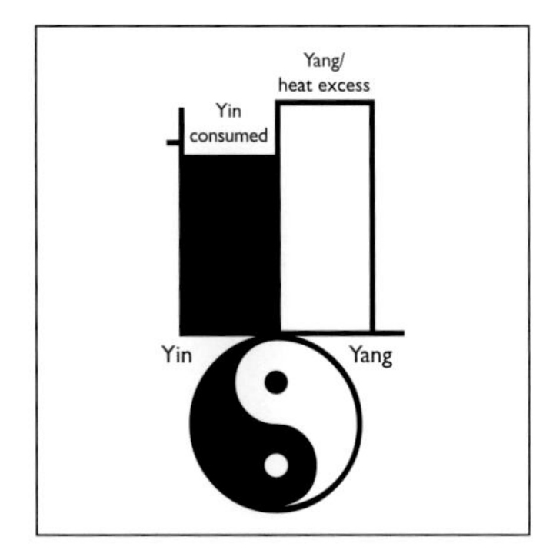

Related images

p.758 Varicose veins and ulcer
p.542 Portal hypertension
p.640 Peripheral arterial disease
p.541 Peptic ulcer
p.36 Hiatus hernia
p.543 Haemorrhoids
p.561-562 Hepatitis
p.222 Fatty liver
p.222-223 Gallstones
p.223 Jaundice
p.133 Liver failure and ascites
p.470 Pancreatic failure
p.156 Worm gut infestation
p.494 Crohn's disease
p.507 Coeliac disease
p.71 Eczema
p.75 Psoriasis
p.650 Acne rosacea
p.411 Acne vulgaris
p.721 Lichen planus
p.56 Conjunctivitis
p.454 Lymphangitis
p.527-528 Headaches
p.10 Sciatica
p.270 Gout and pseudogout
p.339 & p.660 Osteoarthritis
p.691 Paget's disease
p.619-624 Rheumatoid arthritis
p.347 Polymyalgia rheumatica

then took place. Job's test is a test to be experienced by all of humanity at varying stage of evolution. This is the reversal of disease within humanity, and the clearing of all miasms – but will only be finalised in the last root races and rounds of evolution, far in the future. Job's story therefore pre-empts this crisis point. The story also illustrates the infection by Luciferic forces into the human body and bloodstream. This occurred coincidental with the Fall from Grace. However, such shadow forces were required to provide the impetus and resistance for further evolution. Later stages of humanity will be able to finally clear these Luciferic elements out of the body, leading to a final resolution of the syphilitic miasm within the race.

Of interest, the modern allopathic diagnosis of Job's syndrome is a particular type of staphylococcal-based skin infection, with severe and recurrent infections, unusual eczema-like eruptions and abnormal white cell function with raised immunoglobulin levels of IgE. It is rare and inherited by a dominant pattern. There are also severe lung and joint infections (and any other internal body part may be affected) from the invasion of the pathogenic staphylococcus. Deformities and fractures of the skeleton can occur. Children may retain their milk teeth, resulting in two sets of dentititon at the same time. Although antibiotic treatment is frequent, there is a need for prevention by maintaining good personal hygiene, skin care and preventing skin injury with the invasion of the skin surface flora. 15-40% of healthy people carry Staphylococcus aureus bacteria on their skin, considered in these cases as normal commensals. In Staphylococcal skin infections (of which Job's syndrome is a rare variant) these bacteria either become pathogenic, or the skin is breached with the internal invasion of the bacteria. The very high levels of IgE in Job's syndrome are reminiscent of the duality principle or reacting inappropriately (i.e. without grace) to the breach of the skin defences (the inflictions by Satan's darts).

It is noteworthy that latent neurosyphilis is a particular problem in immunosuppressed patients (typically in HIV positive AIDs). The spinal cord and brain becomes affected by meningeal inflammation, ulcerative damage and tumours – leading to loss of nerve function and/or cognitive deterioration.

FOLLOWING PAGE. Richard Tennant Cooper, 'Provocative woman', watercolour, with gouache and pen. © Wellcome Library, London. An enticing naked young woman lies on a bed, with death as a cloaked skeleton sitting at her side. Meanwhile a naked man walks away from the bed with his head bowed, as if shamed or despairing – a typical mental state of the syphilitic miasm. The crowd of diseased and dying people he is joining appear to suffer from syphilis, which he has also just contracted from his sexual encounter. This also highlights the essential nature of the disease – that it is caused by excessive and inappropriate mixing of genetic, blood and sexual fluids. This leads to dissolution of Self into a collective blend of the selves of other partners throughout time. The sense of Ego becomes fragmented, lost and confused in the morass.

COOPER

Stephen Blankaart (author). 'Treatments for syphilis by sweating, inhalation and cautery.' Engraving of title page (with variations) to the Dutch edition of 'Die belagert une entsetzte Venus' published by J. F. Gleditsch, Leipzig 1690. © Wellcome Library, London.

Original

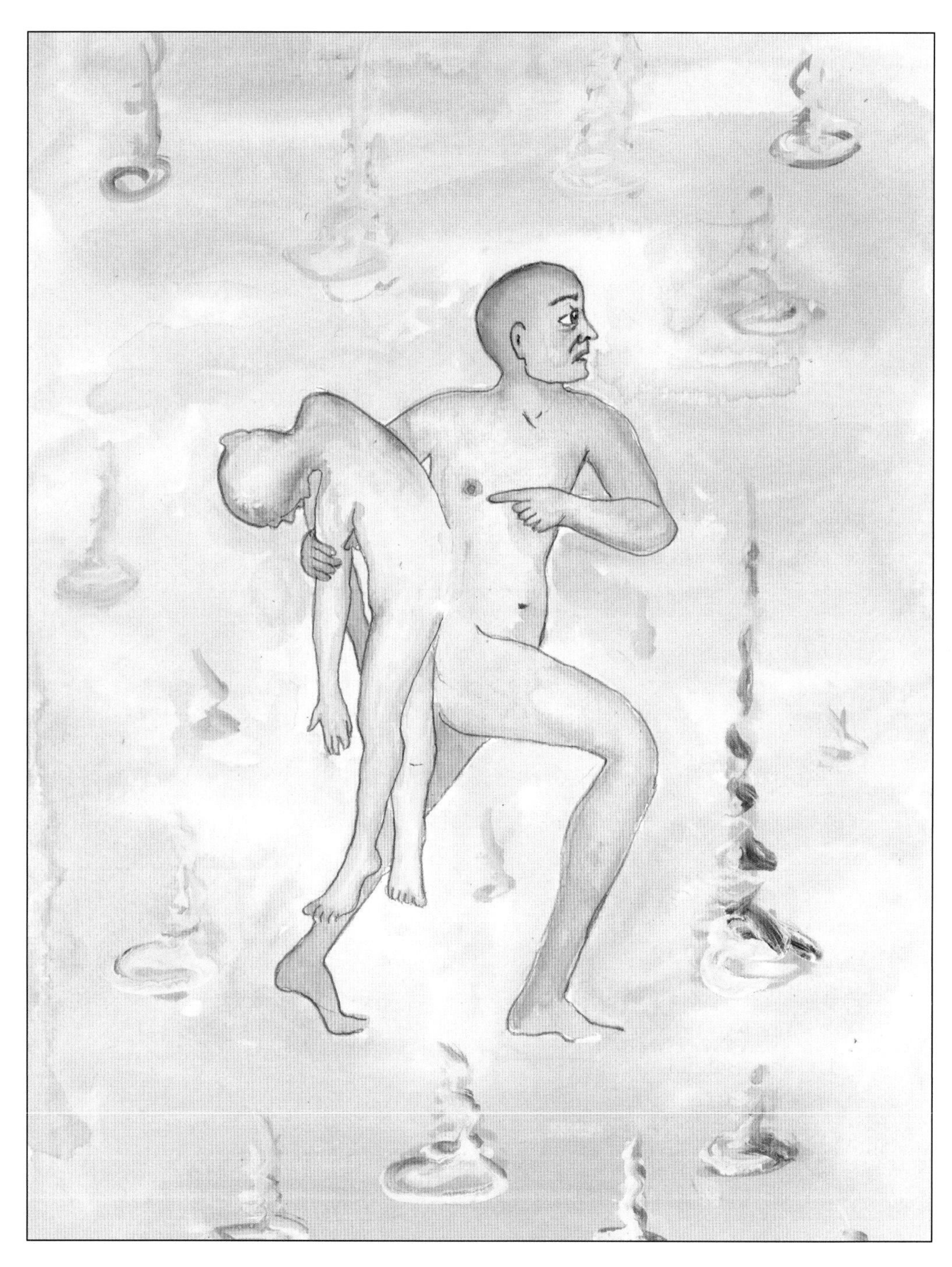

'Syphilinum and carriage of the dead', by Antonia Chetwynd. Several alchemical and esoteric depictions of the mercury process and the miasm of syphilis showed a live person bound to and carrying a dead person. This is also exteriorised by the nature of Mercury as psychopomp (see p.492). Note the spirals suggestive of spirochete bacteria around the figure.

'Syphilinum and the imprisonment of souls', by Tessa Gaynn. The possessed and fragmented nature of the syphilitic psyche is represented here by the image of a prison yard, the inmates drearily walking in a circle as exercise. Unnoticed above are ghostly and malefic entities, perpetuating the negative thinking of the trapped souls. The image is based on that by Gustavé Dore's 'Newgate - Exercise Yard' in London, A Pilgrimage (1872).

'Birth of Hercules - defeat of the two serpents', by Yubraj Sharma. Hercules (Herakles) represents the son of god, his divine attributes re-connecting humanity back to a cosmic vision. The spiritual aspirant may study his labours as a portrayal of the Path of Discipleship. Ultimately he becomes a world saviour, pre-empting the life of Christ. The twelve labours are reflections of initiations within the zodiac, from Aries to Pisces (anticlockwise). Any personal competitive or selfish desires are cleared. The name 'Herakles' means the glory of Hera, indicating the light of the soul shines forth. Within Hercules, as within all humans, resided the inherent duality of Mother-Earthly form and the Father-Divine image. He had to remove himself from all extraneous identification, to find the true essence of soul within. There should be no one-sided character. The duality within Hercules was compounded by the fact that he was one of twins. His brother was born of an earthly mortal father, whilst he was born of a god, Zeus. Two natures met within him, the mortal and the divine. A well developed personality and apparatus (physical, emotional and mental) is able to master all dualistic impulses from the material and spiritual realms. The story of his birth begins with Zeus impersonating King Amphitryon whilst away at war, and thereby laying with his wife Alcmene. Zeus lengthened the intercourse to 36 hours (equivalent to 3 nights) by ordering Helius the Sun to quench his solar fires and become unyoked from the Hours. He ordered Hermes to cause the Moon to travel slowly, and Sleep to make humans so drowsy they did not notice the delayed passing of time. After that 'night', Amphitryon returned from battle victorious and also lay with his wife, leading to a twin conception. Nine months later, Zeus boasted to his wife Hera that he had fathered a mighty son to be called Hercules, to rule the noble house of Perseus. Hera, however, tricked Zeus into promising that the first royal son born before nightfall would be king, and then caused the birth of Hercules to be delayed. The prophecy of kingship was defeated, but this was required in order to later propel Hercules onto the spiritual path rather than that of mundane kingship. When Hercules was 8-10 months of age, Hera caused two serpents to destroy the child in his cradle. His mortal twin brother Iphicles cried out in terror and tried to escape. However, Hercules, without any fear, took great delight in strangling them to death. By this means Amphitryon knew which of his sons was from the god, and sought out the oracle for further advice. The defeat of the serpents is a test of awakening, and of revealing the true nature of the personality-soul unit within. It represents the conquest of duality. He strangled the serpent of matter, thus the corporeal realm no longer imprisoned him. He also strangled the serpent of illusion, representing the karmic binds met by the soul when living outside the laws of spirit and cosmos. Indeed, a third serpent could eventually be revealed to him, representing the inner nature of wisdom.

FOLLOWING PAGE. 'Syphilinum and the choice of Hercules', by Antonia Chetwynd. This is the description of Virtue and Pleasure, making their appearances to Hercules as two beautiful women. Hercules was at last free, having completed his twelve arduous tasks. However, he did not know what to do with the rest of his life, and one day he retired into a desert, where the silence and solitude enabled his meditations. Whilst musing, much perplexed on the path in life he should choose, he saw two large women approach. One of them had a very noble and graceful manner; her beauty was natural, her person clean, her eyes cast towards the ground with an agreeable reserve, her motion full of modesty, and her clothes as white as snow. The other had a great deal of health and floridness in her countenance, which she had helped with makeup, and endeavoured to appear more graceful by her gestures. She had a wonderful confidence and colourful dress to show her complexion to an advantage. She cast her eyes upon herself and on those that were present, to see how they liked her. Upon her nearer approach to Hercules, she stepped before the other lady, and running up to him, stated: "My dear Hercules, I find you are very much divided in your own thoughts upon the way of life you ought to choose: be my friend, and follow me; I'll lead you into the possession of pleasure, and out of the reach of pain, and remove you from all the noise and disquietude of business. The affairs of either war or peace shall have no power to disturb you. Your whole employment shall be to make your life easy, and to entertain every sense with its proper gratification. Sumptuous tables, beds of roses, clouds of perfumes, consorts of music, crowds of beauties, are all in a readiness to receive you. Come along with me into this region of delights, this world of pleasure, and bid farewell for ever to care, to pain, to business–"

Hercules desired to know her name, to which she replied, "My friends, and those who are well acquainted with me, call me Happiness; but my enemies, and those who would injure my reputation, have given me the name of Pleasure."

By this time the other lady spoke to the young hero: "Hercules, I offer myself to you, because I know you are descended from the gods, and give proofs of that descent by your love to virtue, and application to the studies proper for your age. This makes me hope you will gain, both for yourself and me, an immortal reputation. But before I invite you into my society and friendship, I will be open and sincere with you, and must lay down this as an established truth, that there is nothing truly valuable which can be purchased without pains and labour. The gods have set a price upon every real and noble pleasure. If you would gain the favour of the deity, you must be at the pains of worshipping him; if the friendship of good men, you must study to oblige them; if you would be honoured by your country, you must take care to serve it. In short, if you would be eminent in war or peace, you must become master of all the qualifications that can make you so. These are the only terms and conditions upon which I can propose happiness."

Hercules asked this woman her name, to which she replied "Among men I am called Duty," (also Virtue). The goddess of Pleasure here retorted: "You see, Hercules, by her own confession, the way to her pleasure is long and difficult, whereas that which I propose is short and easy."

"Alas, [said the other lady],what are the pleasures you propose? To eat before you are hungry, drink before you are athirst, sleep before you are tired, to gratify appetites before they are raised, and raise such appetites as nature never planted. You never heard the most delicious music, which is the praise of one's self; nor saw the most beautiful object, which is the work of one's own hands. Your votaries pass away their youth in a dream of mistaken pleasures, while they are hoarding up anguish, torment, and remorse for old age. As for me, I am the friend of gods and of good men, an agreeable companion to the artisan, an household guardian to the fathers of families, a patron and protector of servants, and associate in all true and generous friendships. The banquets of my votaries are never costly, but always delicious; for none eat or drink at them who are not invited by hunger and thirst. Their slumbers are sound, and their wakings cheerful. My young men have the pleasure of hearing themselves praised by those who are in years; and those who are in years, of being honoured by those who are young. In a word, my followers are favoured by the gods, beloved by their acquaintance, esteemed by their country and (after the close of their labours) honoured by posterity."

The more Hercules looked at Pleasure the more beautiful she grew; while the face of Duty seemed more stern. However, he realised the need to use his strength to help others. Pleasure would not be able to help him rid the world of the rest of its monsters, whereas Duty would. Thus, Hercules, being the honourable hero, gave up his heart to the woman of Virtue. Sometimes Pleasure or Vice is depicted in art with an alluring face, but ending in snakes and monsters. Here she appears with an fake mask. Virtue is instead shown as a wise man here. So Hercules, instead of being Eurystheus' servant, became, of his own free will, the servant of all humanity. He made it his work to seek out wrong, he travelled the world to enforce the law of justice, and the worship of the gods.

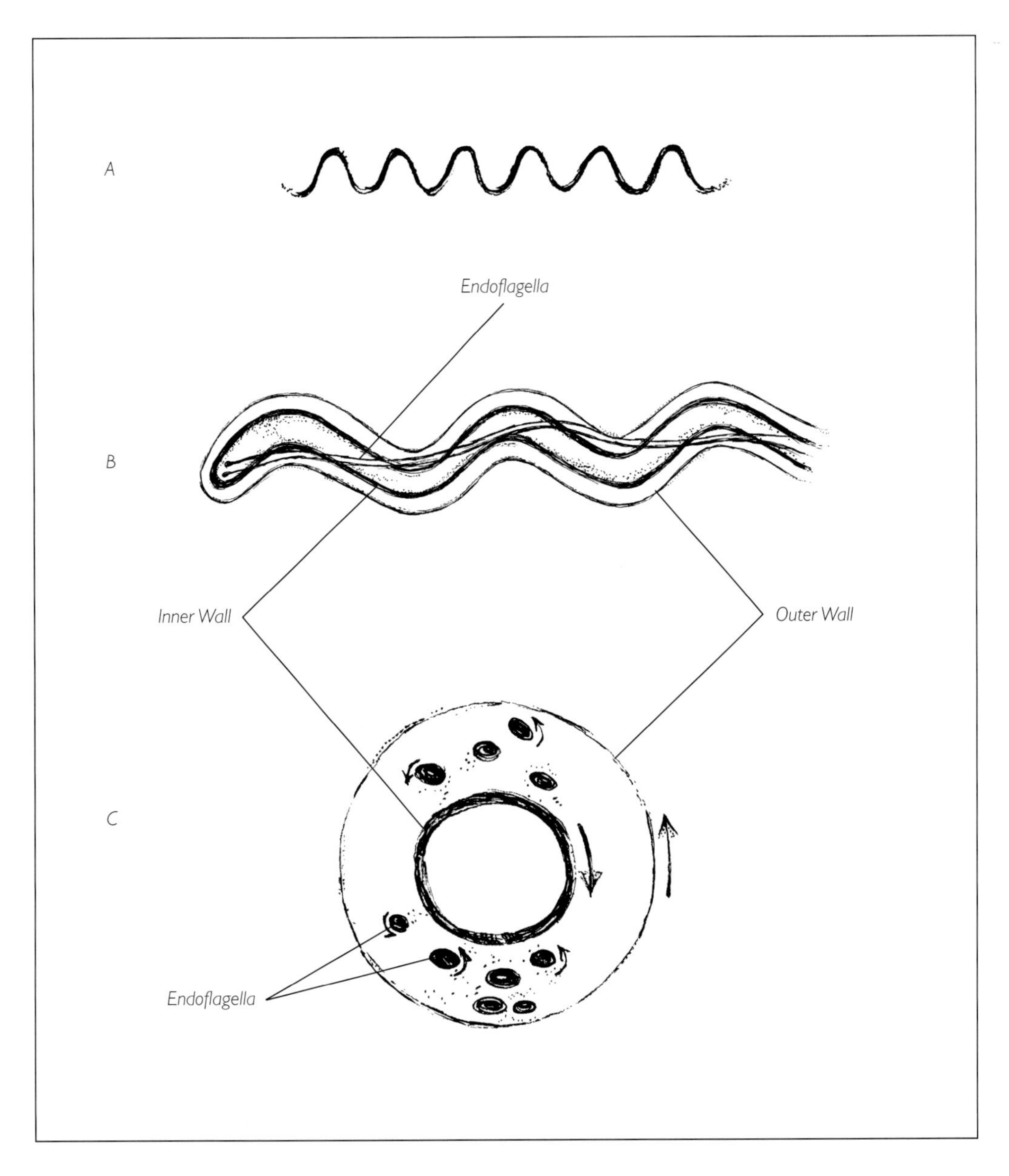

'Syphilinum and morphology of Spirochete bacteria', by Katherine Mynott. Treponema pallidum differs in appearance from the other spirochetes in having a flat waveform rather than the more usual three-dimensional helical shape. It is a long and yet extremely thin cell. It has 6-18 spirals and between 2-40 flagella. The central axial bundle of the protoplasmic cylinder is surrounded by the spiral flagella and the outer sheath membrane. There is an internal semi-rigid cell wall and an outer flexible cell sheath. This internal wall effectively forms what is known as a protoplasmic cylinder with a layer of periplasmic substance between this and the outer sheath. Motility is due to many flagella that are connected to each pole. However, unlike most other bacteria, the flagella do not flex or move outside of the cell boundary but remain within the periplasm. They are thus known as endoflagella. Since they tend to extend for two-thirds the length of the cell there is overlap with the endoflagella from the opposite pole about the middle of the bacteria. The endoflagella rigidly rotate or spin (rather than contracting and swinging) and through resonance cause rotation in the outer flexible sheath in the same direction. However the inner partially rigid cell wall is made to rotate in the reverse direction through torsion effects. This creates a force on the protoplasmic cylinder, causing it to flex. Thus, despite not extending beyond the cell border, the endoflagella rotation leads to a spinning type irregular motion of the whole bacteria. This is rather like a corkscrew movement, rotating and spinning about the central body axis.

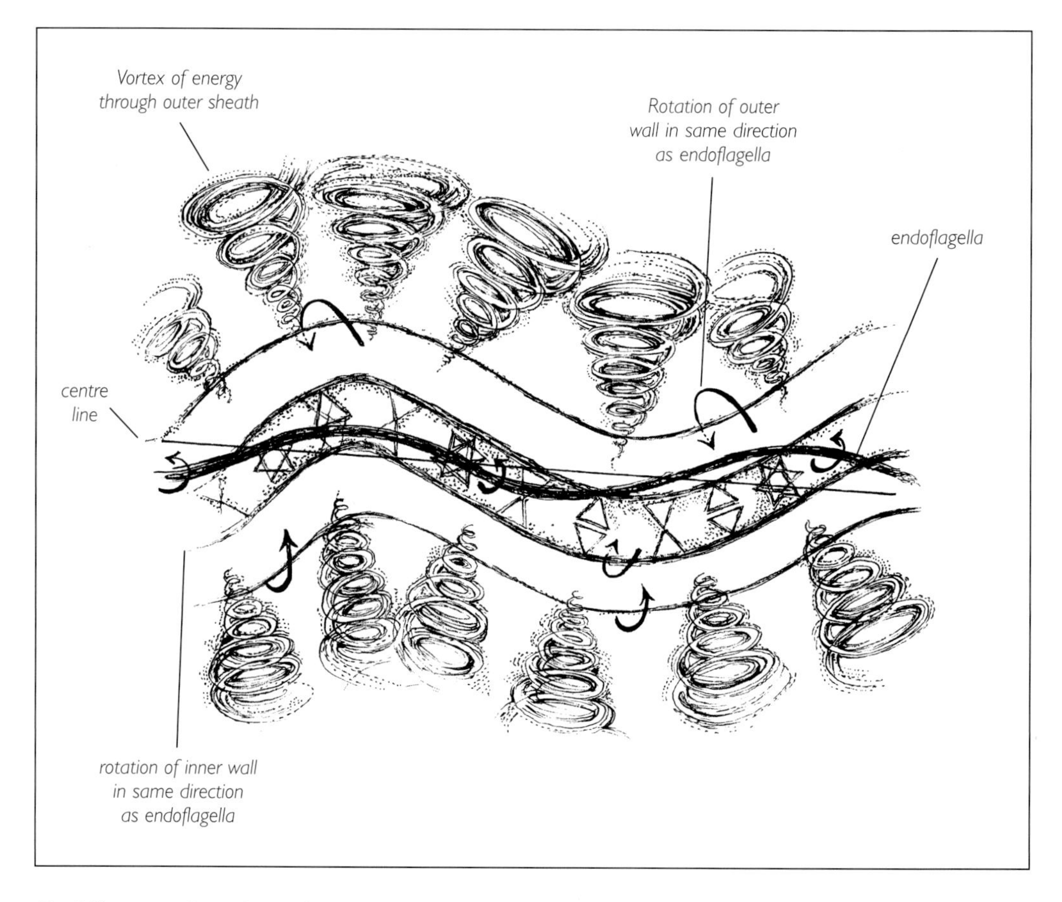

'Syphilinum and vortices of energy flow in Spirochetes', by Katherine Mynott.

However, one cannot explain the motility of cells and organisms simply through mechanical forces. It is the astral body under the guidance of the ego or self-consciousness that leads to motion of the physical vehicle of the organism. Spirochetes and Treponema pallidum bacteria are the result of a disordered Mercury process within the biology of the host. Indeed this species has become flattened and almost two-dimensional in its thinness compared to other more helical spirochetes. The theme within the energy of movement of the spirochetes is communication and transmission of impulses from the higher spiritual realms to the lower material and metabolic realm. The outer flexible bacterial membrane is porous to the influx of these higher energies, whereas the more rigid internal wall holds the geometrical and denser mineralised structure of the material realm. Between the two walls lie the endoflagella that must rotate so as to synchronise and harmonise the signals flowing between the two realms. When this process is disordered then can manifest a syphilitic state of disease, leading to the typical tissue destruction.

Astrology

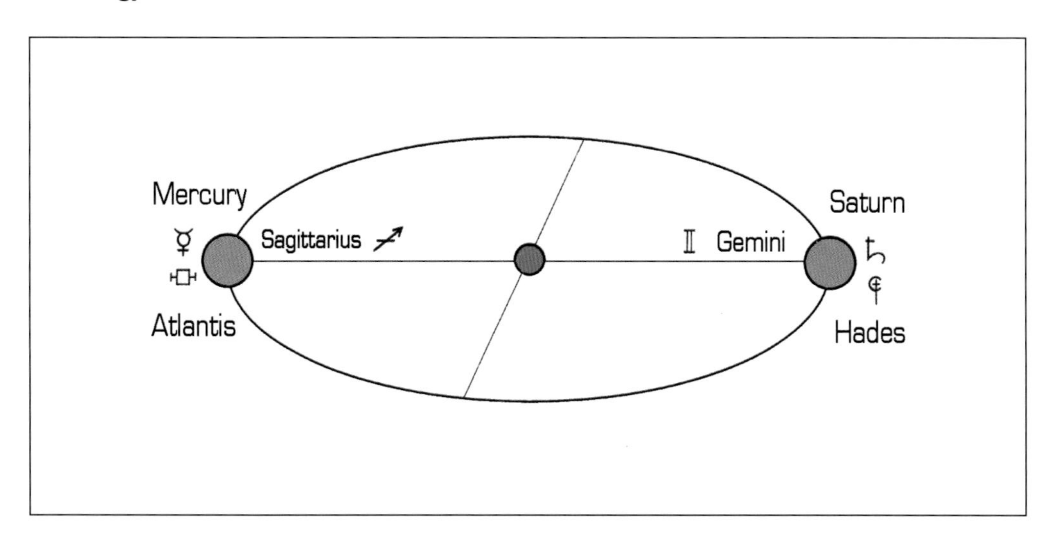

Mercury conjunct Atlantis within Sagittarius, opposite Saturn conjunct Hades within Gemini.

Oriental

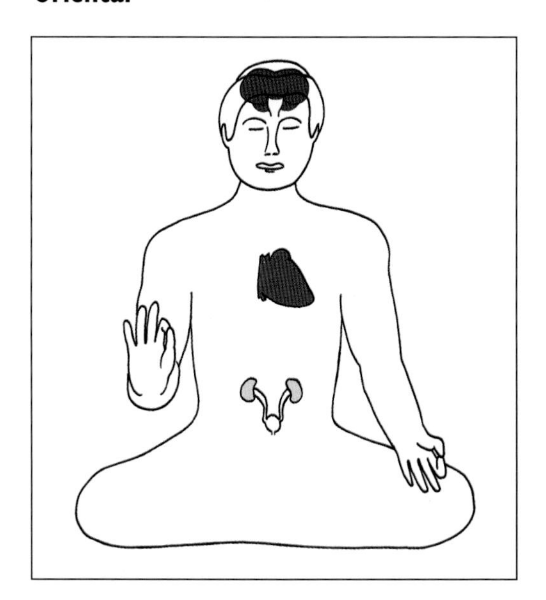

Kidney yin deficiency with heart fire blazing and blood stasis within brain.

Particulars

In primary syphilis, during the initial three weeks after inoculation, the Treponema pallidum microbes spread throughout the body via the blood circulation. After this period the hard chancre appears at the original site of entry, as a painless ulcer.

Syphilis, primary chancre on penis

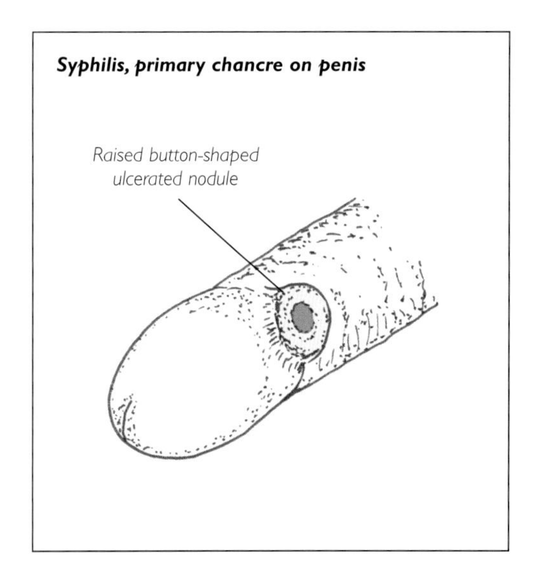

Syphilis, primary chancre on female genitalia

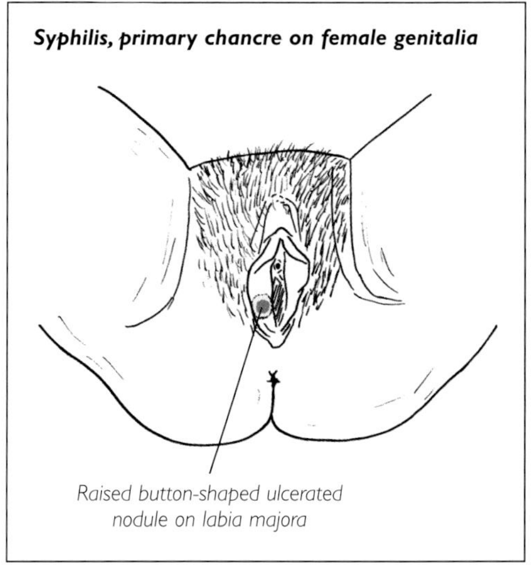

Primary syphilis or chancre is usually present as a single, small, painless, reddish macule or patch which then develops into a papule (lump) and then an ulcer. The ulcer is round or oval in shape with a clear regular grey-yellow scab of dried secretions. The Treponema pallidum microbes are present in the exudates from the ulcer. It can take several weeks to heal, leaving a thin scar. The commonest site in heterosexual men is the penis (glans, inner prepuce, frenum, urethral meatus or shaft of penis). In homosexual men it is usually present in the anal canal, should contact have therein occurred. In women it is typically on the vulva, within the vaginal wall, or rarely on the cervix. In either gender it may also occur on the lips, tonsils, fingers, buttocks or nipples. The local lymph nodes may be enlarged, with a firm, rubbery, mobile consistency and are painless.

Reiter's syndrome, mouth ulcers

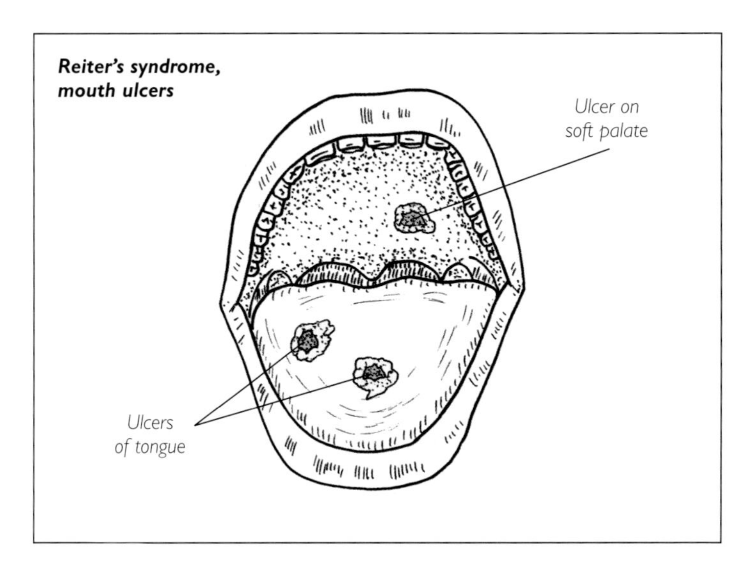

Reiter's syndrome is characterised by a combination of urethritis, conjunctivitis and arthritis. It can also include fevers, myocarditis, pericarditis, cardiac arrhythmias and dermatitis. Erosions or ulcers also typically occur on the soft palate and/or tongue.

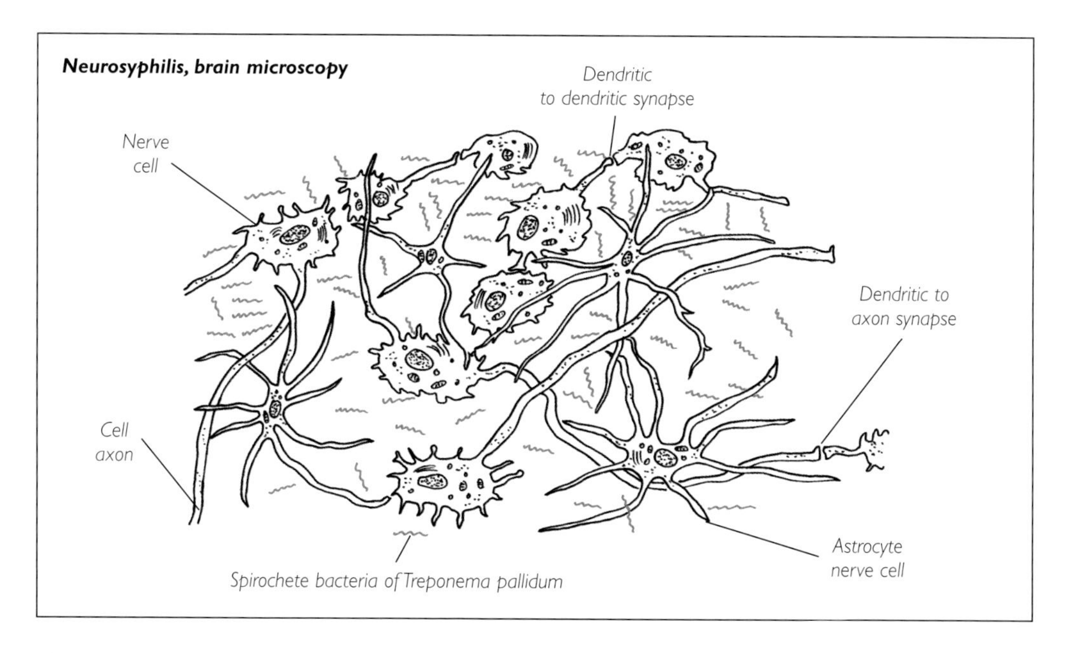

Treponema pallidum, the cause of syphilis, often infects the central nervous system. This causes a chronic inflammation with the initial infiltration into the brain of small lymphocytes and giant macrophages cells. Eventually there is a granulomatous process with degeneration and gumma formation. In this microscopic view there is a general reduction of neurone cells and reactionary proliferation of the astrocyte cells (a cell type which usually supports nerve function). The spiral syphilitic bacteria are also found in copious numbers (coloured green for clarity).

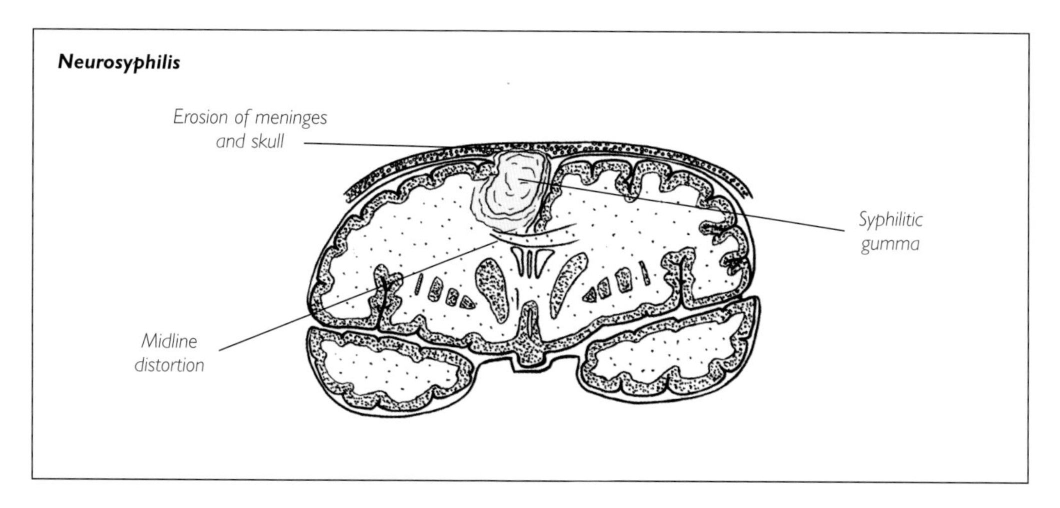

Neurosyphilis can occur in several states. It can cause meningitis, with headaches, stiff neck, fever, and cranial nerve damage. It can cause tabes dorsalis, where degenerative changes occur in the posterior nerve roots and columns of the spinal cord and some of the cranial nerves – causing nerve pains, a spastic gait, failing of vision and urinary disturbance. In dementia paralytica (also known as general paresis of the insane) there is a widespread encephalitis or infection throughout the brain tissue, causing progressive dementia, delusions, slurred speech and tremor. Another form of disease is the gumma of the brain (as shown here) or a focal spinal cord expanding lesion which causes local nerve damage (i.e. similar features to a stroke).

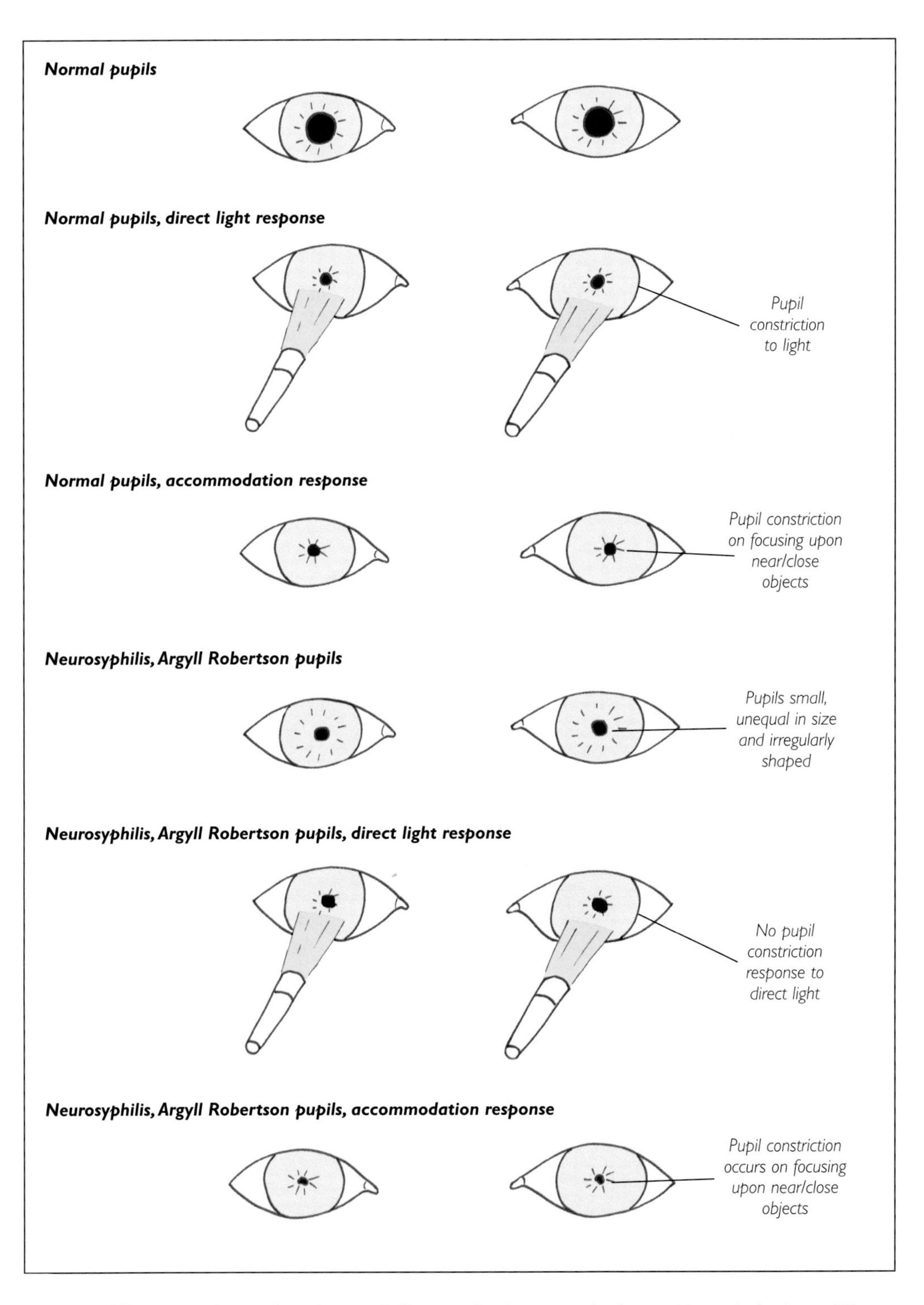

Neurosyphilis causes the pupils to be small (3mm or less), uneven in size and irregularly shaped. There is dissociation of light and near object responses, hence they do not react to light but do constrict on accommodation or convergence to viewing of close objects. Rarely the same papillary responses can be found in diabetes mellitus; otherwise these signs are practically diagnostic of neurosyphilis.

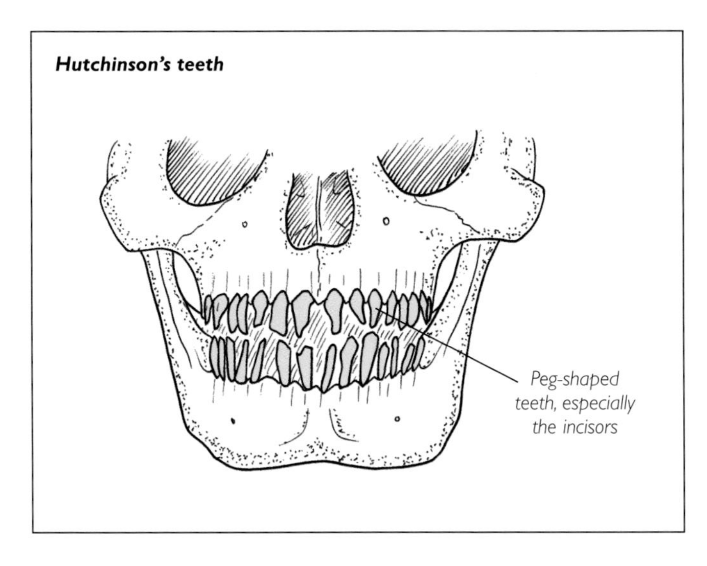

Congenital syphilis occurs when the Treponema pallidum bacteria are transmitted from an infected mother to her foetus. The bacteria proliferate within the foetus to cause inflammatory responses and tissue destruction (and the risk of death). Where the foetus reaches full term and is born the signs are variable, but include a chronic rhinitis or nasal inflammation (snuffles) and a peeling rash. Bone destruction occurs, e.g. a saddle nose, anterior bowing of the legs (sabre shins), and peg-shaped teeth – especially the upper incisors (called Hutchinson's teeth).

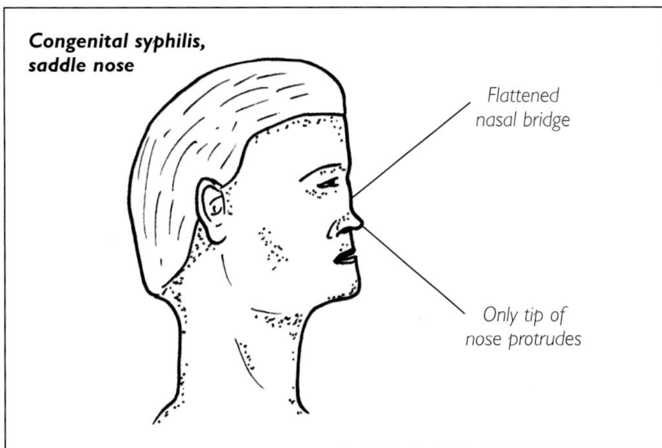

Congenital syphilis (i.e. infection during embryonic life) leads to deficient growth of the nasal septum and bones during childhood. This is aggravated by the persistent rhinitis or nasal inflammation. There is depression of the nasal bridge.

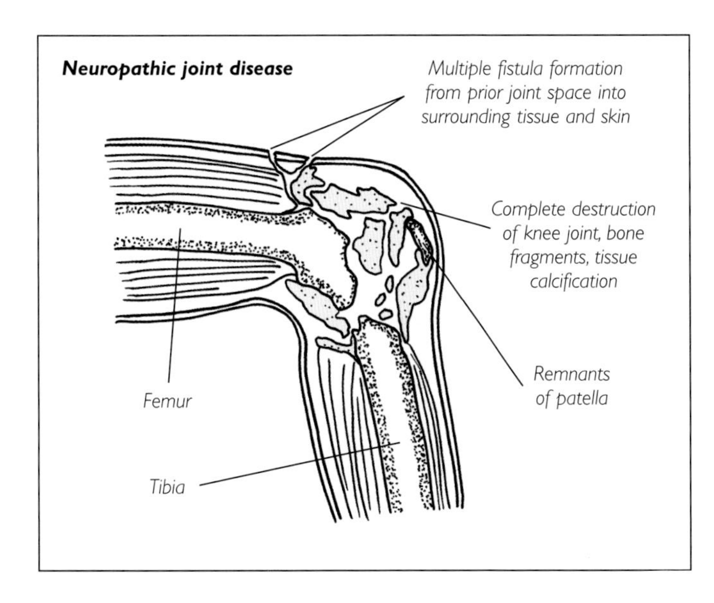

Neuropathic joint disease (Charcot's joint) is caused by disturbed nerve supply to the joint. Causes include syphilis (in the third or tertiary stages), diabetic neuropathy, or syringomyelia. The loss of proprioception (joint position sense) and pain sensation causes the joint structures, such as the ligaments, to relax. The unstable joint progressively deteriorates. Despite this the joint does not feel painful, or only mildly so.

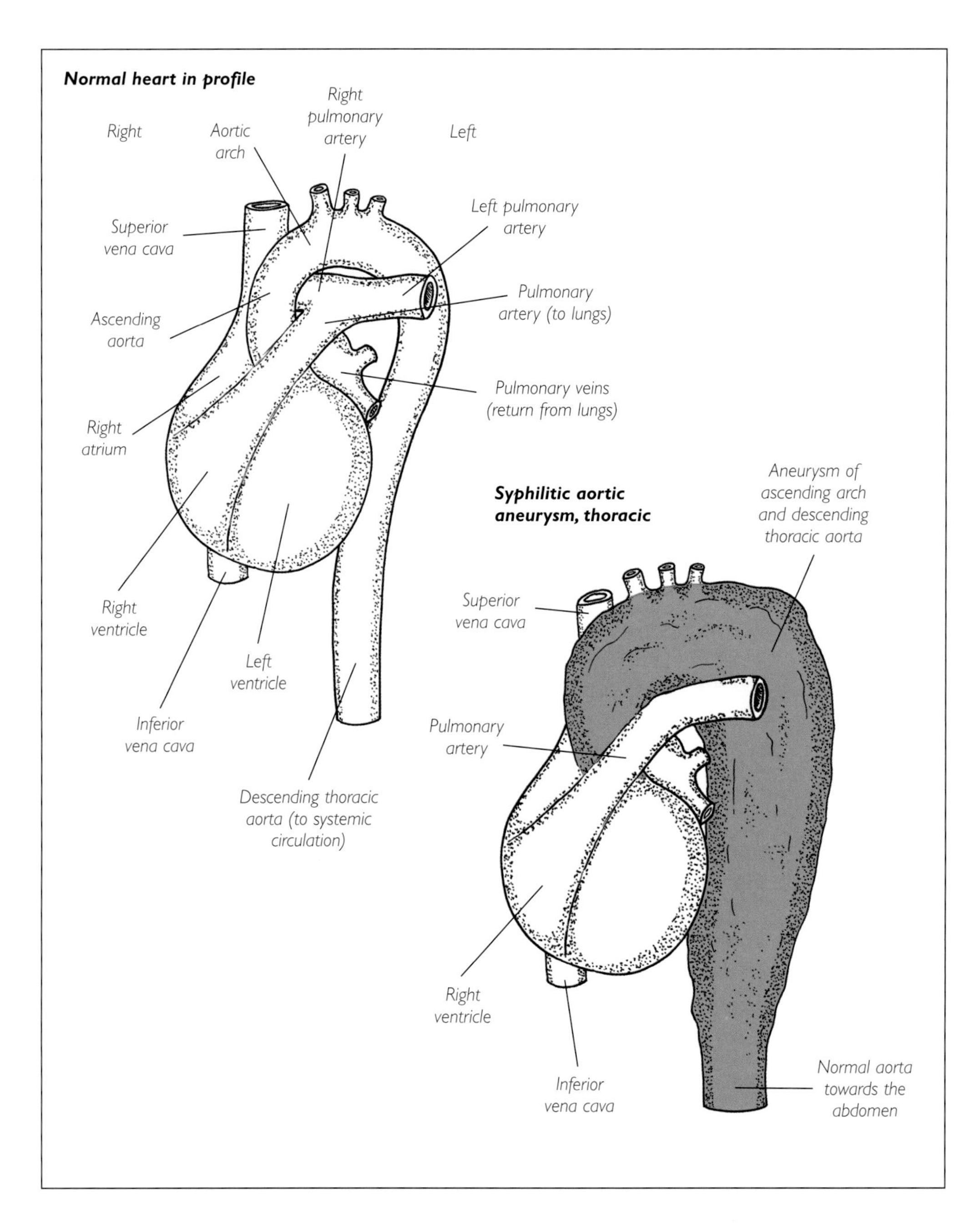

Syphilis in the tertiary phase can cause various cardiac abnormalities, including aortic aneurysm, typically within the thoracic section. There is replacement of the normal wall by scar tissue, fibrous thickening and white cell infiltrates. The aorta widens markedly, although usually only to the level of the diaphragm, sparing the abdominal aorta. Diffuse atherosclerosis occurs in the inner wall, with cholesterol and calcium deposits, and then ulceration. This can cause narrowing of the orifices to the coronary arteries, aggravating any ischaemic heart disease. There is also incompetence of the aortic valve with fixed separated valve cusps, causing aortic regurgitation – which strains the left ventricular function by virtue of the ejected blood partially refluxing back into the ventricle. Another complication is rupture of the aorta, since its wall is significantly weaker.

Related images

p.232 & p.343 Multiple sclerosis
p.586-587 Poliomyelitis
p.277 Motor neurone disease
p.586 Muscle wasting
p.35 Spinal myelitis
p.752 Pineal tumour
p.578 Hypothalamic tumour
p.40-41 Pituitary tumour
p.18 Parkinson's disease
p.55 Encephalitis
p.17 Alzheimer's disease
p.17 Investigation of higher cortical function
p.276 Brain glioma tumour
p.285-286 Cerebrovascular accident
p.281 Endocarditis
p.519-520 Valvular heart disease
p.282 Cardiac muscle sections, cardiomyopathy
p.144 Coronary artery disease
p.81 Post-myocardial infarction aneurysm
p.299 Atrial fibrillation
p.82 Pacemaker ECG
p.264 Multifocal extrasystoles/ectopic beats
p.383 Ventricular arrhythmias
p.300 Heart failure, right-sided
p.172 Osteogenesis imperfecta
p.171-172 Rickets and osteomalacia
p.171-172 Osteoporosis
p.691 Paget's disease
p.623-624 Rheumatoid arthritis, deformities
p.541 Peptic ulcer
p.206-210 Cancer and malignancy
p.247-248 Cleft lip and palate
p.658 Spina bifida
p.239 Incomplete miscarriage
p.640 & p.650 Threatened miscarriage
p.96 Growth chart
p.98 Genital underdevelopment
p.97 Undescended testes
p.505-506 Teeth gum recession
p.171 Teeth crowding, delayed dentition

TABACUM

Original

'Tabacum with astral flight and separation', by Tessa Gaynn. The plant is surrounded by swirling nicotine impregnated gases. The astral bodies of various users can be seen floating upwards into an escapist state into the astral realm.

Astrology

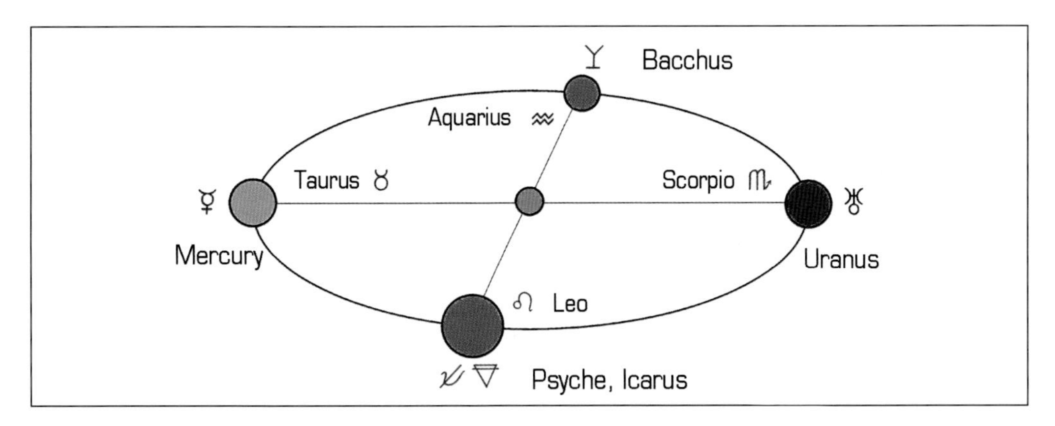

Grand cross, Mercury in Taurus opposite Uranus in Scorpio, and Psyche conjunct Icarus within Leo opposite Bacchus in Aquarius.

Oriental

Heart chi and blood stagnation, with phlegm-heat obstructing the lungs.

Related images

p.144 Coronary artery disease, p.145 Angina & p.451 Myocardial infarction
p.640 Peripheral arterial disease & p.295 Renal artery stenosis
p.258 Labyrinthitis & p.260 Meniere's disease
p.443 Arteriosclerosis & p.574 Hypertension
p.321 Arteriosclerosis and hypertension in eye
p.321-322 Retinal vascular disease & p.571 Retinal degeneration
p.572-573 Visual field defects & p.320 Diabetic maculopathy
p.541 Peptic ulcer & p.36 Hiatus hernia

TARENTULA HISPANICA

Original

'Tarentula and the cosmic nature of spiders', by Esther Lane. The Earth is shown connected to a web of energy, interconnecting 'All That Is' within creation. Myriad spiritual beings work with the Earth, some representatives are shown. However, a huge spider grasps the planet, indicating that the nature of duality has permeated much of Earth life, so as to facilitate a sense of separation or Fall from the cosmos/spiritual realm.

Astrology

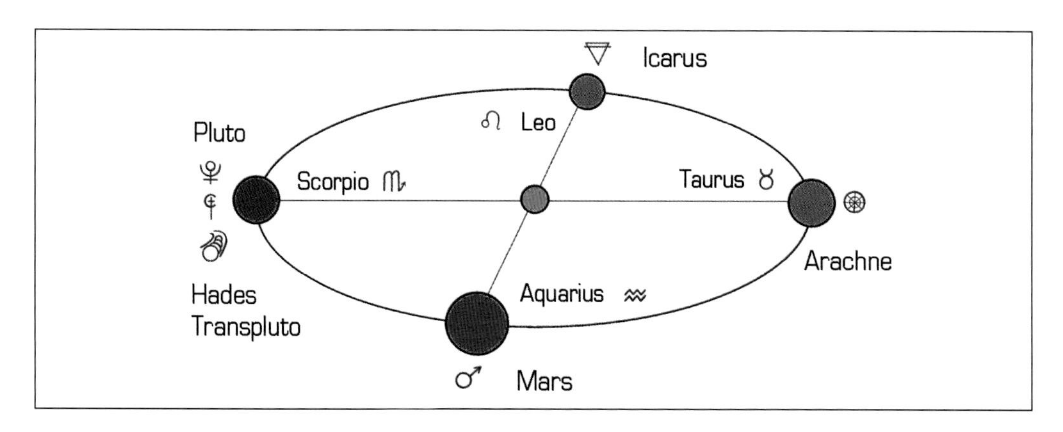

Grand cross, Pluto conjunct Transpluto and Hades within Scorpio opposite Arachne in Taurus, and Mars in Aquarius opposite Icarus in Leo.

Oriental

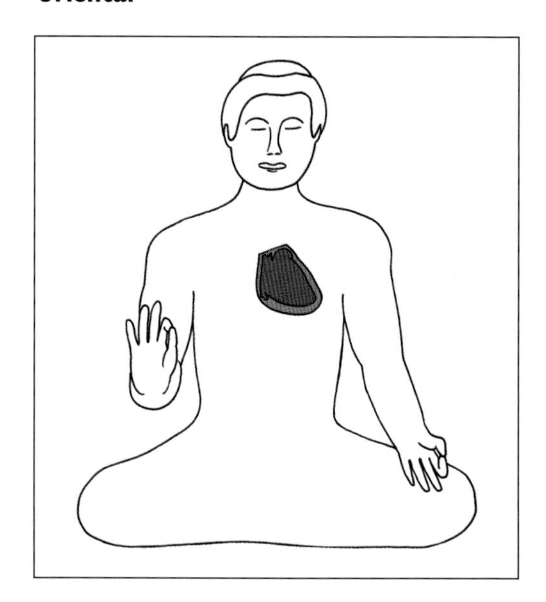

Exterior heat invasion of the pericardium, with phlegm-fire harassing the heart.

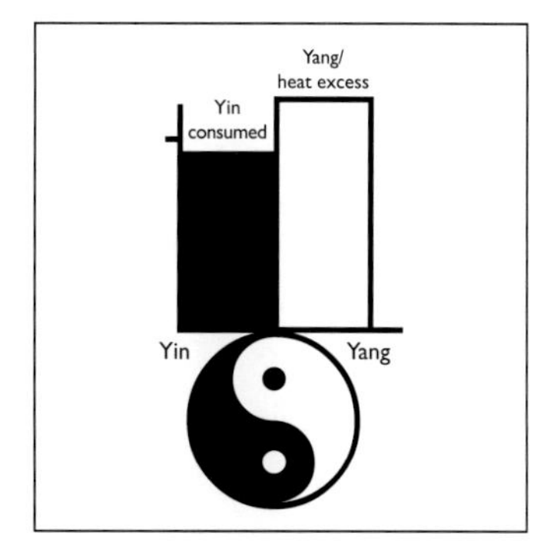

Related images

p.232 & p.343 Multiple sclerosis & p.35 Spinal myelitis
p.586-587 Poliomyelitis
p.277 Motor neurone disease & p.586 Muscle wasting
p.233-234 Epilepsy
p.285-286 Cerebrovascular accident
p.44 Cutaneous necrosis & Necrotic abscess
p.420 Candidiasis
p.314 Osteomyelitis & p.90 Subdiaphragmatic abscess

THUJA OCCIDENTALIS

Museum

'Edward Jenner among patients in the Smallpox and Inoculation Hospital at St. Pancras', also called 'The Cow-Pock, or the Wonderful Effects of the New Inoculation!'(1802), by James Gillray (1757-1815), watercolour. © Wellcome Library, London. The artist/caricaturist, in his usual style of scathing scepticism towards the medical profession, shows Jenner amidst his vaccinated patients, who are sprouting features of a cow, including horns and tails. This was a satirical attack on the dangers of the unknown by injecting animal-derived substances into humans. Smallpox had, however, plagued humanity for millennia. An Egyptian mummy from 1200 BC has been shown to have been infected by smallpox. It was worldwide a major source of mortality. The bacteria has no animal vector, needing enough infected humans before an epidemic can start. There is a flu-like illness, with a rash proceeding from macules, to papules, vesicles and then scabs. Widespread haemorrhage may occur from the skin. Surviving victims are left scarred and disfigured, although with life-long immunity.

In fact, inoculation had been used in Asia and Africa to treat smallpox for centuries, and became introduced into the Americas in 1721, at the severe epidemic in Boston, by a Reverend and a few brave physicians. Indeed, such was the violent reaction against the procedure by most of the American medical community that those who tried it had to barricade themselves for protection from firebombs and attack. The procedure involved deliberately introducing smallpox pus through an incision to a healthy person - having been shown to induce a less serious form of the disease that then provided immunity to further exposure. In parts of Asia, the procedure sometimes was instead to inhale particles of a ground-up smallpox scab through the nose. Another danger was that those inoculated would often transmit the infection to unprotected persons around them, thus actually spreading the disease. Later, isolation of the vaccinated person (for up to a month) was instituted. Much of the American war of Revolution against British rule from the 1770s was affected by troops being smallpox susceptible, without the time for soldiers en masse to be inoculated for protection. Hence severe casualties resulted from the illness. The initial smallpox vaccinations were found to kill about 1% of the patients, and the risk of disease transmission still occurred nonetheless.

In 1796 Edward Jenner discovered that a cowpox vaccine could be protective. Jenner's methods changed the manner of smallpox control. He had noticed that cowmaids did not suffer smallpox, but instead developed the milder less virulent cowpox from cows. He used a sample of this cowpox (or sometimes a horsepox), and found the vaccinated patients experienced milder side-effects compared to smallpox inoculation and without, of course, any risk of transmitting smallpox to others. Although Jenner believed his treatment conferred lifelong immunity, it was confirmed after his death that immunity only lasted 7-10 years. The new vaccine reached the U.S. in 1799. Similar to an earlier debate over the smallpox sourced vaccine, another debate then raged within the clergy and the medical establishment, arguing that "... inoculating a healthy person from a disease animal was repulsive, unsafe and ungodly." Other arguments at the time were that cowpox was some form of bovine syphilis, thus transmitting a new infection into humans. One reason for this may have been the unstable nature of the cow-pus collected to make the vaccine. It was difficult to keep it free from other bacterial contaminants, such as hepatitis or syphilis. It is curious that from 1930, the smallpox vaccine appears not to have been the same as Jenner's original cowpox, but some other distinct related virus. One theory is that the modern vaccine may actually derive from some [now extinct in the wild] horsepox virus. Due to its side effects, use of the vaccine remained controversial until the eradication of smallpox in 1980. Two experimental batches of the smallpox bacteria, one stored in the U.S and the other in the USSR, are supposedly the only remnants of this disease on Earth. These were planned for destruction by the authorities in 1999, but have been maintained, in part due to the cold war between the superpowers. But the scourge of smallpox again rises from potential bio-terrorism if these batches were to be stolen. Furthermore, the world population is now immunologically defenceless again from smallpox, and any vaccination prophylaxis may cause a great deal of harm in normal subjects.

Original

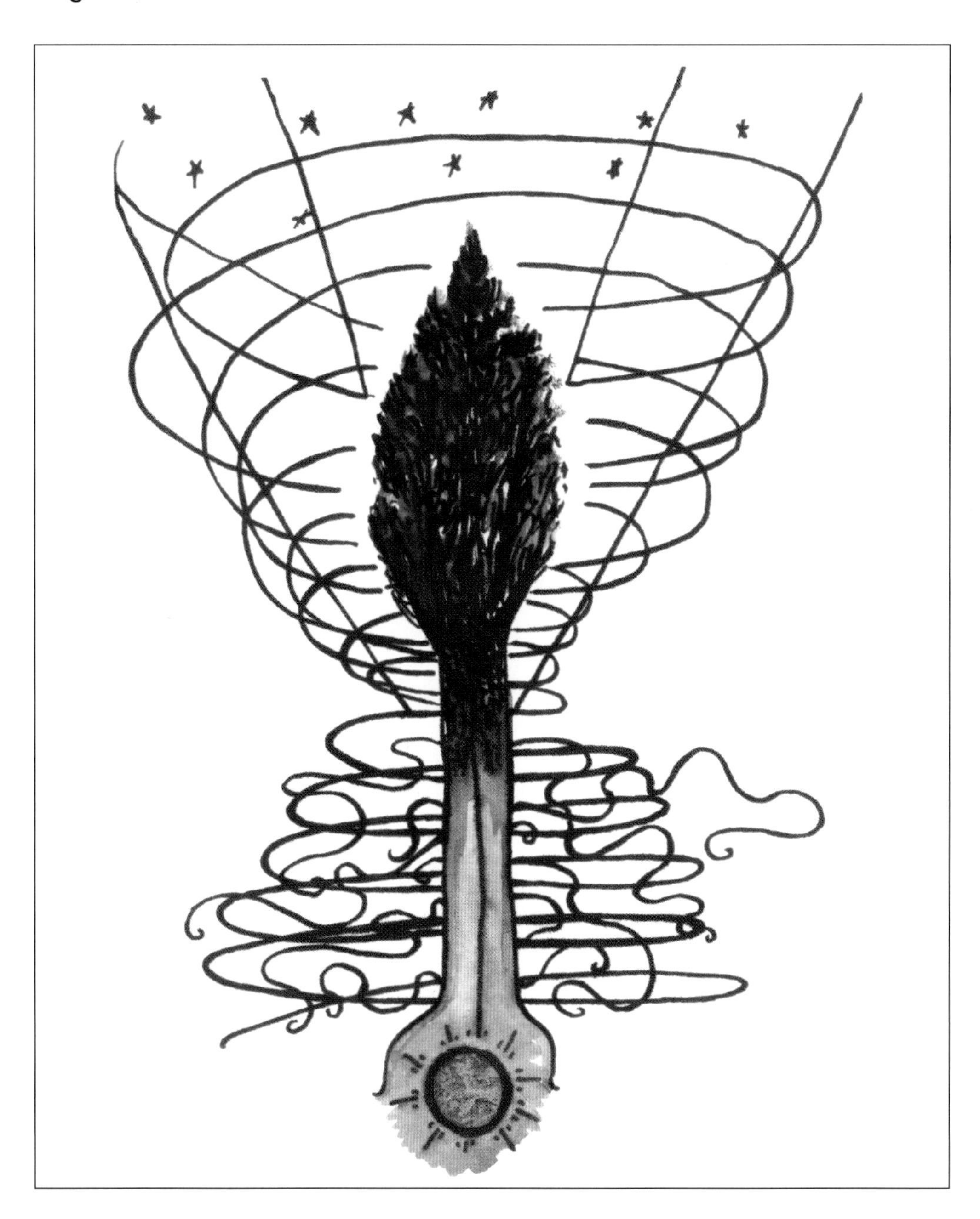

'Thuja and multidimensional pathway to the Earth-core', by Selina Swayne. Moving from the base of the tree is shown a grounding cord of energy to the planetary centre, around which are spiralling and complex energy forms. An expanding spiral of energy also spreads from the tree crown to the spiritual realm above. Feeling appropriately earthbound involves grounding of one's spiritual and other subtle bodies as well as the physical body grounding. For example, an individual may feel 'spaced-out' from a lack of mental body connection to earthly or physical life. This multidimensional grounding is facilitated by the remedy.

Astrology

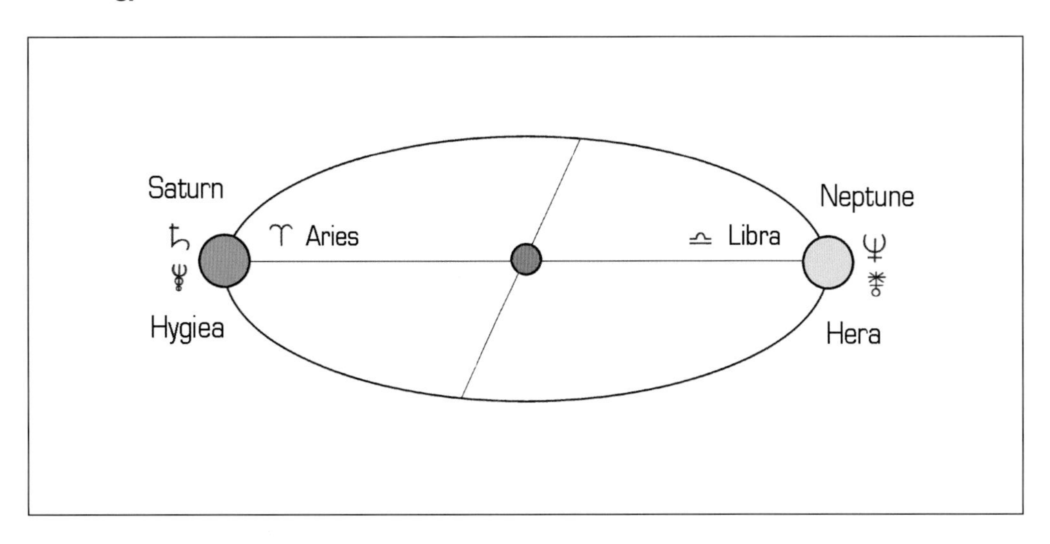

Saturn conjunct Hygiea within Aries, opposite Neptune conjunct Hera within Libra.

Oriental

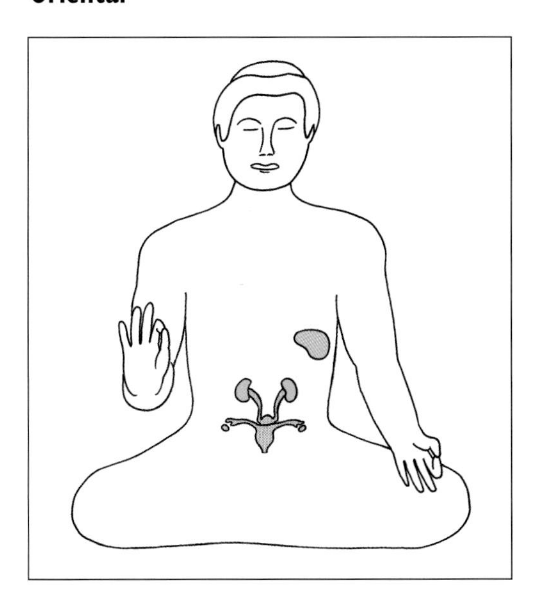

Kidney and spleen yang deficiency, with dampness of lower burner, bladder and uterus/gonads.

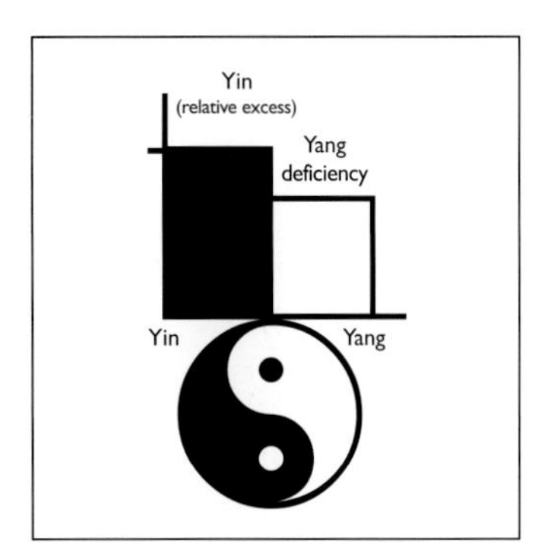

Particulars

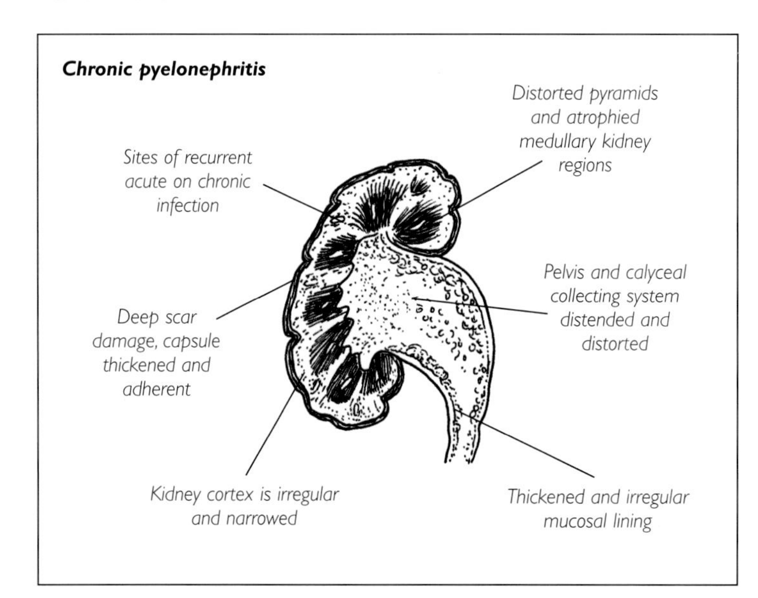

Chronic pyelonephritis of the kidneys is the result of repeated attacks of inflammation (acute pyelonephritis). Kidney infections may occur from ascending spread of cystitis (bladder infection), vesico-ureteric reflux of urine from bladder to kidney, and after distortion of the kidneys by, e.g. stones. The chronic and recurrent inflammation leads to fibrosis and scarring, with progressive destruction of kidney tissue and failure.

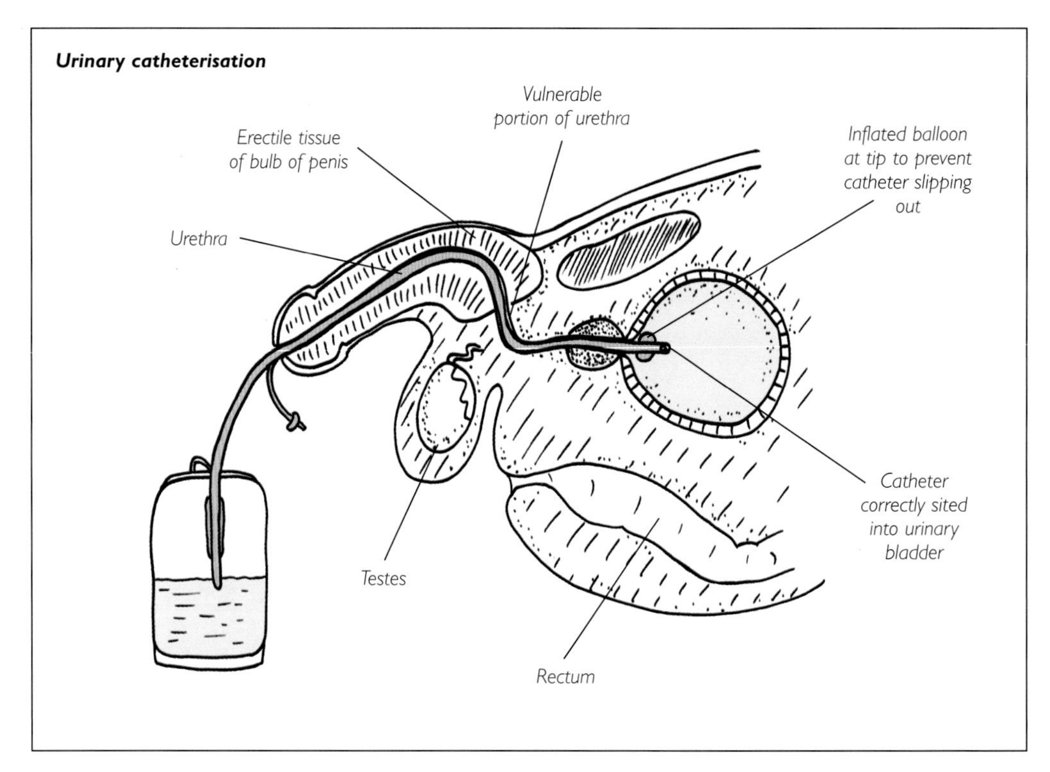

Bladder catheterisation is done to remove urine from a patient unable to micturate, or to irrigate the bladder or to obtain a sample of urine uncontaminated by transit through the urethra. There are different sections and curves of the urethra. The male anatomy is shown here. Just outside the region where the urethra is surrounded by erectile tissue of the penis there is a segment of membranous urethra sensitive to trauma and rupture during the passage of an instrument.

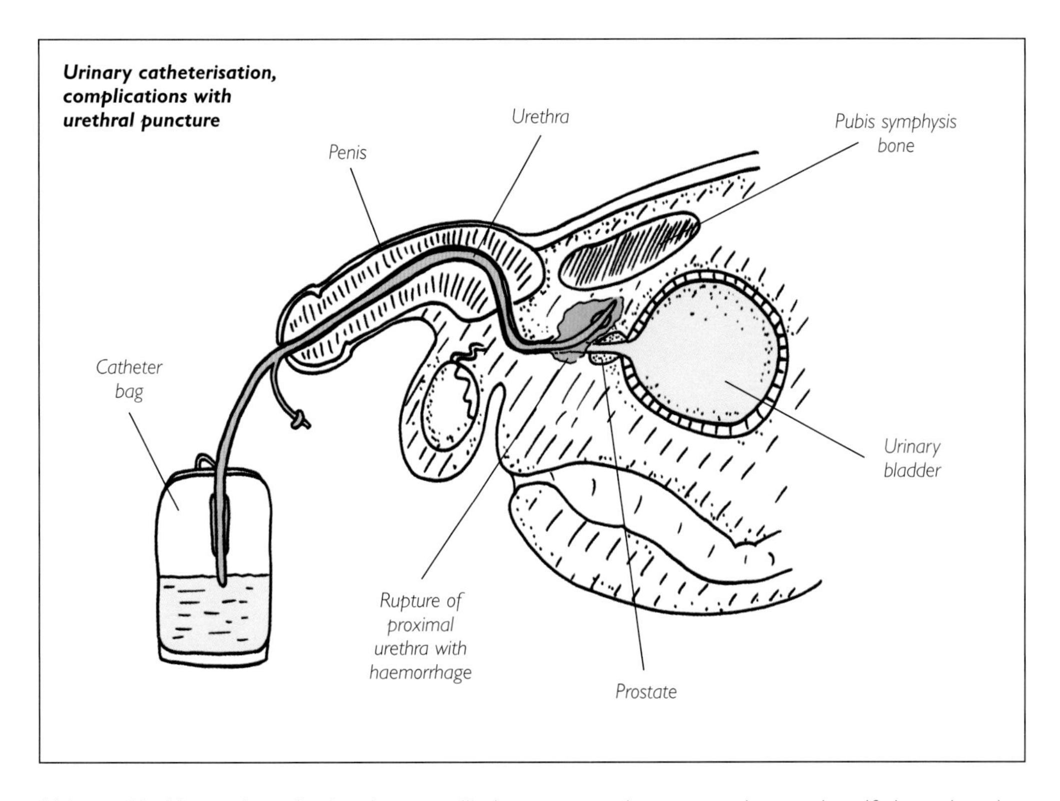

Urinary bladder catheterisation is more likely to cause damage to the urethra if there is prior urethral stricture, chronic urethritis, or congenital anomalies for example. Local haemorrhage at the base of the bladder, muscle spasm and inflammation can obstruct the flow of urine – necessitating suprapubic catheterisation in some cases (i.e. passing a catheter through the lower abdominal wall directly into the bladder). There is also the likely leakage of urine into the retroperitoneal space behind the bladder with the risk of infection. Despite surgical repair of the damaged urethra there is a very likely risk of strictures and narrowing of the urethra in the future.

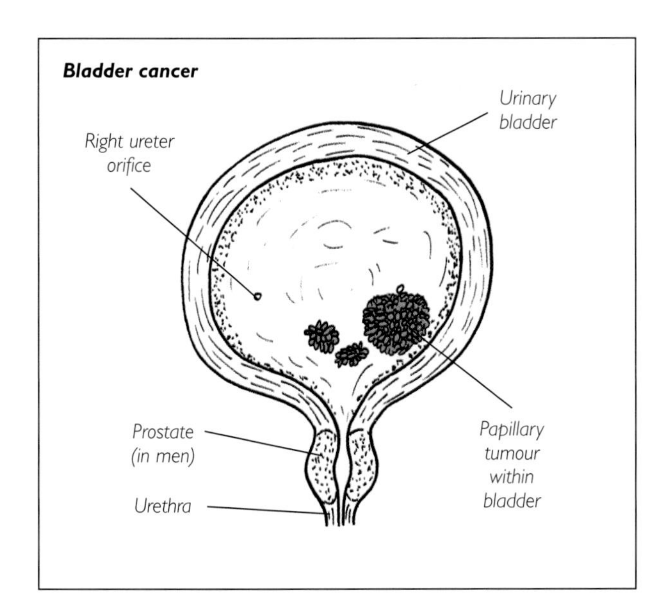

Bladder tumours are usually histologically a transitional cell type, arising from the inner mucous membrane of the bladder wall. They can be benign papillomas (villous shaped warts), sessile (flat) cancers or villous (protruding frond-like) cancers. Certain chemical toxins can trigger bladder cancers, (e.g. beta-naphthylamine used in the aniline dye industry), also smoking, infection by schistosomiasis etc. The cancer can invade through the bladder wall into surrounding blood and lymphatic vessels – to distant organ sites. The symptoms locally are usually haematuria (blood in urine, which can be severe) and pain.

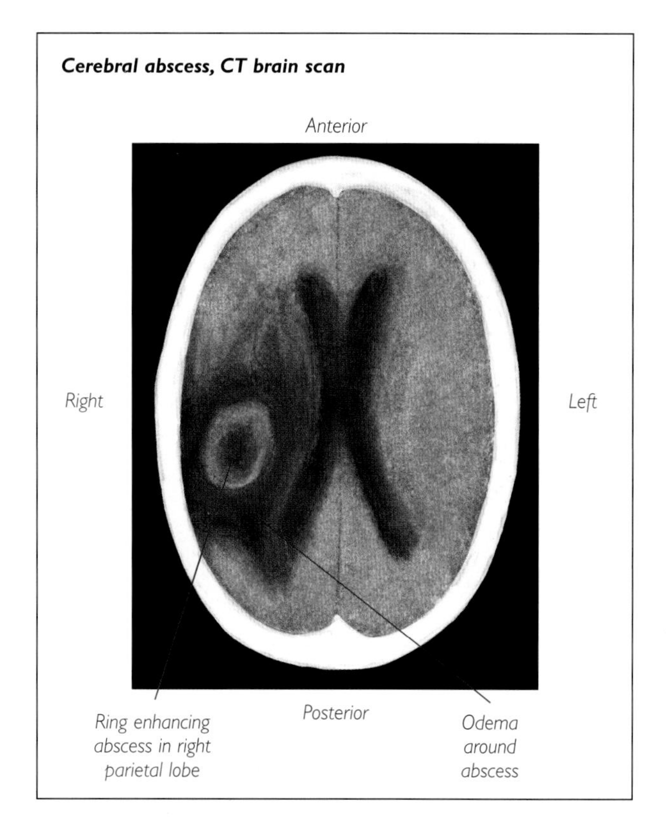

A cerebral abscess is a focal area of bacterial or other microbial (e.g. fungal) infection within the cerebrum. Typical causes are staphylococcus and tuberculosis. Multiple abscesses often occur in immunosuppressed patients, e.g. HIV/AIDs patients. Spread of the microbe could arise from a local infection (e.g. from nose, sinuses) or through the blood from a distant site (e.g. lungs, abdomen). Symptoms include headaches, fevers, raised intracranial pressure (blurred vision, vomiting), fits, or focal neurological deficit (e.g. paralysis of one side of the body or loss of speech). Both the clinical and CT scan appearances are thus similar to a cerebral tumour. Typically there is a ring-enhancing mass (i.e. contrast medium taken up by the rim of the abscess) with a central cavity (containing the pus). The mass is surrounded by odema within the brain as a darkened region.

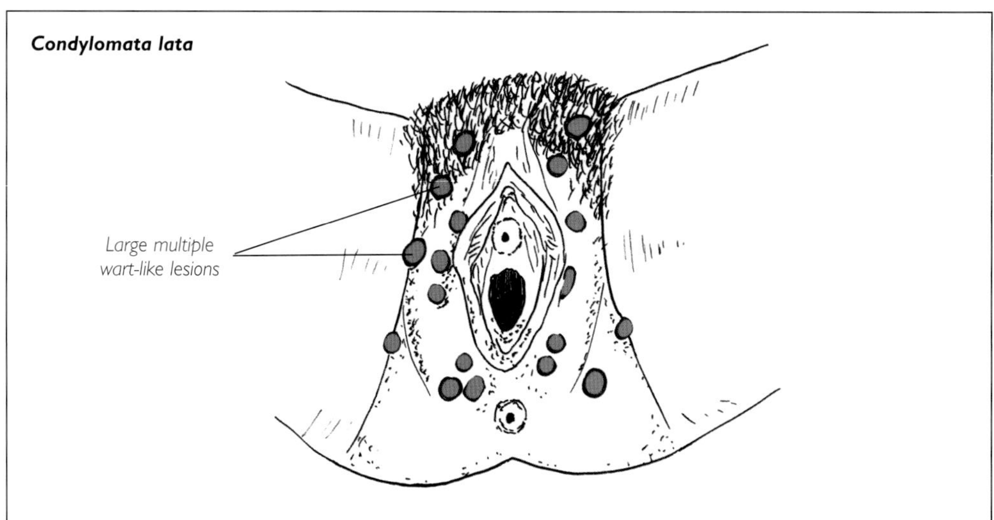

Condylomata lata is due to papilloma (genital wart) virus. This is an infectious pathogen (sexually transmitted) where more than 50% of the contacts are likely to become affected. The initial lesion is a small, single warty growth, and seedling warts soon appear in the same area. They tend to be soft, and pink or white in colour, and can become luxuriant in moister areas. Sometimes ulceration, secondary infection with pus, and/or bleeding occurs. Occasionally they can massively enlarge during pregnancy. Differentiating these lesions from true cancers is required, especially where they occur at the cervix.

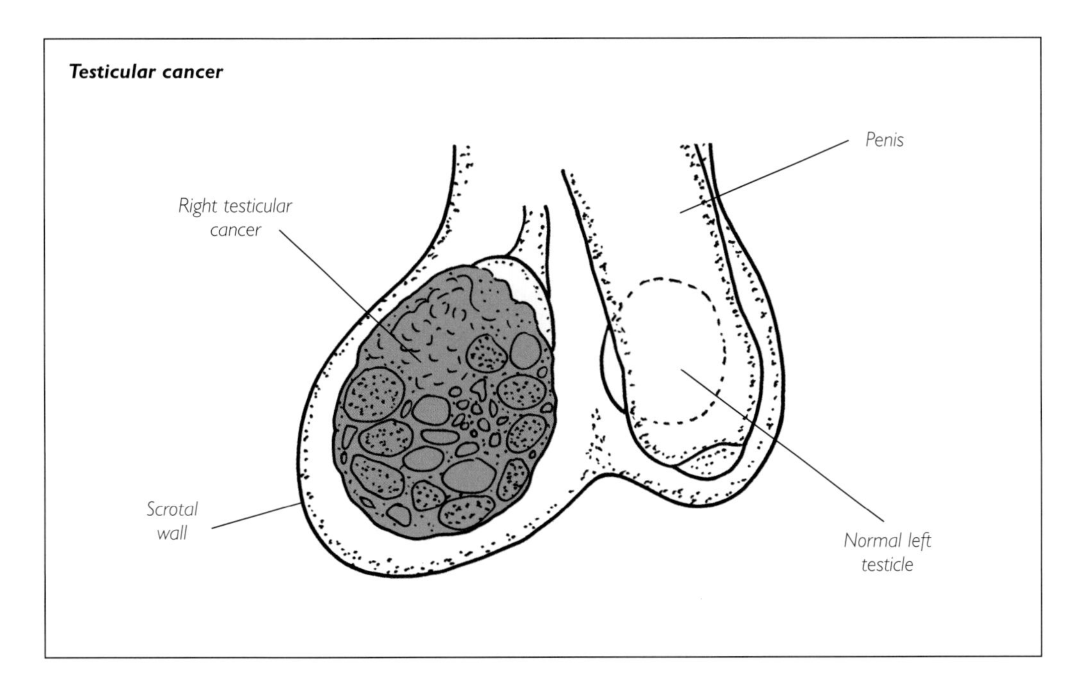

Testicular tumours fall into several types, and are the commonest malignancy in young males. Any mass arising within the testes should therefore be investigated. The usual malignant type derives from the germ cells (which produce sperm), of which two forms are seminoma and teratoma. In a seminoma, there is uniform enlargement of the testicle, with a smooth lobular pattern. Teratomas tend to be irregular in shape and display foci of haemorrhage and necrosis. Spread from both may occur along the lymphatics into the abdominal (para-aortic) lymph nodes, and through the bloodstream - especially to the liver and lungs. Such invasion may be tracked by CT/MRI scanning and assessment of bloodborne tumour markers. Such germ cell tumours tend to be chemotherapy and radiation-sensitive. Less common causes of testicular tumour are lymphoma (primary site). Sometimes leukemia spreads into the testes.

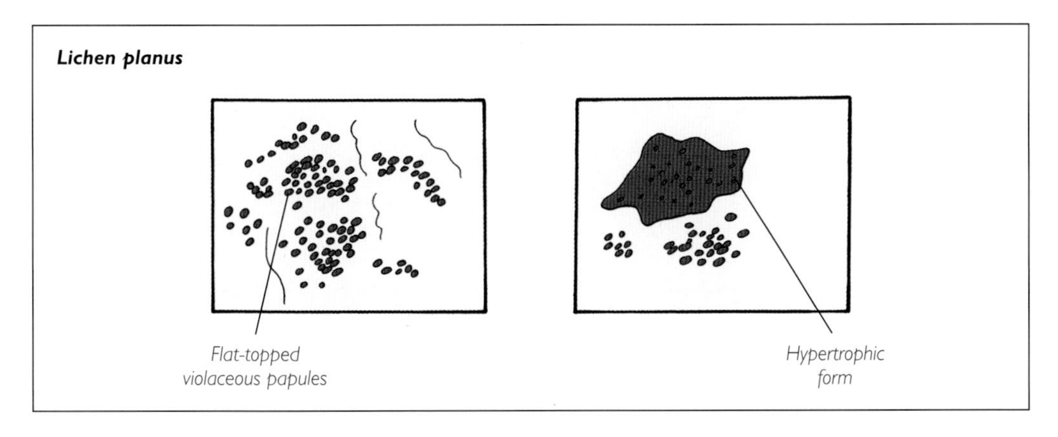

Lichen planus is of unknown allopathic cause, although likely to have an autoimmune factor. There are characteristically small itchy skin lesions, shiny and flat-topped, of a red-violet colour. It usually affects the wrists, forearms, trunk, mouth or genitalia. Lesions may coalesce into larger hypertrophic plaques, especially on the shins.

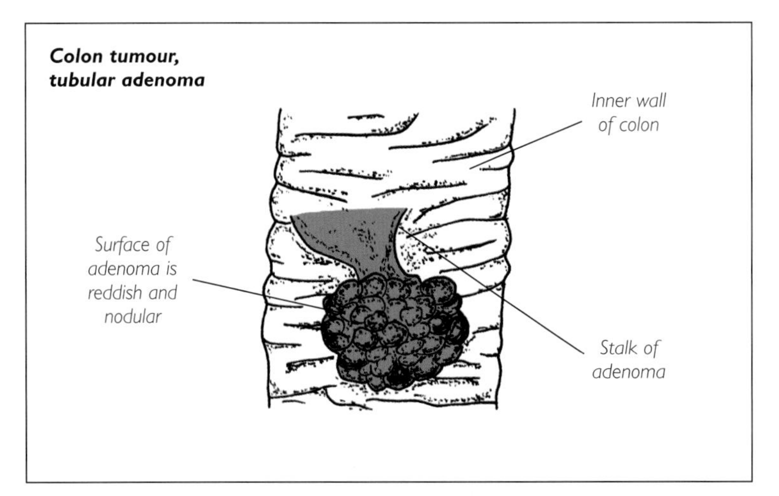

The majority of colonic adenomas (as yet a benign tumour) occur in the rectum and sigmoid colon and may lead to cancer. They often begin as a swelling in the wall, which then becomes pedunculated – developing a stalk. Symptoms include rectal bleeding and a sensation of incomplete bowel evacuation.

Related images

p.376 Bone marrow suppression
p.375 Autoimmune disease
p.408 Sinusitis and nasal polyps
p.501 Otitis media, glue ear
p.504 Chronic bronchitis
p.306 Bronchiectasis
p.95 Cystic fibrosis
p.488-491 Gonorrhoea and sycotic miasm
p.57 Ovarian inflammation
p.335 Endometriosis
p.210 Ovarian cancer
p.421-422 Cervical cancer
p.139 External virilisation
p.209 & p.294 Adrenal tumour
p.294 Adrenal hyperplasia
p.206-210 Cancer and malignancy
p.160 Cushing's syndrome
p.561-562 Hepatitis
p.222 Fatty liver
p.222-223 Gallstones
p.223 Jaundice
p.133 Liver failure and ascites
p.224 Hyperlipidaemia

THYMUS GLAND

Museum

Cornelius van Caukercken (after Peter Paul Rubens). 'Cimon and Pero', engraving on paper. An example of the importance of maternal breastmilk nourishment to the newborn thymus gland is shown (in preparing the infantile immune system for earthly life), but in a different context. The aged Cimon was forced to starve in prison before his execution. However, his devoted daughter Pero secretly visited him to nourish him with her own breastmilk. She is witnessed by the jailor one day and, because of her dedication, won the release of her father. The ancient Roman historian Valerius Maximus, in his 'Memorable Acts and Sayings of the Ancient Romans' presented this act as the highest example of honouring one's parent. Breastfeeding is a typical subject between the Virgin and Christ as an example of Christian devotional love. Even further in history examples include Isis suckling Horus, a forerunner in Egyptian mythology of the Madonna-Christ pair. The universe, and specifically the Milky Way galaxy is said to have formed out of the spurting milk from Greek Hera's breast. Pagan images of breastfeeding were, however, increasingly destroyed after the proclamation of Christianity as the official religion of the Holy Roman Empire (312 AD). Note that Isis lactans statues were worshipped as Maria lactans at least up to the 15th century in regions such as France. Pero is also demonstrating a typical pseudo-zygodactylous hand gesture. The thumb is splayed away, with the second index finger to the top and the remaining fingers held together below. This same hand orientation is shown by the lactating goddesses throughout history, such as Isis nursing Horus, Hera nursing Hercules and the Virgin Mary herself. Indeed, the Virgin is also shown in Medieval and Renaissance art in this nursing altitude even without the Child, showing her maternal care for mortal humans (often older boys and young men) seeking heavenly salvation. In some versions there is no actual mouth to breast contact, instead the milk is squirted in a arcing jet into the devotee's mouth. The hand gesture is also depicted by saints outside the nursing context, showing their power and influence over guiding human souls to the spiritual realm. From a lactating goddess would flow a gift of immortality or spiritual power. The gesture symbolises a communication between the divine and human. Jesus later adopts the hand gesture himself, to demonstrate the wound on his side and on his chest. He then becomes Jesus the Mother of humanity, and indicates his ability to provide salvation. Thus "Like newborn infants, long for pure spiritual milk so that through it you may grow into salvation" (I Peter 2:2).

Original

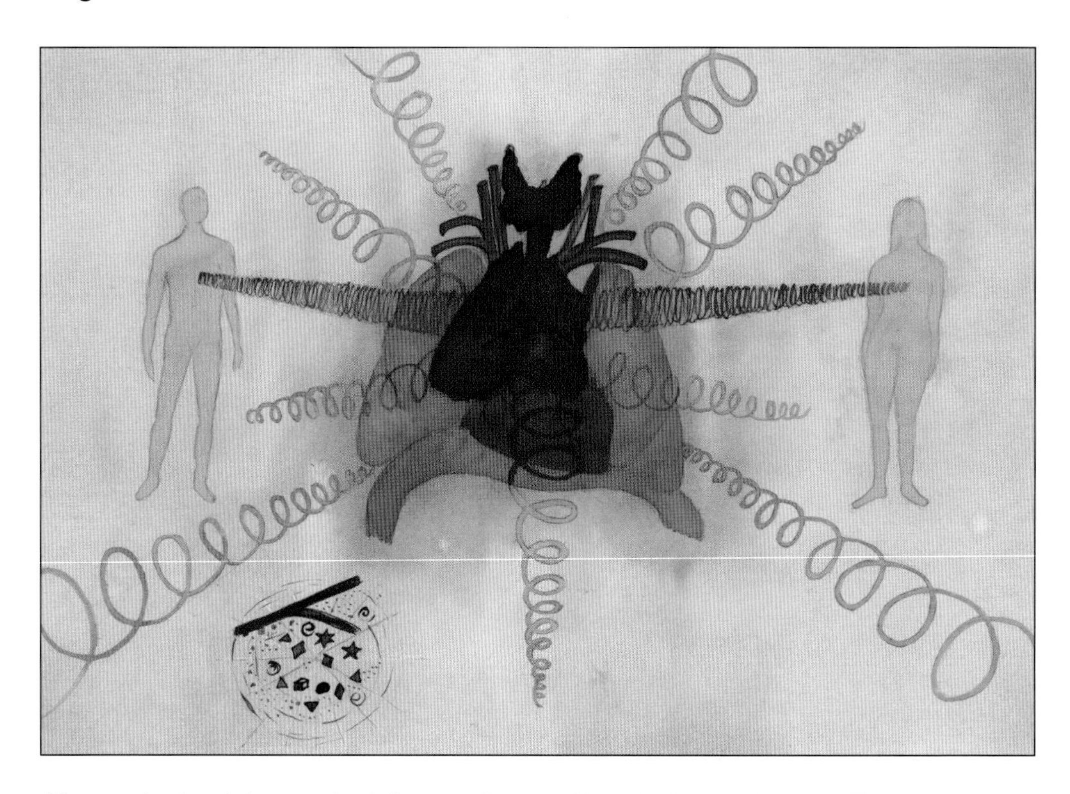

'Thymus gland and the warming influence of parental love', by Nadine Kardesler. The red-coloured thymus gland is shown overlying the heart and lung system, with a Star of David (two tetrahedral shapes overlapping), representing the completed human having a merger of his/her spiritual and physical bodies. In the lower left-side is an expanded view of its cellular structure, showing a matrix of geometric shapes to indicate the gland enables communication and transmission of information. Hence, spirals of reddish light also stream towards and from the thymus gland to 'All That Is' within creation. Streaming towards the thymus gland are warming forces of love from the heart-thymus centres of both parents of the individual (this especially being relevant to the phase of childhood). Without this nurturing energy the thymus gland is liable to prematurely atrophy.

Astrology

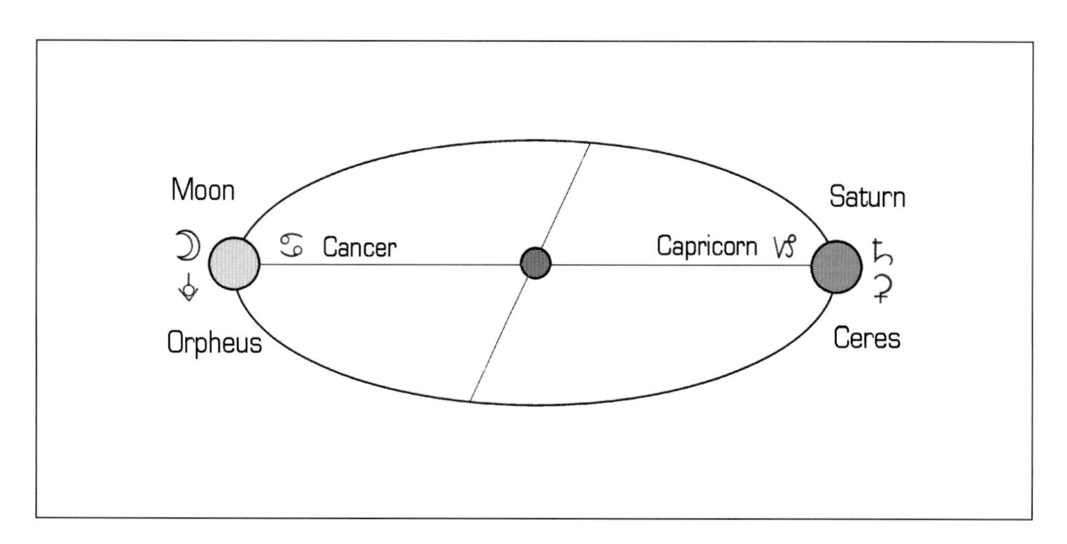

Moon conjunct Orpheus within Cancer, opposite Saturn conjunct Ceres within Capricorn.

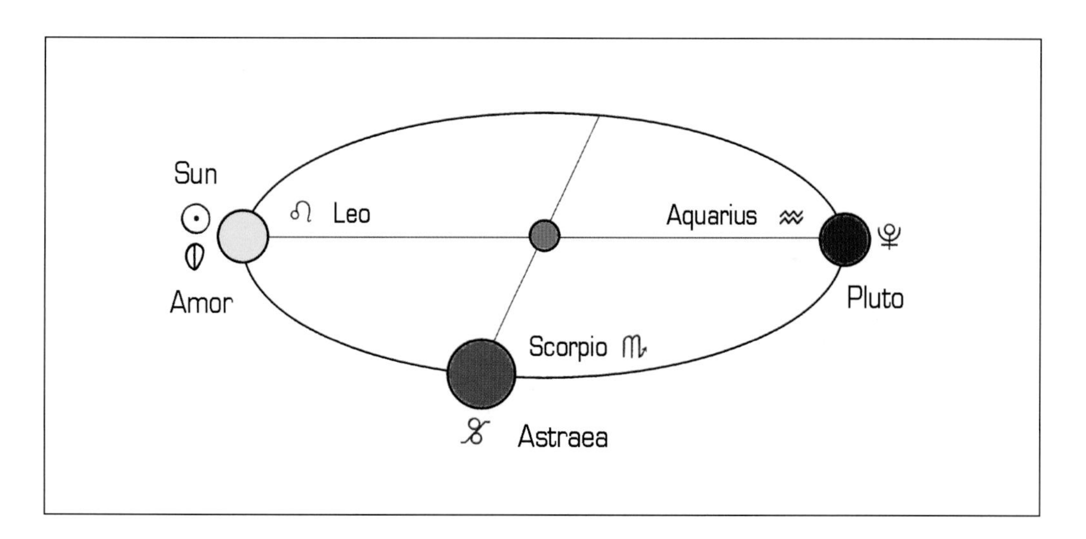

Sun conjunct Amor within Leo, opposite Pluto in Aquarius, squared by Astraea in Scorpio.

Oriental

Chi deficiency of spleen, heart and thymus gland.

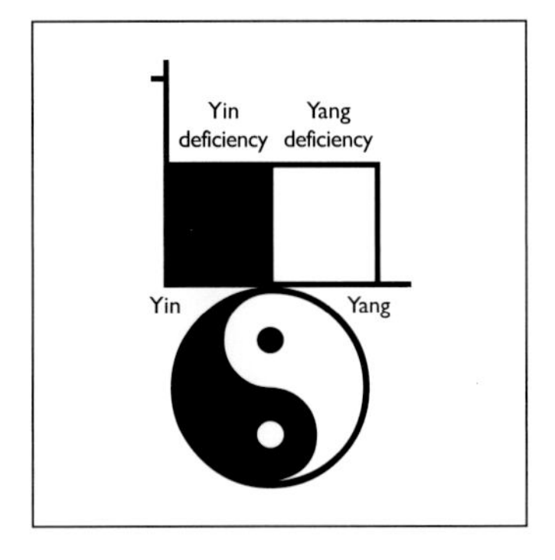

Related images

p.376 Bone marrow suppression
p.504 Chronic bronchitis
p.198 Emphysema
p.306 Bronchiectasis
p.95 Cystic fibrosis
p.375 Autoimmune disease
p.507 Coeliac disease
p.172 Osteogenesis imperfecta
p.171 Osteoporosis
p.206-210 Cancer and malignancy
p.96 Growth chart
p.282 Cardiac muscle sections
p.300 Heart failure, right-sided

THYROIDINUM SARCODE

Original

'Thyroidinum and throat chakra portals', by Yubraj Sharma & Mariam Molokhia. The two lateral lobes of the thyroid gland are shown in blue, overlying the larynx. At the isthmus between the two lobes is a double pyramid with the 'All seeing Eye of God' represented inside. Streaming towards the anterior is a burst of air and at each side are wings, both symbolising the movement of the astral body through the throat through respiration and the strength of the voice. Towards the back is a view of the brainstem and a cosmic star, symbolising the chakra (alta major) that lies posteriorly in line with the throat chakra. Below is a grid to symbolise the grounding to the Earth imparted by the incarnational movement of the astral body into the physical-etheric body.

Astrology

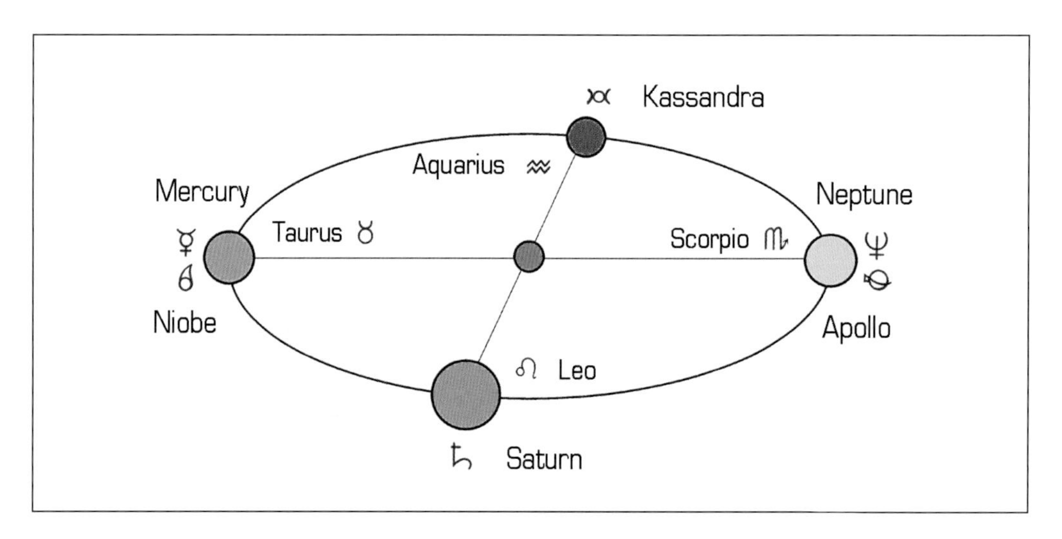

Grand cross, Mercury conjunct Niobe within Taurus opposite Neptune conjunct Apollo within Scorpio, and Saturn in Leo opposite Kassandra in Aquarius.

Oriental

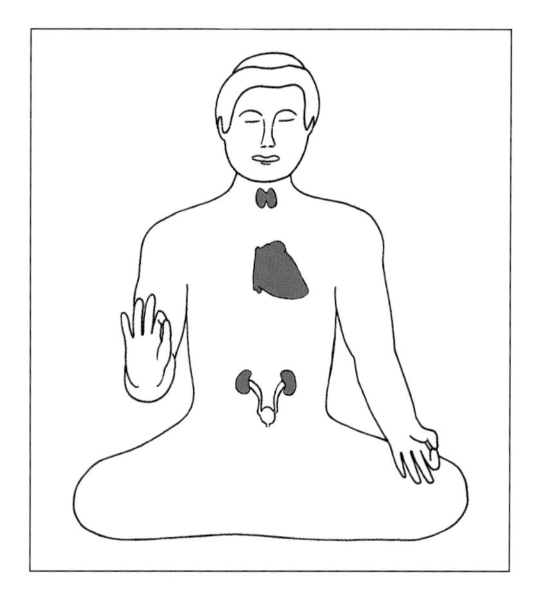

Yang collapse of kidneys, heart and thyroid (hypothyroid states)

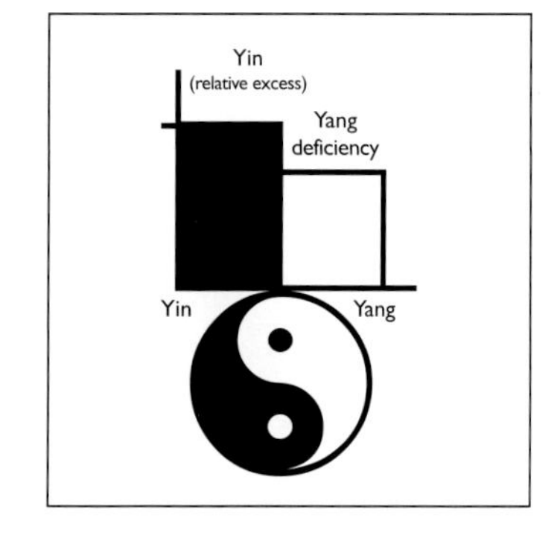

Yin collapse of kidneys, heart and thyroid (hyperthyroid states)

Particulars

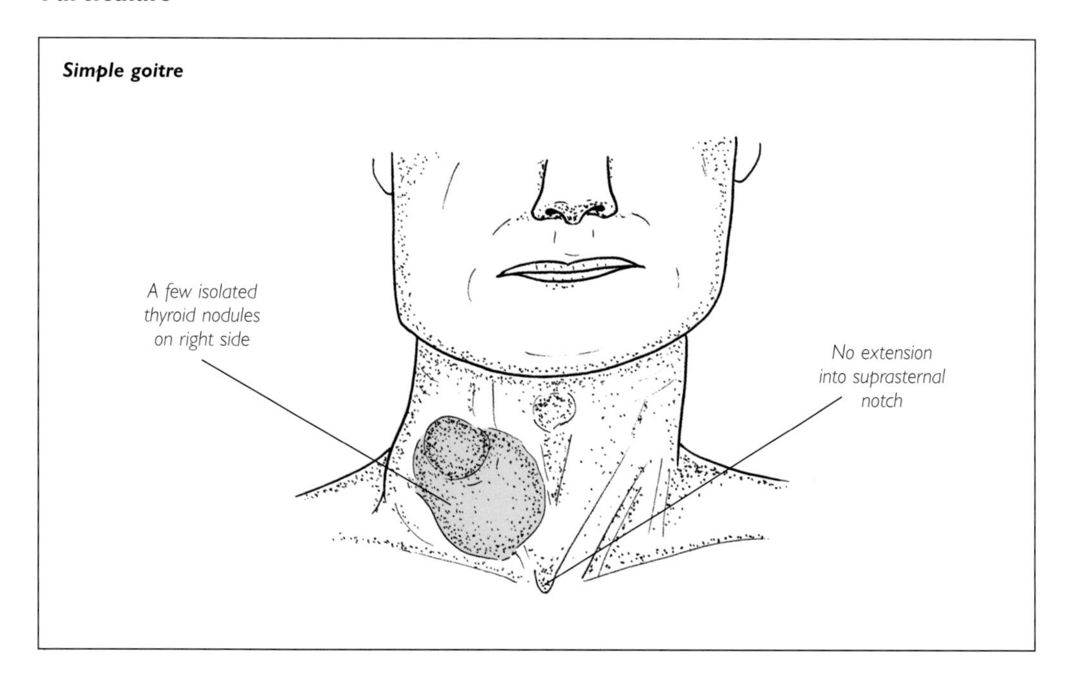

Thyroid enlargement may progress, or level off and/or become smaller. In this example of goitre there is only one area, at the right lobe, of thyroid swelling with nodules, rather than the extensive multinodular appearance shown next.

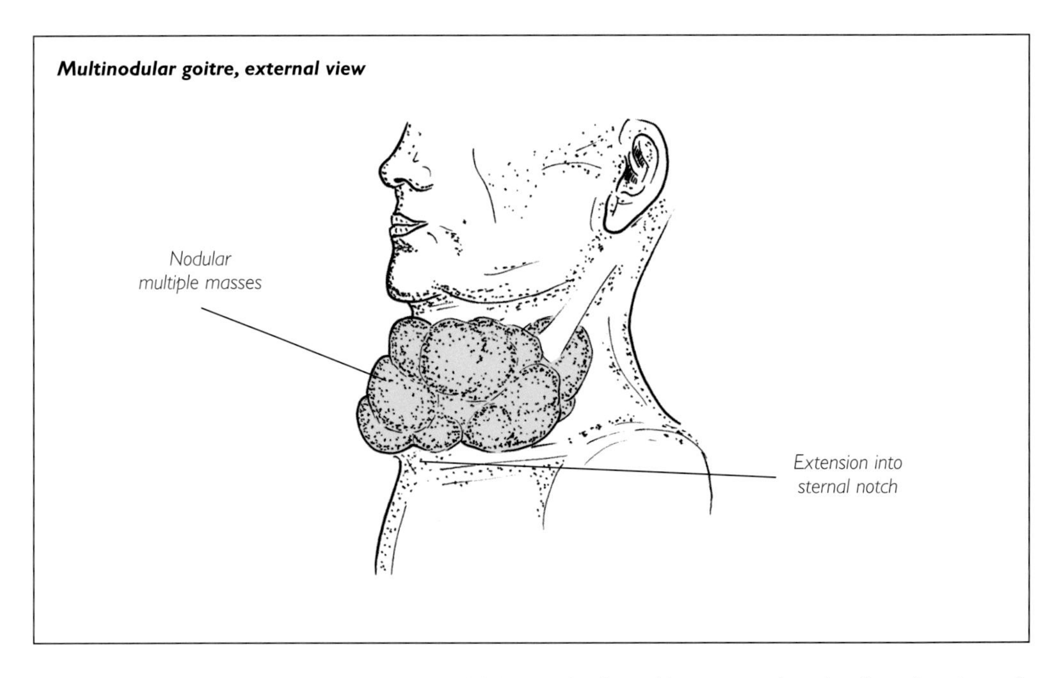

Multinodular goitre, external view

Goitre is enlargement of the thyroid gland. Non-toxic (i.e. without actual endocrine disturbance) goitres are common throughout the world, especially in regions with low iodine content within water and soil (i.e. inland areas). Goitres often initially develop as a diffuse enlargement, later they become nodular or harder with a lumpy consistency. Cystic change may also occur; continued growth can extend beneath the sternum into the thoracic cavity. Large goitres can partially obstruct the trachea or oesophagus, and cause local pain. A single nodular swelling rather than multinodular types are, however, usually more likely to be malignant in nature.

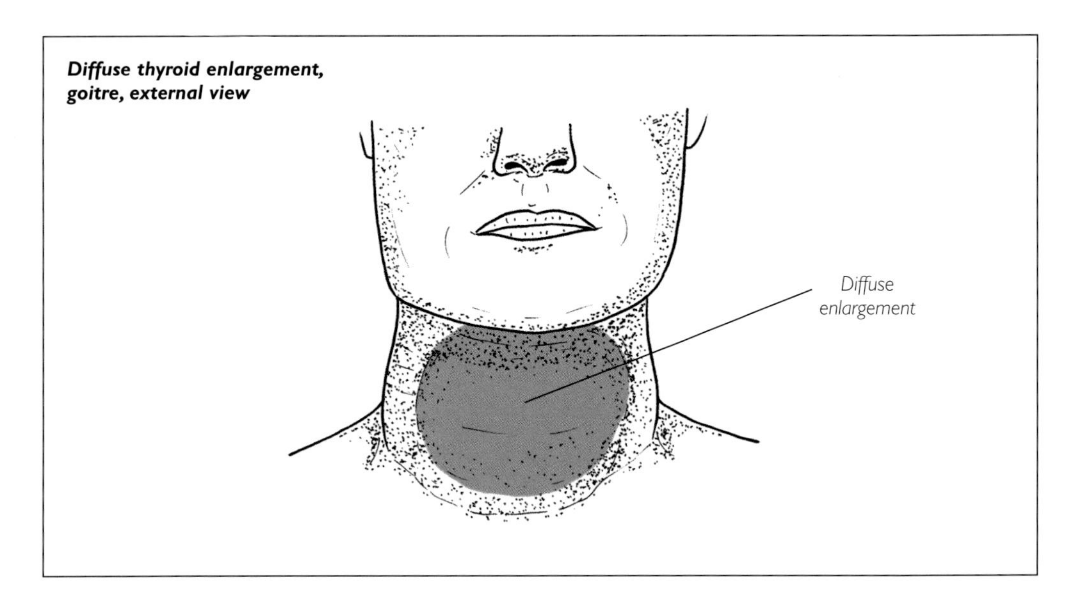

Diffuse thyroid enlargement, goitre, external view

The external appearance of this goitre or swelling is shown. It is a smooth enlargement (rather than irregular and lumpy/nodular) and there may be a palpable thrill (vibration) and audible bruit (a vascular murmur heard by stethoscope) due to the heightened blood flow through the gland.

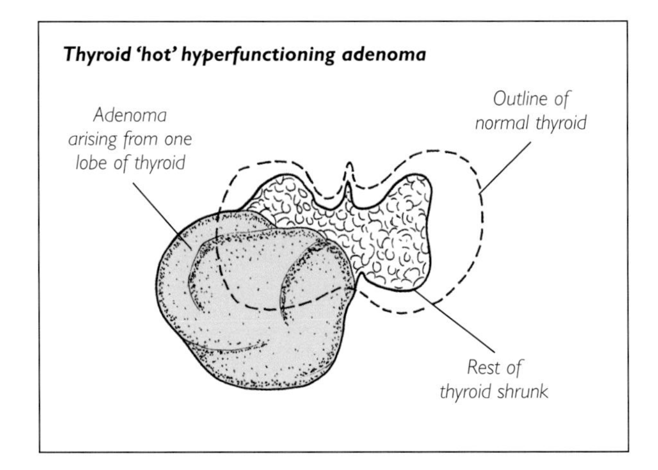

A hot toxic thyroid adenoma is a nodular goitre which is hyperfunctioning. It can also occur as part of a multinodular goitre. The symptoms of hyperthyroidism are present, e.g. a fast heart rate, hypertension etc. In this example the remainder of the thyroid gland is smaller than normal, with a large single nodule in one lobe.

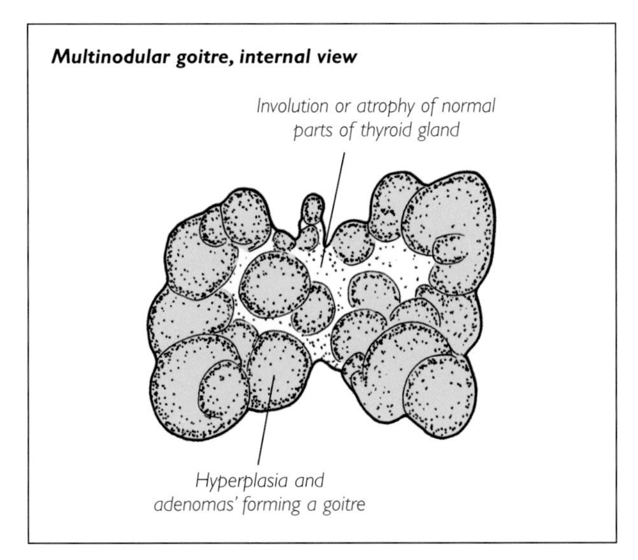

Goitre (of a non-toxic or non-cancerous nature) is due to a deficiency of thyroid hormone secretion.The pituitary then responds with an increased output of thyroid stimulating hormone, which causes hyperplasia or overgrowth of the thyroid gland. Iodine deficiency is one particular cause of goitre, and certain drugs or chemical toxins can also block normal thyroid production to develop a goitre. Thyroid function tests, however, may not show hypothyroidism if the hyperplasia is compensating for the initial deficiency. There is a risk of haemorrhage, cyst formation, fibrosis and calcification of the goitre.

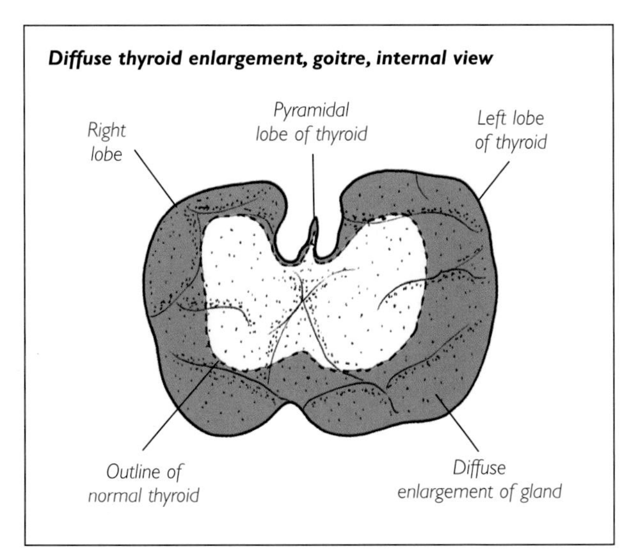

Diffuse enlargement of the thyroid can present as the initial stages of a non-toxic goitre (i.e. without endocrine disturbance). It is also the appearance in diffuse hyperthyroidism (Grave's disease), where the whole thyroid is overactive. There are symptoms of hyperthyroidism. Blood flow and iodine uptake is much increased throughout the gland. This type of hyperthyroidism is associated with exophthalmos or protrusion of the eyes. It is caused by auto-antibodies triggering the thyroid stimulating hormone receptor (TSH) of the thyroid cells.

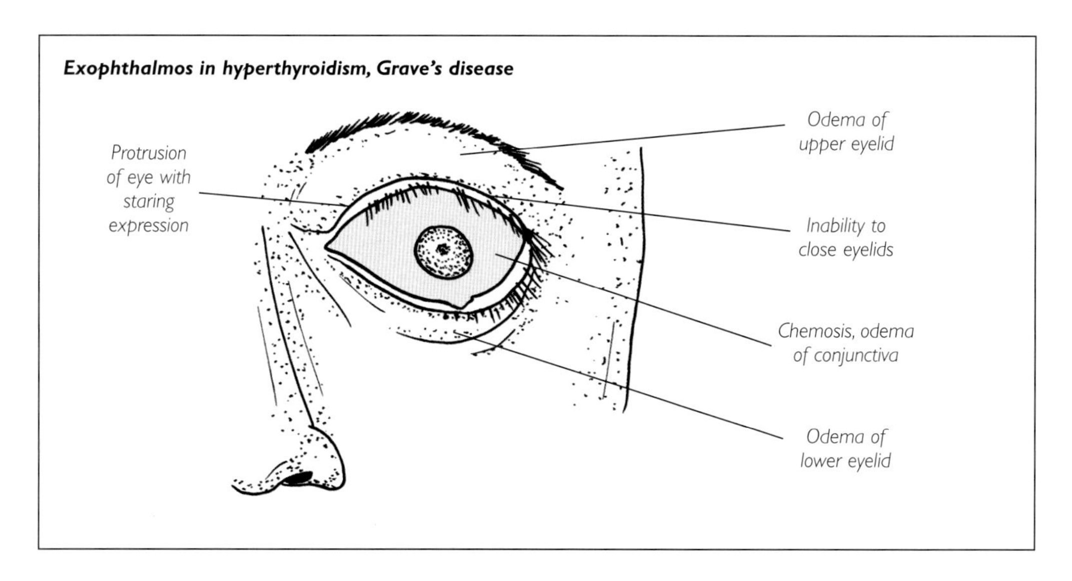

Graves disease is a type of hyperthyroidism associated with exophthalmos or protruding eyes. There is a diffuse enlargement of the thyroid (goitre) with overactive thyroid function. The eye pathology varies from mild to severe, and protrusion is defined by the distance from the canthus to the front of the cornea exceeding 18mm (in the adult). The lids are retracted, with a staring look, dilatation of the pupils, often an eyelid tremor, difficulty in elevating the upper lid and weakness of some of the extra-ocular muscles for eye movement. The eye symptoms often regress once the thyroid function is brought to normal. However, in severe cases with progressive exophthalmos there is odema of the upper and lower eyelids, chemosis (odema of the conjunctiva), increased lacrimation (eye watering) and pain in the orbits. The lids may fail to fully close over the eye, leading to corneal ulceration (which can become infected and cause loss of the eye). The cause of exophthalmos is considered to be an inflammatory (autoimmune) infiltration behind the eye orbits – corresponding to the auto-antibody reaction which triggered hyperactivity within the thyroid gland.

Related images

p.91 Bradycardia
p.130-131 Pleural effusion
p.129 Pericardial effusion
p.300 Pulmonary odema
p.96 Growth chart
p.172 Osteogenesis imperfecta
p.171 Osteoporosis
p.171-172 Rickets and osteomalacia
p.98 Genital underdevelopment
p.434 Mastitis
p.264 Supraventricular tachycardia
p.299 Atrial fibrillation
p.90 Pyrexia of unknown origin
p.586 Muscle wasting

TUBERCULINUM BOVINUM

Museum

Richard Tenant Cooper, 'Sickly female', watercolour, with gouache and pencil. © Wellcome Library, London. The disease represented is tuberculosis, with a sickly female patient sitting up on a balcony with a blanket. She has been coughing bloody sputum; she clenches her handkerchief. Her immense fatigue and wasting is evident, hence the old name for the disease – consumption. There is a beautiful view, yet she cannot appreciate it. This is similar to the tubercular mood, not being able to connect to the beauty of one's surroundings, always feeling that life is elsewhere. Death, the Grim Reaper, stands nearby (as a ghostly skeleton clenching a scythe and an hourglass to indicate her earthly time is expired). In the past, treatment typically included sunlight exposure, especially in high altitude or pine forested mountain retreats. The lack of solar forces nourishing the soul is similar to the phosphoric depletion of light.

Original

'Tuberculinum and the despair of life on Earth: under the arches', by Yubraj Sharma. Homeless individuals sit or lie in despair and forlornness under the bridge and around the riverbank. They cannot see the beauty or splendour of life or the closeness of spirit, as symbolised by the angel above, but remain in a bleak and black attitude towards their corporeal life. Tuberculosis is indeed more prevalent amongst the homeless and disaffected, including asylum and refugee populations. To prevent the personality entering the tubercular mood, there is a need to re-connect to earthly life via the base chakra and adrenal-kidney system. This is analogous to the descent of phosphoric light and acceptance of the journey of incarnation.

FOLLOWING PAGE. 'Tuberculinum and the despair of life on Earth: separation', by Joanna Campion. Above is the gleaming light and structures/temples of the spiritual realm, whilst below is a grey lifeless zone of corporeality. The difference is evident. Very little light trickles down into the individual incarnation. The tubercular mood causes the personality to fly upwards in a vain attempt to escape and return to the spiritual world. It is far better for the personality to become an effective vehicle for the descent of its soul and spirit. This enables the collapse of the illusion of separation between the material and spiritual worlds.

Astrology

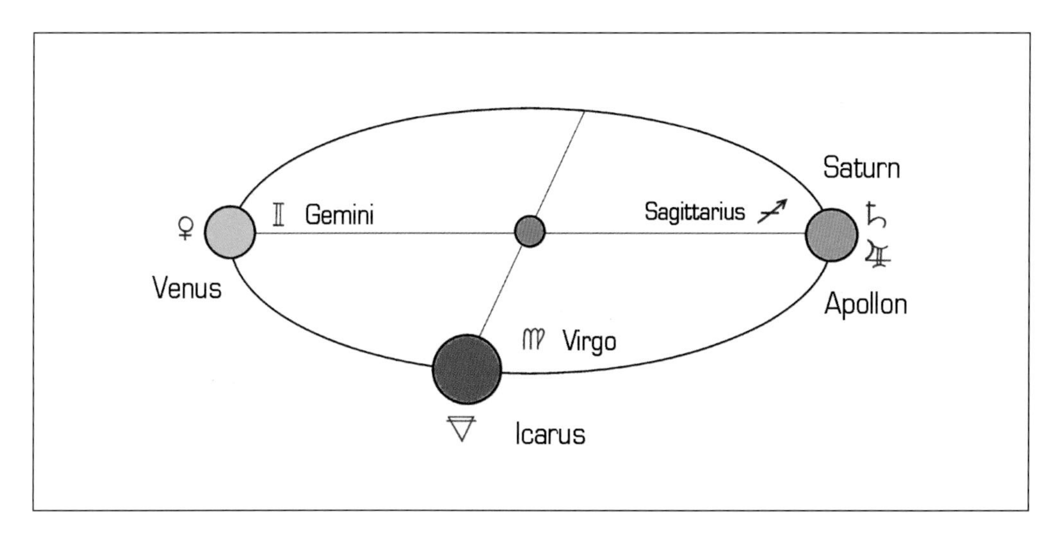

Venus in Gemini opposite Saturn conjunct Apollon within Sagittarius, squared by Icarus in Virgo.

Oriental

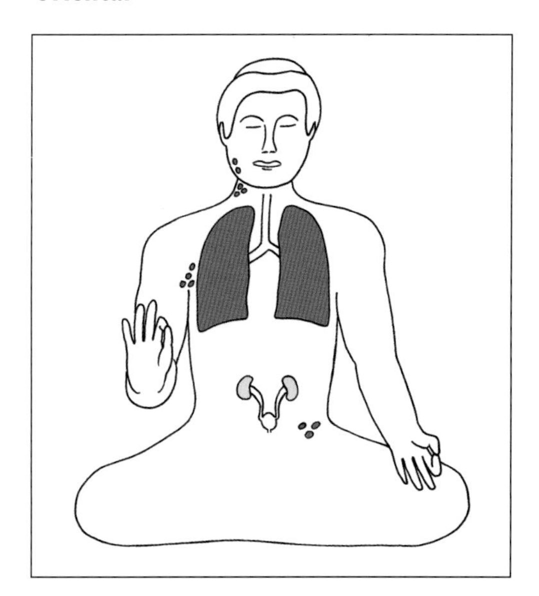

Kidney yin deficiency, with lung chi deficiency and defence chi/lymph node deficiency.

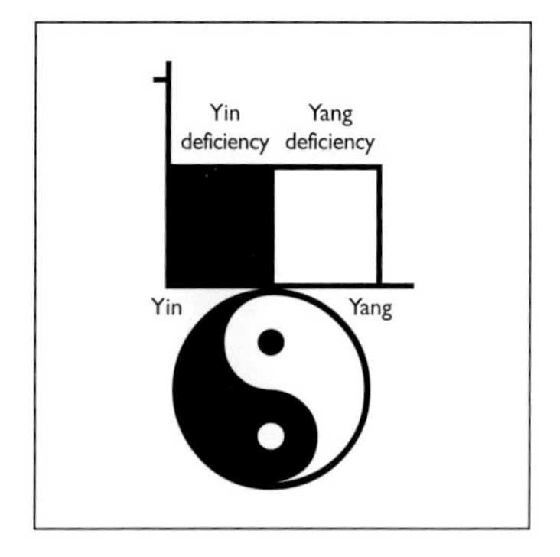

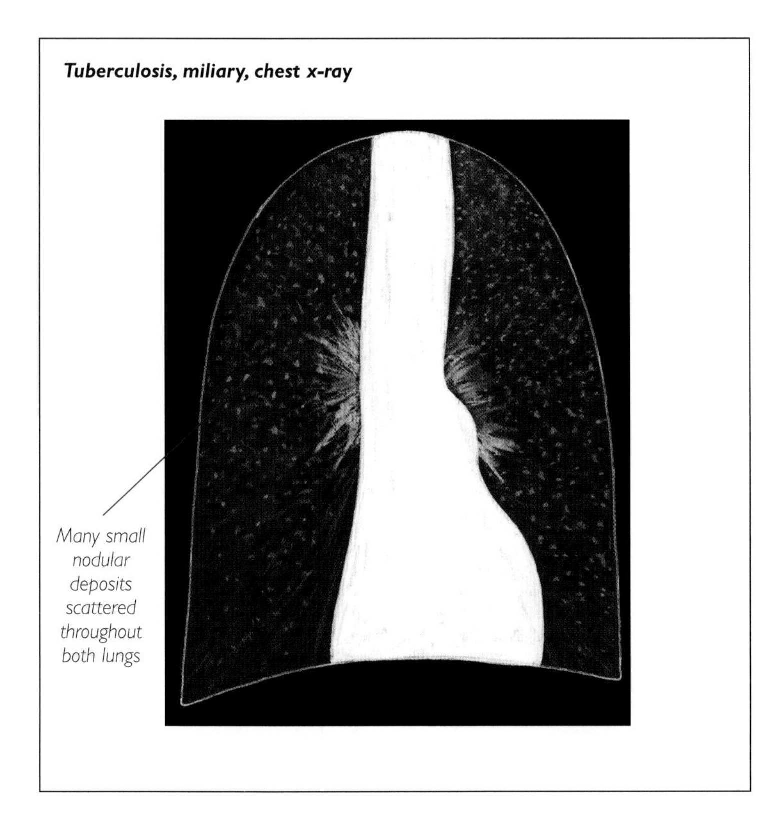

Miliary tuberculosis is due to widespread spread of the TB throughout the lung fields, and is a severe form of the infection with a greater risk of further spread to the brain. There are numerous small lesions scattered throughout the lungs visible as tiny radio-opaque (whitish) nodules.

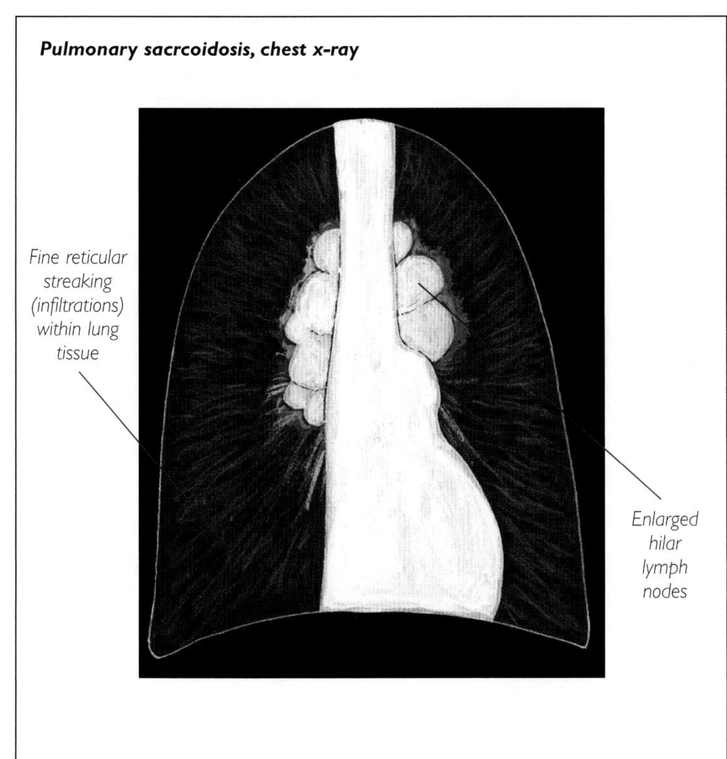

The early chest x-ray features of sarcoidosis are bilateral enlargement of the hilar lymph nodes. Progression of the disease leads to spread into the lung tissue with reticular (appearance of thready lines) and nodular (appearance of small dots or lumps) infiltrations. The chronically scarred lungs will by now have a severe restrictive pattern of dysfunction, with reduced lung volumes, reduced lung tissue elasticity and chronic hypoxemia (deficient blood oxygenation).

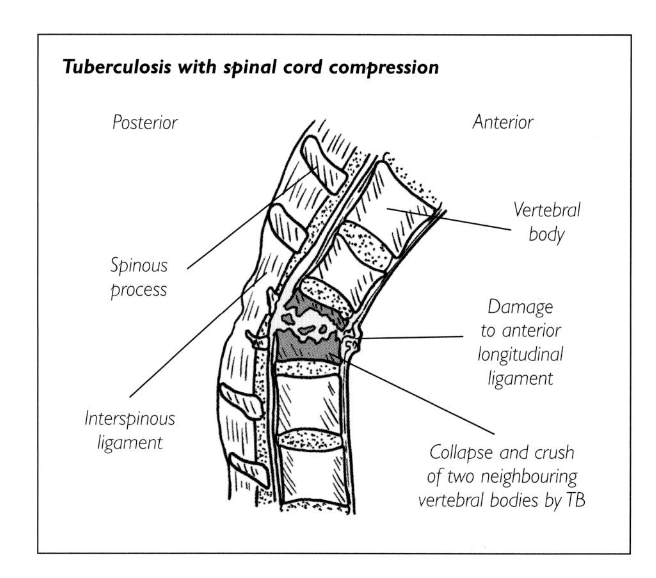

Tuberculosis commonly spreads (through the blood) from the primary infection site (usually the Ghon focus in the lungs) to other organs, such as brain, meninges, bone, kidneys, adrenals or colon. Damage to the bodies of two neighbouring vertebrae causes vertebral collapse. An abscess of infected pus remains, and this can track along the tissues to discharge elsewhere. There are symptoms of local pain and sometimes swelling, alongside the general features of TB (malaise, night sweats and fever). There is the risk of spinal cord compression – the cord lies posterior to the vertebral bodies.

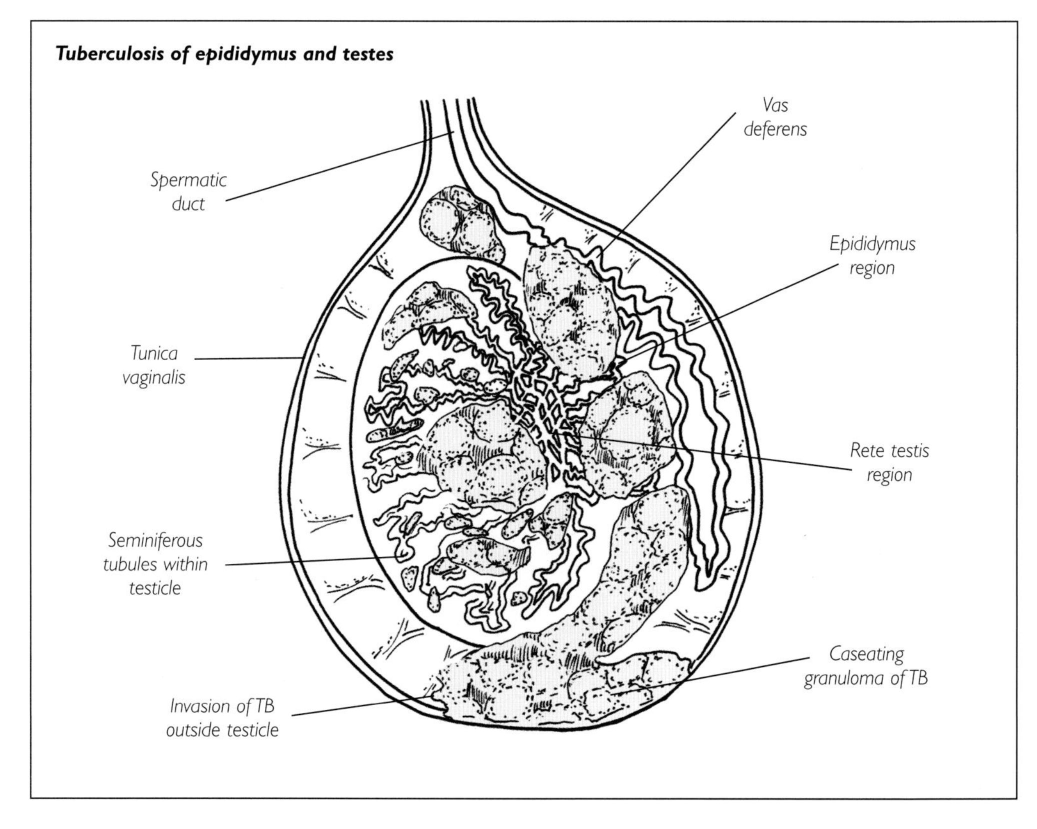

Tuberculosis commonly spreads to the genital tract, although this is generally now a problem mainly in the third world. It has spread from a primary site of infection elsewhere in the body, and the kidneys are almost always infected if spread has also reached the epididymus and testes. There are symptoms of scrotal swelling and pain and sometimes a sinus (hole) discharging pus from the scrotum. It tends to affect both sides of the scrotum. The typical pathology of caseating granuloma has destroyed the normal testes.

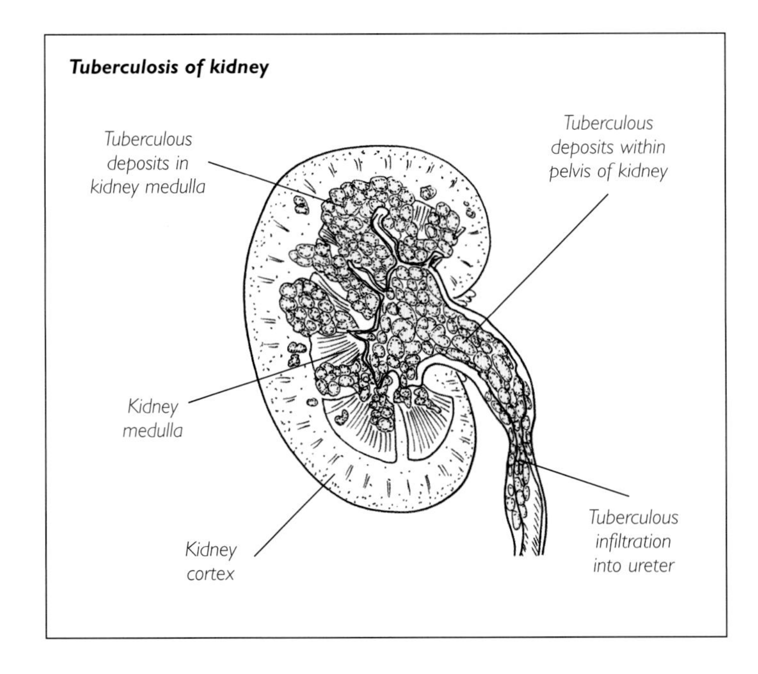

Tuberculosis commonly affects the kidneys, usually spreading from the lungs via the bloodstream. Deposits of tuberculosis usually settle at the upper pole of the kidney. It can spread along the ureters, bladder and furthermore to the prostrate gland, vas deferens, epididymus and testes. The usual tuberculous pathology of fibrosis, scarring, calcification caseation and cavitation can occur. Symptoms are usually vague, but may include burning pain on urination and haematuria (blood within urine).

Related images

p.376 Bone marrow suppression
p.90 Pyrexia of unknown origin
p.504 Chronic bronchitis
p.198 Emphysema
p.306 Bronchiectasis
p.95 Cystic fibrosis
p.506-507 Pneumothorax
p.28 Supplementary oxygen therapy
p.13 Allergic rhinitis
p.461-463 Uterine prolapse
p.603 Splenomegaly
p.103 Tonsillitis
p.408 Sinusitis and nasal polyps
p.718 Pyelonephritis
p.248 & p.250 Renal failure and dialysis
p.593 Adrenal atrophy
p.172 Osteogenesis imperfecta
p.171-172 Rickets and osteomalacia
p.171-172 Osteoporosis
p.278 Spinal cord compression
p.138 Abscess, buttock

URANIUM NITRICUM

Original

'Uranium and castration of the god', by Antonia Chetwynd. The god Uranus is shown at the centre, electricity and blood from his castration wound falling to Gaia to create Titans (as well as the goddess Venus). Saturn/Cronos (his son), having inflicted the injury, is shown on the right. The fiery nature of the astrological Uranus and Saturn are shown as a dragon of creation looping around the two characters.

Astrology

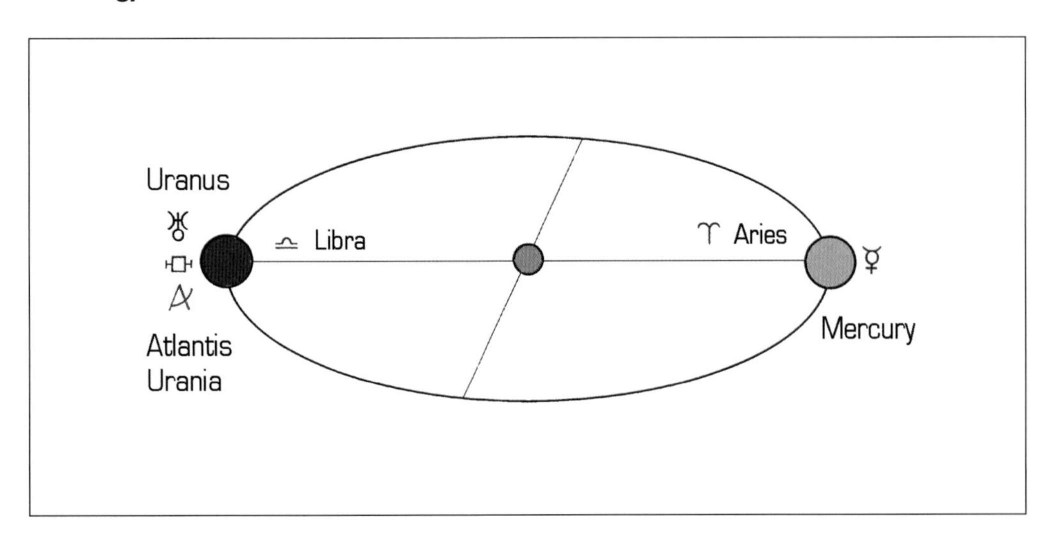

Uranus conjunct Atlantis and Urania within Libra, opposite Mercury in Aries.

Oriental

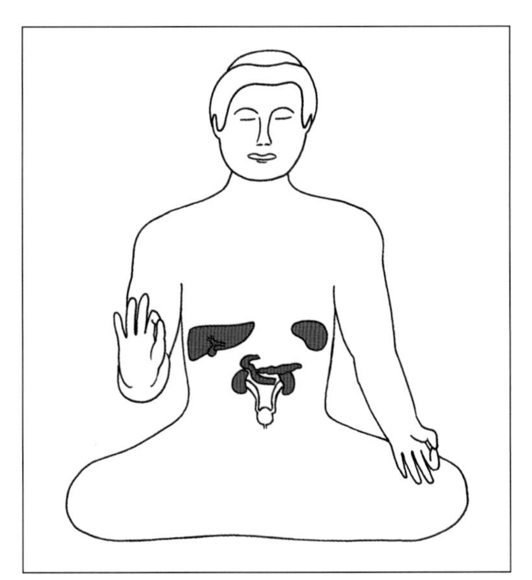

Fire within the liver, spleen, pancreas and kidneys.

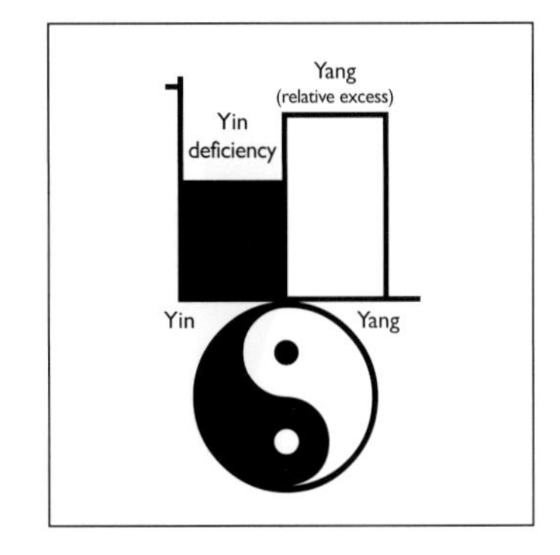

VERATRUM ALBUM

Museum

Francisco de Goya, 'The Colossus'. Prado Museum, Madrid © 1990, Photo Scala, Florence. The image is often described by art historians as an allegory of the Spanish war, either as a representation of Spain itself, or of the crushing power of war. Indeed, a Spanish poet's description of the Napoleonic wars may have inspired the piece: "On a height above yonder cavernous amphitheatre, a pale Colossus rises, caught by the fiery light of the setting sun". Goya had seemed to become consumed by the issue of hatred and the state of hell that resided within humanity. It appears throughout much of his later work that a human being with authority or power over another will abuse it to harm, deprave or destroy. The atmospheric space around the giant appears airless, oppressive. The lower legs of the being are not visible, almost as if it floats in space. It is moving away from the crowd, and its eyes are closed. The clenched fist is not even directed to the people, all suggestive that it has little to do with the war they are caught within on the ground. Nonetheless, the image correlates well with the story in myth of gigantomachy, of the war between the Olympian gods and the titan-giants of ancient Greece. The defeated giants were cast down to Tartarus, an abode within Hades-underworld, not killed but placed into slumber.

Astrology

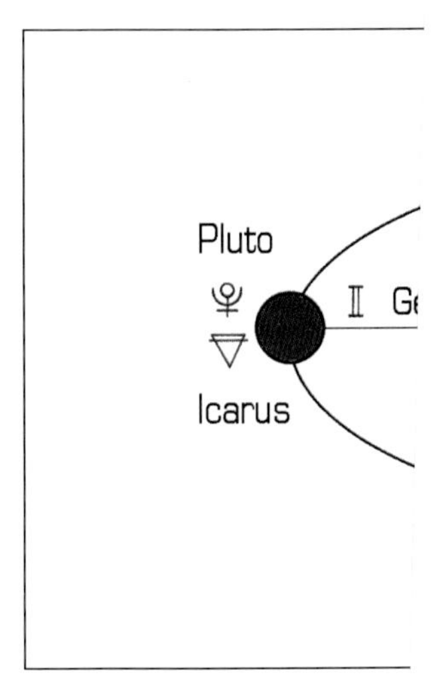

Mercury conjunct Atlantis w

Oriental

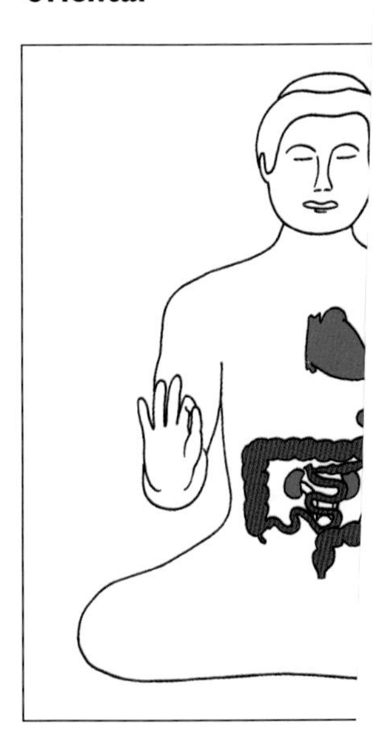

Original

'Veratrum album and animal-human stages of evolution', by Caroline Hamilton (plant) & Yubraj Sharma (animal-human forms). A goat and goat-man is shown on each side, to indicate the mixing of animal genes with human form during human evolution. Progressively these denser codes have been removed from the human gene pool, but incarnation of an animalised state within a human indicates retardant stages.

'Veratrum album and ape-
stage baby primate, with th
Lemurian root race). Howe
into the adult stage ape as
the left-side is a human pr
ape-body nature. The hum
the density in his various p

VIPERA

Original

'Vipera and destruction of the blood circulation', by Caroline Hamilton. On the right-side a snake is shown ascending the inferior vena cava on its way to the right side of the heart, at its tail end the blood has coagulated (as in deep vein thrombosis). On the left-side the viper is travelling along the arch and descending aorta, but an aneurysm has developed within the aorta just proximal to its bifurcation into the iliac vessels. The snake is bursting out of this dilated portion, symbolising the similar rupture that can occur of an aneurysm.

Astrology

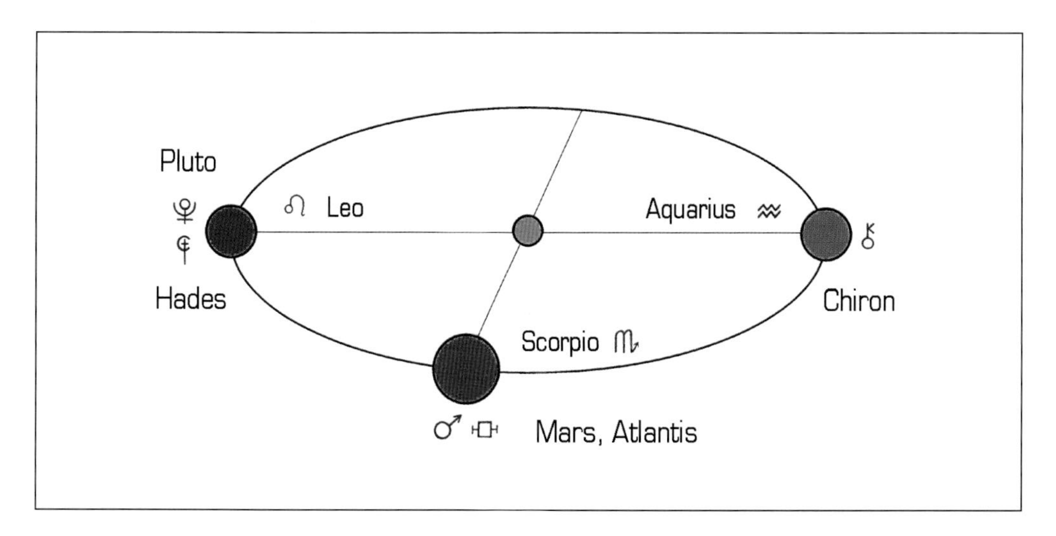

Pluto conjunct Hades within Leo, opposite Chiron in Aquarius, squared by Mars conjunct Atlantis within Scorpio.

Oriental

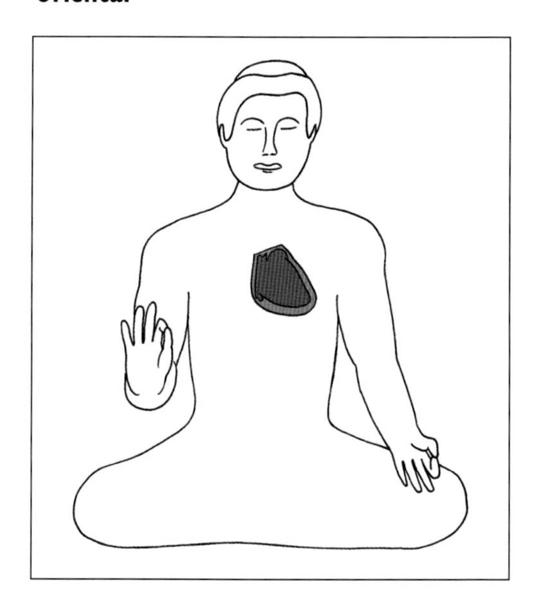

Heat invasion of the pericardium, with fire-heat congealing the heart blood.

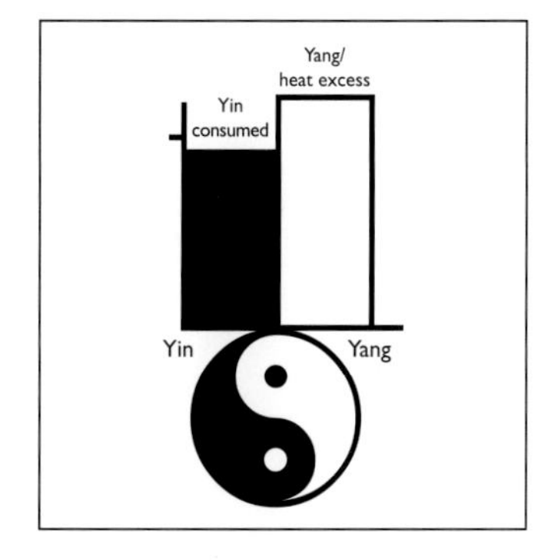

Particulars

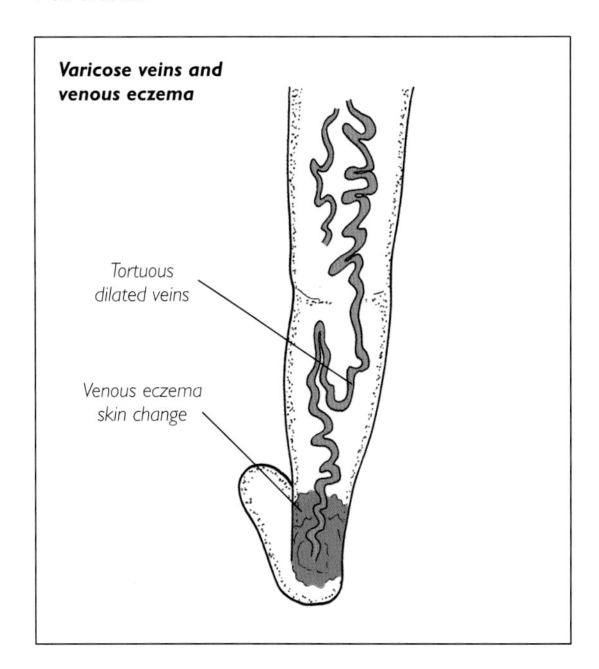

Varicose veins are very common, especially in the elderly and after pregnancy. The veins are dilated, prominent, tortuous and bulge outwards under the skin. Normally the vein conducts blood at low pressures and has a thin musculoelastic wall. When subjected to increased pressure over a long enough period the wall tension causes initial hypertrophy of the elastic tissues in the wall, the lumen dilates and then atrophy of the muscles and elastic tissues within the walls develops. These become replaced by fibrous tissue and cause the wall to stretch and bulge outwards.There are often heredity factors with defective valves in the veins. Increased venous blood pressure can occur with any obstruction to the venous flow, e.g. a pelvic tumour, chronic constipation or pregnancy.

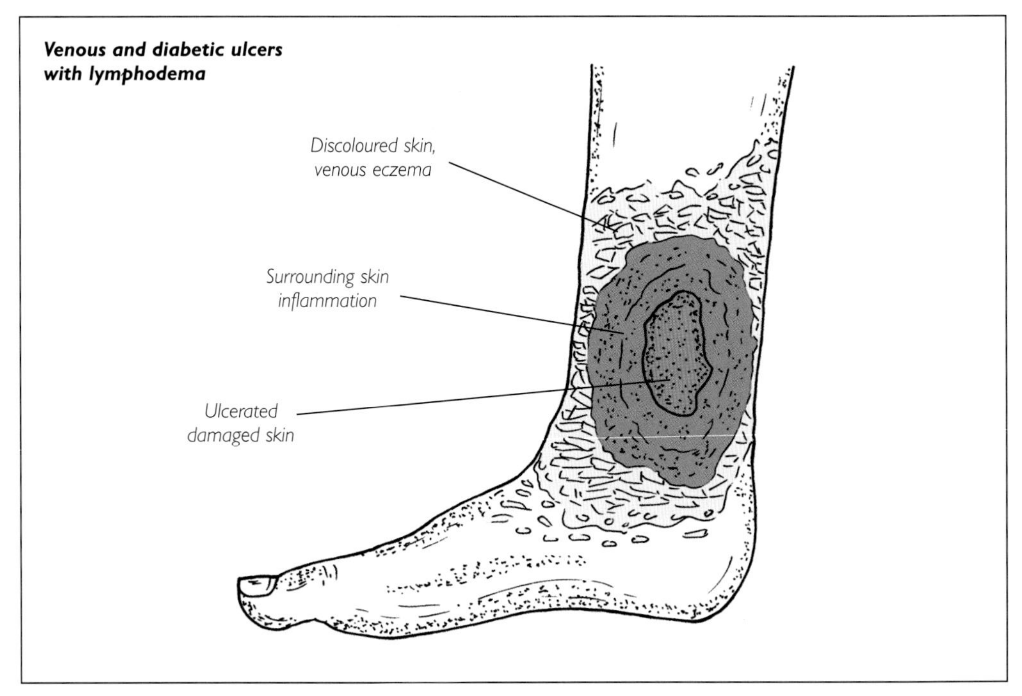

Chronic disease of the veins in the legs, such as varicose veins, thrombosis of the veins, phlebitis (inflammation of the veins) can predispose to venous eczema or skin damage, especially at the medial section of the lower legs near the ankles. The skin ulcerates, with surrounding skin discolouration. A similar problem can occur with poorly controlled diabetes mellitus and in chronic lymphodema (congestion of the lymph vessels).

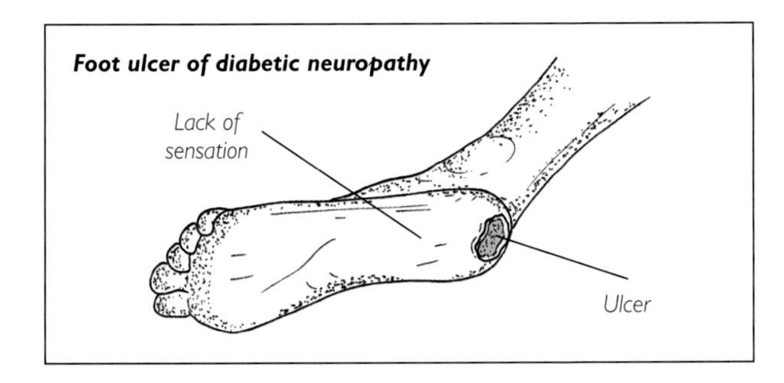

Diabetes can damage either or both motor and sensory nerves, as well as voluntary and/or involuntary nerve control systems. With loss of pain and position sense there is a tendency to foot damage and painless ulcers develop. The arterial blood supply may still be sufficient – the causes are neuropathic rather than ischaemic.

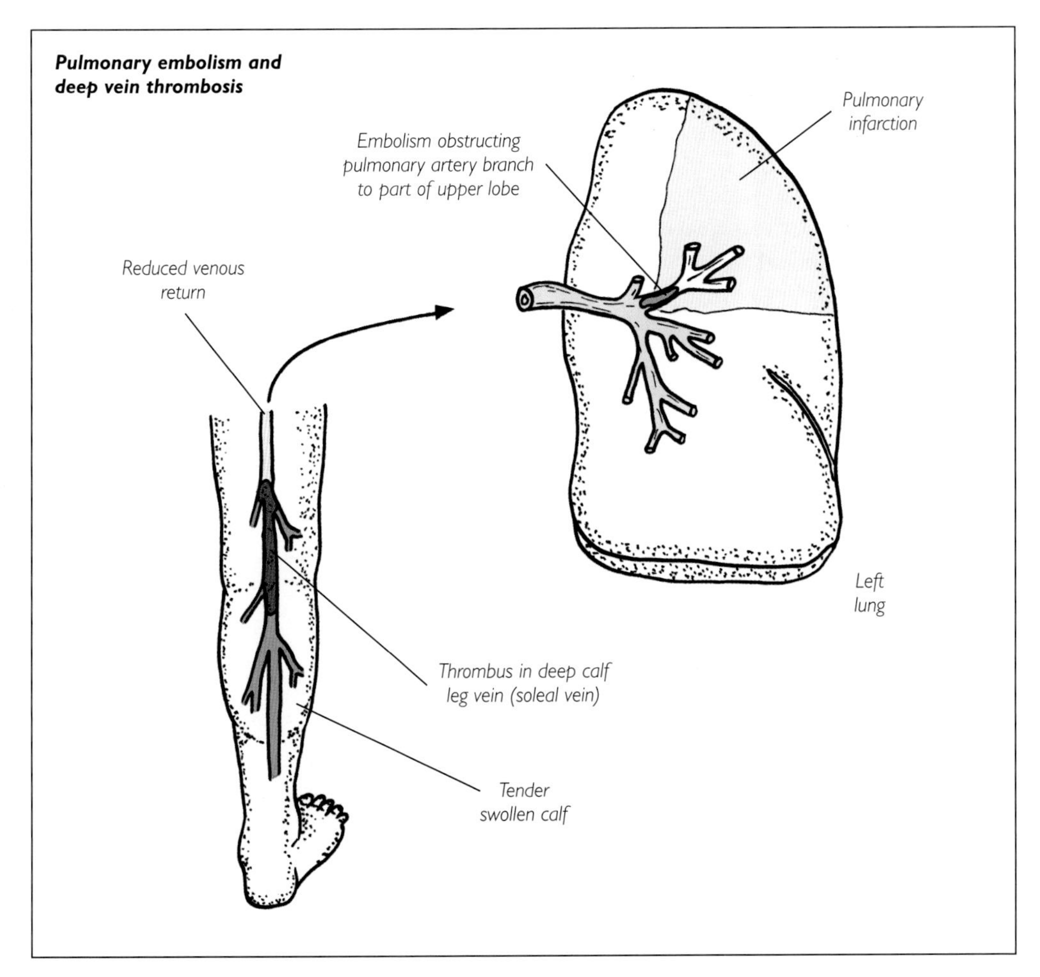

Thrombosis can occur in superficial or deep leg veins, but the risk of embolism is low with the former site. Deep vein thrombosis will usually present with a swollen and tender calf. A fragment of thrombus can embolise to travel through the right-sided heart and lodge at a small pulmonary artery/arteriole. Depending on the degree of arterial obstruction (i.e. size of artery involved, size of embolus and extent of collateral circulation) there is ischaemia and infarction (death) of the lung tissue supplied. The symptoms are acute onset chest pain, coughing of blood and breathlessness. Risk factors for DVT/PE include venous stasis (e.g. prolonged sitting in elderly people with already sluggish venous circulation or incompetent vein valves), post-operative patients, oral contraceptive drugs and those with hyper-coagulation diseases.

Investigation of deep vein thrombosis, venography

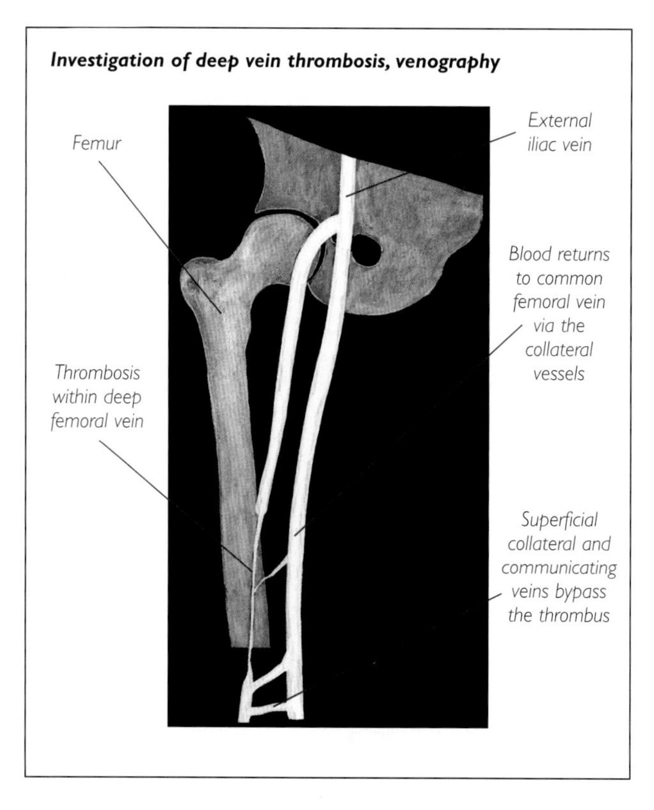

The most accurate method of establishing the diagnosis of a deep vein thrombosis is venography (also called phlebography). Water-soluble contrast solution is injected into a foot vein. The progress of the contrast is followed by x-ray fluoroscopy and spot x-ray films (overhead radiographs). Anatomically the venous system of the leg is categorised into 4 types of vein: (1) the deep veins, running parallel to the arteries, (2) superficial veins, running just under the skin, (3) deep muscle veins and (4) communicating veins, which connect the superficial and deep veins together. As shown in this example, a filling defect is shown within the lumen of the deep femoral vein towards the knee joint. Blood is diverted through the communicating veins and thereby returns through the common femoral vein back to the external iliac vein.

Investigation of pulmonary embolism, ventilation-perfusion scan

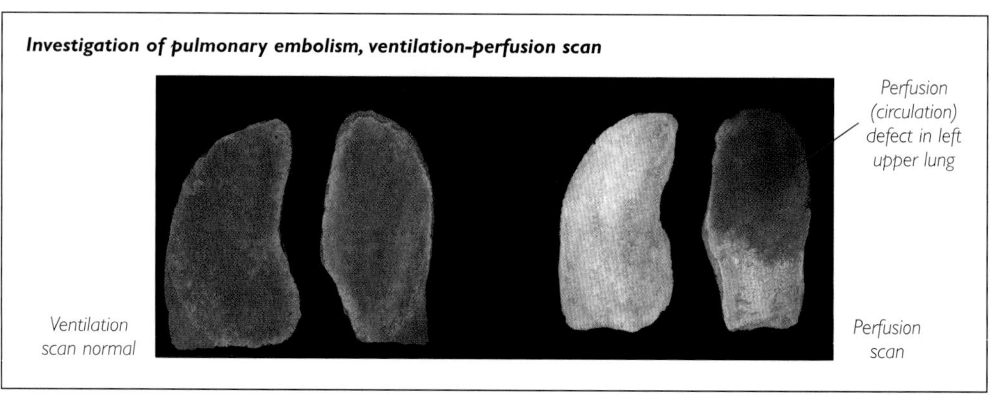

A lung scan, using radio-isotope markers, can establish the presence of a pulmonary embolism. The perfusion scan involves intravenously injecting human albumin protein labelled with technetium-99m. These particles are large enough to impact in the lung capillaries and lodge there for a few hours. A gamma radiation camera is then used to record the location of the albumin, providing a scan pattern of the pulmonary blood flow. Deficient areas of flow therefore imply a pulmonary embolism causing obstruction to the arterial supply for that region. The ventilation scan involves inhalation of xenon-133 gas into the lungs, its distribution is then recorded by a scan. The two scans must be compared in order to see any discrepancy whereby ventilation is intact for a given area of deficient blood flow – as this is more conclusive of a pulmonary embolism. Various lung diseases (e.g. asthma or pneumonia) cause areas of impairment in both the ventilation and perfusion scans, and therefore a perfusion scan by itself may falsely diagnose a pulmonary embolism. This example is a sample V/Q scan that mirrors the pathological site of the embolism shown on p.759.

Related images

p.542 Portal hypertension
p.640 Peripheral arterial disease
p.144 Coronary artery disease
p.145 Angina
p.451 Myocardial infarction
p.281 Endocarditis
p.519-520 Valvular heart disease
p.282 Cardiac muscle sections, cardiomyopathy
p.144 Coronary artery disease
p.81 Post-myocardial infarction aneurysm
p.300 Heart failure, right-sided
p.640 Peripheral arterial disease
p.133 Liver failure and ascites
p.443 Arteriosclerosis
p.574 Hypertension
p.321 Arteriosclerosis and hypertension in eye
p.321-322 Retinal vascular disease
p.571 Retinal degeneration
p.288 Immune thrombocytopenia purpura

ZINCUM METALLICUM

Original

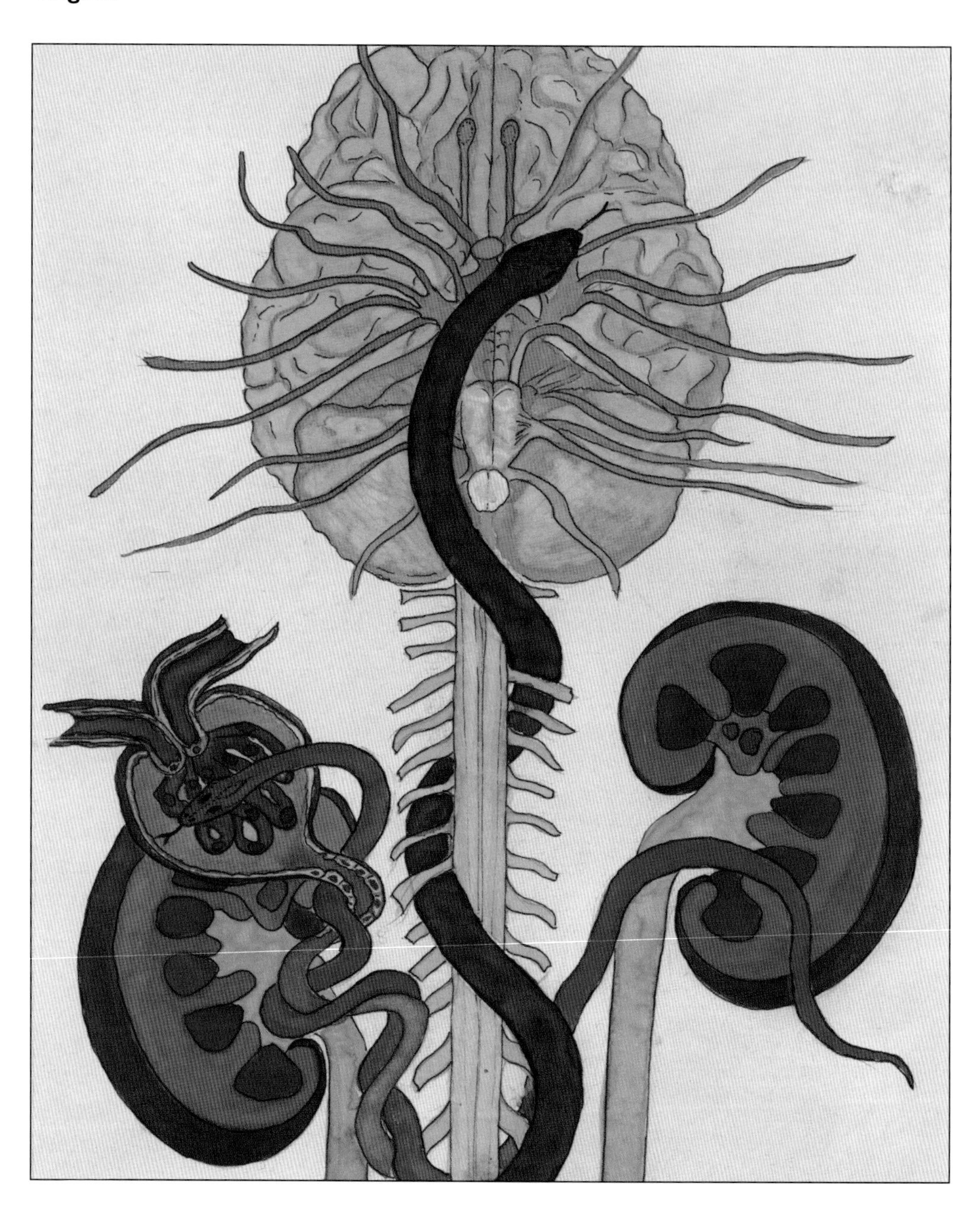

'Zincum and snake activity within the kidney and nervous systems', by Nadine Kardesler. The nervous system is vitalised by radiations of chi from the kidneys, both treatable through zincum. Snake venom has a relationship to zinc, this being an essential ingredient. One snake is shown winding around both kidneys (on the right kidney is a cut-out section of a filtering glomerulus). A second snake is coiled around the spinal cord into the basal brain.

Astrology

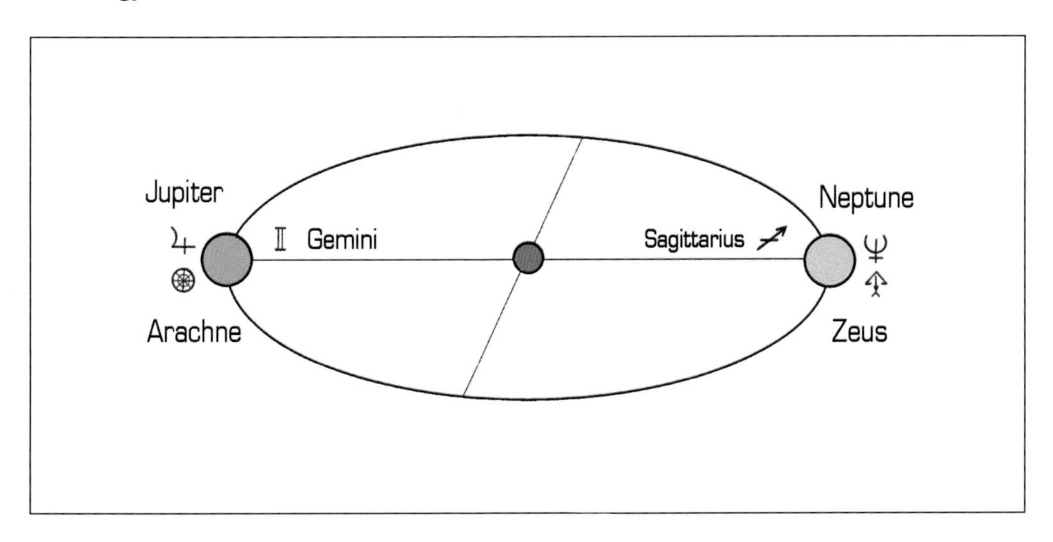

Jupiter conjunct Arachne within Gemini, opposite Neptune conjunct Zeus within Sagittarius.

Oriental

Kidney and liver yin deficiency, with interior wind invading the brain and muscles.

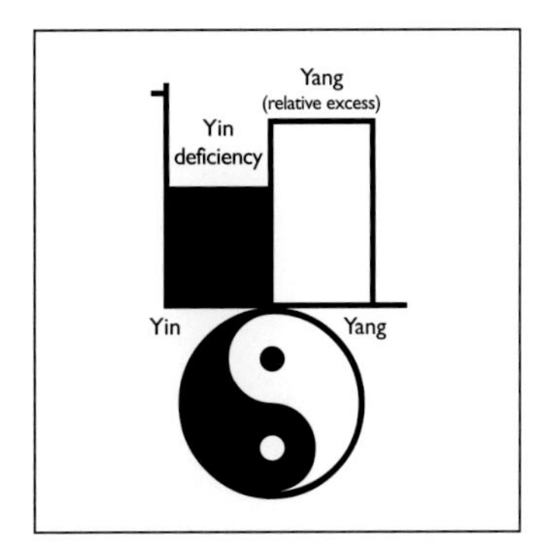

Particulars

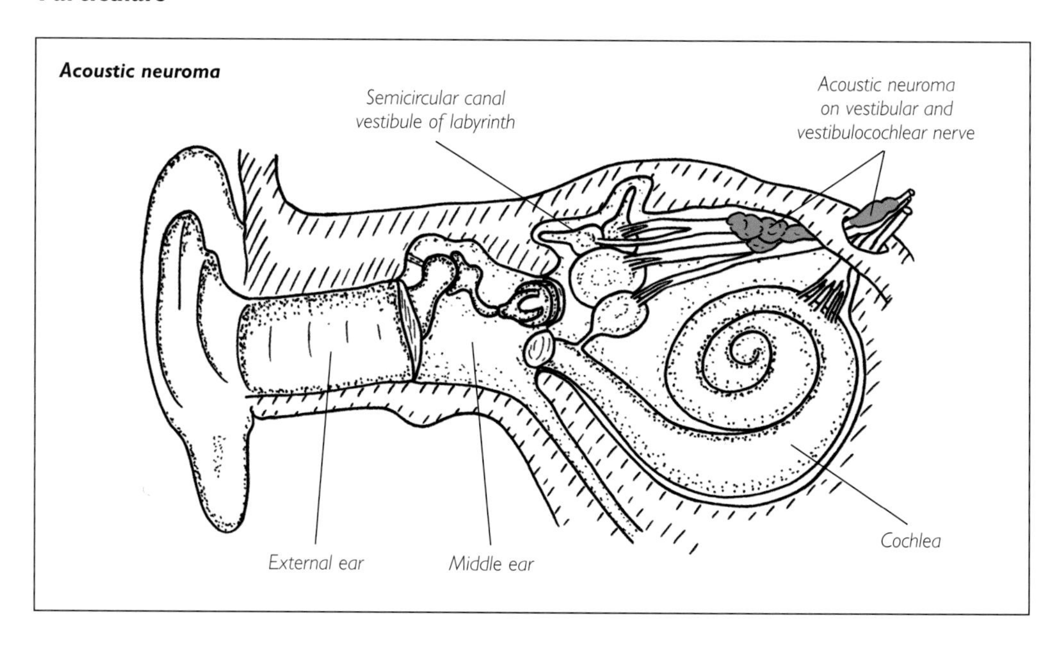

Acoustic neuroma

An acoustic neuroma is a benign tumour (a neurofibroma) of the vestibulocochlear nerve sheath. It can be slow growing and cause progressive deafness, vertigo (sensation of spinning). As it enlarges it can also compress on the nearby trigeminal nerve (5th cranial nerve) to cause numbness on that side of the face, and compress the facial nerve (7th cranial nerve) to cause facial weakness. Ataxia or incoordination is also a feature.

Related images

p.232 & p.343 Multiple sclerosis
p.586-587 Poliomyelitis
p.277 Motor neurone disease
p.586 Muscle wasting
p.35 Spinal myelitis
p.18 Parkinson's disease
p.55 Encephalitis
p.17 Alzheimer's disease
p.17 Investigation of higher cortical function
p.285-286 Cerebrovascular accident
p.574 Peripheral neuropathy
p.364 Syringomyelia
p.3 Trigeminal neuralgia
p.434 Mastitis
p.593 Adrenal atrophy
p.389 Lumbar puncture
p.527-528 Headaches
p.260 Meniere's disease
p.258 Labyrinthitis

APPENDIX: CRANIOSACRAL IMAGES

The images pertain to the Craniosacral glossary of Volume I Spiritual Bioenergetics of Homoeopathic Materia medica and are arranged in the order of that text. It is beyond the scope of this book to define every aspect of the neuro- and cranial anatomical illustration. Within the cranial base images (for instance see p.774), the sutures have been shown as wide spaces between the cranial bones. This space is, nonetheless, a joint (also known as a synchondrosis) which has either retained a fibrous flexibility or has become fused into bone. A space is, however, utilised to demonstrate some of the various compression pathologies possible. Not all the remedies pertaining to the many cranial base pathologies possible have been provided, partly due to the long listings possible. Also, only the more extreme pathological states of cranial base compression or strain have been illustrated. Excessive separation of the cranial base or vault bones at their sutures has not been illustrated, although being relevant for certain remedies (such as Fluoric acid). However, a short list of remedies for such excess laxity at the sutures has been listed within the image of the normal cranial base, p.774.

Nonetheless, where possible, each remedy has been listed with the relevant pathology heading, or alongside the main image. This analysis is not exhaustive of all the effects of a homoeopathic prescription, which should be properly found only on an individual case analysis of the patient. Hence, the craniosacral profile of a remedy is to be regarded as a guideline to understanding the remedy and prescription. Furthermore, the craniosacral system functions as a holism. For example, all the remedies should technically improve the synchronicity or transmission of the cranial to spinal rhythm, but a view has been taken to list some of the most useful remedies in each pathology rather than everything. Most of the remedies would influence the sphenoid bone, this being a central pivot for the cranial base and vault and flow of the cerebrospinal fluid. Therefore, practically every remedy could be feasibly listed somewhere with the sphenoid-basilar junction distortions on p.775-777. Only those remedies specifically linked to sphenoid-basilar joint deviations have been listed adjoining these images.

Note that some new terms have been created to define the ventricular system. Hence, the 6th ventricle for cerebrospinal fluid is defined as the central aqueduct within the spinal cord, and the 7th ventricle is regarded as the subarachnoid spaces around the brain. These are not labels used in other textbooks, for the time being.

Each remedy should ideally also be consulted within volume I. Thus, in the image 'Circulation of cerebrospinal fluid disorders' on p.767, the listing of remedies under the pathology 'Mucus or damp congestion within csf' contains a wide range of possible pathology. Allium cepa and Euphrasia could relate to allergic and sinusitis related head mucus congestion pervading the cerebrospinal fluid (e.g. after suppression by antihistamines or from a deeply acting sycotic miasm). On the other hand, Apis, Bryonia or Pyrogenium are more particular to meningitis induced pus within the csf. Carcinosin is more suited to inflammatory cells of a malignant morphology entering the csf space, for example through metastatic disease or after disease suppression.

Circulation of cerebrospinal fluid (csf)

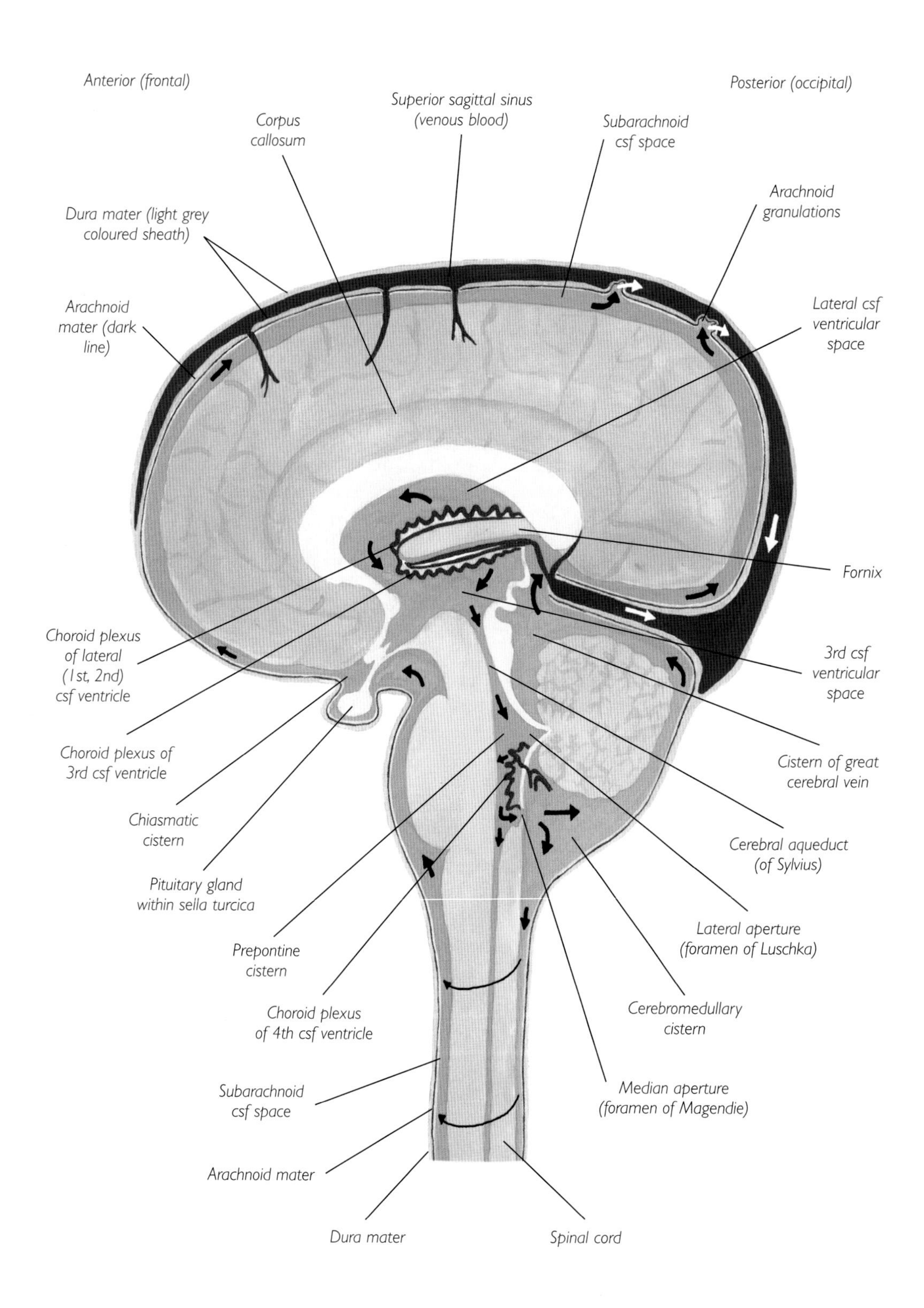

Circulation of cerebrospinal fluid disorders

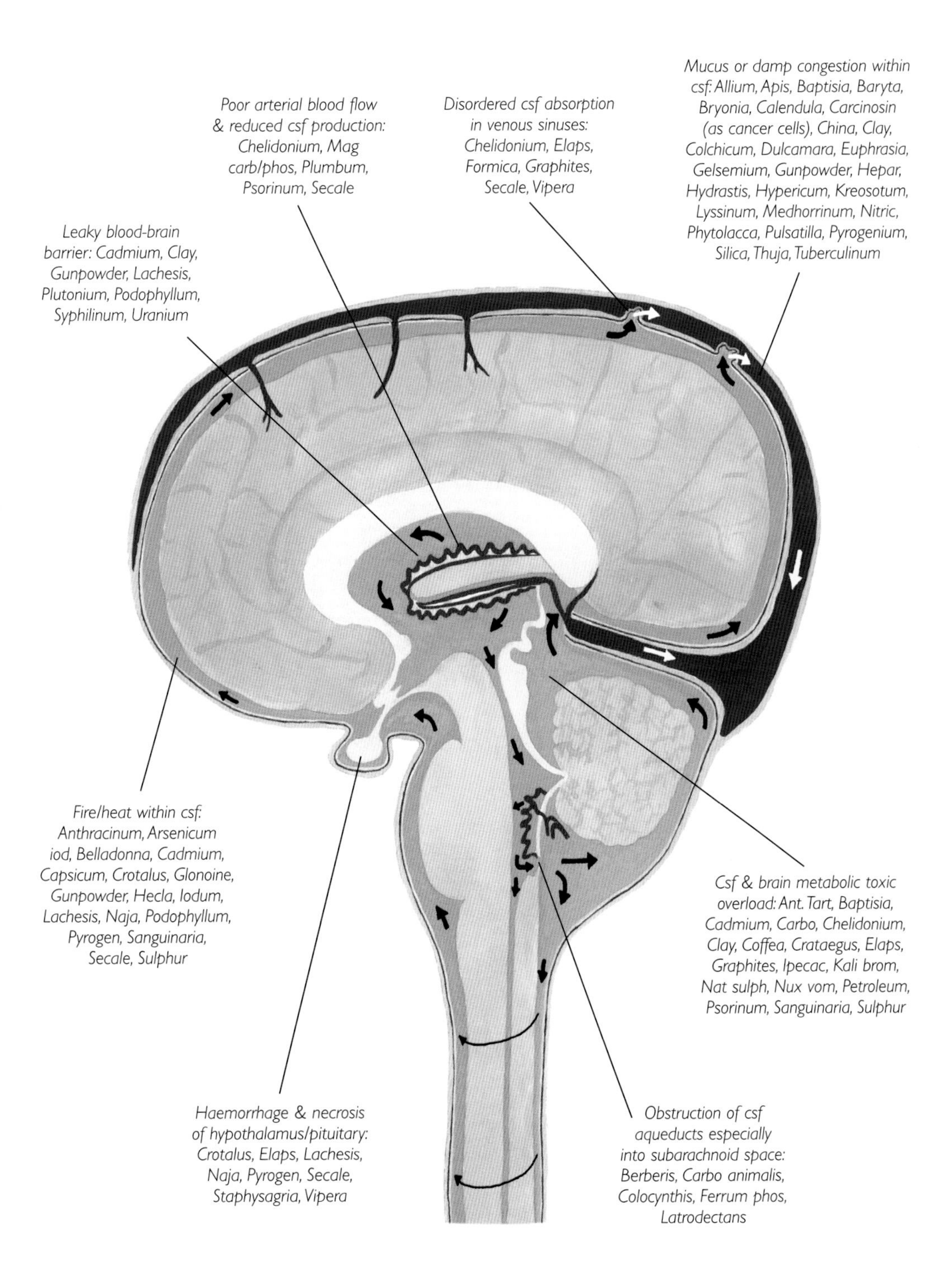

CSF ventricular system of brain

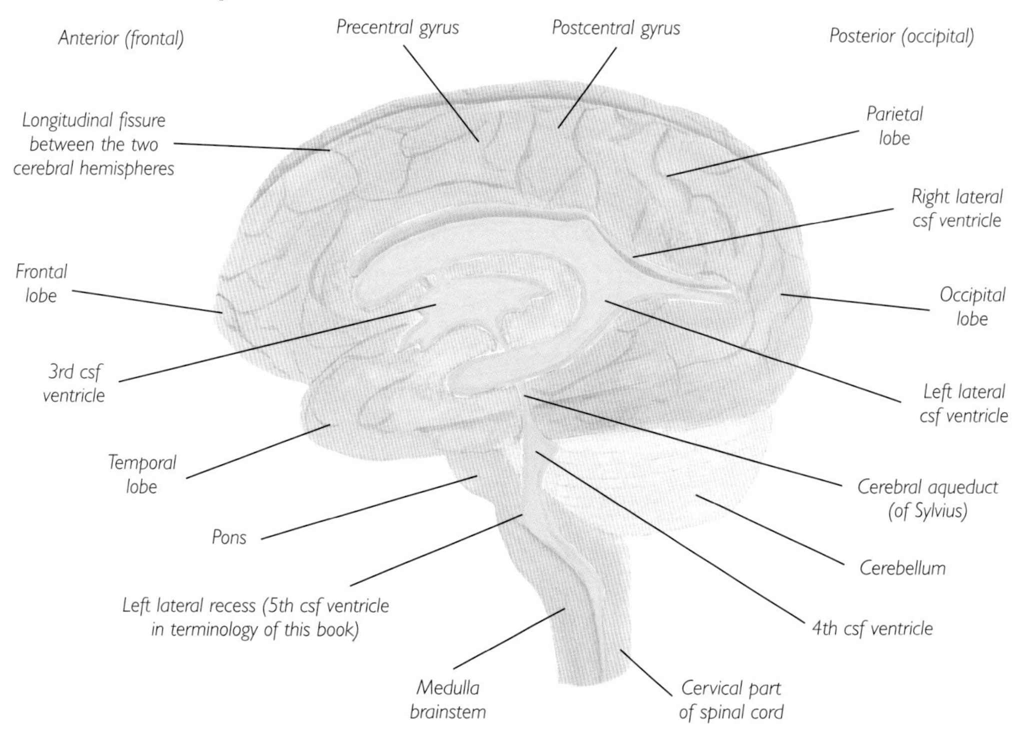

Ventricular system of brain (expanded view)

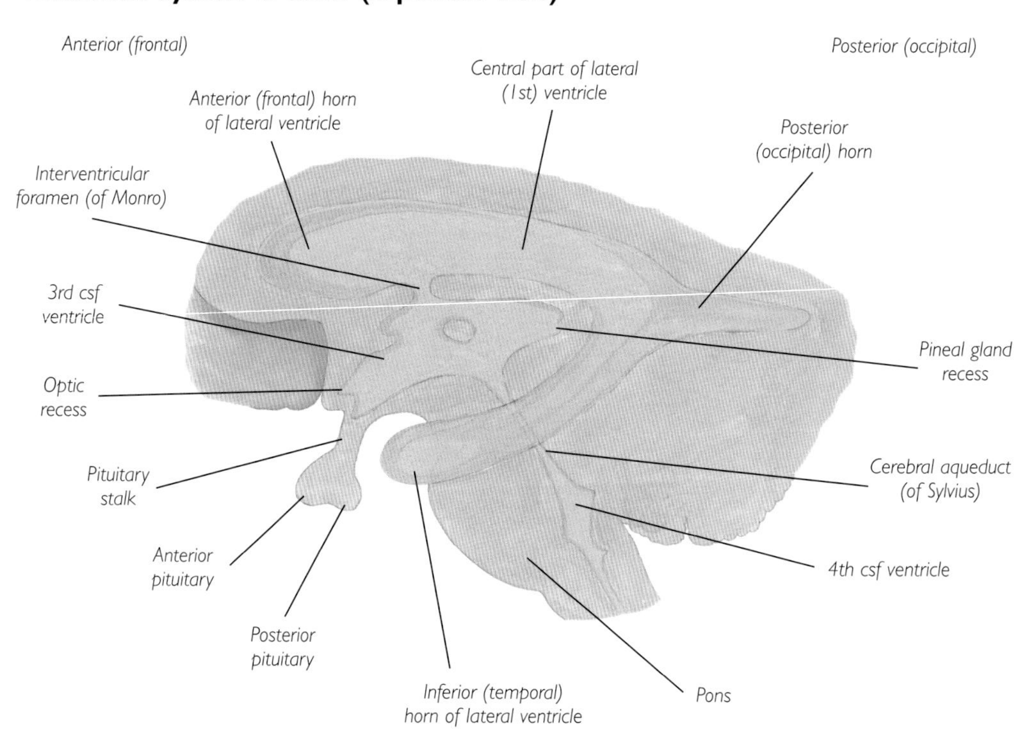

Ventricular disorders

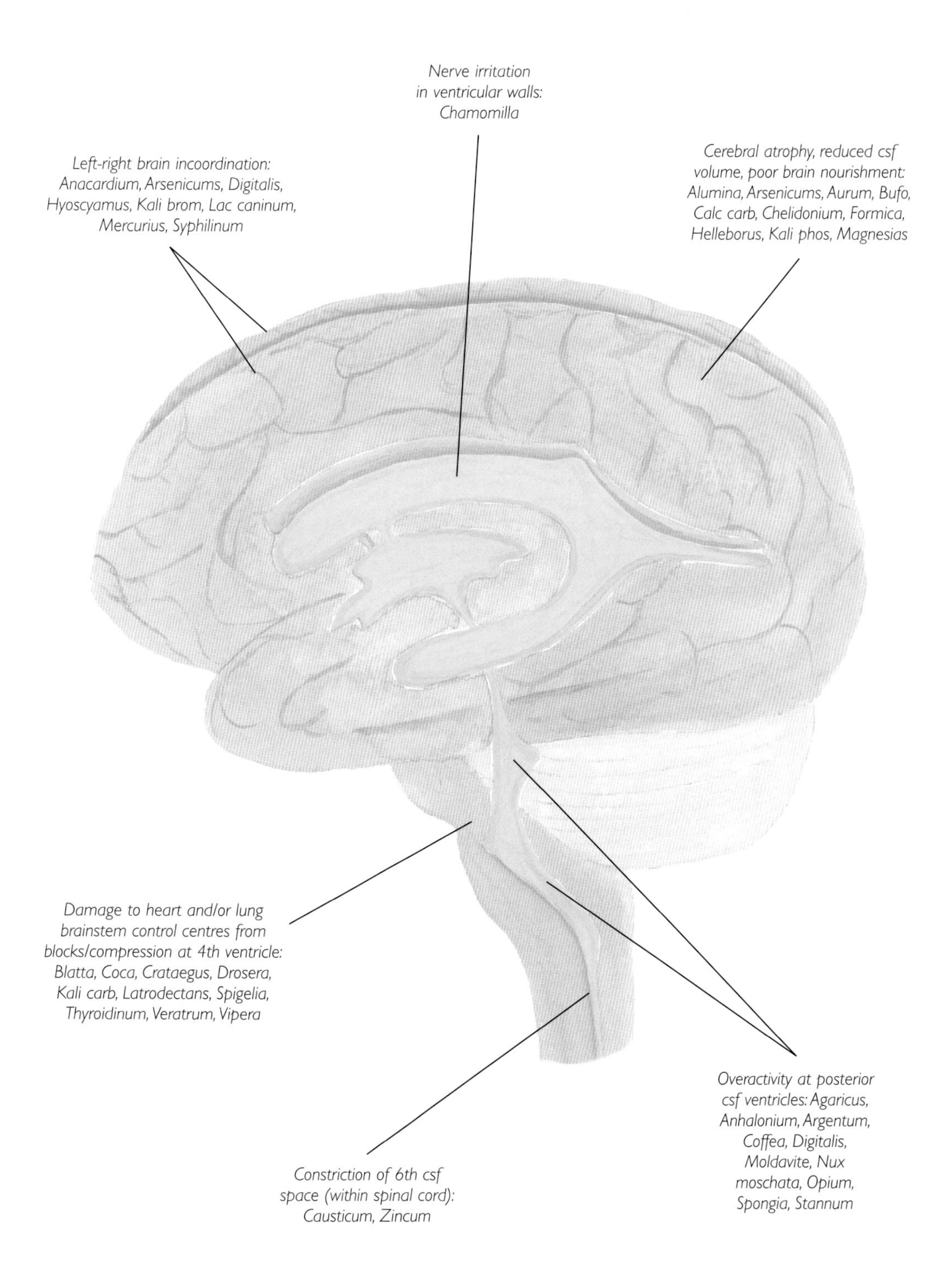

Dural membrane system in brain

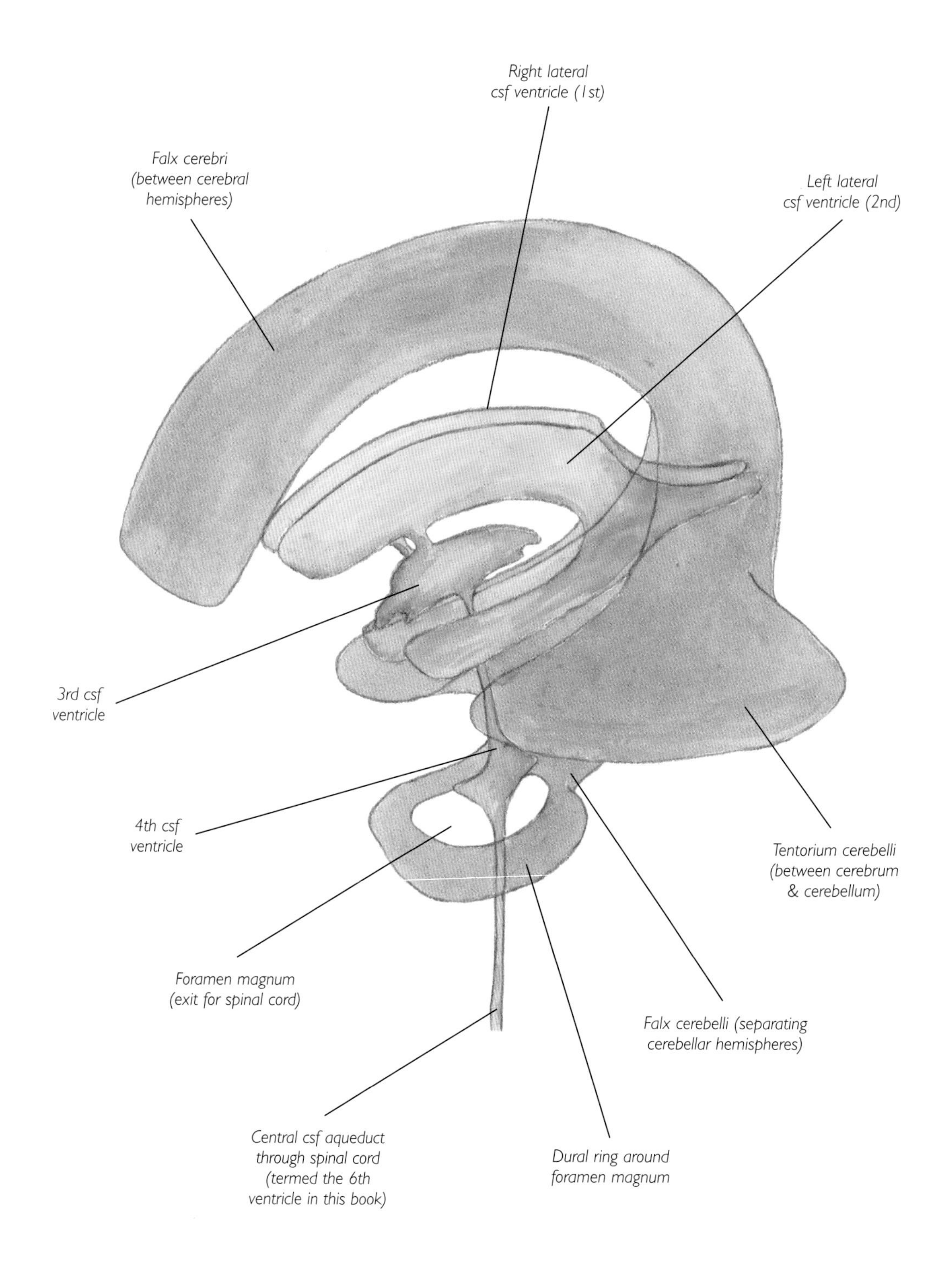

Cranial base, sphenobasilar junction at mid-position, side view

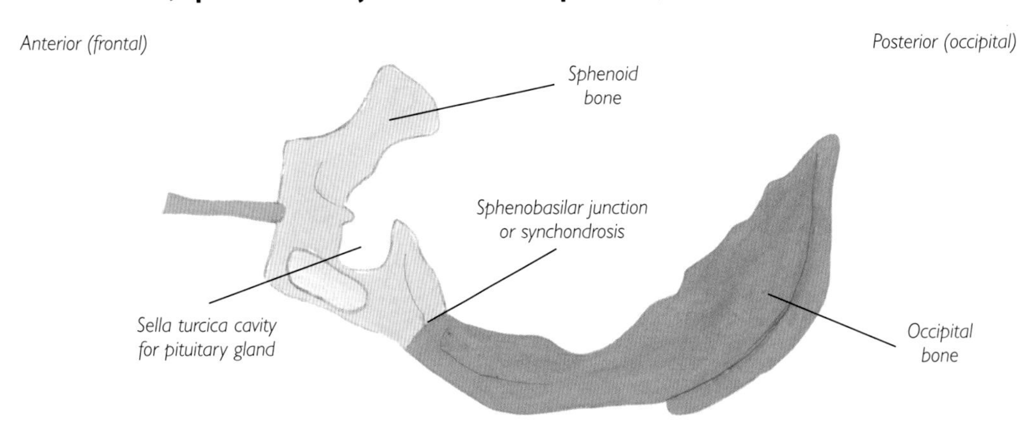

Cranial base, sphenobasilar junction in extension, side view

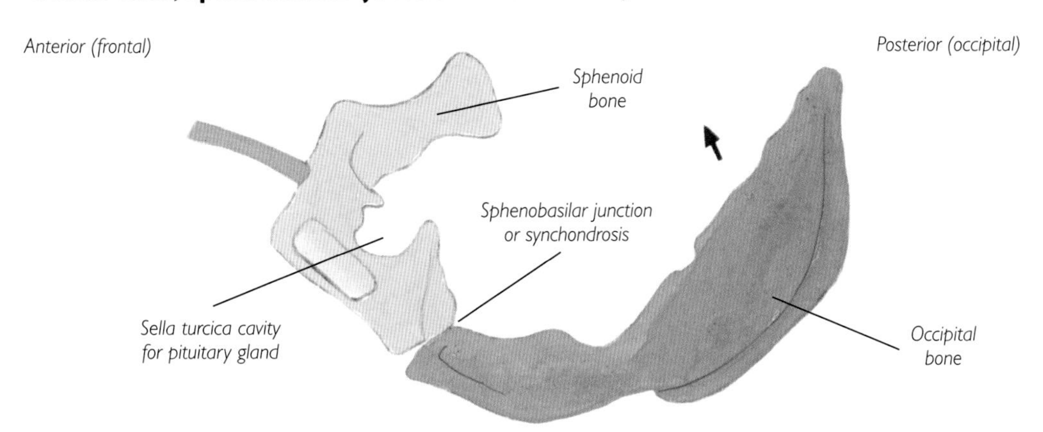

Remedies: Carbo veg, Fluoric acid, Iodum, Platina

Cranial base, sphenobasilar junction in flexion, side view

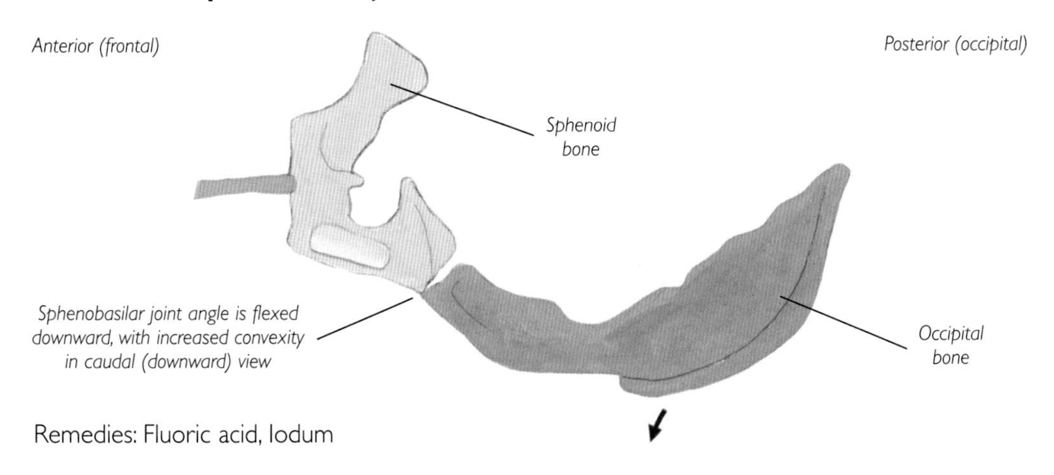

Remedies: Fluoric acid, Iodum

Cranial base, sphenobasilar junction in normal alignment, top view

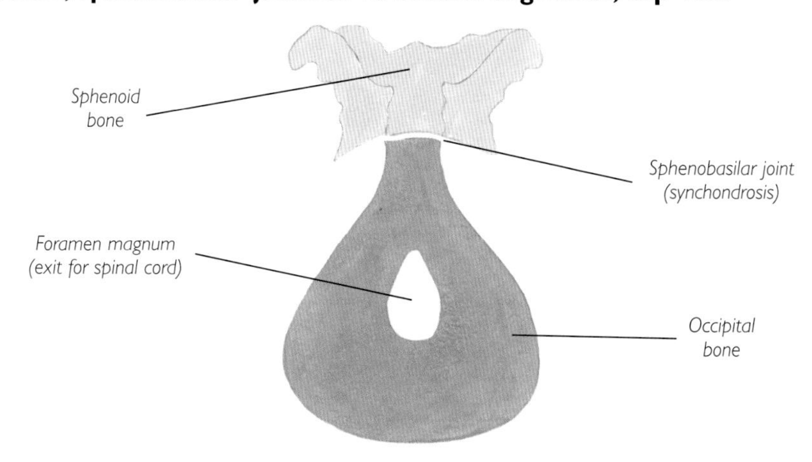

Cranial base, sphenobasilar junction with sidebending, top view

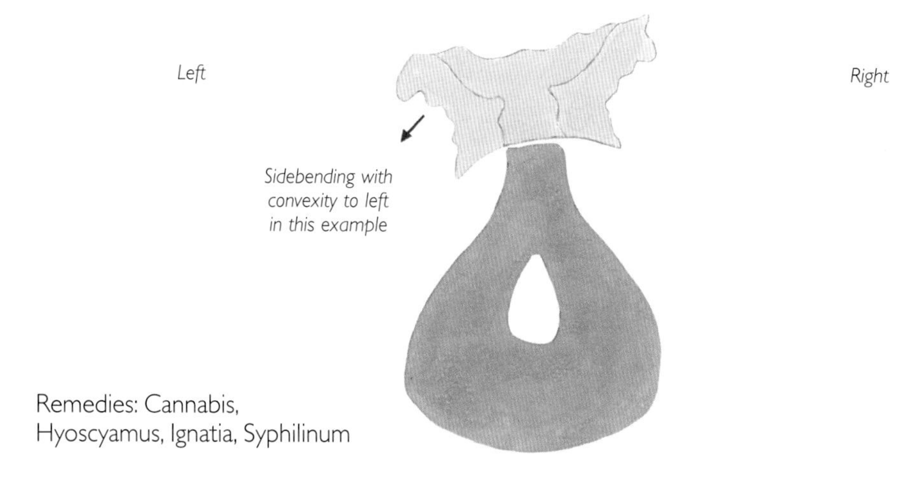

Remedies: Cannabis, Hyoscyamus, Ignatia, Syphilinum

Cranial base, sphenobasilar junction in torsion, top view

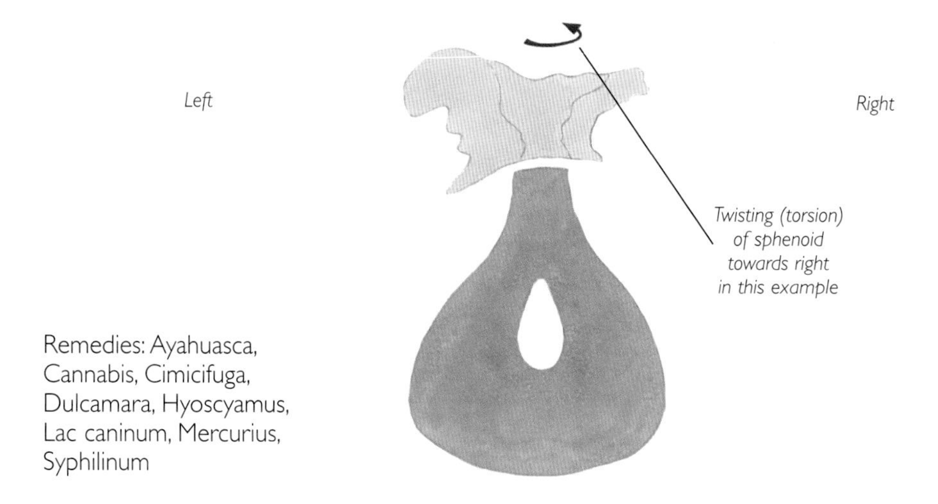

Remedies: Ayahuasca, Cannabis, Cimicifuga, Dulcamara, Hyoscyamus, Lac caninum, Mercurius, Syphilinum

Cranial base, sphenobasilar junction in superior vertical strain, side view

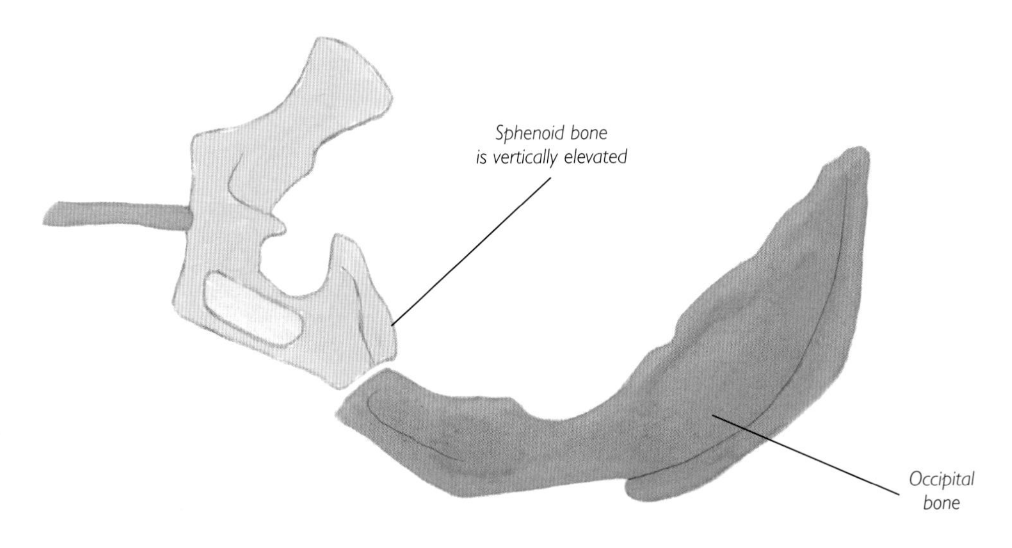

Remedies: Chamomilla, Drosera, Fluoric acid,
Hecla, Iodum, Thyroidinum (hyperthyroid state)

Cranial base, sphenobasilar junction in inferior vertical strain, side view

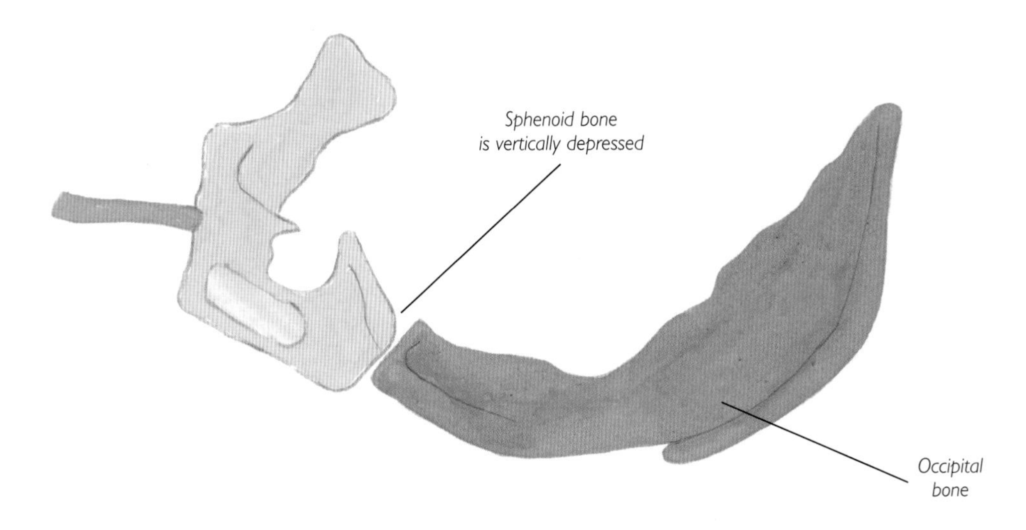

Remedies: Argentum, Cantharis, Folliculinum,
Hecla, Petroleum, Thyroidinum (hypothyroid state)

Cranial base, anterior-posterior compression of whole base, top view

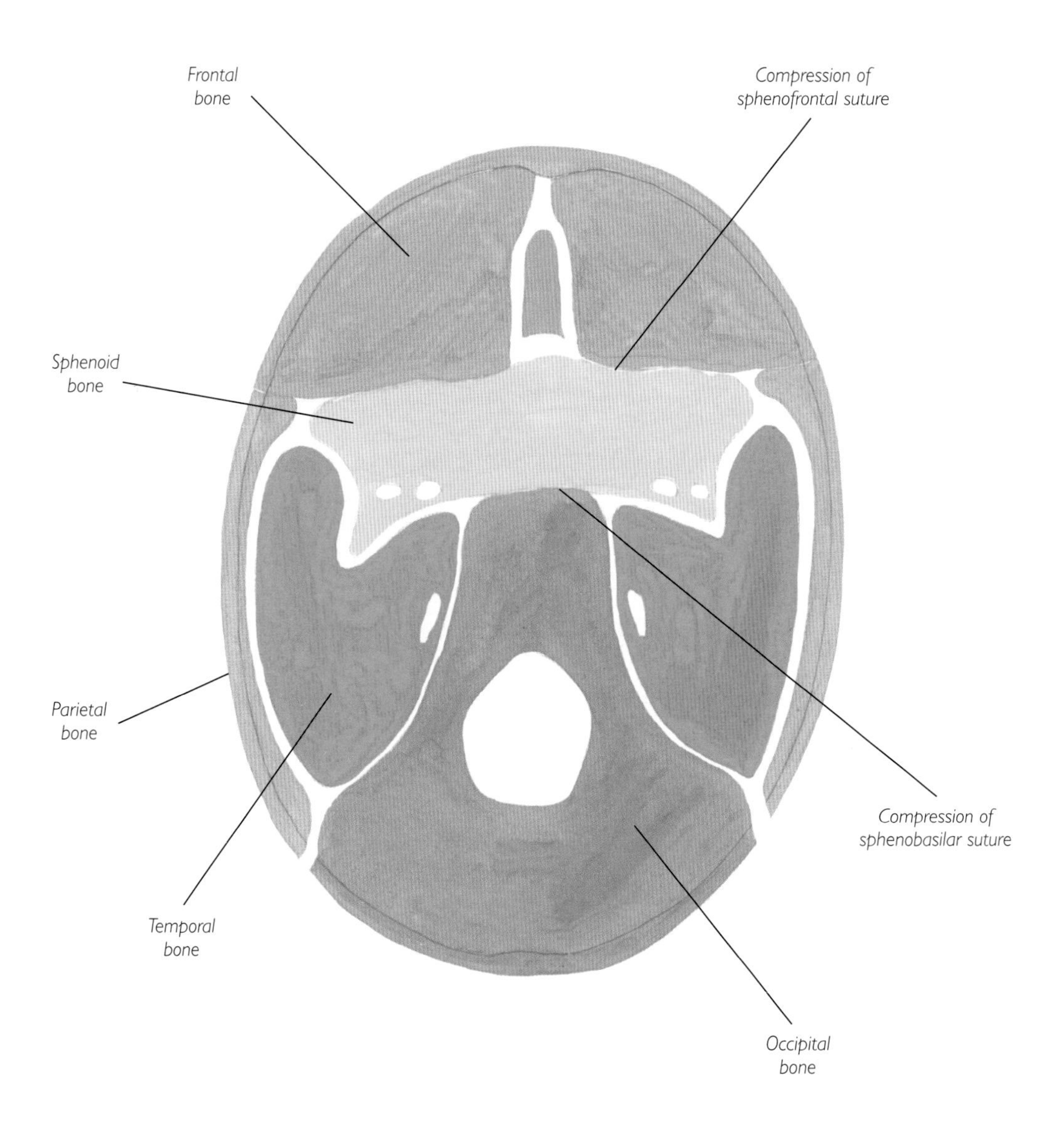

Remedies: Arnica, Carbo animalis, Cicuta, Cimicifuga, Cuprum, Euphrasia, Ipecac, Iris, Kali bich, Natrums, Nux vom, Opium, Phytolacca, Pulsatilla

INDEX OF ARTISTS

INDEX OF ARTISTS

INDEX OF MUSEUMS/COLLECTIONS

Prentenkabinet Rijksuniversiteit te Leiden, Netherlands

Reunion des Musees

Rodin Museum, Paris

Scala

Tate Gallery

© Tate, London 2006

Wellcome Institute

All © Wellcome Library, London

Private collections

Astrology	Chinese	Pathology
Sun	Wind	Normal tissue
Moon	Cold	Blood vessels/blood
Mercury	Wind-cold	Absent blood flow
Venus	Heat	Fluid lighter than csf
Mars	Fire	Nerve tissue
Jupiter	Mucus-damp	Mucus
Saturn	Yin/blood deficiency	Inflammation/allergy
Uranus	Yang deficiency	Microbes
Neptune	Chi deficiency and defence chi def	Cysts/stones
Pluto	Essence deficiency	Stones
Asteroids	Chi constraint/ stagnation	Gangrene/necrosis
Transuranian	Blood stasis/ congealed	Ectopic/misplaced tissues
Centaur	Yang collapse	Medical instruments/ devices
Miscellaneous	Yin collapse	Moles
Earth	Rebellious chi	Light rays